THE BEDSIDE TALES

THE BEDSIDE TALES

A GAY COLLECTION

With an Introduction
by

Peter Arno

WM. PENN PUBLISHING CORP.
NEW YORK   1945

PRINTED IN THE UNITED STATES OF AMERICA
BY J. J. LITTLE & IVES COMPANY, NEW YORK

INTRODUCTION

LOOK AT THE THING REALISTICALLY. THERE *are* NIGHTS WHEN YOU want to go to bed with a book.

On this point, I was in perfect accord with the publisher of this volume. There was no argument. But when he confronted me with the assignment of writing the introduction to this collection, I balked at the suggestion, for I have always believed that there are two things that it is *presumptuous* in one man to recommend to another. These are—a wife and a book.

A wife can turn into a personal misfortune of the first magnitude. While a book, however sincerely suggested, can become in the mind of the wrong receiver, an accusation of bad taste or lack of learning capable of rankling the pride for a long time.

However, reading for pleasure, as old as literature itself, is one of the few aristocratic delights left to us. Books, free of prudery, pretense and pomp. Books wise in their understanding of human nature—and candid in their treatment of it.

Such a book is this choice collection of tales. It is a luscious package, with something in it for every bedtime mood and need. To tickle your risibilities: I recommend Clarence Day describing how he was taught the violin and what effect it had on the solid citizens of Madison Avenue; or Bemelmans on a "cutie" from Paris. Suppose it's the kind of laugh that hurts a little: may I please call your attention to Mr. Damon Runyon and his hideously funny piece about a sucker for women. And if you enjoy the sly humor that you sometimes find in the best reporter of the peculiar things that happen in reality: then it's Liebling you want. I could go on classifying, but you can do it for yourself, out of a list of contributions by names that include George Jean Nathan, Robert Benchley, John Collier, H. L. Mencken, Oscar Levant, et al.

That was Part I, a sort of pot-pourri of humorous pieces of all kinds. With Part II we really get to the uninhibited laughs of the book. It ranges over the field of *amour* and other interesting, unrestrained relationships. You are not, of course, to take the division

1

too seriously. There is sex in Part I. Have you read "Mary" by John Collier—and what do you think Bemelmans is talking about? And there is joyful humor in Part II: for example, that wonderful zany Perelman writes a philosophical and statistical description of bedtime. If you read them through with a dead pan, life is no longer worth living for you! And snickers will be out of place when you read Thurber and White on frigidity in men. There are other kinds of pieces too—a little gem by Woollcott on the sentimental heart of a courtesan, a great piece of historical report-ing by Herbert Asbury on the gaudiest bawdy houses of them all, Gallico's wistful irony on the female athlete, Dorothy Parker's little story of newlyweds, H. Allen Smith's interview with a burlesque queen whom God had not blessed with much above the collar bone.

I pause for a moment to philosophize with myself about the fact that Part I (humor) and Part II (sex) seem to be all mixed up. I reach no conclusions that I didn't reach when I was sixteen years old. I am merely pleased to have my lifelong opinions confirmed and flattered to discover that I was precocious.

There is nothing mixed up in Part III. It is a beautiful little library of more serious literature, also by the best writers of our day. This is the fifth time I have read Hemingway's "The Short Happy Life" and it is just as good as the first time. It is good to re-read, after all these years, Scott Fitzgerald's pathetic "Winter Dreams." I am glad to have this opportunity to salute Irwin Shaw's wonderful little story "Welcome to the City." It is almost an insult today to say anything in praise of Ring Lardner's "The Love Nest" or Dorothy Parker's "Big Blonde." Better men than I said it all long ago. Mitchell's "On the Wagon" and Brendan Gill's "The Knife" will stay with me. There is more. In fact, you get your money's worth out of this part alone—some of it sad and some of it happy, but all of it finished, perfect and terrifically absorbing.

Part IV is a portfolio of chills, dreads, and terrors. Stories of this kind are the hardest of all to write. They call for superlative slickness, pace, atmosphere. They have to make your skin crawl and bones rattle. If I can stay dry and warm when I read one of these stories it is no good. If I get cold and feel damp and something begins to catch me in my Adam's apple, then it is good—and then there is no other kind of story that can pick me up and carry me out of this world the way one of these can. There are exactly ten stories in Part IV and every one of them did it to me in its different way. I am still breathing hard over things I read—like Straus' "The Most Maddening Story in the World."

There is nothing else to say. I have been trying to tell you about a book—really four books in one. This is a little new for me. I have promoted a few things before, but never a book for bedtime entertainment. After all, there are nights when a book wouldn't do you any good whatever. Let it stand about the way I started. If it's a book you want tonight, this is the one.

Peter Arno

CONTENTS

CONTENTS

CONTENTS

ACKNOWLEDGMENTS

THE PUBLISHERS OF THIS VOLUME GRATEFULLY ACKNOWLEDGE THE KINDNESS OF THE authors, agents, and publishers who have given permission to reproduce copyright material, as follows:

BRANDT & BRANDT: for permission to reprint "The Sobbin' Women" from *Thirteen O'Clock* by Stephen Vincent Benét, published by Farrar & Rinehart, copyright 1926 by Stephen Vincent Benét; "The Most Dangerous Game" by Richard Connell, copyright 1924 by Richard Connell.

W. R. BURNETT: for "Dressing Up," copyright 1930 by Harper & Brothers. Reprinted by permission of W. R. Burnett.

JAMES M. CAIN: for permission to reprint "Dead Man" by James M. Cain.

JACQUES CHAMBRUN, INC.: for permission to reprint "The Shadow" by Ben Hecht.

DODD, MEAD & COMPANY, INC.: for "Ring Out, Wild Bells" from *A Bed of Neuroses* by Wolcott Gibbs, copyright 1937 by Wolcott Gibbs. Reprinted by permission of Dodd, Mead & Company, Inc.

DOUBLEDAY, DORAN & COMPANY, INC.: for "Memoirs of a Mute" from *A Smattering of Ignorance* by Oscar Levant, copyright 1939, 1940 by Doubleday, Doran & Company, Inc.; "The Jollity Building" from *Telephone Booth Indian* by A. J. Liebling, copyright 1937, 1939, 1940, 1941, 1942 by A. J. Liebling, reprinted by permission of Doubleday, Doran & Company, Inc.; "Red" from *Trembling of a Leaf* by W. Somerset Maugham, copyright 1921 by Doubleday, Doran & Company, Inc.; "Barefooted—Up to Her Chin" from *Low Man on a Totem Pole* by H. Allen Smith, copyright 1941 by Doubleday, Doran & Company, Inc.

DUELL, SLOAN & PEARCE, INC.: for "Over the Green Mountains" from *Jackpot* by Erskine Caldwell; "On the Wagon" from *McSorley's Wonderful Saloon* by Joseph Mitchell; "Days" from *Files on Parade* by John O'Hara. Reprinted by permission of the publishers, Duell, Sloan & Pearce, Inc.

HARCOURT, BRACE AND COMPANY, INC.: for "Mr. K*a*p*l*a*n and Shakespeare" from *The Education of Hyman Kaplan* by Leonard Q. Ross, copyright 1937 by Harcourt, Brace and Company, Inc.

HARPER & BROTHERS: for "Polyp with a Past" and "They're Off" from *Benchley Beside Himself* by Robert Benchley; "Frigidity in Men" from *Is Sex Necessary* by James Thurber and E. B. White. Reprinted by permission of the publishers, Harper & Brothers.

LELAND HAYWARD, INC.: for "Two Sharp Knives" by Dashiell Hammett. Reprinted by permission of the author.

ALFRED A. KNOPF, INC.: for the selections from *The Barbary Coast* by Herbert Asbury, copyright 1933 by Alfred A. Knopf, Inc.; "There's No Future in It" from *There's Something in the Air* by H. E. Bates, copyright 1943 by Alfred A. Knopf, Inc.; "The Noblest Instrument" from *Life with Father* by Clarence Day, copyright 1920, 1922, 1923, 1924, 1933, 1934, 1935 by Clarence Day; "Farewell to Muscle Molls" from *Farewell to Sport* by Paul Gallico, copyright 1937, 1938 by Paul Gallico; "The Noble Experiment" from *Heathen Days* by H. L. Mencken, copyright 1941, 1942, 1943 by Alfred A. Knopf, Inc. Reprinted by permission of and special arrangement with Alfred A. Knopf, Inc.

J. B. LIPPINCOTT COMPANY: for "The Brain Goes Home" from *Guys and Dolls* by Damon Runyon, reprinted by permission of the publishers, J. B. Lippincott Co., copyright 1929 by Damon Runyon.

HAROLD MATSON: for permission to reprint "Mary" and "Thus I Refute Beelzy" by John Collier.

HAROLD OBER: for "I Want to Know Why" from *The Triumph of the Egg* by Sherwood Anderson, copyright 1921 by Eleanor Anderson. Reprinted by permission of Eleanor Anderson.

AUGUSTUS PETERS: for permission to reprint "The Most Maddening Story in the World" by Ralph Straus.

RANDOM HOUSE, INC.: for "A Rose for Emily" from *These 13* by William Faulkner, copyright 1931 by William Faulkner; "Beat Me Post-Impressionist Daddy" from *Crazy Like a Fox* by S. J. Perelman, copyright 1944 by Random House, Inc.; "70,000 Assyrians" from *The Daring Young Man on the Flying Trapeze* by William Saroyan, copyright 1934 by Random House, Inc.; "Welcome to the City" from the book of the same title by Irwin Shaw, copyright 1942 by Irwin Shaw. Reprinted by permission of Random House, Inc.

REYNAL AND HITCHCOCK, INC.: for the selection from *The Bachelor Life* by George Jean Nathan, by permission of the publishers, Reynal & Hitchcock, Inc.

CHARLES SCRIBNER'S SONS: for "Winter Dreams" from *All the Sad Young Men* by F. Scott Fitzgerald; "Mae West and John Riddell: A Correspondence" from *In the Worst Possible Taste* by Corey Ford; "The Short, Happy Life of Francis Macomber" from *The Fifth Column and the First Forty-Nine* by Ernest Hemingway; "The Love Nest" from *Round-Up* by Ring Lardner. Reprinted by permission of the publishers, Charles Scribner's Sons.

SIMON AND SCHUSTER, INC.: for "The Tuxedos" from *The Horse That Could Whistle Dixie* by Jerome Weidman. Reprinted by permission of the publishers, Simon and Schuster, Inc.

VANGUARD PRESS, INC.: for "Helen, I Love You" reprinted from *The Short Stories of James T. Farrell*, copyright 1934 by Vanguard Press, Inc.; the selection reprinted from *Bed Manners* by Dr. Ralph Y. Hopton and Anne Balliol, copyright 1934 by Vanguard Press, Inc. Reprinted by permission of The Vanguard Press.

THE VIKING PRESS, INC.: for "Watch the Birdie" from *I Love You, I Love You, I Love You* by Ludwig Bemelmans, copyright 1939, 1940, 1941, 1942 by Ludwig Bemelmans; "The Open Window" from *The Short Stories of Saki* (H. H. Munro), copyright 1930 by the Viking Press, Inc.; "Here We Are" and "Big Blonde" from *The Portable Dorothy Parker*, copyright 1939, 1944 by Dorothy Parker; "The Murder" from *The Long Valley* by John Steinbeck, copyright 1938 by John Steinbeck; "Entrance Fee" and "The Vanishing Lady" from *While Rome Burns* by Alexander Woollcott. Reprinted by permission of The Viking Press, Inc., New York.

ANN WATKINS, INC.: for permission to reprint "Suspicion" by Dorothy L. Sayers.

A. P. WATT & SON: for permission to reprint "Caterpillars" from *The Room in the Tower* by E. F. Benson.

The following stories are reprinted by courtesy of *The New Yorker* in which they originally appeared.

"The Works" by Nathan Asch (page 173) copyright 1940 The F-R. Publishing Corporation.

"I Went to See a Queen" by Ralph Faye (page 90) copyright 1944 The F-R. Publishing Corporation.

"The Knife" by Brendan Gill (page 258) copyright 1940 The F-R. Publishing Corporation.

"Letter from the Bronx" by Arthur Kober (page 76) copyright 1937 The F-R. Publishing Corporation.

"Sleepy-Time Extra" by S. J. Perelman (page 125) copyright 1944 The F-R. Publishing Corporation.

PART I

"Laugh when I am merry, and claw
no man in his humour."
—SHAKESPEARE: *Much Ado About Nothing*

WATCH THE BIRDIE

By LUDWIG BEMELMANS

DURING THAT SOFT, GREEN, MAY-WINE-AND-GUITAR-MUSIC PERIOD when Mozart, von Hofmannsthal, and Salzburg were the fashion and Queen Marie of Rumania came to the Passion Play at Oberammergau in a Schiaparelli dirndl, the young Polish photographer Zygmunt Pisik arrived in Salzburg, let his hair grow long over his ears, and changed his name to Johann von Schönberg.

He photographed everything in Salzburg, and he loved an ample, pink woman who was like a peasant commode with wide drawers that were filled with kindness, honesty, and submission —the cold Mamsell of the Hotel zum Frommen Brunnen. She was called the cold Mamsell because she supervised the buffet where salami, ham, and other cold delicatessen were served. She, too, wore a dirndl. Her hair was braided. She walked and stood in solid footgear. With a clop, clop, clop, gallop, she came out every evening and met Johann von Schönberg at a certain bench under a linden tree, and there was always a roll in her handbag, buttered and weighed down with a considerable slice of tender ham. "Here, darling," she handed him the roll and gave him a kiss that was like the butter on the roll.

After one Salzburg season von Schönberg went to Berlin and worked for *Die Dame*, a German imitation of *Vogue*. He also contributed photographs to other magazines, and his art flourished when he began to photograph the nude.

The pictures he took of unclad young women in the snow, on skis, of two of them playing with a pushball, of one kneeling in dejection, of one with eyes half closed under a thin black veil, of one on a polar-bear rug and labeled "Baroness X," found their way through the editorial room to the press with miraculous ease.

Von Schönberg was known among his colleagues as the worm photographer. He took most of his pictures lying flat on his stomach, with the camera tilted up. Girls photographed from that angle became his trademark. It was inevitable that such talent should take him to Paris. He wrapped up the polar-bear rug, packed in a leisurely fashion, and was boarding the train at the moment when an agent of the Goebbels Ministry appeared at *Die Dame* to request a list of the personnel. Schönberg was a certified Aryan with all his grandparents in order, but he disliked Nazis and on several occasions had said so, quite loudly. He was, besides, a Pole, with burnt-sienna skin and thick, shiny black hair, and there were a good many golden-haired and blue-eyed youths around who also could take pictures.

He arrived in Paris in German pants that rode high over his shoes. His hat suggested an excursion into the Black Forest and his shirt choked him.

He found a girl to pose for him and to clean his studio. Her name was Denise and she wore colored ribbons in her hair and she was always cold. They went out to eat together and she sat with a heavy sweater on, listening to him across one of the tables of the Restaurant Cécile, where the *choucroute à l'ancienne*, with napkin and bread and butter included, was seven francs. She didn't mind his German clothes. She loved him as he was.

His life changed when he met Roxanne Colombo and photographed her glossy Italian beauty backstage at the Bal Tabarin. She had him change his name to Henri de Beaumont. She saw to it that his hair was cut. He became thinner. He walked with elegance. Roxanne went with him to the tailor and the shoemaker. A thin mustache bloomed under his nose. Denise disappeared from his life.

Besides photographing pretty women, de Beaumont invented an editorial game which consisted of printing, side by side, pictures that complemented each other. There would be, for example, on the left-hand page a photograph of an old sea lion who looked like an ancient mariner, and on the opposite page a photograph of an ancient mariner who looked like an old sea lion. In his new habitat, a studio on the fifth floor of a modern building near the Observatoire, he pasted up a layout in which a pig and Julius Streicher were juxtaposed.

De Beaumont got several assignments after the layout appeared,

together with a group of his nudes, in a French imitation of *Vogue*.
He was sent to take photographs of a circus party given by Lady
Mendl. He took snaps at Auteuil and at the various fêtes that
were arranged by the Syndicat d'Initiative of the City of Paris,
and in between these routine jobs he lay on his stomach in the
sands of Le Touquet and Deauville and in the early, unpoliced
morning mists of the Bois de Boulogne. He moved to Clichy, and
went to the Tabarin every evening in a midnight-blue dinner
jacket with a blood-red carnation in his lapel. The maître d'hôtel
sat him at a table while he waited for Roxanne to sing the quatrain
that ended the show:

> *Princesses, duchesses, et marquises,*
> *Féerie lumière, oubli décor,*
> *Plus de cafard, à bas la crise;*
> *On peut rire de tout encore.*

Roxanne appeared in the nude on one negative after another
until there were stacks of them. She did her turn on the polar-bear
rug and she was shown holding up a balloon. She was the veiled
nymph in the Bois and also was photographed with her clothes on.
A boy who did de Beaumont's errands and helped him in the
darkroom sometimes was worked into the compositions, the most
successful of which showed the Left Bank arch of the Pont Royal.
Roxanne, in a shabby coat, leaned on a lamppost and the apprentice leaned on her. De Beaumont screwed the lens out of focus
to obtain the mood of waterfront and despair. He called it *Sous
les Ponts de Paris*, and it won the first prize at an exhibition and
made him famous. He raised his prices, had his sofa newly covered,
and bought Roxanne a silver-fox jacket.

Into this idyll came a fashion model from Cleveland, Ohio,
whom everyone greeted with "*Allo*, Toots." She had been re-
cruited, together with six other girls, to pose in Paris when the
great French couturiers had their shows for American buyers.
The young women lived together in three rooms at an eminently
respectable *pension de famille* in the environs of the Eiffel Tower.
Toots had taken French in high school and did her best to converse in that language, although most of the people she found her-

self with were polyglots, like de Beaumont, and spoke some English.

Backgrounds against which to photograph Toots immediately suggested themselves to de Beaumont—the great stairway at Versailles, the Madeleine, the fountains on the Place de la Concorde, marble horses, onyx columns, silvery trees. He looked at her professionally, optically, through a square made of his two hands, studying all her possibilities.

He stopped taking pictures of Roxanne, indeed forgot about her entirely, and lay on the grass in the Tuileries and on the pavement of the Champs-Élysées and looked up at Toots in sports clothes leaning on Daimler cabriolets, sitting at sidewalk tables. After a week the line of her body were as familiar to him as those of the Arc de Triomphe.

On a lovely morning in May, after photographing Toots in a governess cart in the Bois, de Beaumont suggested that she come to his studio that afternoon. He gave himself time to prepare lights, he sent the apprentice away, and then he called for her in his Citroën. When they got to the studio he opened a bottle of Sauternes and arranged some blue grapes on a plate. He asked her not to eat the grapes until he was through taking pictures. He brought out a large portfolio and from it spilled an assortment of fashion shots, the best of his life's work. He also casually drew from his files a picture of a classic Greek statue. He said that he would like to use that in a magazine layout on the left-hand page and opposite, in the same pose, Toots. He said that up to now he had not found anyone worthy of that arrangement.

"*Je n'aime pas de poser dans le nude*," said Toots.

"What are you—Snow White or something?" said de Beaumont. "What is the matter with you? Look, darling, it is only for the pleasure of the eye. There is a lot of precedent. Here, in this *dossier*——"

Toots shook her head.

"What an extraordinary child!" said de Beaumont. He put his face close to hers. "We still can do it. We will do it like the Venus de Milo—half nude, dressed from the waist down."

"I told you, *je n'aime pas du tout—du tout—de poser* that way. *C'est tout*," she said.

While Toots straightened herself out and arranged her hair, de Beaumont poured out two glasses of the wine. He sat silent, with clouded eyes; then he said, "I wish you wouldn't be such a silly child. This has never happened to me before. This is not what you think it is. You must imagine that I am like a doctor——"

"Ha-ha," said Toots, and then, "what are you looking so sad for?"

"Oh, nothing," said de Beaumont.

"All right," she said, "I'll let you take one."

De Beaumont fished around the back of her dress until he found the locket of the zipper, but Toots shook herself and said that she'd rather do it herself. She undid the back and the tight sleeves of the black blouse and slipped it over her head. De Beaumont ran into his darkroom to get his plates. He whistled in there and knocked about and said to himself, "God, what a sweet business!" When he came out, Toots was standing in the middle of the room fully dressed. She had her hat on and she was pulling on a glove. De Beaumont made a mental note never to leave a model alone again.

"Does this furniture belong to you?" asked Toots.

"No," he said. "It goes with the apartment. Only the sofa there belongs to me. It's French Provincial. Do you like it?"

"*Ah, oui!* I had a grandmother on my mother's side who was French."

"I'm hungry," de Beaumont said.

They let themselves down in the automatic elevator.

"*Après vous,*" said de Beaumont, and held open the outside door. He had never been that gallant to the others.

They drove to one of the large *brasseries* along the Champs-Élysées, went down to the basement, and sat in a corner.

"We must speak French," Toots said while he studied the menu. "I, *moi*"—pointing at herself—"*je aime beaucoup le théâtre. Vous savez?* Sarah Bernhardt, Sacha Guitry, *la Comédie-Française. Tous les soirs,* when I can, *quand je peux,* I go to the theater, you understand. I, *moi, je veux être grande artiste—du théâtre,* or moving picture——"

"*Ça c'est très intéressant,*" said de Beaumont.

She suggested that they go to the theater together, to see a performance of *Oscar Wilde* in English. *"Vous allez apprendre* English," Toots said, "and I will improve my French by translating the hard parts for you." A tight squeeze of his arm sealed this *entente cordiale,* and de Beaumont said to himself, "Time. Patience. Perhaps the next time, if I don't go out of the room. Perhaps then."

He drove her to a little theater he had never heard of. It turned out to be only one street away from the Bal Tabarin. De Beaumont bought two tickets in an upstairs loge. The curtain was painted to resemble a tapestry. It went up on a set showing the terrace of a hotel in Algiers—two broken-down wicker chairs, a tabouret on which stood an ashtray advertising the Galeries Lafayette, and a potted palm.

Lord Alfred Douglas, in a platinum-blond wig, his thin-fingered hands hanging on one hip, danced toward the place from which Oscar was to make his entrance. Toots started to translate the dialogue.

After the second act she sighed. "I have learned so much," she said. *"Avez vous remarqué le* business *abec les* gloves?"

She had tears in her eyes when the final curtain came down. She shouted "Bravo!" and applauded to six curtain calls. They stopped in a bar for a drink, and afterward de Beaumont said good night to her on the steps of the *pension de famille* near the Eiffel Tower.

For the next two weeks he did fashion shots of Toots during the day and in the evenings they met, ate, and ended up in that little island of people who huddled together in the emptiness of the Odéon Theatre and sat through dreary performances of Racine and Molière. Neither the statue of the Venus de Milo nor the polar-bear rug was brought up again.

In the summer of 1939, when the political horizon grew dark with storm clouds, Toots took the S.S. *Manhattan* back to America. De Beaumont drove her down to Boulogne-sur-Mer and waved good-by from the pier. Then he turned his Citroën around and went back to Paris. Toward midnight he was in the neighborhood of the Tabarin. He dropped in. Roxanne was still singing the same quatrain:

Princesses, duchesses, et marquises . . .

The next spring, a few weeks before the invasion of the Low Countries, de Beaumont aroused himself sufficiently from the melancholia which the American girl had imposed on him to do a montage of Winston Churchill and a bulldog. This was an instant and international success. A New York magazine cabled for de Beaumont, and again, just in time, he packed and left.

His table companions aboard the ship on which he left Boulogne-sur-Mer were two Poles. One was an author's agent, Sylvan Pogoda, who had just sold the American motion-picture rights of a play and two novels. He had once spent two years in America and was returning there now for the filming of a new story. The other was the son of a painter, who was taking his father's work across. He had also been to America before. The three agreed on the character of American women.

"You will rarely see a woman in America who is bad-looking," said Pogoda. "Some of them are ravishingly beautiful. They call them long-stemmed American Beauties, and, you know, they are. The long legs, the beautiful, slim long legs. They talk with them."

"I know," said de Beaumont. "I have had experience with them."

"But it is all a *trompe-l'œil* proposition," said Pogoda. "They are wonderful to look at and they have the soul of a tennis player, or a cash register. You could cry blood over the beauty of their eyes and hair and faces, but it is all false. They do not love the dog, neither the grandfather, neither the child, least of all the husband—not even the lover. The climate also is abominable."

Day after day, usually when they walked the deck after meals, the three men continued to discuss in bad French the unalluring prospects of life in the United States.

"Where does one eat in New York?" de Beaumont asked the day before they landed.

"Ah, that too is hopeless," the others said.

"There are good restaurants in New York," Pogoda explained. "But you must be a millionaire, an American millionaire, to go there. They are out of the question for people like you and me.

If you are lucky, after a while, when you meet a friend, he may take you to his *bistro*. They are hidden away in side streets, or on the avenues where the high trains run, upstairs in apartments that are fixed up as small restaurants."

"My contract runs for a year," de Beaumont said. "I will live in a cheap little room and eat in the *bistro*. I will not buy a hat, a shirt, shoes, or clothes. I will save every penny and hurry back to France."

The editor of the American publication was delighted with the fearless approaches of his new photographer. He found that the girls in college clothes taken on the lids of sandboxes along Fifth Avenue, straddling the stairs at Vassar, or the bulwarks surrounding the base of the Statue of Liberty, had great appeal for his readers. At the end of a year, de Beaumont's contract with the American publication was renewed and his visa extended.

One day he met the agent, Pogoda, who also had managed to stay in America, in the office of a publisher who wanted to bring out a photographic manual for which he, de Beaumont, was to supply the material. Pogoda and de Beaumont went to lunch together at an expensive restaurant in the Fifties. As they followed the headwaiter, Pogoda waved to a girl in a large felt hat and said, "*Allo*, Toots."

"It's Toots!" cried de Beaumont. "I know Toots."

They went over to her table. Toots introduced de Beaumont to the man lunching with her. His name was Horace. He was a dramatic critic. Horace seemed to know Pogoda. He nodded briefly and then studied the color of his beer while the others talked with Toots. She had just returned from Hollywood, she said, and was about to start rehearsals in a play Horace had picked for her.

"I didn't know you knew her," de Beaumont said when he and Pogoda were seated at their own table. "I knew her in Paris a couple of years ago. I didn't know she was in Hollywood."

"Oh, she's been out there two years. Her name is now Sandra Watteau. I went out there with her," said Pogoda. "It's a funny story."

As they sat down they waved once more to Toots, and she waved back.

"Ah, she's lovely," said Pogoda, with his finger pointing at the oysters-and-hors-d'œuvres part of the menu. To the waiter he said, "*Donnez-moi des* bluepoints. You know, I love oysters now. I used to detest them. It's a matter of getting over the first plate. Bluepoints and *stchi à la russe.*"

"And for me, some *escargots* to start with," said de Beaumont. "But coming back to Toots. Ah, what a darling! What a body!" While Pogoda ate the oysters, he gave a short account of a very satisfactory stretch of life with Toots.

"*Entendez,*" he said. "I worked on her with flowers, bon-bons, tickets, and restaurants," he said. "Absolutely nothing happens. Kiss. Good night. Thank you for a lovely time. Good-by. I went almost crazy. Do you know where their weakness lies, Henri? They are sentimental. They are sentimental, like dogs. I will explain to you—where were we? Oh, yes. I tried everything. I tried to make her jealous. I keep away. I come back. Nothing happens. So one day I met her here in this restaurant. She was with that same fellow. I tell her that I am flying to Hollywood on the eleven o'clock plane the next day to see about the filming of *Le Moulin de la Galette.* 'I'll see you there,' she says. 'I'm taking the train for Hollywood myself to-morrow. I'm going out for a part in a picture.' I said to her, 'Oh, I can't take the plane if you go by train. Never. I will go by train also.' 'All right,' she said. And I thought perhaps on a train it will be easier. You know how easy and relaxed women are on shipboard.

"She told me what train she was taking. I wanted to engage a compartment, but it was fifty-four eighty-five for the compartment and the fare was ninety-one fifty. So I thought, one always can make arrangements with the conductor. I was glad I didn't get the compartment when I arrived at the train. Who is there? Horace. I thought that he had come to say good-by, but he stayed. He had a compartment for two, and when she came she put her things in with his. . . . The soup is for me," Pogoda said to the waiter, and then he continued. "I thought it was again all for nothing, but then something *épatant* happened, something glorious. Horace got off to go to a place called Central City. That is where they hold an annual festival, a sort of cowboy celebration. Ah, Toots is on the train alone. She had the compartment all the way to Los Angeles. It happened in Salt Lake City. I will always love that name, SALT-LAKE-CITY. It was morning, and while the train stopped in the station, Toots went out to walk up and down, and she bought a paper. All at once she came running back to the car. She held up the front page for me to look at, and through the window I read: PLANE CRASHES WEST OF ALBUQUERQUE. ALL ABOARD DEAD.

" 'I am so glad,' she said, as she climbed aboard. I didn't understand right away what she meant, but when the train was under way again, while we stood on one of those drafty passages between our car and the diner, wobbling in that canvas tunnel that looks like the inside of a concertina, she embraced and kissed me, and said, 'The plane that crashed was most probably the plane you would have been on if I'd let you go, darling.'

"I put my things in with hers all the way to Hollywood, from Salt Lake City on, *cher ami*, it was as easy—" he fiddled about in the air with his soupspoon, searching for the proper words—"it was as easy as putting a letter through the mail."

THE MYTHOLOGY OF BACHELOR LIFE

By GEORGE JEAN NATHAN

Legendary Premise

ONE OF THE MANY THINGS THAT AMUSE THE BACHELOR IS THE prevalent and apparently irrevocable idea, entertained chiefly by very young girls and the older married folk, that he is always having a hell of a gay time. The circumstance that the idea in point is encouraged by the vainer idiots among bachelors themselves only adds to the diversion of the more realistic and self-analytical bachelor. As a member of the latter order in long and at least comparatively honorable standing, I take the liberty of dispelling several of the more popular misconceptions.

The first of these is that it must be wonderful not to be tied down to any one woman and with the field constantly to choose from. On the joys of connubial bliss I am, of course, unqualified to speak, but on the theoretically superior and overwhelming joy of being free to keep company with a plurality of women I should like to say a few words.

Out of every fifty women of all ages and conditions whom a bachelor meets, he is lucky if he can find one of sufficient charm, intelligence, and loveliness to interest him in the slightest. That is, for any length of time and presuming him to be moderately intelligent and of any experience and accuracy of taste. More bachelors spend evenings alone at home, or at their clubs, or having dinner with other lonely bachelors than the generality of legend-lovers imagines, and it isn't always because they wish to. It is because, against their will, they do it rather than sit around with nine-tenths of the women available to them and listen to the same old routine feminine chatter on all the routine subjects from sex, Dorothy Thompson, and the novels of D. H. Lawrence on the one hand to the ineffable delights of the conga and the deep problem dramas of Noel Coward on the other, not forgetting, of course, how come such a charming and interesting man as oneself (that is, if one has ordered eight dollars' worth of caviar and a bottle of vintage Bollinger and has brushed one's hair that day) has never married but how wonderful it must be anyway not to be tied down to any one woman.

A second misconception is the bachelor's enormous popularity with hostesses, it apparently being the theory that, simply because one happens to be a bachelor, hostesses constantly fall all over themselves in a mad scramble for one's company. That bachelors, by virtue of their estate, are relatively easy and available prey for hostesses seeking to fill out dinner tables, dance floors, and the attentions of the more silly, voluble, and neglected dowagers, is not to be denied. But that any hostess of experience doesn't in turn know from that experience that a bachelor is something of a problem and may be even an instrument of disconcerting pain is to be doubted only by those whom the aforesaid hostess has never taken into her confidence.

The trouble with bachelors in this respect is threefold. In the first place, they usually seem to have mysterious engagements of one sort or another, not always entirely mythical, which remove them from the party at least an hour or two before the hostess has reckoned, thus leaving a number of extra women seated forlornly in corners with no one to talk to and with the hostess herself, to her distress, compelled to weary herself being solicitous about them. In the second place, the bachelor is more inclined to be quickly bored than the non-bachelor, and is hence a further concern to his hostess. The reasons for the bachelor's relative ennui are several. Whereas a married man finds diversion in mingling for a change with women other than his wife, the bachelor, to whom such mingling is a commonplace, finds neither novelty nor any particular excitement in it. Again, whereas a married man has from long training in the art made himself adaptable to formality and as a matter of fact secretly likes it, the bachelor finds it rather uncomfortable and tedious and prefers his own somewhat looser punctilio. And in the third and final place, the bachelor is above all usually an irritatingly selfish fish and demands twice as much attention from a hostess as a married man. He feels, doodle that he essentially is, that he is doing his hostess a favor by the mere act of contributing his presence and he expects it to be appreciated. This is especially true if he falls into the social category of the "extra man," that is, the bachelor equivalent of military reinforcements, the fellow who is called upon at the last moment to fill in the dinner chair next to some particularly dull female (the aforesaid chair having been deserted, also at the last moment, by some more independent and assertive bachelor), to sit through a show he has already been summoned to sit through at least five times, or to attempt to loosen up some visiting duchess's joints sufficiently to persuade the onlookers that it is a rumba and not a minuet that is being danced.

A further popular misconception is that a bachelor is extremely fortunate in being able to go home late at night, lock himself in from outside bothers, be alone with himself, and meditate quietly to his heart's content. Anyone who believes that doesn't know the truth by half. The telephone companies' records will attest to the fact that most of the peremptory requests for changes of phone numbers come regularly from bachelors. The bachelor who, when he gets home at night, finds peace and quiet is largely a product of others' romantic imaginations. If he isn't awakened by telephone calls of all varieties, he is disturbed by all kinds of friends in the shape of visitors and droppers-in who somehow imagine that a bachelor is synonymous with a bartender, a guide to the night life of the city, a confidential directory of all the great stage beauties since Lily Langtry, a prestidigitator of sandwiches, and a sweet reprobate generally. The biggest laugh that the poor bachelor can evoke on such occasions is to remark that he has to get up early the next morning and work.

The notion that a bachelor is especially blessed by Providence and is a combination William Wycherley, Casanova, and recherché maître d'hôtel, with slight overtones of Florenz Ziegfeld, Basil Zaharoff, and Moët and Chandon, is shared even by the world's law-makers, who every now and again seek to make him conscious of and pay for his theoretical great privilege. Taxes on bachelors are regularly proposed in the various nations; in Italy, in Germany, and in Greece today, indeed, a considerable fee is ordained. And in other countries the fight to make him cough up handsomely is making big strides. But the last straw came recently in a press dispatch from Dover, Delaware, in this, our great republic. The dispatch was as follows: "The Legislature has received a proposal to tax bachelors for the support of a home for unwed expectant mothers. A bill introduced recently by Representative William R. Ringler would require all bachelors over thirty to pay fifty dollars a year."

There are, of course, it is to be admitted, certain compensations, hereinafter to be duly and gratefully noted, which the bachelor enjoys, but they are assuredly not the ones that the layman, in his profound ignorance, conjures up. The bachelor's admired freedom is often a yoke, for the freer a man is to himself the greater slave he often is to the whims of others. The bachelor as envied Lothario is frequently a migraine to the bachelor himself, for Lotharioism is simply monogamy's doldrums multiplied, and with thrice monogamy's duties, penalties, and wear and tear. And the bachelor's respected privacy, as before observed, is frequently the privacy of a monkey in a zoo. The day when everyone begins properly laughing at bachelors instead of envying and admiring them will see a wholesale bachelor stampede to the altar, God forbid.

Corollary

The persistence of the myth that the bachelor is the most enviable of men is further attested to by the beaver-like industry of others hypothetically less fortunate in attempting to dislodge him from his offensively happy estate. The campaign against him, indeed, partakes of sheer venom, its bitterness ill-concealed. In witness whereof, consider the above-mentioned frequent proposals, in some instances already put into harsh practice, to impose a heavy public tax on him in revenge for the softness of his existence. In Italy the assault has reached its height. There the government has inflicted a particularly severe assessment against him to pay for the births, care, and upbringing of married men's babies. But even this has not persuaded the authentic and determined wop bachelor to give up the self-fancies luxurious delights of single blessedness. Of 1,800,000 of the species only 17,683 have thus far permitted the impost to wobble them. The rest not only have taken it in their stride with a complacent grin but have not permitted even a new supplementary levy over and above the normal income tax to move them half an inch nearer to the altar.

It is commonly assumed that women are the greatest foes of bachelorhood. While no one can say that they do not do their thorough damnedest to wean the bachelor from his single heaven, they are hardly more assiduous than the males to whom the fellow irritatingly and even painfully represents their own lost gala independence.

The technique of these males is generally as obvious as it is devious. Through statistics dubiously arrived at, and which they have foxily spread far and wide, they inform their enemy that married men live longer than single men, thus hoping to alarm the bachelor into sudden matrimony. Their philosophy hurled at their foe, they then proceed to try to argue him into a conviction that he is ruining his digestion with restaurant food, whereas good home-cooking, hypothetically obtainable only in the houses of the married, would be of immense comfort and therapeutical benefit to him. This second philosophy, humorously meditates the bachelor, is apparently based on the theory that the chef at the Colony, Larue's, the Voisin, the Passy, or even the Canari d'Or is a Simon-pure lug compared with the least Polish female cook to be found in the average household.

Observing that the bachelor does not seem to be properly impressed, the crusading benedick now has at him with the sentimental whimsy that it's wonderful to have a real home with a loving and solicitous wife and a warm grate-fire and a comfortable dressing gown and soft slippers—there's nothing like it, take it from me, old man! At this juncture the bachelor glances covertly at his watch and notes, not without a trace of analytical drollery, that it is now 2:30 A.M. and that his vis-à-vis is about to order up still another round of drinks.

Another pet weapon in the benedick's arsenal is babies. You don't know, old man, what you're missing; until you have a child you're only half living! It presently develops, however, that the philosopher's two offspring are somehow not doing their romantic duty by papa. His son, it appears, has been kicked out of three jobs for playing craps an hour at a stretch in the washroom and his daughter, it seems, spends most of her time dancing the rumba with a bunch of gigolos in the night clubs and getting home in the small hours of the morning smelling like a gin bottle.

Still another argument is that the bachelor wastes a lot of time spreading his affections over a quorum of women when he might much more profitably and enjoyably confine them to one who would truly appreciate him. At this point the bachelor calls for a copy of the *World Almanac* and ruminates on the steadily increasing national divorce statistics of recent years, the number for the last available year establishing an all-time high record.

The female foes of the bachelor display what they evidently esteem as a greater cunning still, poor girls. Their strategy is best reflected in the sly philosophies which they expound in the daily, weekly, and monthly prints. These are recommended to the fair sex generally in their sniping war on the celibate.

By way of luring the bachelor into matrimony, we read such recommendations as the following:

1. "Study up on his hobbies, even if it means knowing your DiMaggio or a straight-grain briar from a calabash."

Critical footnote: Any woman who gabbles superficially about a bachelor's hobbies, whatever they may be, strikes him as something of an idiot. The woman, for example, who thinks to make a hit with him by telling him her ideas on Joe DiMaggio or briar pipes drives him posthaste to some cutie who doesn't know head or tail about his hobbies, who doesn't know exactly whether you smoke DiMaggio or make home runs with briar pipes, and who contents herself simply in every once in a while accidentally brushing his knee with hers under the table.

2. "When he suggests the movies or a show for entertainment, play up the quiet-evening-at-home idea."

Critical footnote: Inasmuch as the bachelor in all likelihood really wants to see the movie or the show, any such proposal that he stay quietly at home and be bored to death listening about DiMaggio and briar pipes makes him pretty mad. If he wanted a quiet evening at home he would have remained at his own home in the first place.

3. "Make yourself useful about his apartment."

Critical footnote: This will literally drive him crazy. The busybody who goes about doing things to a bachelor's quarters is his bête noire. He likes his quarters the way they are, even, in point of fact, if the place looks like a Chinese outhouse, and any woman who tries to alter it may count herself on his index expurgatorius. His maid and valet will do all the fixing necessary, if any, and when they do it he doesn't relish even their ministrations.

4. "Don't let him think marriage will change his life."

Critical footnote: If he imagines for a moment that marriage is in a woman's mind, he will run like the very devil. If it is in anyone's mind, he wants it to be solely in his own. If and when conceivably he marries, you will usually find he marries the girl who wasn't much thinking about it one way or another.

5. "When you telephone him, don't tell him your name. Make him guess who it is."

Critical footnote: Try any such nonsense and he'll hang up.

6. "Most bachelors like to be considered helpless babies who need looking after."

Critical footnote: Any such damned fool, bachelor or benedick, isn't worth any intelligent woman's effort. Go after one who not only knows how to take care of himself perfectly but who knows how to take care of you.

Such slivers of moonshine sufficiently suggest the general tenor.

In conclusion, possibly the greatest testimonial to bachelordom appeared not long ago in an editorial in the estimable *New Yorker*. I quote it:

"Bachelors, we've noticed, are seldom troubled by moths, and this is curious because few of them take any precautions whatever. Let a man marry, however, and there is no bag or spray or clever trap that will keep them out. We have spent years trying to get to the bottom of this phenomenon, but without much success. The fact nevertheless remains that bachelors don't have moths."

THE NOBLEST INSTRUMENT

By CLARENCE DAY

FATHER HAD BEEN AWAY, REORGANIZING SOME OLD UPSTATE RAIL-road. He returned in an executive mood and proceeded to shake up our home. In spite of my failure as a singer, he was still bound to have us taught music. We boys were summoned before him and informed that we must at once learn to play on something. We might not appreciate it now, he said, but we should later on. "You, Clarence, will learn the violin. George, you the piano. Julian—well, Julian is too young yet. But you older boys must have lessons."

I was appalled at this order. At the age of ten it seemed a disaster to lose any more of my freedom. The days were already too short for our games after school; and now here was a chunk to come out of playtime three days every week. A chunk every day, we found afterward, because we had to practice.

George sat at the piano in the parlor, and faithfully learned to pound out his exercises. He had all the luck. He was not an inspired player, but at least he had some ear for music. He also had the advantage of playing on a good robust instrument, which he didn't have to be careful not to drop, and was in no danger of breaking. Furthermore, he did not have to tune it. A piano had some good points.

But I had to go through a blacker and more gruesome experience. It was bad enough to have to come in from the street and the sunlight and go down into our dark little basement where I took my lessons. But that was only the opening chill of the struggle that followed.

The whole thing was uncanny. The violin itself was a queer, fragile, cigar-boxy thing, that had to be handled most gingerly. Nothing sturdy about it. Why, a fellow was liable to crack it putting it into its case. And then my teacher, he was queer too. He had a queer pickled smell.

I dare say he wasn't queer at all really, but he seemed so to me, because he was different from the people I generally met. He was probably worth a dozen of some of them, but I didn't know it. He was one of the violins in the Philharmonic, and an excellent player; a grave, middle-aged little man—who was obliged to give lessons.

He wore a black, wrinkled frock coat, and a discolored gold watch-chain. He had small, black-rimmed glasses; not tortoise-shell, but thin rims of metal. His violin was dark, rich, and polished, and would do anything for him.

Mine was balky and awkward, brand new, and of a light, common color.

The violin is intended for persons with a passion for music. I wasn't that kind of person. I liked to hear a band play a tune that we could march up and down to, but try as I would, I could seldom whistle such a tune afterward. My teacher didn't know this. He greeted me as a possible genius.

He taught me how to hold the contraption, tucked under my chin. I learned how to move my fingers here and there on its handle or stem. I learned how to draw the bow across the strings, and thus produce sounds. . . .

Does a mother recall the first cry of her baby, I wonder? I still remember the strange cry at birth of that new violin.

My teacher, Herr M., looked as though he had suddenly taken a large glass of vinegar. He sucked in his breath. His lips were drawn back from his teeth, and his eyes tightly shut. Of course, he hadn't expected my notes to be sweet at the start; but still, there was something unearthly about that first cry. He snatched the violin from me, examined it, readjusted its pegs, and comforted it gently, by drawing his own bow across it. It was only a new and not especially fine violin, but the sounds it made for him were more natural—they were classifiable sounds. They were not richly musical, but at least they had been heard before on this earth.

He handed the instrument back to me with careful directions. I tucked it up under my chin again and grasped the end tight. I held my bow exactly as ordered. I looked up at him, waiting.

"Now," he said, nervously.

I slowly raised the bow, drew it downward. . . .

This time there were *two* dreadful cries in our little front basement. One came from my new violin and one from the heart of Herr M.

Herr M. presently came to, and smiled bravely at me, and said if I wanted to rest a moment he would permit it. He seemed to think I might wish to lie down awhile and recover. I didn't feel any need of lying down. All I wanted was to get through the lesson. But Herr M. was shaken. He was by no means ready to let me proceed. He looked around desperately, saw the music book, and said he would now show me that. We sat down side by side on the window-seat, with the book in his lap, while he pointed out the notes to me with his finger, and told me their names.

After a bit, when he felt better, he took up his own violin, and instructed me to watch him and note how he handled the strings. And then at last, he nerved himself to let me take my violin again. "Softly, my child, softly," he begged me, and stood facing the wall. . . .

We got through the afternoon somehow, but it was a ghastly experience. Part of the time he was maddened by the mistakes I kept making, and part of the time he was plain wretched. He covered his eyes. He seemed ill. He looked often at his watch, even shook it as though it had stopped; but he stayed the full hour.

That was Wednesday. What struggles he had with himself before Friday, when my second lesson was due, I can only dimly imagine, and of course I never even gave them a thought at the time. He came back to recommence teaching me, but he had changed—he had hardened. Instead of being cross, he was stern; and instead of sad, bitter. He wasn't unkind to me, but we were no longer companions. He talked to himself, under his breath; and sometimes he took bits of paper, and did little sums on them, gloomily, and then tore them up.

During my third lesson I saw the tears come to his eyes. He went up to Father and said he was sorry but he honestly felt sure I'd never be able to play.

Father didn't like this at all. He said he felt sure I would. He dismissed Herr M. briefly—the poor man came stumbling back down in two minutes. In that short space of time he had gallantly

gone upstairs in a glow, resolved upon sacrificing his earnings for
the sake of telling the truth. He returned with his earnings still
running, but with the look of a lost soul about him, as though he
felt that his nerves and his sanity were doomed to destruction.
He was low in his mind, and he talked to himself more than ever.
Sometimes he spoke harshly of America, sometimes of fate.

But he no longer struggled. He accepted this thing as his destiny. He regarded me as an unfortunate something, outside the
human species, whom he must simply try to labor with as well
as he could. It was a grotesque, indeed a hellish experience, but
he felt he must bear it.

He wasn't the only one—he was at least not alone in his suf-
ferings. Mother, though expecting the worst, had tried to be hopeful about it, but at the end of a week or two I heard her and
Margaret talking it over. I was slaughtering a scale in the front
basement, when Mother came down and stood outside the door
in the kitchen hall and whispered, "Oh, Margaret!"

I watched them. Margaret was baking a cake. She screwed up
her face, raised her arms, and brought them down with hands
clenched.

"I don't know what we shall do, Margaret."

"The poor little feller," Margaret whispered. "He can't make
the thing go."

This made me indignant. They were making me look like a
lubber. I wished to feel always that I could make anything go. . . .

I now began to feel a determination to master this thing. History shows us many examples of the misplaced determinations of
men—they are one of the darkest aspects of human life, they
spread so much needless pain: but I knew little history. And I
viewed what little I did know romantically—I should have seen in
such episodes their heroism, not their futility. Any role that seemed
heroic attracted me, no matter how senseless.

Not that I saw any chance for heroism in our front basement,
of course. You had to have a battlefield or something. I saw only
that I was appearing ridiculous. But that stung my pride. I hadn't
wanted to learn anything whatever about fiddles or music. But
since I was in for it, I'd do it, and show them I could. A boy will

often put in enormous amounts of his time trying to prove he isn't as ridiculous as he thinks people think him.

Meanwhile Herr M. and I had discovered that I was near-sighted. On account of the violin's being an instrument that sticks out in front of one, I couldn't stand close enough to the music book to see the notes clearly. He didn't at first realize that I often made mistakes from that cause. When he and I finally comprehended that I had this defect, he had a sudden new hope that this might have been the whole trouble, and that when it was corrected I might play like a human being at last.

Neither of us ventured to take up this matter with Father. We knew that it would have been hard to convince him that my eyes were not perfect, I being a son of his and presumably made in his image; and we knew that he immediately would have felt we were trying to make trouble for him, and would have shown an amount of resentment which it was best to avoid. So Herr M. instead lent me his glasses. These did fairly well. They turned the dim grayness of the notes into a queer bright distortion, but the main thing was they did make them brighter, so that I now saw more of them. How well I remember those little glasses. Poor dingy old things. Herr M. was nervous about lending them to me; he feared that I'd drop them. It would have been safer if they had been spectacles: but no, they were pince-nez; and I had to learn to balance them across my nose as well as I could. I couldn't wear them up near my eyes because my nose was too thin there; I had to put them about half-way down where there was enough flesh to hold them. I also had to tilt my head back, for the music-stand was a little too tall for me. Herr M. sometimes mounted me on a stool, warning me not to step off. Then when I was all set, and when he without his glasses was blind, I would smash my way into the scales again.

All during the long winter months I worked away at this job. I gave no thought, of course, to the family. But they did to me. Our house was heated by a furnace, which had big warm air pipes; these ran up through the walls with wide outlets into each room, and sound traveled easily and ringingly through their roomy, tin passages. My violin could be heard in every part of the house. No one could settle down to anything while I was practicing.

If visitors came they soon left. Mother couldn't even sing to the baby. She would wait, watching the clock, until my long hour of scalework was over, and then come downstairs and shriek at me that my time was up. She would find me sawing away with my forehead wet, and my hair wet and stringy, and even my clothes slowly getting damp from my exertions. She would feel my collar, which was done for, and say I must change it. "Oh, Mother! Please!"—for I was in a hurry now to run out and play. But she wasn't being fussy about my collar, I can see, looking back; she was using it merely as a barometer or gauge of my pores. She thought I had better dry myself before going out in the snow.

It was a hard winter for Mother. I believe she also had fears for the baby. She sometimes pleaded with Father; but no one could ever tell Father anything. He continued to stand like a rock against stopping my lessons.

Schopenhauer, in his rules for debating, shows how to win a weak case by insidiously transferring an argument from its right field, and discussing it instead from some irrelevant but impregnable angle. Father knew nothing of Schopenhauer, and was never insidious, but, nevertheless, he had certain natural gifts for debate. In the first place his voice was powerful and stormy, and he let it out at full strength, and kept on letting it out with a vigor that stunned his opponents. As a second gift, he was convinced at all times that his opponents were wrong. Hence, even if they did win a point or two, it did them no good, for he dragged the issue to some other ground then, where he and Truth could prevail. When Mother said it surely was plain enough that I had no ear, what was his reply? Why, he said that the violin was the noblest instrument invented by man. Having silenced her with this solid premise he declared that it followed that any boy was lucky to be given the privilege of learning to play it. No boy should expect to learn it immediately. It required persistence. Everything, he had found, required persistence. The motto was, Never give up.

All his life, he declared, he had persevered in spite of discouragement, and he meant to keep on persevering, and he meant me to, too. He said that none of us realized what he had had to go through. If he had been the kind that gave up at the very first obstacle, where would he have been now—where would any of the family have been? The answer was, apparently, that we'd either have been in a very bad way, poking round for crusts in the gutter, or else nonexistent. We might have never even been born if Father had not persevered.

Placed beside this record of Father's vast trials overcome, the little difficulty of my learning to play the violin seemed a trifle. I faithfully spurred myself on again, to work at the puzzle. Even my teacher seemed impressed with these views on persistence. Though older than Father, he had certainly not made as much money, and he bowed to the experience of a practical man who was a success. If he, Herr M., had been a success he would not have had to teach boys; and sitting in this black pit in which his need of money had placed him, he saw more than ever that he must learn the ways of this world. He listened with all his heart, as to a god, when Father shook his forefinger, and told him how to climb to the heights where financial rewards were achieved. The idea he got was that perserverance was sure to lead to great wealth.

Consequently our front basement continued to be the home of lost causes.

Of course, I kept begging Herr M. to let me learn just one tune. Even though I seldom could whistle them, still I liked tunes; and I knew that, in my hours of practicing, a tune would be a comfort. That is, for myself. Here again I never gave a thought to the effect upon others.

Herr M., after many misgivings, to which I respectfully listened —though they were not spoken to me, they were muttered to himself, pessimistically—hunted through a worn old book of selections, and after much doubtful fumbling chose as simple a thing as he could find for me—for me and the neighbors.

It was spring now, and windows were open. That tune became famous.

What would the musician who had tenderly composed this air, years before, have felt if he had foreseen what an end it would have, on Madison Avenue; and how, before death, it would be execrated by that once peaceful neighborhood. I engraved it on their hearts; not in its true form but in my own eerie versions. It was the only tune I knew. Consequently I played and replayed it.

Even horrors when repeated grow old and lose part of their sting. But those I produced were, unluckily, never the same. To be sure, this tune kept its general structure the same, even in my sweating hands. There was always the place where I climbed unsteadily up to its peak, and that difficult spot where it wavered, or staggered, and stuck; and then a sudden jerk of resumption— I came out strong on that. Every afternoon when I got to that difficult spot, the neighbors dropped whatever they were doing to wait for that jerk, shrinking from the moment, and yet feverishly impatient for it to come.

But what made the tune and their anguish so different each day? I'll explain. The strings of a violin are wound at the end around pegs, and each peg must be screwed in and tightened till the string sounds just right. Herr M. left my violin properly tuned when he went. But suppose a string broke, or that somehow I jarred a peg loose. Its string then became slack and soundless. I had to re-tighten it. Not having an ear, I was highly uncertain about this.

Our neighbors never knew at what degree of tautness I'd put such a string. I didn't myself. I just screwed her up tight enough to make a strong reliable sound. Neither they nor I could tell which string would thus appear in a new role each day, nor foresee the profound transformations this would produce in that tune.

All that spring this unhappy and ill-destined melody floated out through my window, and writhed in the air for one hour daily, in sunshine or storm. All that spring our neighbors and I daily toiled to its peak, and staggered over its hump, so to speak, and fell wailing through space.

Things now began to be said to Mother which drove her to act. She explained to Father that the end had come at last. Absolutely. "This awful nightmare cannot go on," she said.

Father pooh-poohed her.

She cried. She told him what it was doing to her. He said that she was excited, and that her descriptions of the sounds I made were exaggerated and hysterical—must be. She was always too vehement, he shouted. She must learn to be calm.

"But you're downtown, *you* don't have to hear it!"

Father remained wholly skeptical.

She endeavored to shame him. She told him what awful things the neighbors were saying about him, because of the noise I was making, for which he was responsible.

He couldn't be made to look at it that way. If there really were any unpleasantness then I was responsible. He had provided me with a good teacher and a good violin—so he reasoned. In short, he had done his best, and no father could have done more. If I made hideous sounds after all that, the fault must be mine. He said that Mother should be stricter with me, if necessary, and make me try harder.

This was the last straw. I couldn't try harder. When Mother told me his verdict I said nothing, but my body rebelled. Self-discipline had its limits—and I wanted to be out: it was spring. I skimped my hours of practice when I heard the fellows playing outside. I came home late for lessons—even forgot them. Little by little they stopped.

Father was outraged. His final argument, I remember, was that my violin had cost twenty-five dollars; if I didn't learn it the money would be wasted, and he couldn't afford it. But it was put to him that my younger brother, Julian, could learn it instead, later on. Then summer came, anyhow, and we went for three months to the seashore; and in the confusion of this Father was defeated and I was set free.

In the autumn little Julian was led away one afternoon, and imprisoned in the front basement in my place. I don't remember how long they kept him down there, but it was several years. He had an ear, however, and I believe he learned to play fairly well. This would have made a happy ending for Herr M. after all; but it was some other teacher, a younger man, who was engaged to teach Julian. Father said Herr M. was a failure.

RING OUT, WILD BELLS

By Wolcott Gibbs

WHEN I FINALLY GOT AROUND TO SEEING MAX REINHARDT'S CINEMA version of "A Midsummer-Night's Dream," and saw a child called Mickey Rooney playing Puck, I remembered suddenly that long ago I had taken the same part.

Our production was given on the open-air stage at the Riverdale Country School, shortly before the war. The scenery was only the natural scenery of that suburban dell, and the cast was exclusively male, ranging in age from eleven to perhaps seventeen. While we had thus preserved the pure, Elizabethan note of the original, it must be admitted that our version had its drawbacks. The costumes were probably the worst things we had to bear, and even Penrod, tragically arrayed as Launcelot in his sister's stockings and his father's drawers, might have been embarrassed for us. Like Penrod, we were costumed by our parents, and like the Schofields, they seemed on the whole a little weak historically. Half of the ladies were inclined to favor the Elizabethan, and they had constructed rather bunchy ruffs and farthingales for their offspring; others, who had read as far as the stage directions and learned that the action took place in an Athenian wood, had produced something vaguely Athenian, usually beginning with a sheet. Only the fairies had a certain uniformity. For some reason their parents had all decided on cheesecloth, with here and there a little ill-advised trimming with tinsel.

My own costume was mysterious, but spectacular. As nearly as I have ever been able to figure things out, my mother found her inspiration for it in a Maxfield Parrish picture of a court jester. Beginning at the top, there was a cap with three stuffed horns; then, for the main part, a pair of tights that covered me to my wrists and ankles; and finally slippers with stuffed toes that curled up at the ends. The whole thing was made out of silk in alternate

37

green and red stripes, and (unquestionably my poor mother's most demented stroke) it was covered from head to foot with a thousand tiny bells. Because all our costumes were obviously perishable, we never wore them in rehearsal, and naturally nobody knew that I was invested with these peculiar sound effects until I made my entrance at the beginning of the second act.

Our director was a man who had strong opinions about how Shakespeare should be played, and Puck was one of his favorite characters. It was his theory that Puck, being "the incarnation of mischief," never ought to be still a minute, so I had been coached to bound onto the stage, and once there to dance up and down, cocking my head and waving my arms.

"I want you to be a little whirlwind," this man said.

Even as I prepared to bound onto the stage, I had my own misgivings about those dangerously abundant gestures, and their probable effect on my bells. It was too late, however, to invent another technique for playing Puck, even if there had been room for anything but horror in my mind. I bounded onto the stage.

The effect, in its way, must have been superb. With every leap I rang like a thousand children's sleighs, my melodies foretelling God knows what worlds of merriment to the enchanted spectators. It was even worse when I came to the middle of the stage and went into my gestures. The other ringing had been loud but sporadic. This was persistent, varying only slightly in volume and pitch with the vehemence of my gestures. To a blind man, it must have sounded as though I had recklessly decided to accompany myself on a xylophone. A maturer actor would probably have made up his mind that an emergency existed, and abandoned his gestures as impracticable under the circumstances. I was thirteen, and incapable of innovations. I had been told by responsible authorities that gesture went with this part, and I continued to make them. I also continued to ring—a silvery music, festive and horrible.

If the bells were hard on my nerves, they were even worse for the rest of the cast, who were totally unprepared for my new interpretation. Puck's first remark is addressed to one of the fairies, and it is mercifully brief.

I said, "How now, spirit! Whither wander you?"

This unhappy child, already embarrassed by a public appearance in cheesecloth and tinsel, was also burdened with an opening speech of sixteen lines in verse. He began bravely:

> "Over hill, over dale,
>   Through bush, through brier,
> Over park, over pale,
>   Through flood, through fire . . ."

At the word "fire," my instructions were to bring my hands up from the ground in a long, wavery sweep, intended to represent fire. The bells pealed. To my startled ears, it sounded more as if they exploded. The fairy stopped in his lines and looked at me sharply. The jingling, however, had diminished; it was no more than as if a faint wind stirred my bells, and he went on:

> "I do wander every where,
>   Swifter than the moone's sphere . . ."

Here again I had another cue, for a sort of swoop and dip indicating the swiftness of the moone's sphere. Again the bells rang out, and again the performance stopped in its tracks. The fairy was clearly troubled by these interruptions. He had, however, a child's strange acceptance of the inscrutable, and was even able to regard my bells as a last-minute adult addition to the program, nerve-racking but not to be questioned. I'm sure it was only this that got him through that first speech.

My turn, when it came, was even worse. By this time the audience had succumbed to a helpless gaiety. Every time my bells rang, laughter swept the spectators, and this mounted and mingled with the bells until everything else was practically inaudible. I began my speech, another long one, and full of incomprehensible references to Titania's changeling.

"Louder!" said somebody in the wings. "You'll have to talk louder."

It was the director, and he seemed to be in a dangerous state.

"And for heaven's sake, stop that jingling!" he said.

I talked louder, and I tried to stop the jingling, but it was no use. By the time I got to the end of my speech, I was shouting and so was the audience. It appeared that I had very little control over the bells, which continued to jingle in spite of my passionate efforts to keep them quiet.

All this had a very bad effect on the fairy, who by this time had many symptoms of a complete nervous collapse. However, he began his next speech:

> "Either I mistake your shape and making quite,
> Or else you are that shrewd and knavish sprite
> Call'd Robin Goodfellow: are you not he
> That . . ."

At this point I forgot that the rules had been changed and I was supposed to leave out the gestures. There was a furious jingling, and the fairy gulped.

"Are you not he that, that . . ."

He looked miserably at the wings, and the director supplied the next line, but the tumult was too much for him. The unhappy child simply shook his head.

"Say anything!" shouted the director desperately. "Anything at all!"

The fairy only shut his eyes and shuddered.

"All right!" shouted the director. "All right, Puck, *You* begin *your* next speech."

By some miracle, I actually did remember my next lines, and had opened my mouth to begin on them when suddenly the fairy spoke. His voice was a high, thin monotone, and there seemed to be madness in it, but it was perfectly clear.

"Fourscore and seven years ago," he began, "our fathers brought forth on this continent a new nation, conceived . . ."

He said it right through to the end, and it was certainly the most successful speech ever made on that stage, and probably one of the most successful speeches ever made on any stage. I don't remember, if I ever knew, how the rest of us ever picked up the dull, normal thread of the play after that extraordinary performance, but we must have, because I know it went on. I only remember that in the next intermission the director cut off my bells with his penknife, and after that things quieted down and got dull.

POLYP WITH A PAST

The Story of an Organism With a Heart

By ROBERT BENCHLEY

OF ALL FORMS OF ANIMAL LIFE, THE POLYP IS PROBABLY THE MOST neglected by fanciers. People seem willing to pay attention to anything, cats, lizards, canaries, or even fish, but simply because the polyp is reserved by nature and not given to showing off or wearing its heart on its sleeve, it is left alone under the sea to slave away at coral-building with never a kind word or a pat on the tentacles from anybody.

It was quite by accident that I was brought face to face with the human side of a polyp. I had been working on a thesis on "Emotional Crisis in Sponge Life," and came upon a polyp formation on a piece of coral in the course of my laboratory work. To say that I was astounded would be putting it mildly. I was surprised.

The difficulty in research work in this field came in isolating a single polyp from the rest in order to study the personal peculiarities of the little organism, for, as is so often the case (even, I fear, with us great big humans sometimes), the individual behaves in an entirely different manner in private from the one he adopts when there is a crowd around. And a polyp, among all creatures, has a minimum of time to himself in which to sit down and think. There is always a crowd of other polyps dropping in on him, urging him to make a fourth in a string of coral beads or just to come out and stick around on a rock for the sake of good-fellowship.

The one which I finally succeeded in isolating was an engaging organism with a provocative manner and a little way of wrinkling up its ectoderm which put you at once at your ease. There could be no formality about your relations with this polyp five minutes after your first meeting. You were just like one great big family.

Although I have no desire to retail gossip, I think that readers

41

of this treatise ought to be made aware of the fact (if, indeed, they do not already know it) that a polyp is really neither one thing nor another in matters of gender. One day it may be a little boy polyp, another day a little girl, according to its whim or practical considerations of policy. On gray days, when everything seems to be going wrong, it may decide that it will be neither boy nor girl but will just drift. I think that if we big human cousins of the little polyp were to follow the example set by these lowliest of God's creatures in this matter, we all would find ourselves much better off in the end. Am I not right, little polyp?

What was my surprise, then, to discover my little friend one day in a gloomy and morose mood. It refused the peanut-butter which I had brought it and I observed through the microscope that it was shaking with sobs. Lifting it up with a pair of pincers I took it over to the window to let it watch the automobiles go by, a diversion which had, in the past, never failed to amuse. But I could see that it was not interested. A tune from the Victrola fell equally flat, even though I set my little charge on the center of the disc and allowed it to revolve at a dizzy pace, which frolic usually sent it into spasms of excited giggling. Something was wrong. It was under emotional stress of the most racking kind.

I consulted Klunzinger's "Die Korallenthiere des Rothen Meeres" and there found that at an early age the polyp is quite likely to become the victim of a sentimental passion which is directed at its own self.

In other words, my tiny companion was in love with itself, bitterly, desperately, head-over-heels in love.

In an attempt to divert it from this madness, I took it on an extended tour of the Continent, visiting all the old cathedrals and stopping at none but the best hotels. The malady grew worse, instead of better. I thought that perhaps the warm sun of Granada would bring the color back into those pale tentacles, but there the inevitable romance in the soft air was only fuel to the flame, and, in the shadows of the Alhambra, my little polyp gave up the fight and died of a broken heart without ever having declared its love to itself.

I returned to America shortly after not a little chastened by what I had witnessed of Nature's wonders in the realm of passion.

THE BRAIN GOES HOME

By Damon Runyon

ONE NIGHT THE BRAIN IS WALKING ME UP AND DOWN BROADWAY, in front of Mindy's Restaurant, and speaking of this and that, when along comes a red-headed raggedy doll selling apples at five cents per copy, and The Brain, being very fond of apples, grabs one out of her basket and hands her a five-dollar bill.

The red-headed raggedy doll, who is maybe thirty-odd and is nothing but a crow as far as looks are concerned, squints at the finnif, and says to The Brain like this:

"I do not have change for so much money," she says, "but I will go and get it in a minute."

"You keep the change," The Brain says, biting a big hunk out of the apple and taking my arm to start me walking again.

Well, the raggedy doll looks at The Brain again, and it seems to me that all of a sudden there are large tears in her eyes as she says:

"Oh, thank you, sir! Thank you, thank you, and God bless you, sir!"

And then she goes on up the street in a hurry, with her hands over her eyes and her shoulders shaking, and The Brain turns around very much astonished, and watches her until she is out of sight.

"Why, my goodness!" The Brain says. "I give Doris Clare ten G's last night, and she does not make half as much fuss over it as this doll does over a pound note."

"Well," I say, "maybe the apple doll needs a pound note more than Doris needs ten G's."

"Maybe so," The Brain says. "And of course, Doris gives me much more in return than just an apple and a God bless me. Doris gives me her love. I guess," The Brain says, "that love costs me about as much dough as any guy that ever lives."

43

"I guess it does," I say, and the chances are we both guess right, because off-hand I figure that if The Brain gets out on three hundred G's per year for love, he is running his love business very economically indeed, because it is well known to one and all that The brain has three different dolls, besides an ever-loving wife.

In fact, The Brain is sometimes spoken of by many citizens as the "Love King," but only behind his back, because The Brain likes to think his love affairs are a great secret to all but maybe a few, although the only guy I ever see in this town who does not know all about them is a guy who is deaf, dumb, and blind.

I once read a story about a guy by the name of King Solomon who lives a long time ago and who has a thousand dolls all at once, which is going in for dolls on a very large scale indeed, but I guarantee that all of King Solomon's dolls put together are not as expensive as any one of The Brain's dolls. The overhead on Doris Clare alone will drive an ordinary guy daffy, and Doris is practically frugal compared to Cynthia Harris and Bobby Baker.

Then there is Charlotte, who is The Brain's ever-loving wife and who has a society bug and needs plenty of coconuts at all times to keep her a going concern. I once hear The Brain tell Bobby Baker that his ever-loving wife is a bit of an invalid, but as a matter of fact there is never anything the matter with Charlotte that a few bobs will not cure, although of course this goes for nearly every doll in this world who is an invalid.

When a guy is knocking around Broadway as long as The Brain, he is bound to accumulate dolls here and there, but most guys accumulate one at a time, and when this one runs out on him, as Broadway dolls will do, he accumulates another, and so on, and so on, until he is too old to care about such matters as dolls, which is when he is maybe a hundred and four years old, although I hear of several guys who beat even this record.

But when The Brain accumulates a doll he seems to keep her accumulated, and none of them ever run out on him, and while this will be a very great nuisance to the average guy, it pleases The Brain no little because it makes him think he has a very great power over dolls.

"They are not to blame if they fall in love with me," The Brain says to me one night. "I will not cause one of them any sorrow for all the world."

Well, of course, it is most astonishing to me to hear a guy as smart as The Brain using such language, but I figure he may really believe it, because The Brain thinks very good of himself at all times. However, some guys claim that the real reason The Brain keeps all his dolls is because he is too selfish to give them away, although personally I will not take any of them if The Brain throws in a cash bonus, except maybe Bobby Baker.

Anyway, The Brain keeps his dolls accumulated, and furthermore he spends plenty of dough on them, what with buying them automobiles and furs and diamonds and swell places to live in—especially swell places to live in. One time I tell The Brain he will save himself plenty if he hires a house and bunches his dolls together in one big happy family, instead of having them scattered all over town, but The Brain says this idea is no good.

"In the first place," he says, "they do not know about each other, except Doris and Cynthia and Bobby know about Charlotte, although she does not know about them. They each think they are the only one with me. So if I corral them all together they will be jealous of each other over my love. Anyway," The Brain says, "such an arrangement will be very immoral and against the law. No," he says, "it is better to have them in different spots, because think of the many homes it gives me to go to in case I wish to go home. In fact," The Brain says, "I guess I have more homes to go to than any other guy on Broadway."

Well, this may be true, but what The Brain wants with a lot of different homes is a very great mystery on Broadway, because he seldom goes home, anyway, his idea in not going home being that something may happen in this town while he is at home that he is not in on. The Brain seldom goes anywhere in particular. He never goes out in public with any one of his dolls, except maybe once or twice a year with Charlotte, his ever-loving wife, and finally he even stops going with her because Doris Clare says it does not look good to Doris's personal friends.

The Brain marries Charlotte long before he becomes the biggest guy in gambling operations in the East, and a millionaire two or three times over, but he is never much of a hand to sit around home and chew the fat with his ever-loving wife, as husbands often do. Furthermore, when he is poor he has to live in a neighborhood which is too far away for it to be convenient for him to go home, so finally he gets out of the habit of going there.

But Charlotte is not such a doll as cares to spend more than one or two years looking at the pictures on the wall, because it seems the pictures on her wall are nothing but pictures of cows in the meadows and houses covered with snow, so she does not go home any more than necessary, either, and has her own friends and is very happy indeed, especially after The Brain gets so he can send in right along.

I will say one thing about The Brain and his dolls: he never picks a crow. He has a very good eye for faces and shapes, and even Charlotte, his ever-loving wife, is not a crow, although she is not as young as she used to be. As for Doris Clare, she is one of the great beauties on the Ziegfeld roof in her day, and while her day is by no means yesterday, or even the day before, Doris holds on pretty well in the matter of looks. Giving her a shade the best of it, I will say that Doris is thirty-two or -three, but she has plenty of zing left in her, at that, and her hair remains very blonde, no matter what.

In fact, The Brain does not care much if his dolls are blonde or brunette, because Cynthia Harris's hair is as black as the inside of a wolf, while Bobby Baker is betwixt and between, her hair being a light brown. Cynthia Harris is more of a Johnny-come-lately than Doris, being out of Mr. Earl Carroll's "Vanities," and and I hear she first comes to New York as Miss Somebody in one of these beauty contests which she will win hands down if one of the judges does not get a big wink from a Miss Somebody Else.

Of course, Cynthia is doing some winking herself at this time, but it seems that she picks a guy to wink at thinking he is one of the judges, when he is nothing but a newspaper man and has no say whatever about the decision.

Well, Mr. Earl Carroll feels sorry for Cynthia, so he puts her in the "Vanities" and lets her walk around raw, and The Brain sees her, and the next thing anybody knows she is riding in a big foreign automobile the size of a rum chaser, and is chucking a terrible swell.

Personally, I always consider Bobby Baker the smartest of all
The Brain's dolls, because she is just middling as to looks and she
does not have any of the advantages of life like Doris Clare and
Cynthia Harris, such as jobs on the stage where they can walk
around showing off their shapes to guys such as The Brain. Bobby
Baker starts off as nothing but a private secretary to a guy in
Wall Street, and naturally she is always wearing clothes, or anyway, as many clothes as an ordinary doll wears nowadays, which
is not so many, at that.

It seems that The Brain once has some business with the guy
Bobby works for and happens to get talking to Bobby, and she
tells him how she always wishes to meet him, what with hearing
and reading about him, and how he is just as handsome and romantic-looking as she always pictures him to herself.

Now I wish to say I will never call any doll a liar, being at all
times a gentleman, and for all I know, Bobby Baker may really
think The Brain is handsome and romantic-looking, but personally
I figure if she is not lying to him, she is at least a little excited when
she makes such a statement to The Brain. The best you can give
The Brain at this time is that he is very well dressed.

He is maybe forty years old, give or take a couple of years, and
he is commencing to get a little bunchy about the middle, what
with sitting down at card-tables so much and never taking any
exercise outside of walking guys such as me up and down in front
of Mindy's for a few hours every night. He has a clean-looking
face, always very white around the gills, and he has nice teeth
and a nice smile when he wishes to smile, which is never at guys
who owe him dough.

And I will say for The Brain he has what is called personality.
He tells a story well, although he is always the hero of any story
he tells, and he knows how to make himself agreeable to dolls in
many ways. He has a pretty fair sort of education, and while dolls
such as Cynthia and Doris, and maybe Charlotte, too, will rather
have a charge account at Cartier's than all the education in Yale
and Harvard put together, it seems that Bobby Baker likes high-
brow gab, so naturally she gets plenty of same from The Brain.

Well, pretty soon Bobby is riding around in a car bigger than
Cynthia's, though neither is as big as Doris's car, and all the neigh-

bors' children over in Flatbush, which is where Bobby hails from, are very jealous of her and running around spreading gossip about her, but keeping their eyes open for big cars themselves. Personally, I always figure The Brain lowers himself socially by taking up with a doll from Flatbush, especially as Bobby Baker soon goes in for literary guys, such as newspaper scribes and similar characters around Greenwich Village.

But there is no denying Bobby Baker is a very smart little doll, and in the four or five years she is one of The Brain's dolls, she gets more dough out of him than all the others put together, because she is always telling him how much she loves him, and saying she cannot do without him, while Doris Clare and Cynthia Harris sometimes forget to mention this more than once or twice a month.

Now what happens early one morning but a guy by the name of Daffy Jack hauls off and sticks a shiv in The Brain's left side. It seems that this is done at the request of a certain party by the name of Homer Swing, who owes The Brain plenty of dough in a gambling transaction, and who becomes very indignant when The Brain presses him somewhat for payment. It seems that Daffy Jack, who is considered a very good shiv artist, aims at The Brain's heart, but misses it by a couple of inches, leaving The Brain with a very bad cut in his side which calls for some stitching.

Big Nig, the crap shooter, and I are standing at Fifty-second Street and Seventh Avenue along about 2 A.M., speaking of not much, when The Brain comes stumbling out of Fifty-second Street, and falls in Big Nig's arms, practically ruining a brand-new topcoat which Big Nig pays sixty bucks for a few days back with the blood that is coming out of the cut. Naturally, Big Nig is indignant about this, but we can see that it is no time to be speaking to The Brain about such matters. We can see that The Brain is carved up quite some, and is in a bad way.

Of course, we are not greatly surprised at seeing The Brain in this condition, because for years he is practically no price around this town, what with this guy and that being anxious to do something or other to him, but we are never expecting to see him carved up like a turkey. We are expecting to see him with a few slugs in him, and both Big Nig and me are very angry to think that there are guys around who will use such instruments as a knife on anybody.

But while we are thinking it over, The Brain says to me like this:

"Call Hymie Weissberger, and Doc Frisch," he says, "and take me home."

Naturally, a guy such as The Brain wishes his lawyer before he wishes his doctor, and Hymie Weissberger is The Brain's mouthpiece, and a very sure-footed guy, at that.

"Well," I say, "we better take you to a hospital where you can get good attention at once."

"No," The Brain says. "I wish to keep this secret. It will be a bad thing for me right now to have this get out, and if you take me to a hospital they must report it to the coppers. Take me home."

Naturally, I say which home, being somewhat confused about The Brain's homes, and he seems to study a minute as if this is a question to be well thought out.

"Park Avenue," The Brain says finally, so Big Nig stops a taxicab, and we help The Brain into the cab and tell the jockey to take us to the apartment house on Park Avenue near Sixty-fourth where The Brain's ever-loving wife Charlotte lives.

When we get there, I figure it is best for me to go up first and break the news gently to Charlotte, because I can see what a shock it is bound to be to any ever-loving wife to have her husband brought home in the early hours of the morning all shivved up.

Well, the door man and the elevator guy in the apartment house give me an argument about going up to The Brain's apartment, saying a blow out of some kind is going on there, but after I explain to them that The Brain is sick, they let me go. A big fat butler comes to the door of the apartment when I ring, and I can see there are many dolls and guys in evening clothes in the apartment, and somebody is singing very loud.

The butler tries to tell me I cannot see Charlotte, but I finally convince him it is best, so by and by she comes to the door, and a very pleasant sight she is, at that, with jewelry all over her. I stall around awhile, so as not to alarm her too much, and then I tell her The Brain meets with an accident and that we have him outside in a cab, and ask here where we shall put him.

"Why," she says, "put him in a hospital, of course. I am entertaining some very important people tonight, and I cannot have them disturbed by bringing in a hospital patient. Take him to a hospital, and tell him I will come and see him tomorrow and bring him some broth."

I try to explain to her that The Brain does not need any broth, but a nice place to lie down in, but finally she gets very testy with me and shuts the door in my face, saying as follows:

"Take him to a hospital, I tell you. This is a ridiculous hour for him to be coming home, anyway. It is twenty years since he comes home so early."

Then as I am waiting for the elevator, she opens the door again just a little bit and says:

"By the way, is he hurt bad?"

I say we do not know how bad he is hurt, and she shuts the door again, and I go back to the cab again, thinking what a heartless doll she is, although I can see where it will be very inconvenient for her to bust up her party, at that.

The Brain is lying back in the corner of the cab, his eyes half-closed, and by this time it seems that Big Nig stops the blood somewhat with a handkerchief, but The Brain acts somewhat weak to me. He sort of rouses himself when I climb in the cab, and when I tell him his ever-loving wife is not home he smiles a bit and whispers:

"Take me to Doris."

Now Doris lives in a big apartment house away over on West Seventy-second Street near the Drive, and I tell the taxi jockey to go there while The Brain seems to slide off into a doze. Then Big Nig leans over to me and says to me like this:

"No use taking him there," Big Nig says. "I see Doris going out tonight all dressed up in her ermine coat with this actor guy, Jack Walen, she is stuck on. It is a very great scandal around and about the way they carry on. Let us take him to Cynthia," Nig says. "She is a very large-hearted doll who will be very glad to take him in."

Now Cynthia Harris has a big suit of rooms that cost fifteen

G's a year in a big hotel just off Fifth Avenue, Cynthia being a doll who likes to be downtown so if she hears of anything coming off anywhere she can get there very rapidly. When we arrive at the hotel I call her on the house phone and tell her I must see her about something very important, so Cynthia says for me to come up.

It is now maybe three-fifteen, and I am somewhat surprised to find Cynthia home, at that, but there she is, and looking very beautiful indeed in a négligée with her hair hanging down, and I can see that The Brain is no chump when it comes to picking them. She gives me a hello pleasant enough, but as soon as I explain what I am there for, her kisser gets very stern and she says to me like this:

"Listen," she says, "I got trouble enough around this joint, what with two guys getting in a fight over me at a little gathering I have here last night and the house copper coming in to split them out, and I do not care to have any more. Suppose it gets out that The Brain is here? What will the newspapers print about me? Think of my reputation!"

Well, in about ten minutes I can see there is no use arguing with her, because she can talk faster than I can, and mostly she talks about what a knock it will be to her reputation if she takes The Brain in, so I leave her standing at the door in her négligée, still looking very beautiful, at that.

There is now nothing for us to do but take The Brain to Bobby Baker, who lives in a duplex apartment in Sutton Place over by the East River, where the swells set up a colony of nice apartments in the heart of an old tenement-house neighborhood, and as we are on our way there with The Brain lying back in the cab just barely breathing, I say to Big Nig like this:

"Nig," I say, "when we get to Bobby's, we will carry The Brain in without asking her first and just dump him on her so she cannot refuse to take him in, although," I say, "Bobby Baker is a nice little doll, and I am pretty sure she will do anything she can for him, especially," I say, "since he pays fifty G's for this apartment we are going to."

So when the taxicab stops in front of Bobby's house, Nig and I take The Brain out of the cab and lug him between us up to the door of Bobby's apartment, where I ring the bell. Bobby opens the door herself, and I happen to see a guy's legs zip into a room in the apartment behind her, although of course there is nothing wrong in such a sight, even though the guy's legs are in pink pajamas.

Naturally, Bobby is greatly astonished to see us with The Brain dangling between us, but she does not invite us in as I explain to her that The Brain is stabbed and that his last words are for us to take him to his Bobby. Furthermore, she does not let me finish my story which will be very sad indeed, if she keeps on listening.

"If you do not take him away from here at once," Bobby says, before I am down to the pathetic part, "I will call the cops and you guys will be arrested on suspicion that you know something about how he gets hurt."

Then she slams the door on us, and we lug The Brain back down the stairs into the street, because all of a sudden it strikes us that Bobby is right, and if The Brain is found in our possession all stabbed up, and he happens to croak, we are in a very tough spot, because the cops just naturally love to refuse to believe guys like Big Nig and me, no matter what we say.

Furthermore, the same idea must hit the taxicab jockey after we lift The Brain out of the cab, because he is nowhere to be seen, and there we are away over by the East River in the early morning, with no other taxis in sight, and a cop liable to happen along any minute.

Well, there is nothing for us to do but get away from there, so Big Nig and I start moving, with me carrying The Brain's feet, and Big Nig his head. We get several blocks away from Sutton Place, going very slow and hiding in dark doorways when we hear anybody coming, and now we are in a section of tenement houses, when all of a sudden up out of the basement of one of these tenements pops a doll.

She sees us before we can get in a dark place, and she seems to have plenty of nerve for a doll, because she comes right over to us and looks at Big Nig and me, and then looks at The Brain, who loses his hat somewhere along the line, so his pale face is plain to be seen by even the dim street light.

"Why," the doll says, "it is the kind gentleman who gives me the five dollars for the apple—the money that buys the medicine that saves my Joey's life. What is the matter?"

"Well," I say to the doll, who is still raggedy and still red-headed, "there is nothing much the matter except if we do not get him somewhere soon, this guy will up and croak on us."

"Bring him into my house," she says, pointing to the joint she just comes out of. "It is not much of a place, but you can let him rest there until you get help. I am just going over here to a drug store to get some more medicine for Joey, although he is out of danger now, thanks to this gentleman."

So we lug The Brain down the basement steps with the doll leading the way, and we follow her into a room that smells like a Chinese laundry and seems to be full of kids sleeping on the floor. There is only one bed in the room, and it is not much of a bed any way you take it, and there seems to be a kid in this bed, too, but the red-headed doll rolls this kid over to one side of the bed and motions to us to lay The Brain alongside the kid. Then she gets a wet rag and starts bathing The Brain's noggin.

He finally opens his eyes and looks at the red-headed raggedy doll, and she grins at him very pleasant. When I think things over afterwards, I figure The Brain is conscious of much of what is going on when we are packing him around, although he does not say anything, maybe because he is too weak. Anyway, he turns his head to Big Nig, and says to him like this:

"Bring Weissberger and Frisch as quick as you can," he says. "Anyway, get Weissberger. I do not know how bad I am hurt, and I must tell him some things."

Well, The Brain is hurt pretty bad, as it turns out, and in fact he never gets well, but he stays in the basement dump until he dies three days later, with the red-headed raggedy doll nursing him alongside her sick kid Joey, because the croaker, old Doc Frisch, says it is no good moving The Brain, and may only make him pop off sooner. In fact, Doc Frisch is much astonished that The Brain lives at all, considering the way we lug him around.

I am present at The Brain's funeral at Wiggins's Funeral Parlors, like everybody else on Broadway, and I wish to say I never see more flowers in all my life. They are all over the casket and knee-deep on the floor, and some of the pieces must cost plenty, the price of flowers being what they are in this town nowadays. In fact, I judge it is the size and cost of the different pieces that makes me notice a little bundle of faded red carnations not much bigger than your fist that is laying alongside a pillow of violets the size of a horse blanket.

There is a small card tied to the carnations, and it says on this card, as follows: "To a kind gentleman," and it comes to my mind that out of all the thousands of dollars' worth of flowers there, these faded carnations represent the only true sincerity. I mention this to Big Nig and he says the chances are I am right, but that even true sincerity is not going to do The Brain any good where he is going.

Anybody will tell you that for off-hand weeping at a funeral The Brain's ever-loving wife Charlotte does herself very proud indeed, but she is not one-two-seven with Doris Clare, Cynthia Harris, and Bobby Baker. In fact, Bobby Baker weeps so loud that there is some talk of heaving her out of the funeral altogether.

However, I afterwards hear that loud as they are at the funeral, it is nothing to the weep they all put on when it comes out that The Brain has Hymie Weissberger draw up a new will while he is dying and leaves all his dough to the red-headed raggedy doll, whose name seems to be O'Halloran, and who is the widow of a bricklayer and has five kids.

Well, at first all the citizens along Broadway say it is a wonderful thing for The Brain to do, and serves his ever-loving wife and Doris and Cynthia and Bobby just right; and from the way one and all speaks you will think they are going to build a monument to The Brain for his generosity to the red-headed raggedy doll.

But about two weeks after he is dead, I hear citizens saying the chances are the red-headed raggedy doll is nothing but one of The Brain's old-time dolls, and that maybe the kids are his and that he leaves them the dough because his conscience hurts him at the finish, for this is the way Broadway is. But personally I know it cannot be true, for if there is one thing The Brain never has it is a conscience.

MR. K*A*P*L*A*N AND SHAKESPEARE

By LEONARD Q. ROSS

IT WAS MISS HIGBY'S IDEA IN THE FIRST PLACE. SHE HAD SUGGESTED to Mr. Parkhill that the students came to her class unaware of the *finer* side of English, of its beauty and, as she put it, "the glorious heritage of our literature." She suggested that perhaps poetry might be worked into the exercises of Mr. Parkhill's class. The beginners' grade had, after all, been subjected to almost a year of English and might be presumed to have achieved some linguistic sophistication. Poetry would make the students conscious of precise enunciation; it would make them read with greater care and an ear for sounds. Miss Higby, who had once begun a master's thesis on Coventry Patmore, *loved* poetry. And, it should be said in all justice, she argued her cause with considerable logic. Poetry *would* be excellent for the enunciation of the students, thought Mr. Parkhill.

So it was that when he faced the class the following Tuesday night, Mr. Parkhill had a volume of Shakespeare on his desk, and an eager, almost an expectant, look in his eye. The love that Miss Higby bore for poetry in general was as nothing compared to the love that Mr. Parkhill bore for Shakespeare in particular. To Mr. Parkhill, poetry meant Shakespeare. Many years ago he had placed Polonius in his senior class play.

"Tonight, class," said Mr. Parkhill, "I am going to try an experiment."

The class looked up dutifully. They had come to regard Mr. Parkhill's pedagogical innovations as part of the natural order.

"I am going to introduce you to poetry—great poetry. You see—" Mr. Parkhill delivered a modest lecture on the beauty of poetry, its expression of the loftier thoughts of men, its economy of statement. He hoped it would be a relief from spelling and composition exercises to use poetry as the subject matter of the

55

regular Recitation and Speech period. "I shall write a passage on the board and read it for you. Then, for Recitation and Speech, you will give short addresses, using the passage as the general topic, telling us what it has brought to your minds, what thoughts and ideas."

The class seemed quite pleased by the announcement. Miss Mitnick blushed happily. (This blush was different from most of Miss Mitnick's blushes; there was aspiration and idealism in it.) Mr. Norman Bloom sighed with a business-like air you could tell that for him poetry was merely another assignment, like a speech on "What I Like to Eat Best" or a composition on "A Day at a Picnic." Mrs. Moskowitz, to whom any public performance was unpleasant, tried to look enthusiastic, without much success. And Mr. Hyman Kaplan, the heroic smile on his face as indelibly as ever, looked at Mr. Parkhill with admiration and whispered to himself: "Poyetry! Now is poyetry! My! Mus' be progriss ve makink awreddy!"

"The passage will be from Shakespeare," Mr. Parkhill announced, opening the volume.

An excited buzz ran through the class as the magic of that name fell upon them.

"Imachine!" murmured Mr. Kaplan. "Jakesbeer!"

"*Shake*speare, Mr. Kaplan!"

Mr. Parkhill took a piece of chalk and, with care and evident love, wrote the following passage on the board in large, clear letters:

Tomorrow, and tomorrow, and tomorrow
Creeps in this petty pace from day to day,
To the last syllable of recorded time;
And all our yesterdays have lighted fools
The way to dusty death. Out, out, brief candle!
Life's but a walking shadow, a poor player
That struts and frets his hour upon the stage,
And then is heard no more; it is a tale
Told by an idiot, full of sound and fury,
Signifying nothing.

A reverent hush filled the classroom, as eyes gazed with wonder on this passage from the Bard. Mr. Parkhill was pleased at this.

"I shall read the passage first," he said. "Listen carefully to my enunciation—and—er—let Shakespeare's thoughts sink into your minds."

Mr. Parkhill read: " 'Tomorrow, and tomorrow, and tomorrow . . .' " Mr. Parkhill read very well and this night, as if some special fire burned in him, he read with rare eloquence. "Out, out, brief candle!" In Miss Mitnick's eyes there was inspiration and wonder. "Life's but a walking shadow . . ." Mrs. Moskowitz sat with a heavy frown, indicating cerebration. "It is a tale told by an idiot . . ." Mr. Kaplan's smile had taken on something luminous; but his eyes were closed: it was not clear whether Mr. Kaplan had surrendered to the spell of the Immortal Bard or to that of Morpheus.

"I shall—er—read the passage again," said Mr. Parkhill, clearing his throat vociferously until he saw Mr. Kaplan's eyes open. " 'Tomorrow, and tomorrow, and tomorrow. . . .' "

When Mr. Parkhill had read the passage for the second time, he said: "That should be quite clear now. Are there any questions?"

There were a few questions. Mr. Scymzak wanted to know whether "frets" was "a little kind excitement." Miss Schneiderman asked about "struts." Mr. Kaplan wasn't sure about "cripps." Mr. Parkhill explained the words carefully, with several illustrative uses of each word. "No more questions? Well, I shall allow a few minutes for you all to—er—think over the meaning of the passage. Then we shall begin Recitation and Speech."

Mr. Kaplan promptly closed his eyes again, his smile beatific. The students sank into that revery miscalled thought, searching their souls for the symbols evoked by Shakespeare's immortal words.

"Miss Caravello, will you begin?" asked Mr. Parkhill at last.

Miss Caravello went to the front of the room. "Da poem isa gooda," she said slowly. "Itsa have—"

"It *has*."

"It hasa beautiful wordsa. Itsa lak Dante, Italian poet—"

"Ha!" cried Mr. Kaplan scornfully. "Shaksbeer you metchink mit Tante? *Shaksbeer?* Mein Gott!"

It was obvious that Mr. Kaplan had identified himself with Shakespeare and would tolerate no disparagement of his *alter ego*.

"Miss Caravello is merely expressing her own ideas," said Mr. Parkhill pacifically. (Actually, he felt completely sympathetic to Mr. Kaplan's point of view.)

"Hau Kay," agreed Mr. Kaplan, with a generous wave of the hand. "But to me is no comparink a high-cless man like Shaksbeer mit a Tante, dat's all."

Miss Caravello, her poise shattered, said a few more words and sat down.

Mrs. Yampolsky's contribution was brief. "This is full deep meanings," she said, her eyes on the floor. "Is hard for a person not so good in English to unnistand. But I like."

" '*Like!*' " cried Mr. Kaplan with a fine impatience. " '*Like?*' Batter *love*, Yampolsky. Mit Shaksbeer mus' be *love!*"

Mr. Parkhill had to suggest that Mr. Kaplan control his aesthetic passions. He did understand how Mr. Kaplan felt, however, and sensed a new bond between them. Mrs. Yampolsky staggered through several more nervous comments and retired.

Mr. Bloom was next. He gave a long declamation, ending: "So is passimistic ideas in the poem, and I am optimist. Life should be happy—so we should remember this is only a poem. Maybe is Shakespeare too passimistic."

"You wronk, Bloom!" cried Mr. Kaplan with prompt indignation. "Shaksbeer is passimist because is de *life* passimist also!"

Mr. Parkhill, impressed by this philosophical stroke, realized that Mr. Kaplan, afire with the glory of the Swan of Avon, could not be suppressed. Mr. Kaplan was the kind of man who brooked no criticism of his gods. The only solution was to call on Mr. Kaplan for his recitation at once. Mr. Parkhill was, indeed, curious about what fresh thoughts Mr. Kaplan would utter after his passionate defences of the Bard. When Mr. Parkhill had corrected certain parts of Mr. Bloom's speech, emphasizing Mr. Bloom's failure to use the indefinite article he said: "Mr. Kaplan, will *you* speak next?"

Mr. Kaplan's face broke into a glow; his smile was like a rainbow. "Soitinly," he said, walking to the front of the room. Never had he seemed so dignified, so eager, so conscious of a great destiny.

"Er—Mr. Kaplan," added Mr. Parkhill, suddenly aware of the possibilities which the situation (Kaplan on Shakespeare) involved: "Speak *carefully*."

"*Spacially* careful vill I be," Mr. Kaplan reassured him. He cleared his throat, adjusted his tie, and began: "Ladies an' gantleman, you hoid all kinds minninks abot dis piece poyetry, an'—"

"*Poetry*."

"—about dis piece *po*etry. But to me is a difference minnink altogadder. Ve mus' tink abot Julius Scissor an' how *he* falt!"

Mr. Parkhill moved nervously, puzzled.

"In dese exact voids is Julius Scissor sayink—"

"Er—Mr. Kaplan," said Mr. Parkhill once he grasped the full import of Mr. Kaplan's error. "The passage is from 'Macbeth.'"

Mr. Kaplan looked at Mr. Parkhill with injured surprise. "*Not* fromm 'Julius Scissor'?" There was pain in his voice.

"No. And it's—er—'Julius *Cae*sar.'"

Mr. Kaplan waited until the last echo of the name had permeated his soul. "Podden me, Mr. Pockheel. Isn't '*seezor*' vat you cotting somting op mit?"

"That," said Mr. Parkhill quickly, "is 'scissor.' You have used 'Caesar' for 'scissor' and 'scissor' for 'Caesar.'"

Mr. Kaplan nodded, marvelling at his own virtuosity.

"But go on with your speech, please." Mr. Parkhill, to tell the truth, felt a little guilty that he had not announced at the very beginning that the passage was from "Macbeth." "Tell us *why* you thought the lines were from 'Julius Caesar.'"

"Vell," said Mr. Kaplan to the class, his smile assuming its normal serenity. "I vas positiff, becawss I can *see* de whole ting." He paused, debating how to explain this cryptic remark. Then his eyes filled with a strange enchantment. "I see do whole scinn. It's in a tant, on de night bafore dey makink Julius de Kink fromm Rome. So he is axcited an' ken't slip. He is layink in bad, tinking: 'Tomorrow an' tomorrow an' tomorrow. How slow dey movink! Almost cripps! Soch a pity de pace!'"

Before Mr. Parkhill could explain that 'petty pace" did not mean "Soch a pity de pace!" Mr. Kaplan had soared on.

"De day go slow, fromm day to day like leetle tsyllables on phonograph racords fromm time."

Anxiety and bewilderment invaded Mr. Parkhill's eyes.

" 'An' vat abot yestiddy?' tinks Julius Scissor. Ha! 'All our yestiddays are only makink a good light for fools to die in de dost!' "

" 'Dusty death' doesn't mean—" There was no interrupting Mr. Kaplan.

"An' Julius Scissor is so tired, an' he vants to fallink aslip. So he hollers, mit fillink, 'Go ot! Go ot! Short candle!' So it goes ot."

Mr. Kaplan's voice dropped to a whisper. "But he ken't slip. Now is bodderink de idea fromm life. 'Vat is de life altogadder?' tinks Julius Scissor. An' he gives enswer, de pot I like de bast. 'Life is like a bum actor, strottink an' hollerink arond de stage for only vun hour bafore he's kicked ot. Life is a tale told by idjots, dat's all, full of fonny sonds an' phooey!' "

Mr. Parkhill could be silent no longer. " 'Full of sound and fury!' " he cried desperately. But inspiration, like an irresistible force, swept Mr. Kaplan on.

" 'Life is monkey business! It don' minn a ting. It signifies nottink!' An' den Julius Scissor closes his ice fest—" Mr. Kaplan demonstrated the Consul's exact ocular process in closing his "ice"—"—an' falls dad!"

The class was hushed as Mr. Kaplan stopped. In the silence, a tribute to the fertility of Mr. Kaplan's imagination and the power of his oratory, Mr. Kaplan went to his seat. But just before he sat down, as if adding a postscript, he sighed: "Dat vas mine idea. But ufcawss is all wronk, becawss Mr. Pockheel said de voids ain't bot Julius Scissor altogadder. It's all abot an Irishman by de name Macbat."

Then Mr. Kaplan sat down.

It was some time before Mr. Parkhill could bring himself to criticize Mr. Kaplan's pronunciation, enunciation, diction, grammar, idiom, and sentence structure. For Mr. Parkhill discovered that he could not easily return to the world of reality. He was still trying to tear himself away from that tent outside Rome, where "Julius Scissor," cursed with insomnia, had thought of time and life—and philosophized himself to a strange and sudden death. Mr. Parkhill was distinctly annoyed with Miss Higby.

MARY

By John Collier

THERE WAS IN THOSE DAYS—I HOPE IT IS THERE STILL—A VILLAGE
called Ufferleigh, lying all among the hills and downs of North
Hampshire. In every cottage garden there was a giant apple tree,
and when these trees were hung red with fruit, and the newly
lifted potatoes lay gleaming between bean-row and cabbage-patch,
a young man walked into the village who had never been there
before.

He stopped in the lane just under Mrs. Hedges's gate, and
looked up into her garden. Rosie, who was picking the beans,
heard his tentative cough, and turned and leaned over the hedge
to hear what he wanted. "I was wondering," said he, "if there
was anybody in the village who had a lodging to let."

He looked at Rosie, whose cheeks were redder than the apples,
and whose hair was the softest yellow imaginable. "I was wondering," said he in amendment, "if *you* had."

Rosie looked back at him. He wore a blue jersey such as seafaring men wear, but he seemed hardly like a seafaring man. His
face was brown and plain and pleasant, and his hair was black.
He was shabby and he was shy, but there was something about
him that made it very certain he was not just a tramp. "I'll ask,"
said Rosie.

With that she ran for her mother, and Mrs. Hedges came out
to interview the young man. "I've got to be near Andover for a
week," said he, "but somehow I didn't fancy staying right in
the town."

"There's a bed," said Mrs. Hedges. "If you don't mind having
your meals with us——"

"Why, surely, ma'am," said he. "There's nothing I'd like
better."

Everything was speedily arranged; Rosie picked another handful of beans, and in an hour he was seated with them at supper. He told them his name was Fred Baker, but, apart from that, he was so polite that he could hardly speak, and in the end Mrs. Hedges had to ask him outright what his business was. "Why, ma'am," said he, "looking her straight in the face, "I've done one thing and another ever since I was so high, but I heard an old proverb once, how to get on in the world. 'Feed 'em or amuse 'em,' it said. So that's what I do, ma'am. I travel with a pig."

Mrs. Hedges said she had never heard of such a thing.

"You surprise me," said he. "Why, there are some in London, they tell me, making fortunes on the halls. Spell, count, add up, answer questions, anything. But let them wait," said he, smiling, "till they see Mary."

"Is that the name of your pig?" asked Rosie.

"Well," said Fred, shyly, "it's what I call her just between ourselves. To her public, she's Zola. Sort of Frenchified, I thought. Spicy, if you'll excuse the mention of it. But in the caravan I call her Mary."

"You live in a caravan?" cried Rosie, delighted by the doll's-house idea.

"We do," said he. "She has her bunk, and I have mine."

"I don't think I should like that," said Mrs. Hedges. "Not a pig. No."

"She's as clean," said he, "as a new-born babe. And as for company, well, you'd say she's human. All the same, it's a bit of a wandering life for her—up hill and down dale, as the saying goes. Between you and me I shan't be satisfied till I get her into one of these big London theatres. You can see us in the West End!"

"I should like the caravan best," said Rosie, who seemed to have a great deal to say for herself, all of a sudden.

"It's pretty," said Fred. "Curtains, you know. Pot of flowers. Little stove. Somehow I'm used to it. Can't hardly think of myself staying at one of them big hotels. Still, Mary's got her career to think of. I can't stand in the way of her talent, so that's that."

"Is she big?" asked Rosie.

"It's not her size," said he. "No more than Shirley Temple. It's her brains and personality. Clever as a wagonload of monkeys! You'd like her. She'd like you, I reckon. Yes, I reckon she would.

Sometimes I'm afraid I'm a bit slow by way of company for her, never having had much to do with the ladies."

"Don't tell me," said Mrs. Hedges archly, as convention required.

" 'Tis so, ma'am," said he. "Always on the move, you see, ever since I was a nipper. Baskets and brooms, pots and pans, then some acrobat stuff, then Mary. Never two days in the same place. It don't give you the time to get acquainted."

"You're going to be here a whole week, though," said Rosie artlessly, but at once her red cheeks blushed a hundred times redder than before, for Mrs. Hedges gave her a sharp look, which made her see that her words might have been taken the wrong way.

Fred, however, had noticed nothing. "Yes," said he, "I shall be here a week. And why? Mary ran a nail in her foot in the market place, Andover. Finished her act—and collapsed. Now she's at the vet's, poor creature."

"Oh, poor thing!" cried Rosie.

"I was half afraid," said he, "it was going wrong on her. But it seems she'll pull round all right, and I took opportunity to have the van repaired a bit, and soon we'll be on the road again. I shall go in and see her tomorrow. Maybe I can find some blackberries, to take her by way of a relish, so to speak."

"Colley Bottom," said Rosie. "That's the place where they grow big and juicy."

"Ah! If I knew where it was—" said Fred tentatively.

"Perhaps, in the morning, if she's got time, she'll show you," said Mrs. Hedges, who began to feel very kindly disposed towards the young man.

In the morning, surely enough, Rosie did have time, and she showed Fred the place, and helped him pick the berries. Returning from Andover, later in the day, Fred reported that Mary had tucked into them a fair treat, and he had little doubt that, if she could have spoken, she would have sent her special thanks. Nothing is more affecting than the gratitude of a dumb animal, and Rosie was impelled to go every morning with Fred to pick a few more berries for the invalid pig.

On these excursions Fred told her a great deal more about

Mary, a bit about the caravan, and a little about himself. She saw that he was very bold and knowing in some ways, but incredibly simple and shy in others. This, she felt, showed he had a good heart.

The end of the week seemed to come very soon, and all at once they were coming back from Colley Bottom for the last time. Fred said he would never forget Ufferleigh, nor the nice time he had had there.

"You ought to send us a postcard when you're on your travels," said Rosie.

"Yes," he said. "That's an idea. I will."

"Yes, do," said Rosie.

"Yes," said he again, "I will. Do you know, I was altogether downhearted at going away, but now I'm half wishing I was on the road again already. So I could be sending that card right away," said he.

"At that rate," said Rosie, looking the other way, "you might as well make it a letter."

"Ah!" said he. "And do you know what I should feel like putting at the bottom of that letter? If you was my young lady, that is. Which, of course, you're not. Me never having had one."

"What?" said Rosie.

"A young lady," said he.

"But what would you put?" said she.

"Ah!" said he. "What I'd put. Do you know what I'd put? if—*if*, mind you—if you was my young lady?"

"No," said she, "what?"

"I don't hardly like to tell you," said he.

"Go on," she said. "You don't want to be afraid."

"All right," said he. "Only mind you, it's *if*." And with his stick he traced three crosses in the dust.

"If I was anybody's young lady," said Rosie, "I shouldn't see anything wrong in that. After all, you've got to move with the times."

Neither of them said another word, for two of the best reasons in the world. First, they were unable to; second, it was not necessary. They walked on with their faces as red as fire, in an agony of happiness.

Fred had a word with Mrs. Hedges, who had taken a fancy to him from the start. Not that she had not always looked down upon caravan people, and could have been knocked over with a feather, had anyone suggested, at any earlier date, that she would allow a daughter of hers to marry into such a company. But right was right: this Fred Baker was different, as anyone with half an eye could see. He had kept himself to himself, almost to a fault, for his conversation showed that he was as innocent as a new-born babe. Moreover, several knowledgeable people in the village had agreed that his ambitions for Mary, his pig, were in no way unjustified. Everyone had heard of such talented creatures, reclining on snowwhite sheets in the best hotels of the metropolis, drinking champagne like milk, and earning for their fortunate owners ten pounds, or even twenty pounds, a week.

So Mrs. Hedges smilingly gave her consent, and Rosie became Fred's real, genuine, proper young lady. He was to save all he could during the winter, and she to stitch and sing. In the spring, he would come back and they were to get married.

"At Easter," said he.

"No," said Mrs. Hedges, counting on her fingers. "In May. Then tongues can't wag, caravan or no caravan."

Fred had not the faintest idea what she was driving at, for he had lived so much alone that no one had told him certain things that every young man should know. However, he well realized that this was an unusually short engagement for Ufferleigh, and represented a great concession to the speed and dash of the entertainment industry, so he respectfully agreed, and set off on his travels.

My Darling Rosie,

Well here we are in Painswick having had a good night Saturday at Evesham. Mary cleverer than ever that goes without saying now spells four new words thirty-six in all and when I say now Mary how do you like Painswick or Evesham or wherever it is she picks F I N E it goes down very well. She is in the best of health and hope you are the same. Seems to understand every word I say more like a human being every day. Well I suppose I

must be getting our bit of supper ready she always sets up her
cry for that specially when I am writing to you.

With true love

FRED XXX

In May the apple trees were all in bloom, so it was an apple-blossom wedding, which in those parts is held to be an assurance of flowery days. Afterwards they took the bus to the market town, to pick up the caravan, which stood in a stable yard. On the way Fred asked Rosie to wait a moment, and dived into a confectioner's shop. He came out with a huge box of chocolates. Rosie smiled all over her face with joy. "For me?" she said.

"Yes," said he. "To give to her as soon as she claps eyes on you. They're her weakness. I want you two to be real pals."

"All right," said Rosie, who was the best-hearted girl in the world.

The next moment they turned into the yard: there was the caravan. "Oh, it's lovely!" cried Rosie.

At the sound of his voice a falsetto squeal rose from within.

"Here we are, old lady," said Fred, opening the door. "Here's a friend of mine come to help look after you. Look, she's brought you something you'll fancy."

Rosie saw a middle-sized pig, flesh-coloured, neat, and with a smart collar. It had a small and rather calculating eye. Rosie offered the cholocates: they were accepted without any very effusive acknowledgment.

Fred put the old horse in, and soon they were off, jogging up the long hills to the west. Rosie sat beside Fred on the driving seat; Mary took her afternoon nap. Soon the sky began to redden where the road divided the woods on the far hill-top. Fred turned into a green lane, and they made their camp.

He lit the stove, and Rosie put on the potatoes. They took a lot of peeling, for it seemed that Mary ate with gusto. Rosie put a gigantic rice pudding into the oven, and soon had the rest of the meal prepared.

Fred set the table. He laid three places.

"I say," said Rosie.

"What?" said Fred.

"Does she eat along with us?" said Rosie. "A pig?"

Fred turned quite pale. He beckoned her outside the caravan. "Don't say a thing like that," said he. "She won't never take to you if you say a thing like that. Didn't you see her give you a look?"

"Yes, I did," said Rosie. "All the same— Well, never mind, Fred. I don't care, really. I just thought I did."

"You wait," said Fred. "You're thinking of ordinary pigs. Mary's different."

Certainly Mary seemed a comparatively tidy eater. All the same, she gave Rosie one or two very odd glances from under her silky straw-coloured lashes. She seemed to hock her rice pudding about a bit with the end of her nose.

"What's up, old girl?" said Fred. "Didn't she put enough sugar in the pudden? Never mind—can't get everything right first time."

Mary, with a rather cross hiccup, settled herself on her bunk. "Let's go out," said Rosie, "and have a look at the moon."

"I suppose we might," said Fred. "Shan't be long, Mary. Just going about as far as that gate down the lane." Mary grunted morosely and turned her face to the wall.

Rosie and Fred went out and leaned over the gate. The moon, at least, was all that it should be.

"Seems funny, being married and all," said Rosie softly.

"Seems all right to me," said Fred.

"Remember them crosses you drew in the dirt in the road that day?" said Rosie.

"That I do," said Fred.

"And all them you put in the letters?" said Rosie.

"All of 'em," said Fred.

"Kisses, that's what they're supposed to stand for," said Rosie.

"So they say," said Fred.

"You haven't given me one, not since we was married," said Rosie. "Don't you like it?"

"That I do," said Fred. "Only, I don't know——"

"What?" said Rosie.

"It makes me feel all queer," said Fred, "when I kiss you. As if I wanted——"

"What?" said Rosie.

"I dunno," said Fred. "I don't know if it's I want to eat you all up, or what."

"Try and find out, they say," said Rosie.

A delicious moment followed. In the very middle of it a piercing squeal rose from the caravan. Fred jumped as if he were shot.

"Oh dear," he cried. "She's wondering what's up. Here I come, old girl! Here I come! It's her bed-time, you see. Here I come to tuck you in!"

Mary, with an air of some petulance, permitted this process. Rosie stood by. "I suppose we'd better make it lights out," said Fred. "She likes a lot of sleep, you see, being a brain worker."

"Where do _we_ sleep?" said Rosie.

"I made the bunk all nice for you this morning," said Fred. "Me, I'm going to doss below. A sack full of straw, I've got."

"But—" said Rosie. "But——"

"But what?" said he.

"Nothing," said she. "Nothing."

They turned in. Rosie lay for an hour or two, thinking what thoughts I don't know. Perhaps she thought how charming it was that Fred should have lived so simple and shy and secluded all these years, and yet be so knowing about so many things, and yet so innocent, and never have been mixed up in bad company— It is impossible to say what she thought.

In the end she dozed off, only to be wakened by a sound like the bagpipes of the devil himself. She sat up, terrified. It was Mary.

"What's up? What's up?" Fred's voice came like the ghost's in _Hamlet_ from under the floor. "Give her some milk," he said.

Rosie poured out a bowl of milk. Mary ceased her fiendish racket while she drank, but the moment Rosie had blown out the light, and got into bed again, she began a hundred times worse than before.

There were rumblings under the caravan. Fred appeared in the doorway, half dressed and with a straw in his hair.

"She _will_ have me," he said, in great distress.

"Can't you— Can't you lie down here?" said Rosie.

"What? And you sleep below?" said Fred, astounded.

"Yes," said Rosie, after a rather long pause. "And me sleep below."

Fred was overwhelmed with gratitude and remorse. Rosie couldn't help feeling sorry for him. She even managed to give him a smile before she went down to get what rest she could on the sack of straw.

In the morning, she woke feeling rather dejected. There was a mighty breakfast to be prepared for Mary; afterwards Fred drew her aside.

"Look here," he said. "This won't do. I can't have you sleeping on the ground, worse than a gippo. I'll tell you what I'm going to do. I'm going to get up my acrobat stuff again. I used to make a lot that way, and I liked it fine. Handsprings, double somersaults, bit of conjuring: it went down well. Only I didn't have time to keep in practice with Mary to look after. But if you'd do the looking after her, we'd make it a double turn, and soon we'd have a good bit of cash. And then—"

"Yes?" said Rosie.

"Then," said Fred, "I could buy you a trailer."

"All right," said Rosie, and turned away. Suddenly she turned back with her face flaming. "You may know a lot about pigs," she said bitterly. "And about somersaults, and conjuring and baskets and brooms and I don't know what-all. But there's *one* thing you don't know." And with that she went off and cried behind a hedge.

After a while she got the upper hand of it, and came back to the caravan. Fred showed her how to give Mary her morning bath, then the depilatory—that was very hard on the hands—then the rubbing with Cleopatra Face Cream—and not on her face merely—then the powdering, then the manicuring and polishing of her trotters.

Rosie, resolved to make the best of it, conquered her repugnance, and soon mastered these handmaidenly duties. She was relieved at first that the spoiled pig accepted her ministrations without protest. Then she noticed the gloating look in its eye.

However, there was no time to brood about that. No sooner was the toilet finished than it was time to prepare the enormous lunch. After lunch Mary had her little walk, except on Saturdays when there was an afternoon show, then she took her rest. Fred explained that during this period she liked to be talked to, and have her back scratched a bit. Mary had quite clearly decided that in future she was going to have it scratched a lot. Then she had her massage. Then tea, then another little walk, or the evening show, according to where they were, and then it was time to prepare dinner. At the end of the day Rosie was thankful to curl up on her poor sack of straw.

When she thought of the bunk above, and Fred, and his simplicity, her heart was fit to break. The only thing was, she loved him dearly, and she felt that if they could soon snatch an hour alone together, they might kiss a little more, and a ray of light might dispel the darkness of excessive innocence.

Each new day she watched for that hour, but it didn't come. Mary saw to that. Once or twice Rosie suggested a little stroll, but at once the hateful pig grumbled some demand or other that kept her hard at work till it was too late. Fred, on his side, was busy enough with his practising. He meant it so well, and worked so hard—but what did it lead to? A trailer!

As the days went by, she found herself more and more the slave of this arrogant grunter. Her back ached, her hands got chapped and red, she never had a moment to make herself look nice, and never a moment alone with her beloved. Her dress was spotted and spoiled, her smile was gone, her temper was going. Her pretty hair fell in elf locks and tangles, and she had neither time nor heart to comb it.

She tried to come to an explanation with Fred, but it was nothing but cross purposes and then cross words. He tried in a score of little ways to show that he loved her: these seemed to her a mere mockery, and she gave him short answers. Then he stopped, and she thought he loved her no longer. Even worse, she felt she no longer loved him.

So the whole summer went by, and things got worse and worse, and you would have taken her for a gipsy indeed.

The blackberries were ripe again; she found a whole brake of them. When she tasted one, all sorts of memories flooded into her heart: she went and found Fred. "Fred," she said, "the blackberries are ripe again. I've brought you one or two." She held out some in her grubby hand. Fred took them and tasted them; she watched to see what the result would be.

"Yes," said he, "they're ripe. They won't gripe her. Take her and pick her some this afternoon."

Rosie turned away without a word, and in the afternoon she took Mary across the stubbles to where the ripe berries grew. Mary, when she saw them, dispensed for once with dainty service, and began to help herself very liberally. Rosie, finding she had nothing more urgent to attend to, sat down on a bank and sobbed bitterly.

In the middle of it all she heard a voice asking what was the matter. She looked up and there was a fat, shrewd, jolly-looking farmer. "What is it, my girl?" said he. "Are you hungry?"

"No," said she, "I'm fed up."

"What with?" said he.

"A pig!" said she, with a gulp.

"You've got no call to bawl and cry," said he. "There's nothing like a bit of pork. I'd have the indigestion for that, any day."

"It's not pork," she said. "It's a pig. A live pig."

"Have you lost it?" said he.

"I wish I had," said she. "I'm that miserable I don't know what to do."

"Tell me your troubles," said he. "There's no harm in a bit of sympathy."

So Rosie told him about Fred, and about Mary, and what hopes she'd had and what they'd all come to, and how she was the slave of this insolent, spoiled, jealous pig, and in fact she told him everything except one little matter which she could hardly bring herself to repeat, even to the most sympathetic of fat farmers.

The farmer, pushing his hat over his eyes, scratched his head very thoughtfully. "Really," said he. "I can't hardly believe it."

"It's true," said Rosie, "every word."

"I mean," said the farmer. "A young man—a young gal—the young gal sleeping down on a sack of straw—a pretty young gal like you. Properly married and all. Not to put too fine a point on it, young missus, aren't the bunks wide enough, or what?"

"He doesn't know," sobbed Rosie. "He just doesn't know no more'n a baby. And she won't let us ever be alone a minute. So he'd find out."

The farmer scratched his head more furiously than ever. Looking at her tear-stained face, he found it hard to doubt her. On the other hand it seemed impossible that a pig should know so much and a young man should know so little. But at that moment Mary came trotting through the bushes, with an egotistical look on her face, which was well besmeared with the juice of the ripe berries.

"Is this your pig?" said the farmer.

"Well," said Rosie, "I'm just taking her for a walk."

The shrewd farmer was quick to notice the look that Rosie got from the haughty grunter when it heard the expression "your pig." This, and Rosie's hurried, nervous disclaimer, convinced the worthy man that the story he had heard was well founded.

"You're taking her for a walk?" said he musingly. "Well! Well! Well! I'll tell you what. If you'd ha' been here this time tomorrow you'd have met *me* taking a walk, with a number of very dear young friends of mine, all very much like her. You might have come along. Two young sows, beautiful creatures, though maybe not so beautiful as that one. Three young boars, in the prime of their health and handsomeness. Though I say it as shouldn't, him that's unattached—he's a prince. Oh, what a beautiful young boar that young boar really is!"

"You don't say?" said Rosie.

"For looks and pedigree both," said the farmer, "he's a prince. The fact is, it's their birthday, and I'm taking 'em over to the village for a little bit of a celebration. I suppose this young lady has some other engagement tomorrow."

"She has to have her sleep just about this time," said Rosie, ignoring Mary's angry grunt.

"Pity!" said the farmer. "She'd have just made up the party. Such fun they'll have! Such refreshments! Sweet apples, cakes, biscuits, a bushel of chocolate creams. Everything most refined, of course, but plenty. You know what I mean—plenty. And that young boar—you know what I mean. If she *should* be walking by—"

"I'm afraid not," said Rosie.

"Pity!" said the farmer. "Ah, well. I must be moving along."

With that, he bade them good afternoon, raising his hat very politely to Mary, who looked after him for a long time, and then walked sulkily home, gobbling to herself all the way.

The next afternoon Mary seemed eager to stretch out on her bunk, and, for once, instead of requiring the usual number of little attentions from Rosie, she closed her eyes in sleep. Rosie took the opportunity to pick up a pail and go off to buy the evening ration of fresh milk. When she got back Fred was still at his practice by the wayside, and Rosie went round to the back of the caravan, and the door was swinging open, and the bunk was empty.

She called Fred. They sought high and low. They went along the road, fearing she might have been knocked over by a motor car. They went calling through the woods, hoping she had fallen asleep under a tree. They looked in ponds and ditches, behind haystacks, under bridges, everywhere. Rosie thought of the farmer's joking talk, but she hardly liked to say anything about it to Fred.

They called and called all night, scarcely stopping to rest. They sought all the next day. It grew dark, and Fred gave up hope. They plodded silently back to the caravan.

He sat on his bunk, with his head in his hand.

"I shall never see her again," he said. "Been pinched, that's what she's been."

"When I think," he said, "of all the hopes I had for that pig——"

"When I think," he said, "of all you've done for her! And what it's meant to you——"

"I know she had some faults in her nature," he said. "But that was artistic. Temperament, it was. When you got a talent like that——"

"And now she's gone!" he said. With that he burst into tears.

"Oh, Fred!" cried Rosie. "Don't!"

Suddenly she found she loved him just as much as ever, more than ever. She sat down beside him and put her arms round his neck. "Darling Fred, don't cry!" she said again.

"It's been rough on you, I know," said Fred. "I didn't ever mean it to be."

"There! There," said Rosie. She gave him a kiss, and then she gave him another. It was a long time since they had been as close as this. There was nothing but the two of them and the caravan; the tiny lamp, and darkness all round; their kisses, and grief all round. "Don't let go," said Fred. "It makes it better."

"I'm not letting go," she said.

"Rosie," said Fred. "I feel— Do you know how I feel?"

"I know," she said. "Don't talk."

"Rosie," said Fred, but this was sometime later. "Who'd have thought it?"

"Ah! Who would, indeed?" said Rosie.

"Why didn't you tell me?" said Fred.

"How could I tell you?" said she.

"You know," said he. "We might never have found out—never! —if she hadn't been pinched."

"Don't talk about her," said Rosie.

"I can't help it," said Fred. "Wicked or not, I can't help it— I'm glad she's gone. It's worth it. I'll make enough on the acrobat stuff. I'll make brooms as well. Pots and pans, too."

"Yes," said Rosie. "But look! It's morning. I reckon you're tired, Fred—running up hill and down dale all day yesterday. You lie abed now, and I'll go down to the village and get you something good for breakfast."

"All right," said Fred. "And tomorrow I'll get yours."

So Rosie went down to the village, and bought the milk and the bread and so forth. As she passed the butcher's shop she saw some new-made pork sausages of a singularly fresh, plump, and appetizing appearance. So she bought some, and very good they smelled while they were cooking.

"That's another thing we couldn't have while she was here," said Fred, as he finished his plateful. "Never no pork sausages, on account of her feelings. I never thought to see the day I'd be glad she was pinched. I only hope she's gone to someone who appreciates her."

"I'm sure she has," said Rosie. "Have some more."

"I will," said he. "I don't know if it's the novelty, or the way you cooked 'em, or what. I never ate a better sausage in my life. If we'd gone up to London with her, best hotels and all, I doubt if ever we'd have had as sweet a sausage as these here."

A LETTER FROM THE BRONX

By Arthur Kober

BELLA GROSS RIFFLED THE PAGES OF THE DICTIONARY, PAUSED AT A leaf headed "dike," ran her finger down a column of words and, when she came to "dilatory," wrote "tardy and inactive" on a slip of paper. She thumbed the book again, hunted for "epistle," and snagged it after a little difficulty owing to her uncertainty over its spelling. She made the notation, "a formal letter."

Fortified by these two items, Bella was ready to plunge into the writing of the grave and important letter she had long planned. Whenever she engaged in such elaborate preliminaries—unearthing the coverless dictionary and bringing it into the dining room, placing pen, ink, and paper on the oilcloth table cover, using her "good" stationery, bought at a sale at Macy's—it was an indication that she was going to compose something of momentous importance.

And this letter to Monroe Rosenblatt, written in her mind time and time again, was of importance. Bella was finally going to do what she had so very often told her friends Jennie and Sarah she would do: "Give Monroe back to the Indians." It was one thing to make fine promises under a romantic summer moon at Kamp Kill Kare. It was another thing, she thought with burning indignation, to fulfill those pretty promises under the harsh and prosaic moon over the Bronx.

Bella reached for a sheet of her good stationery, so impressively monogrammed with the letter "G." No, she thought, no use wasting the paper. This letter needed careful construction. It would be better to make a rough draft first and then rewrite it. She disappeared into her bedroom for a moment and returned with several sheets of business stationery which she had filched from her office.

She dipped her pen in the ink, corrugated her forehead in deep

76

reflection, and then, under several printed lines which read "Solomon Silk Mills, Harry I. Solomon, Pres., Silks, Acetates—Plain and Novelty, 'A Satisfied Customer Is Our Best Recommendation,' " she wrote, "Dear Monroe."

She studied this a moment. "Dear Monroe." No, that sounded too warm, too inviting, too intimate. That was hardly her present attitude toward him. Dear Monroe, indeed! She suddenly had it! All that was necessary was to add "Rosenblatt" to the salutation. "Dear Monroe Rosenblatt." That was it—formal, severe, cold, implacable. "I should have written"—she stopped to consult her notes, and then went on, slowly and painstakingly, employing an almost childish chirography—"this epistle before the present inst. but the reason"—again there was a visual consultation with the notes— "I was so dilatory was because I wanted to carefully weigh what was on my chest. Now that I have weighed same I am going to get it off my chest irregardless of whom it affects even though it be—" There was only a moment's pause to consider grammar, and then she wrote, "I."

"First of all," she went on, "I don't want to throw up anything to your face but I feel this matter must be thrown up. Namely you might of forgotten about the fact that when I left 'Kamp Kill Kare' you declared yourself with all sorts of promises galore. I took you at your word in connection with the matter and gave up some 'contacts' which to me I didn't want to give up, at the same time I thought inasmuch as you declared yourself the fair and square thing to do was not to go 'galvinating' around, not that I am the 'galvinating' type girl inasmuch as I wouldn't stoop to be that common. But still in all I wanted to be fair and square with you. In fact one 'contact' I had was very serious inasmuch as the certain party was 'matrimonyally-inclined' along the lines of marriage, only I thought he should have his two feet on the ground first because too many marriages end up on the rocks due to circumstances over which the girl in the matter has no control. He's a professional person with a college degree."

Bella allowed her mind to dwell on Max Fine for a moment. Poor Mac! A fine fellow—intelligent, well educated—a Certified Public Accountant. If only he had a substantial income. Well, what's done is done. It's silly to regret. Still in all, Mac's a fine boy, she thought, one whose friendship was certainly well worth keeping. Perhaps she ought to attend the regular meetings of the Excelsior Social Club. She had avoided these because of the embarrassment that would follow upon seeing and talking with Mac, the club's president. Oh, well. She sighed deeply, picked up the pen, and continued writing.

"For some time now we've been going out regularly with each other like clock-work. In fact, so regularly have we been going out with each other that one of my girl friend's (Jennie) commented on same and said, 'We're beginning to look like two peas in a pot' and everybody was taking matters for granted. To be crudely blunt about the matter, I too thought that the issue was understood. I hope you won't think me 'mercinarilly-inclined' if I mention the fact that I didn't bring up the matter of a ring but the matter was brought up by you, yourself. Well all you did was to bring up the matter without bringing up the ring. We been seeing each other regularly like clock-work and not once did you lift a little finger to get same but all you did was to talk 'a poor mouth' about how business was bad and the responsibilities you got and gee whiz, people are not buying merchandise like they used to and this, that and the other thing.

"In other words, Monroe, I suddenly came to the realization that I had no protection whatsoever in giving up my 'contacts' for what? So that you can keep me on tender hooks. So that you can come to my house for supper again and again, compliment my Mother on saying the food is very lucious, and then suddenly we wake up and find we got a boarder with us, only boarders at least pay the rent.

"Well I think that in view of this attitude on your part, in view of the fact that all the time you are saying that business conditions are bad so that we got to assume it don't warrant any serious step on your part, not even to the extent of a ring, in view of the fact that I am giving up chances which to me may prove valuable as I am not growing any younger each day and opportunities don't hang on trees, all a girl has to do is to go out and pick it off the tree just like if it was an apple or some piece fruit, in view of all this, Monroe, suppose we better call it just 'quits.'

"Now please don't get the idea I am calling you 'A Cheap Skate' just because I haven't got a ring to show on my finger. I am not placing you in that category whatsoever inasmuch as you have on several occasions shown me a very good time. Still in all if you had merely said to me 'O.K. Billie. String along with me for another couple months till business conditions gets on its feet and then everything will be O.K.' I would of been only too pleased and happy to have strung along with you. But you didn't even have this common courtesy to the girl to who you apparently seemed so crazy about at camp last summer when you swore to me that this here was no typical summer romance you write down on ice it's quickly forgotten, but would culminate to a mutual union. Oh, no, not you! After all promises are cheap and cost nothing. What have you got to lose? Say, it's a wonder to me I'm opening my eyes now. God knows they were closed long enough before.

"So you see, Monroe, why it's better for me to get this matter off my chest once and for all rather than I should waste my time brooding about it because I just can't dismiss things with a snap of the fingers. Perhaps if I was the type girl who could dismiss things with a snap of the finger I would be better off today, believe me. So, Monroe, leave us call it 'quits' and just say it all comes under the heading of 'Experience.' I'm afraid that even if you should dig up a ring, and judgeing from the way your business is at the moment I can just imagine what type ring you would dig up, I'm afraid I'd still have to say 'I'm sorry, I'm not interested.' You had your chances and too bad, you didn't make the most of them. Better luck with some other girl next time. As for me, don't worry. I got along very nicely without you a long time before I met you, and I'll still get along without you inasmuch as I have some very worth-while 'contacts,' friends who don't talk a 'poor mouth' whenever they have to dig in their pockets, be it a ticket for a movie or just a chocolate ice-cream Sunday.

"This letter means 'finis' so please don't reply nor communicate with me via the phone inasmuch as I will be out. I am not 'sore-headed' the least bit about the matter, but I merely want to drop it once and for all.

"Assuring you of my sincerest feelings about the matter, and trusting that you meet a girl who appreciates you a little more than I do in view of the whole situation, I am—"

Bella wondered if "Very truly yours" wasn't just a bit too businesslike and formal. But that was exactly what she wanted to be. She wrote, "Very truly yours, Bella Gross." There! Signing "Bella" instead of "Billie" would make him realize that their relationship was completely over.

She picked up the scribbled pages and read them carefully. Once or twice she stopped to make a correction and to consult the dictionary about spelling. When she had finished reading what she had written, she added, "P.S. Please excuse the handwriting." She then reached for a sheet of her good paper, inked her pen, glanced at the rough draft, and started to write, "Dear Monroe Rosenblatt."

THE NOBLE EXPERIMENT

By H. L. MENCKEN

PROHIBITION WENT INTO EFFECT ON JANUARY 16, 1920, AND BLEW up at last on December 5, 1933—an elapsed time of twelve years, ten months and nineteen days. It seemed almost a geological epoch while it was going on, and the human suffering that it entailed must have been a fair match for that of the Black Death or the Thirty Years' War, but I should say at once that my own share of the blood, sweat and tears was extremely meagre. I was, so far as I have been able to discover, the first man south of the Mason and Dixon line to brew a drinkable home-brew, and as a result my native Baltimore smelled powerfully of malt and hops during the whole horror, for I did not keep my art to myself, but imparted it to anyone who could be trusted—which meant anyone save a few abandoned Methodists, Baptists and Presbyterians, most of them already far gone in glycosuria, cholelithiasis or gastro-hydrorrhea, and all of them soon so low in mind and body that they could be ignored.

My seminary was run on a sort of chain-letter plan. That is to say, I took ten pupils, and then each of the ten took ten, and so on *ad infinitum*. There were dull dogs in Baltimore who went through the course forty or fifty times, under as many different holders of my degrees, and even then never got beyond a nauseous *Malzsuppe*, fit only for policemen and Sunday-school superintendents. But there were others of a much more shining talent, and I put in a great deal of my time in 1921 and 1922 visiting their laboratories, to pass judgment on their brews. They received me with all the deference due to a master, and I was greatly bucked up by their attentions. In fact, those attentions probably saved me from melancholia, for during the whole of the twelve years, ten months and nineteen days I was a magazine editor, and a magazine editor is a man who lives on a sort of spiritual Bataan, with bombs of odium taking him incessantly from the front and torpedoes of obloquy harrying him astern.

But I would not have you think that I was anything like dependent, in that abominable time, upon home-brew, or that I got down any really formidable amount of it. To be sure, I had to apply my critical powers to many thousands of specimens, but I always took them in small doses, and was careful to blow away a good deal of the substance with the foam. This home-brew, when drinkable at all, was a striking proof of the indomitable spirit of man, but in the average case it was not much more. Whenever the mood to drink purely voluptuously was on me I preferred, of course, the product of professional brewmasters, and, having been born lucky, I usually found it. Its provenance, in those days, was kept a kind of military secret, but now that the nightmare is over and jails no longer yawn I do not hesitate to say that, in so far as my own supply went, most of it came from the two lowermost tiers of Pennsylvania counties. Dotted over that smiling pastoral landscape there were groups of small breweries that managed successfully, by means that we need not go into, to stall off the Prohibition agents, and I had the privilege and honor of getting down many a carboy of their excellent product both in Baltimore, where I lived, and in New York, where I had my office.

When I say New York I mean the city in its largest sense— the whole metropolitan region. As a matter of fact, the malt liquor on tap on the actual island of Manhattan was usually bad, and often downright poisonous. When I yearned for a quaff of the real stuff I went to Union Hill, N. J., and if not to Union Hill, then to Hoboken. Both of these great outposts radiated a bouquet of malt and hops almost as pungent as Baltimore's, and in Union Hill there was a beer-house that sticks in my memory as the most comfortable I have ever encountered on this earth. Its beers were perfect, its victuals were cheap and nourishing, its chairs were designed by osteological engineers specializing in the structure of the human pelvis, and its waiters, Axel, Otto, Julius and Raymond, were experts at their science.[1]

[1] Raymond, like Axel, was from upper Schleswig-Holstein, and hence technically a Dane. I naturally assumed that his baptismal name was an Americanized

This incomparable dump was discovered by the late Philip Goodman, then transiently a theatrical manager on Broadway and all his life a fervent beer-drinker, and he and I visited it every time I was in New York, which was pretty often. We would ease into our canons' stalls in the early evening and continue in residence until Axel, Otto, Julius and Raymond began to snore in their corner and the colored maintenance engineer, Willie, turned his fire-hose into the washroom. Then back by taxi to Weehawken, from Weehawken to Forty-second street by the six-minute ferry, and from Forty-second street by taxi again to the quick, lordly sleep of quiet minds and pure hearts.

The fact that the brews on tap in that Elysium came from lower Pennsylvania naturally suggested an expedition to the place of their origin, and Goodman and I laid many plans for making the trip in his car. But every time we started out we dropped in on Axel, Otto, Julius and Raymond for stirrup cups, and that was as far as we ever got. Alone, however, I once visited Harrisburg on newspaper business, and there had the felicity of drinking close to the *Urquell*. That was in the primitive days when New York still bristled with peepholes and it was impossible to get into a strange place without a letter from a judge, but in Harrisburg there were no formalities. I simply approached a traffic cop and asked him where reliable stuff was to be had. "Do you see that kaif there?" he replied, pointing to the corner. "Well, just go in and lay down your money. If you don't like it, come back and I'll give you another one." I liked it well enough, and so did not trouble him further.

I should add, however, that I once came so near going dry in Pennsylvania, and in the very midst of a huge fleet of illicit breweries, that the memory of it still makes me shiver. This was at Bethlehem in the Lehigh Valley, in 1924. I had gone to the place with my publisher, Alfred Knopf, to hear the celebrated Bach Choir, and we were astounded after the first day's sessions to discover that not a drop of malt liquor was to be had in the local pubs. This seemed strange and unfriendly, for it is well known

form of the old Teutonic name of Reimund, signifying a sagacious councilor. But one night he told me that his father, a *Stadtpfeiffer*, had named him after the "Raymond" overture by Ambrose Thomas, a work he greatly admired.

to every musicologist that the divine music of old Johann Sebastian cannot be digested without the aid of its natural solvent. But so far as we could make out there was absolutely none on tap in the Lehigh Valley, though we searched high and low, and threw ourselves upon the mercy of cops, taxi-drivers, hotel clerks, the Elks, the rev. clergy, and half the tenors and basses of the choir. All reported that Prohibition agents had been sighted in the mountains a few days before, and that as a result hundreds of kegs had been buried and every bartender was on the alert. How we got through the second day's sessions I don't know; the music was magnificent, but our tonsils became so parched that we could barely join in the final Amen. Half an hour before our train was scheduled to leave for New York we decided to go down to the Lehigh station and telegraph to a bootician in the big city, desiring him to start westward at once and meet us at Paterson, N. J. On the way to the station we discussed this madcap scheme dismally, and the taxi-driver overheard us. He was a compassionate man, and his heart bled for us.

"Gents," he said, "I hate to horn in on what ain't none of my business, but if you feel that bad about it I think I know where some stuff is to be had. The point is, can you get it?"

We at once offered him money to introduce us, but he waived us off.

"It wouldn't do you no good," he said. "These Pennsylvania Dutch never trust a hackman."

"But where is the place?" we breathed.

"I'm taking you to it," he replied, and in a moment we were there.

It was a huge, blank building that looked like a forsaken warehouse, but over a door that appeared to be tightly locked there was the telltale sign, "Sea Food"—the universal euphemism for beer-house in Maryland and Pennsylvania throughout the thirteen awful years. We rapped on the door and presently it opened about half an inch, revealing an eye and part of a mouth. The ensuing dialogue was *sotto voce* but *staccato* and *appassionata*. The eye saw that we were famished, but the mouth hesitated.

"How do I know," it asked, "that you ain't two of them agents?"

The insinuation made us boil, but we had to be polite.

"*Agents!*" hissed Knopf. "What an idea! Can't you *see* us? Take a good look at us."

The eye looked, but the mouth made no reply.

"Can't you tell musicians when you see them?" I broke in. "Where did you ever see a Prohibition agent who looked so innocent, so moony, so dumb? We are actually fanatics. We came here to hear Bach. Is this the way Bethlehem treats its guests? We came a thousand miles, and now—"

"*Three* thousand miles," corrected Knopf.

"*Five* thousand," I added, making it round numbers.

Suddenly I bethought me that the piano score of the B minor mass had been under my arm all the while. What better introduction? What more persuasive proof of our *bona fides?* I held up the score and pointed to the title on the cover. The eye read:

J. S. Bach
Mass in B Minor

The eye flicked for an instant or two, and then the mouth spoke. "Come in, gents," it said. As the door opened our natural momentum carried us into the bar in one leap, and there we were presently immersed in two immense *Humpen.* The quality we did not pause to observe; what we mainly recalled later was the astounding modesty of the bill, which was sixty-five cents for five *Humpen*—Knopf had two and I had three—and two sandwiches. We made our train just as it was pulling out.

It was a narrow escape from death in the desert, and we do not forget all these years afterward that we owed it to Johann Sebastian Bach, that highly talented and entirely respectable man, and especially to his mass in B minor. In the great city of Cleveland, Ohio, a few months later, I had much worse luck. I went there, in my capacity of newspaper reporter, to help cover the Republican national convention which nominated Calvin Coolidge, and I assumed like everyone else that the Prohibition agents would lay off while the job was put through, if only as a mark of respect to their commander-in-chief. This assumption turned out to be erroneous. The agents actually clamped down on Cleveland with the utmost ferocity, and produced a drought that was virtually complete. Even the local cops and newspaper reporters were dry, and many of the latter spent a large part of their time touring the quarters of the out-of-town correspondents, begging for succor. But the supplies brought in by the correspondents were gone in a few days, and by the time the convention actually opened a glass of malt liquor was as hard to come by in Cleveland as an honest politician.

The news of this horror quickly got about, and one morning I received a dispatch in cipher from a Christian friend in Detroit, saying that he was loading a motor-launch with ten cases of bottled beer and ale, and sending it down the Detroit river and across Lake Erie in charge of two of his goons. They were instructed, he said, to notify me the instant they arrived off the Cleveland breakwater. Their notice reached me the next afternoon, but by that time the boys were nominating Cal, so I could not keep the rendezvous myself, but had to send an agent. This agent was Paul de Kruif, then a young man of thirty-four, studying the literary art under my counsel. Paul was a fellow of high principles and worthy of every confidence; moreover, he was dying of thirst himself. I started him out in a rowboat, and he was gone three hours. When he got back he was pale and trembling, and I could see at a glance that some calamity had befallen. When he got his breath he gasped out the story.

The two goons, it appeared, had broken into their cargo on the way down from Detroit, for the weather was extremely hot. By the time they anchored off the Cleveland breakwater they had got down three cases, and while they were waiting for de Kruif they knocked off two more. This left but five—and they figured that it was just enough to get them back to Detroit, for the way was uphill all the way, as a glance at a map will show. De Kruif, who was a huge and sturdy Dutchman with a neck like John L. Sullivan, protested violently and even undertook to throw them overboard and pirate the launch and cargo, but they pulled firearms on him, and the best he could do was to get six bottles. These he drank on his return in the rowboat, for the heat, as I have said, was extreme. As a result, I got nothing whatsoever; indeed, not a drop of malt touched my throat until the next night at 11.57, when the express for Washington and points East crossed the frontier of the Maryland Free State.

This was my worst adventure during Prohibition, and in many ways it remains the worst adventure of my whole life, though I have been shot at four times and my travels have taken me to Albania, Trans-Jordan and Arkansas. In Maryland there was always plenty, and when I was in New York Goodman and I made many voyages to Union Hill. One hot night in 1927, while we were lolling in the perfect beerhouse that I have mentioned, a small but excellent band was in attendance, and we learned on inquiry that it belonged to a trans-Atlantic liner of foreign registry, then berthed at one of the North river docks. Through Axel and Raymond we got acquainted with the leader, and he told us that if we cared to accompany him and his men back to the ship they would set up some real Pilsner. We naturally accepted, and at five o'clock the next morning we were still down in the stewards' dining-room on H-deck, pouring in *Seidel* after *Seidel* and victualing royally on black bread and *Leberwurst*. The stewards were scrupulous fellows and would not bootleg, but Goodman had some talent for mathematics, and it was not hard for him to figure out a tip that would cover what we had drunk of their rations, with a reasonable *Zuschlag* added.

Thereafter, we visited that lovely ship every time it was in port, which was about once every five weeks, and in a little while we began to add other ships of the same and allied lines, until in the end we had a whole fleet of them, and had access to Pilsner about three weeks out of four, and not only to Pilsner but also to Münchner, Dortmunder, Würzburger and Kulmbacher. It was a long hoof down the dark pier to the cargo port we had to use, and a long climb from the water-line down to H-deck, but we got used to the exertion and even came to welcome it, for we were both under medical advice to take more exercise. When we went aboard, usually at 10 or 11 p.m., there was no one on the dock save a customs watchman sitting on a stool at the street entrance, chewing tobacco, and when we debarked at 4 or 5 a.m. the same watchman was still there, usually sound asleep.

Gradually, such being the enticements of sin, we fell into the habit of sneaking a couple of jugs past the watchman—most often, of Germany brandy, or *Branntwein*. It was abominable stuff, but nevertheless it was the real McCoy, and Goodman and I found it very useful—he for drugging his actors and I for dishing out to the poets who infested my magazine office. One night there was some sort of celebration aboard ship—as I recall it, the birthday of Martin Luther—and the stewards put on a special spread. The *pièce de résistance* was a *Wurst* of some strange but very toothsome kind, and Goodman and I got down large rashers of it, and praised it in high, astounding terms. The stewards were so pleased by our appreciation that they gave us two whole ones as we left, and so we marched up the pier to the street, each with a bottle of *Branntwein* in one coat pocket and a large, globulous sausage in the other. To our surprise we found the customs watchman awake. More, he halted us.

"What have you got there in your pockets?" he demanded.

We turned them out, and he passed over the two bottles without a word, but the sausages set him off to an amazing snorting and baying.

"God damn me," he roared, "if I ever seen the like. Ain't you got *no* sense *whatever?* Here I try to be nice to you, and let you get something 100% safe into your system, and what do you hand me? What you hand me is that you try to do some *smuggling* on me. Yes, *smuggling*. I know the law and so do you. If I wanted to turn you in I could send you to Atlanta for the rest of your life. God damn if I ain't *ashamed* of you."

With that he grabbed the two sausages and hugged them to him. Goodman and I, conscious of guilt, stood silent, with flushed faces and downcast eyes. What was there to say? Nothing that we could think of. We had been taken red-handed in a deliberate violation of the just laws of this great Republic. We had tried with malice prepense to rob the Treasury of the duty on two valuable sausages—say, 67½ cents at 25% *ad valorem* on a valuation of $2.50 for the pair. The amount, to be sure, was small, but the principle was precious beyond price. In brief, we were common felons, dirt criminals, enemies to society, and as reprehensible, almost, as so many burglars, hijackers or Prohibition agents.

The watchman howled on for two or three minutes, seeking, apparently, to impress upon us the heinousness of our offense. We

needed no such exposition. Our consciences were devouring us
with red-hot fangs. There was no need for us to say a word, for
we radiated repentance and regret. But finally, as the watchman
dismissed us with a parting blast, Goodman ventured upon a question.

"Do you," he asked, "want the bottles too?"

"Hell, no," replied the watchman. "What *I* am trying to bust
up is *smuggling.*"

I WENT TO SEE A QUEEN

By RALPH FRYE

IT IS STILL A MYSTERY TO ME HOW MY UNCLE 'LISH EVER GOT THE permission of the family to take me, a boy of seven, from Sicasset to Boston to see the parade in honor of Queen Liliuokalani. For my list of proscribed persons was headed by the name of my great-uncle, Captain Elisha Hathaway, retired shipmaster and, as I see it now, probably one of the most scandalous old men of a hard-bitten era. Mother's parting words as I went out to play invariably were "Don't go down to the end of the wharf, and keep away from Uncle 'Lish's house." There was an attraction about the old man's company, combined with a shivery sort of fear, that always made this order hard to obey.

Uncle 'Lish used to sit at a table under the trellis built out from the portico of his four-square old "captain's house" and drink Jamaica rum practically all day. He had a cellar full of it which he had brought in himself on the last of his voyages. The big barque of which he was master and half owner had degenerated and, in her last days, carried molasses from West Indian ports into Medford for the Lawrence distilleries. That was after long years of service as a China trader.

As the day wore on, Uncle 'Lish would get noisy. He used to roar out orders to imaginary seamen, aloft in the big cherry tree above him, to reef a tops'l or set a stuns'l, and the language he employed in giving these orders would blister the paint off the house.

But Sicasset people didn't, in those days, appear to care. Timorous old ladies passing on the street would stop their ears, but most of the neighbors, just said, "By gorry, Cap'n 'Lish, he's givin' her all she'll carry this v'y'ge."

Uncle 'Lish was well on toward seventy-five years. He was very tall, standing more than six feet despite the fact that he was extremely bowed in the legs. He was clean-shaven, with fierce blue eyes, and his jaw was noticeably lopsided. Uncle 'Lish always insisted that this defect was the result of being moonstruck while sleeping on deck in the tropics, but certain old sailors in Sicasset who had shipped out to China with him told another story. They said his jaw was broken in a beating by revengeful members of his crew who waited for him on South Street, in New York, after a particularly trying passage.

His effect of height was enhanced by a tall, narrow-brimmed stovepipe hat which I never saw him remove, in the house or out of it, and by a long-tailed coat of either blue broadcloth or sailor cloth, but with black, not brass, buttons. His trousers were cut very wide, probably to camouflage his bowlegs. He wore high sea boots up to his knees, but they were under his trousers. As to linen, he wore a stiff-bosomed "boiled shirt," and in spite of his slovenly habits when in drink, it always seemed to me immaculate. He never put on a collar or tie, but in the buttonhole under his chin there was always a gold stud of remarkable size and lustre. Finally, he had a rosewood cane with a yellowed ivory knob, which I suppose had punched holes in the streets of most of the ports of the seven seas. I have that cane to this day.

Uncle 'Lish's wife, Mahala, my maternal grandmother's sister, was one of the gentlest of women, but she was far from being browbeaten by her masterful husband. As I look back at it, I believe she was the only person on earth, or beyond, whom he feared. It was this fear of her, I am persuaded, that prompted him to take me with him on that memorable trip to Boston in the year 1886. I was to be his alibi.

I had gone over to his house across the lane one afternoon in spite of orders. Uncle 'Lish, in a fairly sober condition, was sitting with Aunt Mahala under the trellis discussing the dusky royal visitor from the Hawaiian Islands who was to arrive in Boston the following day, and his intention of going to see her. When he noticed me, he broke off in the middle of a sentence.

"And what's more, Mahaly," he roared, "I'm going to take the boy with me! He's never seen a queen. By God, I'll introduce him to my friend Liliuokalani, and show him something of the world. Hell, I ain't seen Lili since I dined in state with her brother, old King Kalakaua, in the royal palace in Honolulu in '67. And of all the damned fish guts and gurry that I ever had served up to me. Yes, b'God, I'm going to ask Mercy to let him go." Mercy was my mother. Off he went to our house.

"I do not believe, Elisha, that Mercy will agree," Aunt Mahala called after him.

Aunt Mahala was wrong. I don't know why, but Mother said yes. So next morning, when the Boston accommodation came screeching into the Sicasset station, with the brakemen winding down on the hand brakes and the cars bumping together on the drawbars, Uncle 'Lish and I were waiting. And an incongruous pair we must have looked.

We got into the smoker and the Captain, taking four-fifths of the seat, began describing to me the wonders and grandeur of the sovereign whom I was about to see. The conductor came and stood beside us and waited for some time for him to come to a stop. Finally he tapped Uncle 'Lish on the elbow with his ticket punch.

I have been sorry ever since for that conductor, a mild little man in a frock coat and a derby hat. Conductors on the Old Colony road didn't wear uniforms in that day and his only insignia of office were a gold shield pinned on his breast and his punch. The conductor's most striking feature was a heavy, sandy beard which reached nearly to his eyes. Captain 'Lish, who had broken off in the middle of a sentence, stared at him for a moment and then turned to me.

"Boy," he said, "I don't like the rig of this bastard. He looks to me like a rat peekin' through a bunch of oakum . . . Go for'ard, you son of a hoor, or I'll keel-haul you under your own train." The conductor fled.

There was a great crowd of people pouring out of the Kneeland Street Station in Boston and from the Albany Depot next door, most of them apparently bound for the parade to see Liliuokalani, who was going to ride in a barouche drawn by six horses, accompanied by the Governor. The Queen's retinue was to follow in hacks. There was a festivity and feeling of carnival in the air as we came out of the station, and I could hear bands playing at a distance.

Naturally I was anxious to follow this gay crowd. But Uncle 'Lish showed no haste.

"Hell, boy," he said, "don't crowd on so much sail. You'll see the Queen, all right. But there's a man over here that I've got to see about a cargo, and that's our first port of call." He steered me across and up Kneeland Street and into the first saloon I had ever been in.

Our entrance into the place had an immediate and, to me, a mysterious effect. Three nautical-looking men who were sitting at a table got up, leaving their drinks, and ran out a side door. A fourth rose and stood at the far end of the bar, where be glowered at Captain Elisha. He was a very big man and I think he, too, was a sailor.

Uncle 'Lish was affable and roared a welcome, and the bartender came up and shook hands. "Welcome aboard, Cap'n," he said. "What's this—your new cabin boy?" But he seemed restless and there was a general air of restraint in the place. Uncle 'Lish laid some money down on the bar.

"A pamikin of rum around for all hands except that goddam swab up there," he said, indicating the man at the far end of the bar. "I wouldn't drink in the same cantina as that pack-rat." They all had drinks, except the big man. I was served some sort of sweet, fruity beverage, which I have never forgotten. Sometimes, in drugstores, or while passing fruit stands, I catch a whiff of odor that brings back, almost visually, that scene, with Captain Elisha leaning over the bar as if it were the taffrail of a ship, the bartender looking worried, and the tall man edging out of the side door.

When he had gone, the bartender seemed more cheerful. He even set up another round of drinks and called on the Captain for a song.

Uncle 'Lish obliged. It was one of those songs dear to sailormen, which related the amorous adventures of a gentleman known as the One-Eyed Riley. I understood little of it at the time and now I have forgotten it.

This sort of thing went on for some time. At last we left the saloon and crossed over to the Albany Depot, where the Captain chartered a herdic, which we boarded, and I felt that at last we were well on our way to seeing the Queen.

The herdic turned south on Washington Street and headed into the South End. Somewhere in the neighborhood of Dover Street, it drew up before a dingy, closely shuttered edifice, evidently once a residence of some pretensions. I was mystified and disturbed to see that there was no particular movement in the street, no people or music or flags, and I was afraid the Captain had some further delay in mind. I wanted to see the Queen.

There was a sinister and forbidding quality about this house, and I noticed that as we got out of the herdic someone was watching us through the shutter of a front-parlor window. I had an impression of something being altogether wrong and this anxiety was not eased by the difficulties of getting into the place—peerings, whisperings, and rattling of chains. Finally the door was opened by a colored maid and the Captain ushered me into the front parlor and the presence of its only occupant.

"There, boy," he shouted, "there, by Almighty God, is the Queen herself!"

I was taken aback by my first sight of the Queen. To begin with, I had formed the idea that she was a black woman, but this personage, who smilingly greeted me, was as fair as Guinevere. She was a plump woman, about fifty, with yellow hair done up high on her head, the front of it falling in frizzy-looking curls over her forehead.

The Queen was wearing a gown made of some red material like plush or velvet, cut very low in the bodice and tight about the waist, and when she stood up, I noticed that she wore a pronounced bustle. Her ears and the fingers of both hands sparkled with what I assumed to be precious stones. Her throne was a red plush sofa with white crocheted antimacassars and at her right hand was a walnut table with a white marble top, on which stood a bottle of beer.

She was very gracious, even regal, in her reception. I had begun to tell her my life at Sicasset when the Captain burst in. "Belay that! How about serving a drink for all hands?"

Evidently the colored maid had been standing within hearing distance, for in a very short time she came in with a large tray, bearing many bottles and glasses, which she set down on the marble table. I wondered at so much preparation for so small a party until the Captain said, "Now, boy, the Queen's ladies in waiting are coming aboard. Stand by!"

I was, of course, a very small boy and the human form divine meant nothing to me, but I remember being distinctly impressed by the Queen's entourage as its ten members entered the room in a body.

They were all very effusive with the Captain and toasted him and seemed anxious to please him. They distributed themselves around the parlor in chairs and sofas. They were all smoking. It was the first time I had ever seen women do that.

As I sat in wide-eyed wonder and watched them, it occurred to me that they were probably the ten most beautiful women in the world. They were of various complexions but mostly their hair was golden-yellow or blue-black, and they had the reddest cheeks and the whitest noses I have ever seen. But none of them was black. I worried about this. The only black woman was the maidservant.

Some of the ladies chatted with me but the attention of most of them was for the Captain, who had already bought another round of drinks. Presently, it seemed that some business matter had come up and that the Captain must go upstairs for a discussion.

"Boy, I'm going aloft, but you stay here," he said to me. "You wanted to see the Queen, didn't you? Well, here she is. Don't be scared to talk to her. Get a bellyful of her. I won't be long." He went away, taking a lady in waiting, the fattest one, with him. Soon the others drifted away and I was left alone with the Queen. Somehow she appeared less gracious now. The gaps in our conversation became longer and longer and I began to feel very lonely and homesick. I think I went to sleep in an uncomfortable plush chair and I may have cried a little, for I was very miserable.

At last there was an outcry from above. The Captain shouting something down the stairs about the timetable, burst into the parlor, saying that we had to leave at once. He bought drinks for the Queen and himself, kissed the Queen, who shook hands with me, and before I realized it we were jingling downtown on a Washington Street horsecar, headed for the depot.

We caught the afternoon train and I was very plad to get on it. On the way to Sicasset, the Captain was silent for a long time, but at last he turned to me and inquired, "You saw the Queen, didn't you?"

I admitted that I had.

"What color was she?"

I said I thought she was sort of yellow.

"Yellow? Goddamit, don't you know brown when you see it? You're a good boy and tomorrow I'm going to buy you a nice present, but if your mother asks you what color the Queen was, by God, you tell her she was brown. And don't forget it. Brown!"

Those devilish little gods who protect the wicked seem to have devoted the next few days to the protection of Uncle 'Lish. Nobody asked me anything about our trip. Some important thing had happened. Somebody had been born, or died, or married, to the exclusion of all other matters. I suppose I was asked if I liked the Queen and said I did, but that was all.

"THEY'RE OFF!"

By ROBERT BENCHLEY

THERE ARE SEVERAL SPECTACULAR WAYS IN WHICH I COULD DIS-sipate a fortune, if I were to have one left to me, but one of them is not horse-racing.

Some day you may read of my daredevil escapades with a team of arch-duchesses on the Riviera in which "Mad Bob" (that will be I) rides up and down the Promenade des Anglais on a high-powered car's running-board throwing out burning mille-franc notes at the people (all of whom love me for my wild, likeable eccentricties). You may read of someone who has discovered me, a grey-haired, distinguished-looking old derelict, pacing the water-front of Port Said, living on the pittance furnished me by friends whom I had wined and dined in the old days when I was known as "The Playboy of Two Continents," before a group of international bankers conspired against me to wipe out my entire fortune at one *coup*. (I hate those bankers already, just thinking about it). But you will never hear about my taking my life at a race-course—unless it is from sheer confusion. That is one thing you don't have to worry about, in case you worry about me at all.

Fond as I am of horses when meeting them personally (and give me a handful of sugar and I will make friends with any horse —or lose my hand up to the wrist in the attempt) I am strangely unmoved when I see them racing each other up and down a track. A great calm descends on me at the cry "They're Off!" and, as the race proceeds, this calm increases in intensity until it is prac-tically a coma, from which I have to be aroused by friends telling me which horse won.

Much of this coolness towards horse-racing is due to the fact that I almost never have any money up. I have no scruples in the matter (except that old New England scruple against losing money), but I never seem to be able to get the hang of just how

97

the betting is done. By the time I have decided what horse I would like to bet on, everybody seems to have disappeared, either through indifference to my betting plans or because the race is on. I hear other people betting, but I never can quite see whom they are betting with. The whole thing is more or less chaotic to me.

In the second place, I never can *see* a horse-race. Of course, when you go to a race in England, like the Grand National, you don't expect to see. All you do is listen very carefully and peer into the mist and, when you hear the crowd murmur "They're Off!" go around back to a refreshment tent and munch on a cold meat-pie until you think it is time for the race to be finished. Then go to the door of the tent and someone (who didn't see the finish either) will tell you who won. That is the Sport of Kings as England knows it.

In this country, you usually can see the course, but I personally have a great deal of trouble in finding out where the horses are. Part of this is due to my inability to manipulate long-range glasses. I can swing them jauntily by my side before the race starts, and I can hold them up to my eyes (until my arms get tired—then to hell with them) but I can't seem to see anything except an in-distinct blur of grass and an object which later turns out to be the back of the head of one of the officials. Even if I find the horses when they are grouped at the barrier, I lose them the minute they start out and spend my time sweeping the horizon for them while my friends are muttering "Look at that! Look at him come up! There goes Captain's Garter! Here comes Onion Soup!" The last time I used field glasses at a horse race I thought I saw a rowboat in the distance manned by a suspiciously large number of oarsmen; so I haven't felt like using the glasses since then. With my naked eye I can at least see the surrounding coun-try, and without the complication of strange rowboats.

I have therefore given up the use of glasses entirely and carry them just for looks. (I am even thinking of giving that up, too, as I have been told that they don't *look* right on me.) With the naked eye at least I can see the grass clearly and, at Belmont Park, there are some very pretty fountains to watch in case the race itself has eluded you. Even with my eyes free to roam as they will, I lose the horses before they have gone a hundred yards. Everyone else seems to know where they are, even people with much worse eyesight than mine (and I may say that my eyesight is very good as a general thing), but the whole affair becomes a mystery to me until suddenly I find that they are at the last turn and into the homestretch. Then comes the problem of finding out which horse is which.

It is, I will admit, a very pretty sight to see a lot of horses coming in at the finish, but it would be much more exciting for me if I could distinguish the various colors. Insofar as I have any favorites at all, they are always the horses who carry a bright red, because that is the only color that means anything to me at the finish. These yellow and pink mixtures get all confused with the baby-blues and blood-oranges when they get bunched together, and I am constantly upset by the spectacle of what seems to me to be two jockeys on one horse. I don't like to admit after the finish that I haven't been able to detect the winner, and so a great many times I am completely in the dark unless I overhear a chance remark or see on early edition of the papers. This makes going to the races something of a mockery.

Then, too, there is another source of confusion for me in the varying lengths of the races they see fit to run. I think that I am correct in saying that one has a right to expect that any race shall finish down in front of the grandstands. I don't mean to be arbitrary about this, but that is the way it seems to me. All right, then. The last race I saw at Belmont Park (New York) began where they all begin—that is, just beyond my range of vision, over at the right. The horses, as near as I could tell, ran straight away along the other side of the course, meaning nothing as far as I was concerned. Then, just as they reached the far turn, they seemed to give the whole thing up as a bad job and began running in different directions. I thought that maybe it was a game like hare-and-hounds, that one bunch of horses went North and another went South and still others East and West, with the ones who got back on to the course first, winning. But no. It seems that the race was over, 'way out there, and they were simply dispersing for the afternoon. In other words, nobody in the stands (unless they happened to know black art and were able to work long-range glasses) had any idea as to which horse won. I was particularly fortunate in not caring.

But, aside from the strain of trying to keep the horses within your range of vision and telling which is which, there is another feature of horse-racing which seems to me a little irksome. That is the intervals between races. If left to myself I would be inclined to read a good book between times, or even during the races themselves. But this, evidently, is not allowed. You must get up as soon as a race is over and go out behind the stands and walk around in the paddock. Just what good this is supposed to do I never could figure out. You look at the horses and you look at the jockeys and you say "How are you?" to a lot of people who are walking around looking at the horses and the jockeys. But as for changing anything at that late hour, even your mind on a bet, the whole thing seems a little futile. Most of the people who walk around in the paddock just before a race don't know whether a horse looks good or not. They just look. They make marks with a pencil and try to appear "in the know" (*slang phrase*), but even *I* know that they aren't getting anywhere by doing it. Unless a horse in the paddock is obviously walking on three legs, or a jockey is obviously cockeyed, this walking around is just walking around and I can just walk around at home or in Times Square. I don't have to go out to a race-course to do it.

Personally, I always get lost when I walk around in the paddock. I start out with, let us say, three friends, whose company is sufficiently pleasing to me to make me leave my comfortable subway or corner drug-store and go out to the track in the first place. We amble around under the trees for a few minutes, look at a couple of horses who would much rather not be looked at, and then, all of a sudden, I am alone. My friends have disappeared into comparatively thin air. I turn to the right and run into a horse. I turn to the left and run into several people who might as well be horses as far as anything in common we have together. Then I get a little panicky. I begin rushing. I try to find the clubhouse. It, too, has disappeared. There are a lot of people about, but I don't seem to know any of them. Once in a while I recognize a man I know who works in the box office of a theater, but he always looks so worried that I dare not speak to

him. I feel that maybe I am out of place. Later I find that I am.
The hot sun beats down on me and I get to crying. The whole
thing takes on the aspect of a bad dream. Even if I do get back
to the stands, I merely am getting back to further confusion.
There really is nothing left for me to do but go home. And I
don't know how to get home. (*I am writing this out by the paddock at the last race-course I went to. Will someone who reads
this, and who lives near Saratoga, come and get me out?*)

THE JOLLITY BUILDING

By A. J. LIEBLING

IN THE JOLLITY BUILDING, WHICH STANDS SIX STORIES HIGH AND covers half of a Broadway block in the high Forties, the term "promoter" means a man who mulcts another man of a dollar, or any fraction or multiple thereof. The verb "to promote" always takes a personal object, and the highest praise you can accord someone in the Jollity Building is to say, "He has promoted some very smart people." The Jollity Building—it actually has a somewhat different name, and the names of its inhabitants are not the ones which will appear below—is representative of perhaps a dozen or so buildings in the upper stories of which the small-scale amusement industry nests like a tramp pigeon. All of them draw a major part of their income from the rental of their stores at street level, and most of them contain on their lower floors a dance hall or a billiard parlor, or both. The Jollity Building has both. The dance hall, known as Jollity Danceland, occupies the second floor. The poolroom is in the basement. It is difficult in such a building to rent office space to any business house that wants to be taken very seriously, so the upper floors fill up with the petty nomads of Broadway—chiefly orchestra leaders, theatrical agents, bookmakers, and miscellaneous promoters.

Eight coin-box telephone booths in the lobby of the Jollity Building serve as offices for promoters and others who cannot raise the price of desk space on an upper floor. The phones are used mostly for incoming calls. It is a matter of perpetual regret to Morty, the renting agent of the building, that he cannot collect rent from the occupants of the booths. He always refers to them as the Telephone Booth Indians, because in their lives the telephone booth furnishes sustenance as well as shelter, as the buffalo did for the Arapahoe and Sioux. A Telephone Booth Indian on the hunt often tells a prospective investor to call him at a certain hour in the afternoon, giving the victim the number of the phone in one of the booths. The Indian implies, of course, that it is a private line. Then the Indian has to hang in the booth until the fellow calls. To hang, in Indian language, means to loiter. "I used to hang in Forty-sixth Street, front of *Variety*," a small book-maker may say, referring to a previous business location. Seeing the Indians hanging in the telephone booths is painful to Morty, but there is nothing he can do about it. The regular occupants of the booths recognize one another's rights. It may be understood among them, for instance, that a certain orchestra leader receives calls in a particular booth between three and four in the afternoon and that a competitor has the same booth from four to five. In these circumstances, ethical Indians take telephone messages for each other. There are always fewer vacancies in the telephone booths than in any other part of the Jollity Building.

While awaiting a call, an Indian may occasionally emerge for air, unless the lobby is so crowded that there is a chance he might lose his place to a transient who does not understand the house rules. Usually, however, the Indian hangs in the booth with the door open, leaning against the wall and reading a scratch sheet in order to conserve time. Then, if somebody rings up and agrees to lend him two dollars, he will already have picked a horse on which to lose that amount. When an impatient stranger shows signs of wanting to use a telephone, the man in the booth closes the door, takes the receiver off the hook, and makes motions with his lips, as if talking. To add verisimilitude to a long performance, he occasionally hangs up, takes the receiver down again, drops a nickel in the slot, whirls the dial three or four times, and hangs up again, after which the nickel comes back. Eventually the stranger goes away, and the man in the booth returns to the study of his scratch sheet. At mealtimes, the Telephone Booth Indians some-times descend singly to the Jollity Building's lunch counter, which is at one end of the poolroom in the basement. The busiest lunch periods are the most favorable for a stunt the boys have worked out to get free nourishment. An Indian seats himself at the counter and eats two or three *pastrami* sandwiches. As he is finishing his lunch, one of his comrades appears at the head of the stairs and shouts that he is wanted on the telephone. The Indian rushes upstairs, absent-mindedly omitting to pay for his meal. Barney, the lunch counter proprietor, is too busy to go after him when he fails to return after a reasonable time. An Indian can rarely fool Barney more than once or twice. The maneuver requires nice timing and unlimited faith in one's accomplice. Should the accomplice fail to make his entrance, the Indian at the counter might be compelled to eat *pastrami* sandwiches indefinitely, acquiring frightful indigestion and piling up an appalling debt.

Morty, the renting agent, is a thin, sallow man of forty whose expression has been compared, a little unfairly, to that of a dead robin. He is not, however, a man without feeling; he takes a personal interest in the people who spend much of their lives in the Jollity Building. It is about the same sort of interest that Curator Raymond Ditmars takes in the Bronx Zoo's vampire bats. "I know more heels than any other man in the world," Morty sometimes says, not without pride. "Everywhere I go around Broadway, I get 'Hello, how are you?' Heels that haven't been with me for years, some of them." Morty usually reserves the appellation "heel" for the people who rent the forty-eight cubicles, each furnished with a desk and two chairs, on the third floor of the Jollity Building. These cubicles are formed by partitions of wood and frosted glass which do not quite reach the ceiling. Sufficient air to maintain human life is supposed to circulate over the partitions. The offices rent for $10 and $12.50 a month, payable in advance. "Twelve and a half dollars with air, ten dollars without air," Morty says facetiously. "Very often the heels who rent them take the air without telling me." Sometimes a Telephone Booth Indian acquires enough capital to rent a cubicle. He thus rises in the social scale and becomes a heel. A cubicle has three advantages over a telephone booth. One is that you cannot get a desk into a telephone booth. Another is that you can play pinochle in a cubicle. Another is that a heel gets his name on the directory in the lobby, and the white letters have a bold, legitimate look.

The vertical social structure of the Jollity Building is subject to continual shifts. Not only do Indians become heels, but a heel occasionally accumulates $40 or $50 with which to pay a month's rent on one of the larger offices, all of them unfurnished, on the fourth, fifth, or sixth floor. He then becomes a tenant. Morty always views such progress with suspicion, because it involves signing a lease, and once a heel has signed a lease, you cannot put him out without serving a dispossess notice and waiting ten days. A tenant, in Morty's opinion, is just a heel who is planning to get ten days' free rent. "Any time a heel acts prosperous enough to rent an office," Morty says, "you know he's getting ready to take you." A dispossessed tenant often reappears in the Jollity Building as an Indian. It is a life cycle. Morty has people in the building who have been Telephone Booth Indians, heels, and tenants several times each. He likes them best when they are in the heel stage. "You can't collect rent from a guy who hangs in the lobby," he says in explanation, "and with a regular tenant of an unfurnished office, you got too many headaches." He sometimes breaks off a conversation with a friendly heel by saying, "Excuse me, I got to go upstairs and insult a tenant."

As if to show his predilection for the heels, Morty has his own office on the third floor. It is a large corner room with windows on two sides. There is a flattering picture of the Jollity Building on one of the walls, and six framed plans, one of each floor, on another wall. Also in the office are an unattractive, respectable-looking secretary and, on Morty's desk, a rather depressing photograph of his wife. The conventionality of this *décor* makes Morty unhappy, and he spends as little time as possible in his office. Between nine o'clock in the morning, when he arrives and dejectedly looks through his mail for rent checks he does not expect to find, and six-thirty in the evening, when he goes home to Rockaway, he lives mostly amid the pulsating activity outside his office door.

The furnished cubicles on the third floor yield an income of about $500 a month, which, as Morty says, is not hay. Until a few years ago, the Jollity Building used to feel it should provide switchboard service for these offices. The outgoing telephone calls of the heels were supposed to be paid for at the end of every business day. This system necessitated the use of a cordon of elevator boys to prevent tenants from escaping. "Any heel who made several telephone calls toward the end of the month, you could kiss him good-by," Morty says. "As soon as he made up his mind to go out of business he started thinking of people to telephone. It was cheaper for him to go out of business than settle for the calls, anyhow. The only way you can tell if a heel is still in business, most of the time, anyway, is to look in his office for his hat. If his hat is gone, he is out of business." A minor annoyance of the switchboard system was the tendency of heels to call the operator and ask for the time. "None of them were going anywhere, but they all wanted to know the time," Morty says resentfully. "None of them had watches. Nobody would be in this building unless he had already hocked his watch." There are lady heels, too, but if they are young Morty calls them "heads." (Morty meticulously refers to all youngish women as "heads," which has the same meaning as "broads" or "dolls" but is newer; he does not want his conversation to sound archaic.) Heads also abused the switchboard system. "One head that used to claim to sell stockings," says Morty, "called the board one day, and when the operator said, 'Five o'clock,' this head said, 'My God, I didn't eat yet!' If there had been no switchboard, she would never have known she was hungry. She would have saved a lot of money."

As a consequence of these abuses, the switchboard was abolished, and practically all the heels now make their telephone calls from three open coin-box telephones against the wall in a corridor that bisects the third floor. The wall for several feet on each side of the telephones is covered with numbers the heels have jotted down. The Jollity Building pays a young man named Angelo to sit at a table in a small niche near the telephones and answer incoming calls. He screams "Who?" into the mouthpiece and then shuffles off to find whatever heel is wanted. On days when Angelo is particularly weary, he just says, "He ain't in," and hangs up. He also receives and distributes the mail for the heels. Angelo is a pallid chap who has been at various periods a chorus boy, a taxi driver, and a drummer in one of the bands which maintain headquarters in the Jollity Building. "Every time a heel comes in," Angelo says, "he wants to know 'Are you sure there isn't a letter for me that feels like it had a check in it? . . . That's funny, the fellow swore he mailed it last night.' Then he tries to borrow a nickel from me so he can telephone."

Not having a nickel is a universal trait of people who rent the cubicles, and they spend a considerable portion of the business day hanging by the third-floor telephones, waiting for the arrival of somebody to borrow a nickel from. While waiting, they talk to Angelo, who makes it a rule not to believe anything they say. There are no booths in the corridor because Morty does not want any Telephone Booth Indians to develop on the third floor.

Morty himself often goes to visit with Angelo and terrifies the heels with his bilious stare. "They all say they got something big for next week," he tells Angelo in a loud, carrying voice, "but the rent is 'I'll see you tomorrow.'" Morty's friends sometimes drop in there to visit him. He likes to sit on Angelo's table with them and tell about the current collection of furnished-office inhabitants. "Who is that phony-looking heel who just passed, you want to know?" he may say during such a recapitulation. "Hey, this is funny. He happens to be legitimate—autos to hire. The heel in the next office publishes a horse magazine. If he gets a winner, he eats. Then there's one of them heels that hires girls to sell permanent waves for fifty cents down, door to door. The girl takes the fifty cents and gives the dame a ticket, but when the dame goes to look for the beauty parlor it says on the ticket, there is no such beauty parlor at that address.

"We got two heels writing plays. They figure they got nothing to do, so they might as well write a play, and if it clicks, they might also eat. Then we got a lady heel who represents Brazilian music publishers and also does a bit of cooking; also a head yho is running a school for hat-check girls, as it seems the hat-check profession is very complicated for some of the type of minds they got in it. Those heads who walk through the hall are going no place. They just stick their potato in every office and say, 'Anything for me today?' They do not even look to see if it is a theatrical office. If they expected to find anything, they would not be over here. What would anybody here have to offer? Once in a while a sap from the suburbs walks into one of the offices on this floor thinking he can get some talent cheap. 'Sure,' some heel says, 'I got just the thing you want.' They run down in the lobby looking for somebody. They ask some head they meet in the lobby, 'Are you a performer?' They try the other little agents that they know. The whole date is worth probably four dollars, and the forty cents' commission they split sometimes four ways."

Morty's favorite heel of the current lot is a tall Chesterfieldian old man named Dr. Titus Heatherington, who is the president of the Anti-Hitlerian League of the Western Hemisphere. Dr. Heatherington for many years lectured in vacant stores on sex topics and sold a manual of facts every young man should know. "The line became, in a manner of speaking, exhausted," Dr. Heatherington says, "because of the increasing sophistication of the contemporary adolescent, so I interested myself in this great crusade, in which I distribute at a nominal price a very fascinating book by Cornelius Vanderbilt, Jr., and everything in it must be exactly as stated, because otherwise Hitler could have sued Mr. Vanderbilt for libel. Incidentally, I sell a lot more books than I have for years. I do particularly well at Coney Island."

Heels are often, paradoxically, more affluent than the official lessees of larger offices. Many fellows who rent the big units take in subtenants, and if there are enough of them, each man's share of the rent may be less than the $10 a month minimum rent a heel has to pay. One two-desk office on the fourth, fifth, or sixth floor may serve as headquarters for four theatrical agents, a band leader, a music arranger, a manager of prize fighters, and a dealer in pawn tickets. They agree on a schedule by which each man has the exclusive use of a desk for a few hours every day, to impress people who call by appointment, and the office is used collectively, when no outsiders are present, for games of rummy. All the fellows in the office receive their telephone calls on a single coin-box machine affixed to the wall. Subtenants often make bets among themselves, the amount of the wager corresponding to each bettor's share of the rent. The loser is supposed to pay double rent, the winner nothing. This causes difficulties for Morty when he comes to collect the rent. The official lessee always protests that he would like to pay on the dot but the other boys haven't paid him. Subtenants who have won bets consider themselves absolved of any responsibility, and the fellows who are supposed to pay double are invariably broke. Morty makes an average of fifteen calls to collect a month's rent on an office, and thus acquires a much greater intimacy with the tenants than the agents of a place like Rockefeller Center or River House.

Desk room in a large office has the advantage of being much

more dignified than a cubicle on the third floor, but there is one drawback: Morty's rule that not more than two firm names may be listed on the directory in the lobby for any one office. Callers therefore have to ask the elevator boys where to find some of the subtenants. If the elevator boys do not like the subtenant in question, they say they never heard of him. Nor will the implacable Morty permit more than two names to be painted on any office door. Junior subtenants get around the rule by having a sign painter put their names on strips of cardboard which they insert between the glass and the wooden frame of the door or affix to the glass by strips of tape. "You cannot let a tenant creep on you," Morty says in justification of his severity. "You let them get away with eight names on the door, and the next thing they will be asking you for eight keys to the men's room."

Morty's parents were named Goldberg, and he was born in the Bensonhurst region of Brooklyn. He almost finished a commercial course in high school before he got his first job, being an order clerk for a chain of dairy-and-herring stores. In the morning he would drive to each of these stores and find out from the store managers what supplies they needed from the company's warehouse. Since he had little to do in the afternoons, he began after a while to deliver packages for a bootlegger who had been a high-school classmate and by chance had an office in the Jollity Building. The name on the door of the office was the Music Writers Mutual Publishing Company. About a quarter of the firms in the building at that time were fronts for bootleggers, Morty recalls. "Repeal was a terrible blow to property values in this district," he says. "Bootleggers were always the best pay." Seeing a greater future in bootlegging than in dairy goods and herring, Morty soon went to work for his old classmate on a full-time basis. The moment Morty decided that his future lay on Broadway, he translated his name from Goldberg into Ormont. " 'Or' is French for gold," he sometimes explains, "and 'mont' is the same as 'berg.' But the point is it's got more class than Goldberg."

By diligent application, Morty worked his way up to a partnership in the Music Writers Mutual Publishing Company. The partners made good use of their company's name. They advertised in pulp magazines, offering to write music for lyrics or lyrics for music, to guarantee publication, and to send back to the aspiring song writer a hundred free copies of his work, all for one hundred dollars. The Music Writers Mutual agreed to pay him the customary royalties on all copies sold. There never were any royalties, because Morty and his partner had only the author's hundred copies printed. They kept a piano in their office and hired a professional musician for thirty-five dollars a week to set music to lyrics. Morty himself occasionally wrote lyrics to the tunes clients sent in, and had a lot of fun doing it. At times the music business went so well that the partners were tempted to give up bootlegging. There were so many similar publishing firms, however, that there was not a steady living in it. "But you would be surprised," Morty says now, "how near it came to paying our overhead." The volume of mail made it look bona fida. They built up a prosperous semi-wholesale liquor business, specializing in furnishing whisky to firms in the Garment Center, which used it for presents to out-of-town buyers. "The idea on that stuff was that it should be as reasonable as possible without killing anybody," Morty says. "It was a good, legitimate dollar." The depression in the garment industry ruined the Music Writers Mutual Publishing Company's business even before repeal and left Morty broke.

The Jollity Building belongs to the estate of an old New York family, and in the twenties the trustees had installed as manager one of the least promising members of the family, a middle-aged, alcoholic Harvard man whom they wanted to keep out of harm's way. Morty had been such a good tenant and seemed so knowing a fellow that the Harvard man offered him a job at twenty-five dollars a week as his assistant. When the manager ran off with eleven thousand dollars in rents and a head he had met in the lobby, Morty took over his job. He had held it ever since. The trustees feel, as one of them has expressed it, that "Mr. Ormont understands the milieu." He now gets fifty dollars a week and two per cent of the total rents, which adds about two thousand a year to his income.

The nostalgia Morty often feels for the opportunities of prohibition days is shared by the senior tenant in the building, the proprietor of the Quick Art Theatrical Sign Painting Company, on the sixth floor. The sign painter, a Mr. Hy Sky—a name made up of the first syllable of his first name, Hyman, and the last syllable of a surname which no one can remember—is a bulky, red-faced man who has rented space in the Jollity Building for twenty-five years. With his brother, a lean, sardonic man known as Si Sky, he paints signs and lobby displays for burlesque and movie houses and does odd jobs of lettering for people in all sorts of trades. He is an extremely fast letterer and he handles a large volume of steady business, but it lacks the exhilaration of prohibition years. Then he was sometimes put to work at two o'clock in the morning redecorating a clip joint, so that it could not be identified by a man who had just been robbed of a bank roll and might return with cops the next day. "Was that fun!" Hy howls reminiscently. "And always cash in advance! If the joint had green walls, we would make them pink. We would move the bar opposite to where it was, and if there was booths in the place, we would paint them a different color and change them around. Then the next day, when the cops came in with the sap, they would say, 'Is this the place? Try to remember the side of the door the bar was on as you come in.' The sap would hesitate, and the cops would say, 'I guess he can't identify the premises,' and they would shove him along. It was a nice, comfortable dollar for me."

Hy has a clinical appreciation of meretricious types which he tries unsuccessfully to arouse in Morty. Sometimes, when Hy has a particularly preposterous liar in his place, he will telephone the renting agent's office and shout, "Morty, pop up and see the character I got here! He is the most phoniest character I seen in several years." The person referred to seldom resents such a description. People in the Jollity Building neighborhood like to be thought of as characters. "He is a real character," they say, with respect, of any fascinatingly repulsive acquaintance. Most promoters are characters. Hy Sky attributes the stability of his own business to the fact that he is willing to "earn a hard dollar." "The trouble with the characters," he says, "is they are always looking for a soft dollar. The result is they knock theirselves out trying too hard to have it easy. So what do they get after all? Only the miss-meal cramps." Nevertheless, it always gives Hy a genteel pleasure to collaborate, in a strictly legitimate way, with any of the promoters he knows. The promoter may engage him to paint a sign saying, "A new night club will open soon on these premises. Concessionaires interested telephone So-and-So at such-and-such a number." The name is the promoter's own, and the telephone given is, as Hy knows, in a booth in the Jollity lobby. The promoter, Hy also knows, will place this sign in front of a vacant night club with which he has absolutely no connection, in the hope that some small hat-check concessionaire with money to invest in a new club will read the sign before someone gets around to removing it and take it seriously. If the concessionaire telephones, the promoter will make an appointment to receive him in a Jollity cubicle borrowed from some other promoter for the occasion and will try to get a couple of hundred dollars as a deposit on the concession. If successful, he will lose the money on a horse in the sixth race at an obscure track in California. The chances of getting any money out of this promotional scheme are exceedingly slight, but the pleasure of the promoter when the device succeeds is comparable to that of a sportsman who catches a big fish on a light line. Contemplation of the ineffectual larceny in the promoter's heart causes Hy to laugh constantly while lettering such a sign. A contributory cause of his laughter is the knowledge that he will receive the only dollar that is likely to change hands in the transaction—the dollar he gets for painting the sign.

Musicians are not characters, in Hy's estimation, but merely a mild variety of phony. As such, they afford him a tempered amusement. When two impressive band leaders in large, fluffy overcoats call upon him for a communal cardboard door sign, toward the cost of which each contributes twenty-five cents, he innocently inquires, "How many of you are there in that office?" One of the band leaders will reply grandiosely, "Oh, we all have separate offices; the sign is for the door to quite a huge suite." Hy laughs so hard he bends double to relieve the strain on his diaphragm. His brother, Si, who lives in continual fear that Hy will die of apolexy, abandons his work and slaps Hy's back until the crowing abates. "A suite," Hy repeats weakly at intervals for a half-hour afterward, "a huge suite they got, like on the subway at six o'clock you could get." Hy also paints, at an average price of twenty-five cents. cardboard backs for music racks. These pieces of cardboard, whose only function is to identify the band, bear in bright letters its name, which is usually something like Everett Winterbottom's Rhumba Raiders. When a Jollity Building band leader has acquired a sign for his door and a set of these lettered cardboards, he is equipped for business. If, by some unlikely chance, he gets an engagement, usually to play a week end in a cabaret in Queens or the Bronx, he hurries out to the curb on Seventh Avenue in front of Charlie's Bar & Grill, where there are always plenty of musicians, and picks up the number of fellows he requires, generally four. The men tapped go over to Eighth Avenue and get their instruments out of pawn. A musician who owns several instruments usually leaves them all in a pawnshop, ransoming one when he needs it to play a date and putting it back the next day. If, when he has a chance to work, he lacks the money to redeem an instrument, he borrows the money from a Jollity Building six-for-fiver, a fellow who will lend you five dollars if you promise to pay him six dollars within twenty-four hours. Meanwhile, the band leader looks up a fellow who rents out orchestra arrangements guaranteed to be exact, illegal copies of those one or another of the big bandsmen has exclusive use of. The band leader puts the arrangements and his cardboards under his arm and goes down to Charlie's to wait for the other musicians to come back from the hock shop. That night Everett Winterbottom's Rhumba Raiders ride again. The only worry in the world the Raiders have, at least for the moment, is that they will have to finish their engagement before a union delegate discovers them and takes away their cards. Each man is going to receive three dollars a night, which is seven dollars below union scale.

MEMOIRS OF A MUTE

By Oscar Levant

FOR MORE THAN FIFTEEN YEARS THE FIRST PERSON THAT ALMOST every visiting celebrity to Hollywood expressed a desire to meet was Charlie Chaplin; inevitably in second place was Harpo Marx. Recently Harpo has been moving ahead in the great Celebrity Sweepstakes, until now the chances are even that as many will ask to meet Harpo as Chaplin. I should not be surprised, indeed, if the lead passes definitely to Marx before the year is out, although Harpo is quite content with his position as runner-up, deferring to the matchless artistry of his predecessor in pantomime.

That the two most celebrated silent men of the now articulate films exercise an irresistible fascination for some of the greatest conversationalists of our time is more than mildly curious. One can only conclude that there must be some subconscious attraction in their silence. Naturally, also, everyone wonders what a man who never says anything sounds like.

Though Harpo is one of the mots ill-informed men I have ever encountered, it was as a consequence of his fascination for savants and celebrities that I had the pleasure of meeting some of the day's most distinguished citizens at his home in Hollywood. One could never be sure in accepting a dinner invitation to Harpo's whether one's companions would be H. G. Wells and Don Budge, or Somerset Maugham and Salvador Dali. Frequently the combinations were even more remarkable—Aldous Huxley and Maxie Rosenbloom.

Despite these efforts to live up to Woollcott's ecstatic characterization of him as an incurable zany (a well-meaning but misguided bit of propaganda which, I am sure, has taxed Harpo's ingenuity now for all of ten years) he is in reality a person of complete conventionality—as Howard Dietz said, "the most normal person I know."

From everything that occurred between us, I would say that Harpo found me a rather amusing person, though he was sometimes shocked by what he considered to be my bad manners. (It was not uncommon for this most celebrated madman to introduce me half-apologetically to a friend as if to prepare him for some outrageous insanity.)

I found him a man generous with money, rather unexciting and a wonderful audience. His qualities were best epitomized on the occasion that I met George S. Kaufman in New York and asked if he had heard recently from Harpo.

"How," he asked, "how can you hear from Harpo? He can't write and he can't talk, so how can you hear from Harpo?"

I first met Harpo at a Gershwin concert at the Stadium in New York eight or nine years ago. He had no ticket and was trying (unsuccessfully) to work his way in through the back gate when I came up with an extra ticket and offered it to him. However, it is now Harpo's story that we had met in some obscure way previously, that I was lonely that night and called him up, begging him to come with me. Further, he contends that he had a date, but that I begged so hard he finally consented to go just to keep me company.

Through our mutual friends, the Gershwins, Irving Berlin, Kaufman, Moss Hart and others, I saw him quite frequently after that, particularly while he was working in New York in various shows. (Somehow, though, I never did get around to seeing any show in which the Marxes appeared.) Sometime after this we went to Woollcott's place in Vermont for a week end together with another mutual friend, Charlie Lederer. We prepared ourselves for the trip and the week end by buying seven "Tarzan" books and two quarts of ice cream before getting on the train.

We had barely pulled out of the station when Harpo, after a short tour of exploration, returned with the information that there was a stunning girl in lower 7. Summoning the porter, we dispatched a message suggesting that she join us for a spot of ice cream. In a moment he returned, followed by a veritable gargoyle. It was by this time too late to rescind the invitation, but while she consumed a full quart of ice cream Harpo quietly disappeared, his tasty little joke consummated.

On another occasion we were driving on Long Island when Harpo spied ahead of us an ancient Baker electric, piloted by two prim dowagers. He drew abreast of them and with his most oafish facial expression leaned from the car, pointed a finger in a generally westerly direction and inquired, "Denver?"

Several weeks later we again went to Long Island, this time to visit Herbert Bayard Swope. (I hope the Swopes do not take offense at this. It's about the only house I have left.) Harpo was accompanied by his man of all work, valet, secretary and trainer, who also drove his car. As Harpo hardly felt that he had attained the dignity of a uniformed chauffeur, his man wore no livery. Moreover, he was an amiable chap who was not above strolling about the grounds and mingling with the guests, watching a game of tennis or whatever interested him. Eventually he came upon Swope, who was engaged in croquet with a group of experts. With his training in public life, Swope prides himself on his ability to remember not only a face, but the name that goes with it, after a single meeting. (His talent in this sphere is said to compare favorably with Jim Farley's.)

When the stranger joined the group, Swope looked at him closely and resumed his play. The shot completed, he glanced up again, more intently this time. Plainly he was searching his mind to recall the identity of this onlooker. Finally confessing defeat, he strode up to the young man, extended his hand and said in his heartiest presidential-timber manner,

"Good afternoon. I'm Herbert Bayard Swope."

"Pleased to meet'cha," he responded. "I'm Benny Murphy, Harpo's chauffeur."

One of Harpo's distinguishing traits is his fondness for receiving guests in the nude, playing the harp in a pair of shorts. Deeply immersed in a Bach "Bourrée" or his *pièce de résistance*, "Mighty Lak' a Rose," with an interminable cadenza, he will greet them blandly, calmly indifferent to their shocked surprise. His pretense of having forgotten the invitation is a beautiful thing to see.

I had a personal experience with that humor several years ago when Harpo, along with the other Marxes, settled permanently to work and live in Hollywood. He had taken quite a large house in Beverly Hills, where there was living with him at the time S. N.

Behrman, the playwright, and Max Gordon, the producer. Nightly when I returned from doing a broadcast in New York I would find wires from Harpo, urging me to come out and spend a few months in Hollywood. He even offered to pay half my fare, and I replied, that was fine, I'd go to Kansas City.

However, as I was playing piano on five radio shows at the time I had good reason for staying in New York. But Harpo's wires became more tantalizing, and I finally picked a fight at the studio—the jobs bored me though I liked the money—and quit.

This accomplished, I sent a wire to Harpo saying,

"Have you room for me?"

He wired back, "Come, but have no room."

Naturally I was furious and poured out my resentment at this treatment in a wire to Behrman. He answered promptly, saying, "Come, will take care of you."

In sequence came a telegram from Harpo, saying,

"I love you, but I can't live in the same house with you."

The matter reached a climax when Behrman sent a mollifying message to me, and I responded that I would accept *his* invitation, but not Harpo's. When I arrived I refused to acknowledge Harpo's greeting or talk to him. I did, however, have a hearty dinner; and for the next four months I had lunch, dinner and supper at Harpo's, without exchanging a word with him. I would, of course, talk with any of the sixteen other persons that invariably sat down to dinner at his table, but never with Harpo.

It was not strange, therefore, that I eventually developed the feeling that Behrman and I owned the place, and that we were merely tolerating Harpo. One night I invited a guest of my own to dinner, at which even Harpo was a little startled. As we sat down at the table Behrman said to me (in the hearing of everyone at the table, including Harpo),

"Why don't you speak to Harpo?"

"The hell with that," I responded. "I'm sore at him."

"But after all," said Behrman, "he's your host."

"No," I answered stubbornly, "he isn't."

"Who is your host?" queried Behrman, puzzled. "And who is the host of your friend who comes as your guest, but you have no host?"

With this Behrman embarked on a flood of causticity, intoxicated by the rhythm of his words. Rocking and rolling like a Talmudic scholar feasting on an insoluble problem, he continued, "You've been eating three meals a day here for four months, and now you even bring a guest. Then you deny that Harpo is your host. This is taking on the clear, unanswerable obscurity of a Pirandello play."

After I had been at Pension Marx for upward of four months thoughts of returning to New York City naturally identified themselves with the hope of a job—possibly with the producer who was the honored guest one night at dinner. We had scarcely disposed of the entrée when Harpo turned to this producer, remarking in a loud, clear voice which no one at the table could ignore. "Oscar says you have no talent." With that, he quietly resumed his dinner.

This was embarrassing to me, even though I do not embarrass easily, and I said,

"Harpo, that's a dirty trick."

Baffled, and not quite sure what to say, the producer attempted to relieve the tension by saying,

"What's the difference as long as I'm a nice fellow?"

To this, Charlie Lederer interposed helpfully,

"That's a moot point."

Harpo, perhaps, valued the presence of his literary guests because their talk acted as a powerful soporific upon him. I have rarely seen the equal of the mellow, easeful mood that would deccend on Harpo after an hour or two at the dinner table. He would be utterly charming to his guests until the inevitable reaction set in. Then he would politely excuse himself and go upstairs to bed.

One of the most enjoyable evenings I had at Harpo's found Maxie Rosenbloom as the lion. Maxie, the celebrated comedian and ex-light-heavyweight boxing champion, was in a perpetual state of retirement, but he would just as soon fight as act. In any case, his past in the ring was still very much with him. On this occasion a fascinating portion of his recitation was devoted to his brother, also a boxer, who had too much pride to trade on the family name of Rosenbloom. Consequently he adopted the *nom de ring* of Sinclair Walsh.

Of his own career, Maxie was most voluble about the portion of his skill which won him the title of "Slapsie-Maxie"—his phenomenal skill as a boxer and particularly his deftness in handling the open glove. In consequence he had built up a remarkable reputation as a boxer and was inordinately proud of the fact that he never resorted to such crude tactics as a knockout to achieve his victories and, indeed, rarely knocked a man down. Thus he was righteously indignant at an episode that happened during a bout in Colorado when he was giving an exhibition of his specialty, dancing about and pecking away with ineffable grace. One of his open gloves made a contact with his dazzled opponent, who promptly collapsed on the canvas.

Enraged, Maxie looked down at him and bellowed,

"Why you dirty double-crossing rat!"

Apropos of prize fighters, I must not omit the saga of the Marxes in their adventures as prize-fighter managers. In some obscure way they had acquired the services of a heavyweight fighter, whom they promptly named "Canvasback." I do not contend that the designation was unjustified, for I had seen "Canvasback" in what might laughingly be called action; but it was always my feeling that the name did not do much to build up his confidence. However, the peak of their enterprise was accomplished on an evening when "Canvasback" exceeded his ordinary quota by being knocked down five times in the first round. As he tottered to his corner Groucho and Harpo leaped into the ring, prepared to exert their skill in readying him for the next round. As he sat down, however, Harpo shoved "Canvasback" brusquely to the floor while Groucho proceeded to fan his brother energetically! . . .

Among Harpo's musical manifestations, not the least was his passion for playing on any stringed instrument, regardless of whether it was guitar, mandolin or banjo. Not infrequently I accompanied him into the remote outskirts of Los Angeles to hear some obscure virtuoso of the frets, and on one occasion he drove me almost to Mexico in search of a superb performer of whom he had been told. He was also a great admirer of Iturbi, whose playing of Mozart with Toscanini had been a cherished memory of a visit to New York. Harpo always went to hear him in Los Angeles with the Philharmonic, and in Hollywood at the Bowl, where he played nothing but Liszt. This rather baffled Harpo.

Though he read less than any man I know, he had a passion for first editions, especially an inscribed Shaw, an early Somerset Maugham (*Liza of Lambeth*, as in walk), and a fine Wells, all three of them extremely valuable. Not even in the British Museum could Harpo's "firsts" have been better preserved than they were on the reading table beside his bed, where he liked to look at them before he retired at night. From time to time I would pass by the door casually and glance at the table to see if the books had changed, but no—the same ones were always there in the same place.

As well as being possessed of one of the most amiable, sweet dispositions I have ever encountered in a man, Harpo was an apostle of generosity. Finding myself short of cash one day, I proposed a loan to him, and he escorted me upstairs to his bathroom (which occupied a total floor space equivalent to that of the Roxy lobby) and opened a small safe beside the shower, from which he extracted, in cash, the $200 I needed. It was always my theory that he kept the first editions there during the day, taking them out at night when his guests came.

There was also a period in which he went in for painting, specializing in nudes. When he first started his career he called an agency for a model but failed to specify the particular type he wanted. When the girl appeared he asked her to strip, which she refused to do. So, instead, Harpo stripped to shorts, and painted her as she donned a smock.

From some unrevealed source he had picked up the name of Czolgosz, the madman who assassinated President McKinley. He made quite a bit of money on this, inveigling friends into a discussion of political assassinations and then wagering that he could supply the assassin's name. He was also greatly fascinated by a story I read to him one day from a Los Angeles newspaper. It was during that period several years ago when Polish athletes who had competed in the Olympics as females were suddenly reappearing as males and vice versa. This story concerned a Polish peasant named Nachman who suddenly, and for no explicable reason (after thirty respectable years as a male) gave birth to a daughter. For weeks after that Harpo would announce himself at a friend's house by pounding loudly on the door and proclaiming, "Nachman is here!"

Perhaps the most remarkable experience I ever had with Harpo followed a studio party at which I encountered a charming young girl, who, it developed, was a highly respected member of Los Angeles society. I pressed her for a date, but she replied that it was out of the question until I had presented myself at her house, met her mother and brought along some member of my family. Accordingly I arranged to call a few evenings later at her home, duly appearing with Harpo, whom I presented as my uncle. We were both on the street five minutes later, after Harpo had insulted the butler, chucked the maid under the chin and chased the girl's mother halfway around the house.

His passion for health is pursued with unremitting zeal, involving arduous tennis, gymnastics, intensive sun-bathing, etc. His sleep is singularly untroubled by dreams, and, indeed, he has a capacity for sleep that I have frequently envied. On that early trip to Vermont our sleeper was buffeted about in Albany between two engines for what seemed to me an eternity. (I was as usual in an upper berth.) Harpo had no recollection of the incident on the following morning and, indeed, boasted of the restful night he had spent. On another occasion, during an airplane trip to the coast, he fell asleep during an incredible passage over the Rockies while I contemplated recourse to a parachute. In a dentist's chair he has even been known to doze quietly while his teeth are being drilled.

It was Harpo, too, who accomplished the prodigious feat of falling asleep in a car on the way to his wedding, with his bride-to-be beside him. But psychologically his sleep symbolized security in his marriage, which has been a happy one. Harpo and Susan subsequently adopted a baby, which elicited a wire from me: "Congratulations on your son. If he needs brother wire terms." And that reminds me that, as a youth, Harpo was a boy soprano in a quartet. When he fortunately lost his voice he found that silence was golden.

PART II

"To bed, to bed: there's knocking at the gate. Come, come, come, come, give me your hand. What's done cannot be undone. To bed, to bed, to bed. . . ."

—SHAKESPEARE: *Macbeth*

SLEEPY-TIME EXTRA

By S. J. Perelman

WHEN IT WAS FIRST NOISED ALONG PUBLISHER'S ROW THAT THE
John B. Pierce Foundation, a non-profit research organization, had
instituted a survey dealing with American family behavior, attitudes, and possessions, public opinion was instantly split into two
camps—into the larger, and drowsier of which I fell. There is
nothing like a good, painstaking survey full of decimal points and
guarded generalizations to put a glaze like a Sung vase on your
eyeball. Even the fact that the results of the poll were to be
printed in that most exciting of current periodicals, *Business
Week*, did little to allay my fatigue. Then, one morning in early
April, hell started popping at my corner stationery store. "What's
good today, Clinton?" I asked, browsing over the magazine rack.
"Well, I tell you," replied Clinton, thoughtfully scratching the
stubble on his chin (he raised corn there last year but is letting
it lie fallow this season), "we just got the new number of *Business
Week* containing the John B. Pierce Foundation survey on American family behavior, attitudes, and possessions." "Well, dog my
cat!" I exclaimed struck all of a heap. "Let's have a nickel's worth
of those licorice gumdrops, will you Clinton?" "Sure," said Clinton reluctantly, "but how about this new number of *Business
Week* containing the John B. Pierce Foundation—" "Listen, Clinton," I said suddenly, "did you hear a funny little click just
then?" "Aha," breathed Clinton, round-eyed. "What was it?"
"A customer closing his account," I snapped, closing my account
and taking my custom elsewhere.

It took a stray copy of the Buffalo *Evening News*, abandoned
late yesterday afternoon on my bus seat by some upstate transient,
to reveal the true nature of the survey and dispel my apathy.
"Married Couples Favor Double Beds," trumpeted the dispatch.
"Eighty-seven per cent of husbands and wives sleep together

in double beds but 5% of the wives are dissatisfied with this and 40% think maybe twin beds would be ideal, *Business Week* Magazine reported today on the basis of a survey by the John B. Pierce Foundation, non-profit research organization. Other conclusions of the survey . . . include: In summer, 70.3% of the wives sleep in nightgowns, 24% in pajamas, 5% in the nude and seven-tenths of 1% in shorts. Sixteen per cent of the women reported they would like to sleep in the nude, causing the Pierce Foundation to comment: 'Here we have clear-cut evidence of an inhibition' . . . Fifty per cent of the husbands report no activity after getting into bed, 22% read, 12% talk, 7% listen to the radio, 3% say their prayers, 4% smoke, 2% eat. Comparable percentages for wives were: 40% no activity, 29% read, 11% talk, 8% listen to the radio, 5% say their prayers, 3% think, 2% smoke, 2% eat."

Though one could speculate on the foregoing until the cows came home and distill all manner of toothsome psychological inferences, I cannot help wondering what machinery the Foundation used to obtain its statistics. Were these delicious confidences stammered into a telephone mouthpiece or haltingly penned in a questionnaire or whispered to a clear-eyed, be-dirndled Sarah Lawrence girl at the kitchen door? Somehow there is a grim, authoritative quality about the project which convinces me that the researchers went right to the source for their data, and I venture to think that more than one must have found himself embroiled in a situation like the following:

[*Scene:* The bedroom of the Stringfellows, a standard middle-aged couple. Monty Stringfellow is a large, noisy extrovert who conceals his insecurity under a boisterous good humor. He affects heavy, hobnailed Scotch brogues and leather patches at the elbows of his sports jackets, is constantly roaring out songs commanding you to quaff the nut-brown ale, and interlards his speech with salty imprecations like "Gadzooks" and "By my halidom." Tanagra, his wife, is a sultry, discontented creature on whom fifteen years of life with a jolly good fellow have left their mark. As the curtain rises, Monty, in a tweed nightgown, is seated upright in their double bed singing a rollicking tune, to which he beats time with a pewter tankard and a churchwarden pipe. Tanagra, sleep mask over her eyes, is trying to catch a little shut-eye and getting nowhere.]

Monty (*con brio*):
"Come quaff the nut-brown ale, lads,
For youth is all too fleeting,
We're holding high wassail, lads,
And life's dull care unheeding,
So quaff the nut-brown ale, lads—"

Tanagra: Oh, shut up, for God's sake! You and your nut-brown ale.

Monty: What's wrong?

Tanagra: Nothing. Nothing at all. What makes you think anything's wrong?

Monty: I don't know—you seem to be on edge lately. Every time I open my mouth, you snap my head off.

Tanagra: Every time you open your mouth, that blasted tune comes out. Haven't you anything else in your song bag?

Monty: Gee, Tanagra, I always looked on it as our theme song, you might say. (*Sentimentally*) Don't you remember that first night at the Union Oyster House in Boston when you made me sing it over and over?

Tanagra: You swept me off my feet. I was just a silly little junior at Radcliffe.

Monty: You—you mean our moment of enchantment has passed?

Tanagra: I'll go further. Many's the night I've lain here awake studying your fat neck and praying for a bowstring to tighten around it.

Monty (*resentfully*): That's a heck of a thing to say. You keep up that kind of talk and pretty soon we'll be sleeping in twin beds.

Tanagra: O. K. by me, chum.

Voice (*under bed*): Aha!

Monty: What's that? Who said that?

Tanagra: I'm sure I don't know.

Monty: There's somebody under this bed!

Voice: There's nobody here except just us researchers from the John B. Pierce Foundation.

Monty: W-what are you doing down there?

Voice: Conducting a survey. (Otis "Speedball" Ismay, ace statistician of the Foundation, a personable young executive, crawls into view from under the Stringfellow fourposter, flips open his notebook.) Evening, friends. Close, isn't it?

Tanagra (*archly*): I never realized how close.

Ismay: You the lady of the house? I'd like to ask a few questions.

Monty: Now just a minute. I don't know whether I approve—

Tanagra: Batten down, stupid, he's not talking to you. (*Brightly*) Yes?

Ismay: Let me see. You prefer sleeping in a nightgown rather than pajamas?

Tanagra: Well, that depends. With this clod, a girl might as well wear a burlap bag.

Ismay (*with a disparaging glance*): Yeah, strictly from Dixie. You know, that's a darned attractive nightie you've got on right now.

Tanagra: What, *this* old thing?

Ismay: It sends *me*, and I'm a tough customer. What do they call these doodads along the top?

Tanagra: Alençon lace.

Ismay: Cunning, aren't they?

Tanagra (*provocatively*): Think so?

Ismay (tickling her): Oootsie-kootsie!

Tanagra: Now you stop, you bad boy.

Monty: Hey, this is a pretty peculiar survey, if you ask me.

Tanagra: Nobody asked you.

Ismay: Wait a second. You *could* tell me one thing, Mister—Mister—

Monty: Stringfellow. Monty Stringfellow.

Ismay: Do you belong to any lodges, fraternal associations, or secret societies?

Monty: What kind do you mean?

Ismay (*impatiently*): It doesn't matter. Any kind that keeps you busy evenings.

Monty: Why, yes. I'm Past Grand Chalice of the Golden Cupbearers of the World, field secretary of the Rice Institute Alumni—

Ismay: Fine, fine. Don't bother to list them. We merely wish to know what evenings you spend away from home.

Monty: Every Tuesday and every other Friday. Is this all part of the survey?

Ismay: Part? It's practically the lifeblood. Well, I think you've given me all the information I need. Oh, just one more detail, Mrs. Stringfellow. You understand there's a high percentage of error in an informal cross-section of this type and naturally we like to check our findings.

Tanagra: Naturally.

Ismay: I'd ask you to drop in at my office, but it's being redecorated.

Tanagra: Yes, I read something in the paper to that effect. Is it serious?

Ismay: No, no, it'll be all right in a day or two. For the time being, I've moved my charts and figures to the Weylin Bar, third table on the left as you come in at four-fifteen tomorrow afternoon.

Tanagra: I'll be there half an hour early.

Ismay: Splendid. (*To Stringfellow*) Thanks, old man, don't bother to show me to the door; I'll use the fire escape. Couple more calls to make in the building. Good night, all! (*He goes.*)

Monty (*chortling*): Ho ho, that bird certainly pulled the wool over your eyes! He's no statician. He didn't even have a fountain pen!

Tanagra (*placidly*): Well, I swan. He sure took me in.

Monty: Yes siree bob, you've got to get up pretty early in the morning to fool old Monty Stringfellow! (*He slaps her thigh familiarly and Tanagra sets her alarm for six forty-five.*)

Curtain

HERE WE ARE

By DOROTHY PARKER

THE YOUNG MAN IN THE NEW BLUE SUIT FINISHED ARRANGING THE glistening luggage in tight corners of the Pullman compartment. The train had leaped at curves and bounced along straightaways, rendering balance a praiseworthy achievement nad a sporadic one; and the young man had pushed and hoisted and tucked and shifted the bags with concentrated care.

Nevertheless, eight minutes for the settling of two suitcases and a hat-box is a long time.

He sat down, leaning back against bristled green plush, in the seat opposite the girl in beige. She looked as new as a peeled egg. Her hat, her fur, her frock, her gloves were glossy and stiff with novelty. On the arc of the thin, slippery sole of one beige shoe was gummed a tiny oblong of white paper, printed with the price set and paid for that slipper and its fellow, and the name of the shop that had dispensed them.

She had been staring raptly out of the window, drinking in the big weathered signboards that extolled the phenomena of codfish without bones and screens no rust could corrupt. As the young man sat down, she turned politely from the pane, met his eyes, started a smile and got it about half done, and rested her gaze just above his right shoulder.

"Well!" the young man said.

"Well!" she said.

"Well, here we are," he said.

"Here we are," she said. "Aren't we?"

"I should say we were," he said. "Eeyop. Here we are."

"Well!" she said.

"Well!" he said. "Well. How does it feel to be an old married lady?"

"Oh, it's too soon to ask me that," she said. "At least—I mean.

130

Well, I mean, goodness, we've only been married about three hours, haven't we?"

The young man studied his wrist-watch as if he were just acquiring the knack of reading time.

"We have been married," he said, "exactly two hours and twenty-six minutes."

"My," she said. "It seems like longer."

"No," he said. "It isn't hardly half-past six yet."

"It seems like later," she said. "I guess it's because it starts getting dark so early."

"It does, at that," he said. "The nights are going to be pretty long from now on. I mean. I mean—well, it starts getting dark early."

"I didn't have any idea what time it was," she said. "Everything was so mixed up, I sort of don't know where I am, or what it's all about. Getting back from the church, and then all those people, and then changing all my clothes, and then everybody throwing things, and all. Goodness, I don't see how people do it every day."

"Do what?" he said.

"Get married," she said. "When you think of all the people, all over the world, getting married just as if it was nothing. Chinese people and everybody. Just as if it wasn't anything."

"Well, let's not worry about people all over the world," he said. "Let's don't think about a lot of Chinese. We've got something better to think about. I mean. I mean—well, what do we care about them?"

"I know," she said. "But I just sort of got to thinking of them, all of them, all over everywhere, doing it all the time. At least, I mean—getting married, you know. And it's—well, it's sort of such a big thing to do, it makes you feel queer. You think of them, all of them, all doing it just like it wasn't anything. And how does anybody know what's going to happen next?"

"Let them worry," he said. "We don't have to. We know darn well what's going to happen next. I mean. I mean—well, we know it's going to be great. Well, we know we're going to be happy. Don't we?"

"Oh, of course," she said. "Only you think of all the people, and you have to sort of keep thinking. It makes you feel funny.

An awful lot of people that get married, it doesn't turn out so well. And I guess they all must have thought it was going to be great."

"Come on, now," he said. "This is no way to start a honeymoon, with all this thinking going on. Look at us—all married and everything done. I mean. The wedding all done and all."

"Ah, it was nice, wasn't it?" she said. "Did you really like my veil?"

"You looked great," he said. "Just great."

"Oh, I'm terribly glad," she said. "Ellie and Louise looked lovely, didn't they? I'm terribly glad they did finally decide on pink. They looked perfectly lovely."

"Listen," he said. "I want to tell you something. When I was standing up there in that old church waiting for you to come up, and I saw those two bridesmaids, I thought to myself, I thought, 'Well, I never knew Louise could look like that!' Why, she'd have knocked anybody's eye out."

"Oh, really?" she said. "Funny. Of course, everybody thought her dress and hat were lovely, but a lot of people seemed to think she looked sort of tired. People have been saying that a lot, lately. I tell them I think it's awfully mean of them to go around saying that about her. I tell them they've got to remember that Louise isn't so terribly young any more, and they've got to expect her to look like that. Louise can say she's twenty-three all she wants to, but she's a good deal nearer twenty-seven."

"Well, she was certainly a knock-out at the wedding," he said. "Boy!"

"I'm terribly glad you thought so," she said. "I'm glad someone did. How did you think Ellie looked?"

"Why, I honestly didn't get a look at her," he said.

"Oh, really?" she said. "Well, I certainly think that's too bad. I don't suppose I ought to say it about my own sister, but I never saw anybody look as beautiful as Ellie looked today. And always so sweet and unselfish, too. And you didn't even notice her. But you never pay attention to Ellie, anyway. Don't think I haven't noticed it. It makes me feel just terrible. It makes me feel just awful, that you don't like my own sister."

"I do so like her!" he said. "I'm crazy for Ellie. I think she's a great kid."

"Don't think it makes any difference to Ellie!" she said. "Ellie's got enough people crazy about her. It isn't anything to her whether you like her or not. Don't flatter yourself she cares! Only, the only thing is, it makes it awfully hard for me you don't like her, that's the only thing. I keep thinking, when we come back and get in the apartment and everything, it's going to be awfully hard for me that you won't want my own sister to come and see me. It's going to make it awfully hard for me that you don't ever want my family around. I know how you feel about my family. Don't think I haven't seen it. Only, if you don't ever want to see them, that's your loss. Not theirs. Don't flatter yourself!"

"Oh, now, come on!" he said. "What's all this talk about not wanting your family around? Why, you know how I feel about your family. I think your old lady—I think your mother's swell. And Ellie. And your father. What's all this talk?"

"Well, I've seen it," she said. "Don't think I haven't. Lots of people they get married, and they think it's going to be great and everything, and then it all goes to pieces because people don't like people's families, or something like that. Don't tell me! I've seen it happen."

"Honey," he said, "what is all this? What are you getting all angry about? Hey, look, this is our honeymoon. What are you trying to start a fight for? Ah, I guess you're just feeling sort of nervous."

"Me?" she said. "What have I got to be nervous about? I mean. I mean, goodness, I'm not nervous."

"You know, lots of times," he said, "they say that girls get kind of nervous and yippy on account of thinking about—I mean. I mean—well, it's like you said, things are all so sort of mixed up and everything, right now. But afterwards, it'll be all right. I mean. I mean—well, look, honey, you don't look any too comfortable. Don't you want to take your hat off? And let's don't ever fight, ever. Will we?"

"Ah, I'm sorry I was cross," she said. "I guess I did feel a little bit funny. All mixed up, and then thinking of all those people all over everywhere, and then being sort of 'way off here, all alone with you. It's so sort of different. It's sort of such a big thing. You can't blame a person for thinking, can you? Yes, don't let's ever, ever fight. We won't be like a whole lot of them. We won't fight or be nasty or anything. Will we?"

"You bet your life we won't," he said.

"I guess I will take this darned old hat off," she said. "It kind of presses. Just put it up on the rack, will you, dear? Do you like it, sweetheart?"

"Looks good on you," he said.

"No, but I mean," she said, "do you really like it?"

"Well, I'll tell you," he said. "I know this is the new style and everything like that, and it's probably great. I don't know anything about things like that. Only I like the kind of a hat like that blue hat you had. Gee, I liked that hat."

"Oh, really?" she said. "Well, that's nice. That's lovely. The first thing you say to me, as soon as you get me off on a train away from my family and everything, is that you don't like my hat. The first thing you say to your wife is you think she has terrible taste in hats. That's nice, isn't it?"

"Now, honey," he said, "I never said anything like that. I only said——"

"What you don't seem to realize," she said, "is this hat cost twenty-two dollars. Twenty-two dollars. And that horrible old blue thing you think you're so crazy about, that cost three ninety-five."

"I don't give a darn what they cost," he said. "I only said— I said I liked that blue hat. I don't know anything about hats. I'll be crazy about this one as soon as I get used to it. Only it's kind of not like your other hats. I don't know about the new styles. What do I know about women's hats?"

"It's too bad," she said, "you didn't marry somebody that would get the kind of hats you'd like. Hats that cost three ninety-five. Why didn't you marry Louise? You always think she looks so beautiful. You'd love her taste in hats. Why didn't you marry her?"

"Ah, now, honey," he said. "For heaven's sakes!"

"Why didn't you marry her?" she said. "All you've done, ever since we got on this train, is talk about her. Here I've sat and sat, and just listened to you saying how wonderful Louise is. I suppose that's nice, getting me all off here alone with you, and then raving about Louise right in front of my face. Why didn't you ask her to marry you? I'm sure she would have jumped at the chance. There aren't so many people asking her to marry them. It's too bad you didn't marry her. I'm sure you'd have been much happier."

"Listen, baby," he said, "while you're talking about things like that, why didn't you marry Joe Brooks? I suppose he could have given you all the twenty-two-dollar hats you wanted, I suppose!"

"Well, I'm not so sure I'm not sorry I didn't," she said. "There! Joe Brooks wouldn't have waited until he got me all off alone and then sneered at my taste in clothes. Joe Brooks wouldn't ever hurt my feelings. Joe Brooks has always been fond of me. There!"

"Yeah," he said. "He's fond of you. He was so fond of you he didn't even send a wedding present. That's how fond of you he was."

"I happen to know for a fact," she said, "that he was away on business, and as soon as he comes back he's going to give me anything I want, for the apartment."

"Listen," he said. "I don't want anything he gives you in our apartment. Anything he gives you, I'll throw right out the window. That's what I think of your friend Joe Brooks. And how do you know where he is and what he's going to do, anyway? Has he been writing to you?"

"I suppose my friends can correspond with me," she said. "I didn't hear there was any law against that."

"Well, I suppose they can't!" he said. "And what do you think of that? I'm not going to have my wife getting a lot of letters from cheap traveling salesmen!"

"Joe Brooks is not a cheap traveling salesman!" she said. "He is not! He gets a wonderful salary."

"Oh yeah?" he said. "Where did you hear that?"

"He told me so himself," she said.

"Oh, he told you so himself," he said. "I see. He told you so himself."

"You've got a lot of right to talk about Joe Brooks," she said. "You and your friend Louise. All you ever talk about is Louise."

"Oh, for heaven's sakes!" he said. "What do I care about Louise? I just thought she was a friend of yours, that's all. That's why I even noticed her."

"Well, you certainly took an awful lot of notice of her today," she said. "On our wedding day! You said yourself when you were standing there in the church you just kept thinking of her. Right up at the altar. Oh, right in the presence of God! And all you thought about was Louise."

"Listen, honey," he said, "I never should have said that. How does anybody know what kind of crazy things come into their heads when they're standing there waiting to get married? I was just telling you that because it was so kind of crazy. I thought it would make you laugh."

"I know," she said. "I've been all sort of mixed up today, too. I told you that. Everything so strange and everything. And me all the time thinking about all those people all over the world, and now us here all alone, and everything. I know you get all mixed up. Only I did think, when you kept talking about how beautiful Louise looked, you did it with malice and forethought."

"I never did anything with malice and forethought!" he said. "I just told you that about Louise because I thought it would make you laugh."

"Well, it didn't," she said.

"No, I know it didn't," he said. "It certainly did not. Ah, baby, and we ought to be laughing, too. Hell, honey lamb, this is our honeymoon. What's the matter?"

"I don't know," she said. "We used to squabble a lot when we were going together and then engaged and everything, but I thought everything would be so different as soon as you were married. And now I feel so sort of strange and everything. I feel so sort of alone."

"Well, you see, sweetheart," he said, "we're not really married yet. I mean. I mean—well, things will be different afterwards. Oh, hell. I mean, we haven't been married very long."

"No," she said.

"Well, we haven't got much longer to wait now," he said. "I mean—well, we'll be in New York in about twenty minutes.

Then we can have dinner, and sort of see what we feel like doing. Or I mean. Is there anything special you want to do tonight?"

"What?" she said.

"What I mean to say," he said, "would you like to go to a show or something?"

"Why, whatever you like," she said. "I sort of didn't think people went to theaters and things on their—I mean, I've got a couple of letters I simply must write. Don't let me forget."

"Oh," he said. "You're going to write letters tonight?"

"Well, you see," she said. "I've been perfectly terrible. What with all the excitement and everything. I never did thank poor old Mrs. Sprague for her berry spoon, and I never did a thing about those book ends the McMasters sent. It's just too awful of me. I've got to write them this very night."

"And when you've finished writing your letters," he said, "maybe I could get you a magazine or a bag of peanuts."

"What?" she said.

"I mean," he said, "I wouldn't want you to be bored."

"As if I could be bored with you!" she said. "Silly! Aren't we married? Bored!"

"What I thought," he said, "I thought when we got in, we could go right up to the Biltmore and anyway leave our bags, and maybe have a little dinner in the room, kind of quiet, and then do whatever we wanted. I mean. I mean—well, let's go right up there from the station."

"Oh, yes, let's," she said. "I'm so glad we're going to the Biltmore. I just love it. The twice I've stayed in New York we've always stayed there, Papa and Mamma and Ellie and I, and I was crazy about it. I always sleep so well there. I go right off to sleep the minute I put my head on the pillow."

"Oh, you do?" he said.

"At least, I mean," she said. " 'Way up high it's so quiet."

"We might go to some show or other tomorrow night instead of tonight," he said. "Don't you think that would be better?"

"Yes, I think it might," she said.

He rose, balanced a moment, crossed over and sat down beside her.

"Do you really have to write those letters tonight?" he said.

"Well," she said, "I don't suppose they'd get there any quicker than if I wrote them tomorrow."

There was a silence with things going on in it.

"And we won't ever fight any more, will we?" he said.

"Oh, no," she said. "Not ever! I don't know what made me do like that. It all got so sort of funny, sort of like a nightmare, the way I got thinking of all those people getting married all the time; and so many of them, everything spoils on account of fighting and everything. I got all mixed up thinking about them. Oh, I don't want ot be like them. But we won't will we?"

"Sure we won't," he said.

"We won't go all to pieces," she said. "We won't fight. It'll all be different, now we're married. It'll all be lovely. Reach me down my hat, will you, sweetheart? It's time I was putting it on. Thanks. Ah, I'm so sorry you don't like it."

"I do so like it!" he said.

"You said you didn't," she said. "You said you thought it was perfectly terrible."

"I never said any such thing," he said. "You're crazy."

"All right, I may be crazy," she said. "Thank you very much. But that's what you said. Not that it matters—it's just a little thing. But it makes you feel pretty funny to think you've gone and married somebody that says you have perfectly terrible taste in hats. And then goes and says you're crazy, beside."

"Now, listen here," he said. "Nobody said any such thing. Why, I love that hat. The more I look at it the better I like it. I think it's great."

"That isn't what you said before," she said.

"Honey," he said. "Stop it, will you? What do you want to start all this for? I love the damned hat. I mean, I love your hat. I love anything you wear. What more do you want me to say?"

"Well, I don't want you to say it like that," she said.

"I said I think it's great," he said. "That's all I said."

"Do you really?" she said. "Do you honestly? Ah, I'm so glad. I'd hate you not to like my hat. It would be—I don't know, it would be sort of such a bad start."

"Well, I'm crazy for it," he said. "Now we've got that settled, for heaven's sakes. Ah, baby. Baby lamb. We're not going to have any bad starts. Look at us—we're on our honeymoon. Pretty soon we'll be regular old married people. I mean. I mean, in a few minutes we'll be getting in to New York, and then we'll be going to the hotel, and then everything will be all right. I mean—well, look at us! Here we are married! Here we are!"

"Yes, here we are," she said. "Aren't we?"

FRIGIDITY IN MEN

By JAMES THURBER *and* E. B. WHITE

I HESITATE TO APPROACH THE SUBJECT OF MALE UNRESPONSIVENESS.
Frigidity in men is a theme sociologists have avoided. Frigidity in
women, on the other hand, forms a vast chapter in the sex research
of today; the part it plays in marital discord is known to students
of sociology as well as to the lay reader, although probably less
well. It has occupied the attention of many noted writers, and has
taken the lives of such men as Zaner and Tithridge, who carried
some of their experiments too far.[1]

Any discussion of frigidity in men calls for an unusual degree
of frankness on the part of the writer, since it entails such factors
as the "recessive knee," Fuller's retort, and the declination of the
kiss. Further, before attacking this subject, it will be necessary to
reëvaluate some of the more fundamental hypotheses of Man's
erotic nature, and what a nuisance that is going to be!

Let us go back a little way. There are two fundamental urges
in nature: the desire to eat and the desire to reproduce one's kind.
Which of these two impulses is the stronger depends somewhat
on the individual and somewhat on the circumstances surrounding
the individual—that is, it is apt to vary with the quality of the
food and of the women. There are, Zaner shows, men who would
rather eat than reproduce, and there are isolated cases of men who
would rather reproduce than eat. But it is the less simple types
that provide the important case histories for the student of masculine frigidity, and no broad conclusions can be drawn about the
relative merits of eating and reproducing without a consideration
of the contributing factors.

Quite regardless of which urge comes first in Man's scheme
of existence, it is safe to state dogmatically that the second urge
(the "sex" urge) has caused more stir in the last few years than

[1] Tithridge especially.

the first, or "nourishment," urge. Sex is less than fifty years old, yet it has upset the whole Western World. The sublimation of sex, called Love, is of course much older—although many purists will question the existence of Love prior to about 1885 on the grounds that there can be no sublimation of a non-existent feeling. What I shall try to show, without carping, will be that there is a very good reason why the erotic side of Man has called forth so much more discussion lately than has his appetite for food. The reason is this: that while the urge to eat is a personal matter which concerns no one but the person hungry (or, as the German has it, *der hungrig Mensch*), the sex urge involves, for its true expression, another individual. It is this "other individual" that causes all the trouble.

Except in rare instances, all of which have been dealt with by Sumner, the urge involves an individual of the opposite sex; that is, for a man it involves a woman, and for a woman it involves a man. I use the word "involve" advisedly. *Just the minute another person is drawn into some one's life, there begin to arise undreamed-of complexities,* and from such a simple beginning as sexual desire we find built up such alarming yet familiar phenomena as *fêtes, divertissements,* telephone conversations, arrangements, plans, sacrifices, train arrivals, meetings, appointments, tardinesses, delays, marriages, dinners, small pets and animals, calumny, children, music lessons, yellow shades for the windows, evasions, lethargy, cigarettes, candies, repetition of stories and anecdotes, infidelity, ineptitude, incompatibility, bronchial trouble, and many others, all of which are entirely foreign to the original urge and way off the subject, and all of which make the person's existence so strangely bewildering that if he could have foreseen these developments his choice would have been the "eating" urge, and he would have just gone quietly out somewhere and ordered himself a steak and some French fried potatoes as being the easier way out.

Still, that is just a hypothetical alternative. Life, as we know, is very insistent; almost daily people become involved with other people. And that brings us to our real theme, namely, frigidity in men.

The Recessive Knee. The first symptom of frigidity in men is what I call the recessive knee. To the study of this phenomenon I have given some of my best years. My laboratory has been the laboratory of life itself. Probably I would never have discovered the recessive knee had I not noticed it, some ten years ago, in myself. Questioning my colleagues, I found to my amazement that they too had had similar experiences which they were unable to account for, and this led me to continue my investigations. Since then I have gone into taxicabs, terminal lunch rooms, boat liveries, and all other places where it is possible or usual for a girl to let her knee rest lightly against that of her companion, have gained the confidence of the young men and women whom I was watching, and have accumulated a mass of data showing that frigidity in men, instead of being almost a non-existent characteristic, is one of the commonest attributes of our national sexual life. Inasmuch as the juxtaposing of the knee by the female, which causes the recessive (or "pulled away") knee in the male, usually occurs fairly fairly soon after dinner, my experiments and observations have had to be made largely in the evening. It has been my custom to sleep late mornings to make up for this.

Simply stated, the knee phenomenon is this: occasions arise sometimes when a girl presses her knee, ever so gently, against the knee of the young man she is out with. The juxtaposing of the knee is brought about by any of a thousand causes. Often the topic of conversation has something to do with it: the young people, talking along pleasantly, will suddenly experience a sensation of compatibility, or of friendliness, or of pity, or of community-of-interests. One of them will make a remark singularly agreeable to the other person—a chance word or phrase that seems to establish a bond between them. Such a remark can cause the knee of the girl to be placed against the knee of the young man. Or, if the two people are in a cab, the turning of a sharp corner will do it. In canoes, the wash from a larger vessel will bring it about. In restaurants and dining-rooms it often takes place under the table, as though by accident. On divans, sofas, settees, couches, davenports, and the like, the slight twist of the young lady's body incident to receiving a light for her cigarette will cause it. I could go on indefinitely, but there is no need. It is not a hard push, you understand—rather the merest touch of knee to knee, light as the brush of a falling blossom against one's cheek, and just as lovely.

Now, a normal male in whom there are no traces of frigidity will allow his knee to retain its original position, sometimes even exerting a very slight counter-pressure. A frigid male, however, will move his knee away at the first suggestion of contact, denying himself the electric stimulus of love's first stirring. Why? That is what my research was conducted to discover. *I found that in 93 per cent of all cases, the male was suspicious; in 4 per cent he was ignorant; and in 3 per cent he was tired.* I have presented these figures to the American Medical Association and am awaiting a reply.

It is the female's subtlety in her laying-on of the knee that annoys the male, I found. His recession is for the purpose of reassuring himself of his own integrity and perspicacity. If the female were to juxtapose in a forthright manner, if she were to preface her gesture with the remark: "I am thinking of letting my knee touch yours for the fun of it, Mortimer," she might gain an entirely different response from the male.

Many men with recessive knees have confided to me that they felt incapable of answering the pressure because of the effect it might have on their minds, with the accompanying loss of self-respect. I have established the fact that no *physical* detriment is incurred by answered pressure—the only harmful effects are psychological. Some males admitted to an unwillingness to give any woman the satisfaction of believing that she was able to take her companion unaware. Still others told me that they feared the consequences of such an act: they were afraid that if ever they let down the bars and failed to turn away from knee pressure, they would likewise be unable to resist other juxtapositions in life and would continually be responding amiably to other amusing stimuli—sales talks, stock promotion, and the like.

It was a young Paterson, N. J., girl by the name of Lillian Fuller who let drop the remark that has epitomized, for the sociological and anthropological world, the phenomenon of the recessive knee. "Fuller's retort" is now a common phrase in the realm of psychotherapy.

Miss Fuller was an unusually beautiful woman—young, accurate, sensitive. She was greatly attached to a man several years her senior in the buffing department; wanted to marry him. To this end she had laid her knee against his innumerable times without a single return of pressure. His frigidity, she realized, was gradually becoming prejudicial to his mental health, and so one evening, after experiencing for the hundredth time the withdrawal of his knee, she simply turned to him with a quiet smile playing on her face and said, "Say, what is the matter with you, anyway?"

Her retort somehow summed up the whole question of frigidity in men.

The Declination of the Kiss.[1] Many men have told me that they would not object to sex were it not for its contactual aspect. That is, they said they would be perfectly willing to express their eroticism if it could be done at a reasonable distance—say fifty paces. These men (the frigid-*plus type*) found kissing intolerable. When they had an opportunity to kiss a young lady, they declined. They made it plain that they would be willing to blow a kiss across the room from their hand, but not execute it with their lips.

I analyzed scores of these cases, questioning both the women and the men. (The women were mad as hornets.) I found that a small number of the kiss-declining men were suffering from a pathology of the eyes—either astigmatism or farsightedness—so that when they got really close to a girl, she blurred on them.[2] The vast majority of cases, however, were quite different. Their unwillingness I traced to a much subtler feeling than eye-strain. Your true anti-contactual, or kiss-decliner, is a very subtle individual indeed.

In effect, he is a throw-back to another period in history, specifically to the Middle Ages. He is a biological sport. (Note: this is very confusing, calling him a "sport," because the ordinary "sport" is not a kiss-decliner at all—anything but. Please keep in mind, then, that when I use the term "sport" I want the strict biological interpretation put upon the word. I want it, and I intend to get it. If there are any of you who think you are going to find

[1] Now we're getting down to business.
[2] Incidentally, I might say that this blurring of the female before the eyes of the male is not entirely unpleasant. It's kind of fun.

the use of the word "sport" in this connection so confusing as to make the rest of the chapter unintelligible, I wish you would drop out. Get something else to read, or, better yet, get some exercise.)

No one can quite comprehend the motives and the successes of a kiss-decliner who does not recall his counterpart in mediæval history. In the Middle Ages, when men were lusty and full of red meat, their women expected as much. A baronial fellow, finishing his meal, made no ado about kissing a Middle Age woman. He just got up from the table and kissed her. Bango, and she was kissed. Love had a simple directness which was not disturbed until the arrival, in the land, of the *minnesingers*. It got so no baronial hall of the Middle Ages was free from these *minnesingers*. They kept getting in. They would bring their harps with them, and after dinner they would twang a couple of notes and then sing a frail, delicate song to the effect that women should be worshiped from afar, rather than possessed. To a baron who had just drunk a goblet of red wine, this new concept of womanhood was screamingly funny. While he was chuckling away to himself and cutting himself another side of beef, his wife, who had listened attentively to the song, would slip out into the alley behind the castle and there the *minnesinger* would join her.

"Sing that one again," she would say.

"Which one?"

"That one about worshiping me from a little distance. I want to hear that one again."

The *minnesinger* would oblige. Then he would illustrate the theme by *not* kissing the woman, but dancing off lightly down the hill, throwing his harp up into the air and catching it again as he went.

"What a nice young man," the baron's wife would think, as she slowly turned and went in to bed.

The kiss-decliner of today is a modern *minnesinger*. He is a sport in that he has varied suddenly from the normal type—which is still baronial. Of course, the amusing thing about his conduct is that oftentimes a woman assumes that she is being worshiped from afar, when as a matter of fact she is merely being *ignored from afar*. That is part of the trick of an anti-contactual person—he takes a perverse delight in allowing the woman whose kiss he has declined, to think of him as more lyrical than other men. When he leaves her presence, she is apt to think of him as off somewhere by the bank of a stream, lying flat on his back, his shaggy head buried in the tall grasses, dreaming of something or other—probably of her, whereas, if she would take the trouble to go to the nearest Liggett's drug store she would probably find him there, getting a sundæ.

By the mere gesture of declining a kiss a man can still make quite a lot of ground, even in these depleted days. The woman thinks: "He would not dream of embracing my body; now that's pretty white of him!" Of course, it would be wrong to ascribe motives of sheer deliberateness to the frigid male. Often he is not a bad sort—merely is a fellow who prefers an imagined kiss to the real kind. An imagined kiss is more easily controlled, more thoroughly enjoyed, and less cluttery than an actual kiss. To kiss in dream is wholly pleasant. First, the woman is the one of your selection, not just anyone who happens to be in your arms at the moment. Second, the deed is garnished with a little sprig of glamour which the mind, in exquisite taste, contributes. Third, the lips, imaginatively, are placed just so, the right hand is placed just so, the concurrent thoughts arrive, just so. Except for the the fact that the whole episode is a little bit stuffy, it is a superior experience all round. When a kiss becomes actual, anything is likely to happen. The lips, failing of the mark, may strike lightly against the end of the lady's nose, causing the whole adventure to crack up; or the right hand may come in contact with the hard, jagged part of the shoulder blade; or, worst of all, the man's thoughts may not clothe the moment with the proper splendor: he may be worrying about something.

So you see, frigidity in men has many aspects, many angles. To me it is vastly more engrossing than frigidity in women, which is such a simple phenomenon you wonder anybody bothers about it at all.

DAYS

By John O'Hara

AFTER THE FIRST FEW DAYS THERE THE HABITS OF LIVING IN A NEW place begin to form. Larkin would lean over and kiss his wife good-by, get out of the car, go inside the station, buy his paper at the news-stand, walk through the station, and stand out there waiting for the train. He liked to get that much air anyway, and that was how he began to notice her.

She, he found, would come out of the large apartment house, the last building before you got to the station. She walked across the graveled space and did not go inside the station at all, not even on rainy days. He had been in the town only a few weeks, and so he did not know whether she stayed inside the station when it was snowing, but from the beginning he was pretty sure she stayed outside, winter and summer.

She carried her paper under her arm. It seemed part of the general neatness of her gloved hands, her bag, her tailored clothes, the scarf at her throat, and even the way she held her head. The paper probably was the one she had delivered at her apartment, because he never saw her buy a paper at the news-stand. On that theory, one day in New York he lingered after everyone had got out of the train, and went back and picked up her paper, hoping it would have her name penciled on top, the way some news-dealers do; but the only mark on the paper was 9-H, obviously the number of her apartment. He felt ashamed that day, and terrified that the conductor, who would have recognized him, would come in and see him at a seat so far forward of the one he always tried to get. He always, after the first week or so, tried to sit behind her so that if she turned her head he could see her profile. She seldom turned her head.

The other habits were merely habits, but there was one of which he was conscious: the habit of knowing all through breakfast and before it that he would see her. In a way it was awful, to be so excited about so little, but it made the mornings good, even some bad Monday mornings after golf tournaments. The excitement would be there until she appeared, then a sort of relief, and, in the train, actual comfort. Yes, comfort, he told himself. The way he wanted to be with her; sort of like being in the same comfortable room, quietly reading, knowing she was there. But then once they were in New York, once people began getting up in the car, it would be different, a different kind of excitement that was not good, but upset him. He knew her path to the subway, and on the way she would pass tunnels that led to hotels. What if he could meet her and then some morning they could take the train as they always did, but this one morning she would turn in at one of those tunnels and wait for him, and they could go to the hotel together?

He would wonder how he could get to meet her. It was too large a suburb, too many people got on the train, for casual good mornings with people you hadn't met. There were two country clubs, and he guessed she belonged to the smaller one, the one with a nine-hole golf course. He sometimes thought of joining that club, but he knew his wife would put her foot down. "Two country clubs?" she would say. "What do you want to join that club for? Lots of other things we could use the money for." And there were, of course, and pretty soon, when his son got home from prep school, the expenses would climb. And anyway, he had no way of knowing she even belonged to the smaller club. The apartment house in which she lived had a lot of tennis-courts, and she probably played tennis. He seldom went to the movies, and he never saw her there, but what if he did? He had a better chance of getting to know her on the train than at any damn movie, with his wife there with him.

He came home one afternoon and said, "I think we ought to have a man here. A chauffeur-gardener."

"What for?"

"We need somebody like that, and they don't cost so much. He could take me to the station in the morning in the big car and you could use him to drive around, and of course, this fellow we have now, he's only a part-time gardener and not so damn good, for that matter."

"I don't see what we need a full-time man for. It's only additional expense."

"Now listen, it wouldn't cost that much more, and we'd get a lot more out of him if we had a full-time man. When Teddy comes home and starts using the Ford all the time you'll be glad of a man to drive you in the big car. You know that yourself. I'm going to call up an agency tomorrow."

"It's your money, but I think you're silly," his wife had said. And so Larkin no longer was driven to the station by his wife. In a way, he told himself, he was doing it for her; he didn't want to stop kissing her good-by, but he didn't want to be seen kissing her by the woman, whoever she was, that he loved.

Well, there it was, acnowledged at last; something he had known all along, more than likely from the first day, when seeing her appear from behind the corner of the station had had an effect on him like—a jolt. Now he began to listen to the words of songs about love, trying to discover a voice on the radio that would be just like a voice he never had heard. In a way he began to envy the people who got into messes in the papers, although that was the last thing he wanted for either of his two women—the one he was married to, and the one he loved. "Mrs. Larkin and two detectives surprised her manufacturer husband at a morning tryst with an attractive brunette at a midtown hotel. The woman, Mrs. Larkin said, was attired in a flimsy négligé, and was about thirty years old. She said her husband had registered under the name of Lawrence. A property settlement . . . alimony . . . custody of their one son." Hell, no! That wasn't the way Anna would do it; not the way he would have it.

Oh, no? Well, if he couldn't have it any other way, he would have it that way. When he went to the station the morning after he lay thinking these things he wanted to explain to her: "If we can't have it that way, if you love me enough, let her go ahead and do as she pleases. I'll give her all the money she wants." And then he had to laugh out loud at what he was thinking, and at that moment she turned, and there was a smile in her eyes. Two other men smiled, too, at him, this man standing alone and laughing out loud at some private joke. But *she* had smiled and it was beautiful. *She* was beautiful. And on the way in on the train he suddenly knew that now it was only a question of days. Days!

BED MANNERS

By DR. RALPH Y. HOPTON *and* ANNE BALLIOL

A POET IN LONDON, LONG AGO, WROTE SOME MEMORABLE LINES
that began:

> Turn out more ale, turn up the light,
> I will not go to bed tonight!
> In bed we laugh, in bed we cry,
> In bed we're born, in bed we die. . . .

Despite this warning, it is likely that you wish you could get
eight hours' rest every night. In other words, you want to spend
a third of your whole life in bed! There is nothing else in your
existence to which you are eager to give so much time.

Are you fond of dancing? Try dancing eight hours every day
for a week, and see how your feet like it. Bridge? Not even Sims
and Culbertson play bridge seventy-two hours a week. They
couldn't find partners, for one thing. For another, they probably
couldn't tell the partners from the kibitzers after a month of this
grind.

You may be fond of work. But the United States Government
won't let you work a seventy-two-hour week. You might try
drinking for eight hours a day, but your health won't stand it.
You might try playing the saxophone, but the neighbors won't
stand it.

Man Is a Bed Animal

Face it frankly. In bed you were born, in bed you will die.
Just as if these two experiences didn't teach you anything, you
now purpose in cold blood to spend thirty-three and one-third
per cent of all your time in bed—and, if you are not married
already, you expect to induce some fellow creature to share bed's
dangers with you.

This you do because you can't help it. The instinct is inherited. Don't be ashamed of it.

The moose is a land animal, the monkey a tree animal, the whale a water animal. But man is a *bed animal*, and the only one in the world (except woman, of course). Considering how fond she is of breakfasting in bed, and of "lying down" on the bed in spare hours, woman is even more of a bed animal than man.

Admitting this fact, the authors have tried to show you how to get into bed as gracefully as possible. If you are an unmarried person, it really doesn't much matter if you hurl your clothes around the room, or festoon them on bureaus and chairs. They offend no eye but your own, while you're in bed. In the morning, after you are out, some humble servitor like your chambermaid, your valet, or your mother, will pick up after you.

In the same way, if you have no bedfellow you can be as sloppy as you like in bed. You can use the sheet for a handkerchief. You can put your muddy boots on the bedspread, when snoozing before dinner. You can drink whisky out of the bottle, spilling some of it on the pillow case. You can burn holes in the blankets with cigarettes. These social errors don't matter except to the menial—be it laundress or mother—who does your wash and your mending.

Try any of these tricks on a bedfellow, however, and you will find yourself out of luck.

It is best to wean yourself of all of them before you ask the Marriage Bureau for a license. Otherwise you will always look back on your wedding night as the night of the Big Blizzard.

Pretty Costumes for Bed

The first great rule is: Wear correct clothes in bed, or none at all. Our ancestors either went to bed with all their clothes on, or else they went to bed raw. Good breeding now decrees the use of nice-looking nightgowns and pajamas. Women are allowed to choose between these articles. Men have no choice. It is pajamas for them or nothing.

The comfortable old-fashioned flannel nightgown, worn with bed socks, is taboo.

So is the practise, common among seamen and lumberjacks, of

going to bed in one's underclothes. A man who does this in the nuptial chamber is crude. This is especially true if you actually *are* a lumberjack, in which case you wear long woollen drawers, and an undershirt with long sleeves, both made of heavy gray or red knit goods.

The eye of a sensitive, delicately reared girl is shocked by such an inartistic sleeping costume. It is your own fault if she screams. You should be wearing a Chinese brocade dressing gown over silk pajamas. Lumberjacks who do this make good husbands. So do other men. Socks are not being worn in bed this year.

The whole art of dressing for bed, in fact, is not to wear anything that could irritate your bolster-buddy or counterpane-chum, call her whatever you will. It is true that "misery makes strange bedfellows," as the proverb says. It is even more true that bedfellows make strange misery—unless they are determined in advance to be nice to one another at all costs.

Etiquette While Horizontal

It is quite easy to show good manners while you are vertical. This is the normal position when taking off your hat to a lady, or selling her a bottle of gin in a store, or any other civilized action.

When you assume a horizontal position, however, whole centuries of traditional good breeding disappear. This is the moment which ordinary writers about etiquette never discuss, the saps. They seem to think you are vertical *all* the time. Standing up, or sitting up. This is nonsense, as we have just proved by showing you that you want to be horizontal so much of your life.

We now answer a few ordinary questions, which everybody wants to ask, but which etiquette authorities have never answered before.

Q. Which goes to bed first, a wife or her husband?
A. The wife who beats her husband into bed leaves him to open the window, fix the shade, and take a last look at the furnace. If she has good sense, she will win this race every night.

*

Q. Who gets up, if there is a noise like burglars?
A. Nobody.

*

Q. What are fashionable topics to discuss in bed?
A. The morals, or lack of morals, of your neighbors; the wretched food and drink served in their houses; the bad manners of their children. These are all safe and reliable themes.

*

Q. Are any topics barred by good manners?
A. Yes. Avoid all discussion of money-worries, of your own morals (or lack of them), of the quality of food and drink served in your own home, and the manners of your own children. All these are dynamite.

*

Q. What does a husband do if the wife is sure the house is on fire.
A. He argues with her till morning, if necessary, taking the negative side of the debate. If he gets up to investigate, there is always the chance that she may be right.

*

Important as all these items are, they are nothing compared to the face cream and hair curler problem. This is the biggest question of the day—excuse us, we mean the night. It cannot be dismissed briefly. It dwarfs even the snoring problem; and the halitosis problem beside it is a pygmy.

All women have been taught, in the past fifteen years, that it is fatal to let the hair and skin alone.

The hair *must* be curled. The skin of the face *must* be covered with cold cream. If these things aren't done just as regularly as the sun sets, a woman loses her membership card in her own sex. She can't even tell you what would happen if she failed just once in this ritual. It is more than a ritual to her. It is a creed.

The average man, we are glad to say, marries a pretty girl. Prettiness and daintiness are the things he values. He remembers Milton's line about some lucky chap who spent a lot of time "lost in the tangles of Neaera's hair"—Neaera being the prettiest nymph of her day and age. The average man also enjoys the ads about that schoolgirl complexion. He adores a soft pink cheek.

And what happens to him?

On tiptoe with expectancy, he finds himself at last alone, behind locked doors, with the pretty girl of his choice. He is on his best behavior. He has used the right soap, the right mouthwash, the right toothpaste, and the right liniment to cure all the unpleasant symptoms mentioned in the other ads he reads. He has fixed his hair brilliantly with slickum. He has bought a lovely silk dressing gown and pajamas. His feet are in costly slippers. He feels and looks on the crest of the wave. His bride, at this moment, comes out of the bathroom.

Where Many Divorces Start

The shock to a sensitive man's feelings, which now occurs, is likely to send him to a lunatic asylum for life.

The bride's head is covered with a network of large, shiny wire gadgets, resembling safety pins, much enlarged. They pull her hair so hard that her eyes are all squinched up. This alters her expression so much that he doesn't at first recognize her. She is wearing a pretty *peignoir*, over a new pink nightgown—the costliest in her trousseau. But he doesn't even see these things. His eyes travel down from her hair to her face. And her face is like a leper's, as white as snow!

When the first shock passes, he realizes that this is the way she is going to look to him every night of their lives. He has heard about curlers and cream. But until he marries, no woman has dared to show them to him. His mother, his sisters, etc., have been too anxious to preserve his good opinion. His wife, on the other hand, feels free from the start to behave naturally.

On that very same night, some lawyer in Reno orders a case of expensive champagne. He knows he can afford it all right. Members of the legal profession, out there, are assured of living on the fat of the land just as long as curlers and cream are made and wives allowed to buy them.

Your Knight Life Has Its Perils

Even if the wife is be-wired and be-whitened, however, and the husband has hung up all his good manners in the closet with his clothes, the nights have to be lived through, some way. The best plan is to say very little.

We have outlined a few harmless topics, which are fun for both persons. Still, almost any chatter can lead, before you know it, to a hail of abuse like machine-gun fire. Any mention of money is an extrahazardous occupation.

Having settled the neighbors' hash with a few well chosen remarks, you should quickly steer the conversation to art, literature, and national politics. This will soon put your pillow-pal to sleep. You can now cautiously doze off yourself, taking great pains not to snore.

If you snore like a foghorn of an ocean steamer, your mattress-mate will wake up, and all's to do over again.

Never despair, however. Practise makes perfect in knight life, as in everything else. Avoid mumbling and talking in your sleep. This is discourteous, and it may also be too interesting to the hearer. Do not walk in your sleep. Getting up to do this admits a blast of cold air into the bed, which will cause discomfort to your bedfellow.

Do not grind your teeth in your sleep, thrash around with your clenched fists, or toss and twist so much that you wind the bed-clothes into a tight cocoon around yourself, leaving your pillow-partner bare. Try to turn off the radio at an early moment after midnight. All these things require some self-denial, but remember what Emerson said.

"Good manners," he said, "are made up of petty sacrifices." If you don't like this quotation, we'll hand you another one from the poet we quoted at the head of this chapter:

> Oh, I've been born, and I've been wed.
> All of man's perils come in bed!

SLUMMER'S PARADISE

By HERBERT ASBURY

AT TWELVE MINUTES AND SIX SECONDS PAST FIVE O'CLOCK ON THE
morning of April 18, 1906, the San Francisco peninsula began to
shiver in the grip of an earthquake which, when its ultimate consequences are considered, was the most disastrous in the recorded
history of the North American continent. The shocks continued
for one minute and five seconds, and while the actual damage
done to property by the temblor was comparatively slight, it
made possible the greater calamity of fire by shaking down chimneys and breaking water-mains and electrical connections throughout San Francisco. Within a few minutes after the earth had
ceased to rock, sixteen fires were throwing their menacing glare
against the morning sky from as many sections of the city south
of Market Street. No water was available except a relatively small
quantity found in a few abandoned cisterns, and the Fire Department was practically helpless. By noon a square mile had been
devastated, and during the early afternoon the conflagration
crossed Market Street at Third and Kearny Streets. Driven by a
strong southeast wind, it spread rapidly northward and westward,
through the business and financial districts, the Barbary Coast, and
Chinatown. For two days the holocaust raged unchecked, while
the trains and ferries, and the roads throughout the countryside,
were crowded with frightened and unhappy refugees. The fire
finally burned itself out, but not until it had destroyed 28,188
buildings in 522 blocks, covering an area of more than four square
miles, or 2,593 acres of which 1,088 acres were north of Market
Street. The property loss was estimated at about four hundred
million dollars, while 315 persons were known to have lost their
lives, and 352 had been reported to the police as missing. Only a
few were ever found.

The destruction of Sodom and Gomorrah by fire and brimstone

157

from heaven was scarcely more complete than the devastation of
Chinatown and the Barbary Coast by fire and earthquake from,
perhaps, the same source. On the morning of April 20, 1906, the
opium dives and slave dens, the cow-yards and parlor houses, the
cribs and deadfalls, the dance-halls and bar-rooms, the melodeons
and concert saloons—all the abode and paraphernalia of vice, from
the waterfont to Grant Avenue and from Morton Street to Telegraph Hill, lay a mass of smoking ruins. Only an occasional dive
or brothel remained, looming stark and solitary in the cloud of
murky smoke which overhung the whole of San Francisco, and
they were immediately closed by the police and the troops of the
United States Army, who patrolled the burned area to protect
the city from looters. At the request of the San Francisco authorities, the bagnios in Oakland, across the Bay, were likewise compelled to shut their doors. But they were reopened almost at once.
As Walter J. Peterson, Chief of the Oakland Police Department,
told Pauline Jacobson of the San Francisco *Bulletin* in an interview seven years later:

> "San Francisco was still smoldering, the earth still rocking,
> and we didn't know when the Almighty might send another
> visitation, yet on the incessant demand the authorities [of
> Oakland] had to open up the houses of prostitution. All day
> long and at night men were lined up for blocks waiting in
> front of the houses, like at a box at a theater on a popular
> night."

As an organized center of vice and crime Chinatown virtually
came to an end on that catastrophic spring day; the underworld
of the Oriental quarter was never able fully to overcome the
cleansing effect of the fire and earthquake, and very few of the
opium resorts and slave cribs were rebuilt. But unlike Chinatown
and its own Biblical prototypes, the Barbary Coast immediately
rose, phœnix-like, from its ashes. While the municipal and military
authorities, aided by committees of reputable citizens, struggled
with the vast problems of reconstruction and rehabilitation which
the disaster had created, the overlords of vice loosened their purse-
strings and devoted their ill-gotten treasure to the erection of a

new and bigger Barbary Coast upon the ruins of the old. Within three months after the flames had subsided, half a dozen brothels and as many deadfalls and dance-halls were in prosperous operation in Pacific and adjacent streets, and by the beginning of 1907 the Barbary Coast was once more roaring in full blast. The final cycle of its career of vice and crime had begun.

The distinction of being the first important resort to flaunt its iniquities after the fire—and the further glory of being perhaps the lowest dive in all the post-earthquake period—belongs to the Seattle Saloon and Dance Hall, which was opened in Pacific Street, near Kearny Street, during the early summer of 1906 by Ed Pincus and Tom Magee, with Billy Harrington as manager. The Seattle was not as pretentious a place as the old Bull Run of more or less hallowed memory, but otherwise it suffered little by comparison with that celebrated dive of an earlier day. The Pincus-Magee enterprise was housed in a large, two-story frame building, with a U-shaped entrance lobby decorated by framed panels containing gaudy paintings of women in varying stages of undress. The upper floor was occupied by an assignation house, and the saloon and dance-hall were downstairs in a long, rectangular room, at one end of which was a small stage whereon bawdy shows and hoochy-coochy dances were presented. Behind the stage were a few small dressing-rooms hung with curtains, where the performers changed their costumes and into which drunken men were enticed and robbed. Rough tables, chairs and benches were scattered about the dance-floor.

Pincus and Magee employed twenty girls, who were paid, as wages, from fifteen to twenty dollars a week, according to their beauty and popularity. They wore thin blouses cut very low, skirts cut very high, and black silk stockings held in place by fancy garters. Mindful of the success of the notorious deadfall and dance house at Kearny and California streets, which in preearthquake days had aroused a considerable commotion throughout the Barbary Coast by its rule forbidding underwear, Pincus and Magee enforced a similar fashion in their establishment and advertised the fact by cards discreetly distributed in saloons and other places where men were wont to gather. In general, duties of the women employed in the Seattle were the same as those of the pretty waiter girls, but in one respect Pincus and Magee introduced an innovation which was soon adopted by most of the other Barbary Coast resorts. They employed men to serve drinks to customers at the tables and benches on the dance-floor and thus gave their girls more time to dance with and otherwise entertain the men who succumbed to their charms. Drinks could be purchased over the bar of the Seattle at the prices which prevailed in ordinary saloons, but if a man seated himself at a bench or table with one of the dive's female attachées and ordered liquor, he paid a dollar for a pony of whisky, the same for a pint of beer, three dollars for a small bottle of bitter wine known as Dago red, and five dollars a bottle for a beverage labeled champagne, which was in reality aerated cider. The girls were paid a small percentage on drinks sold in the dance-hall and were also entitled to half of whatever they managed to abstract from their partners' pockets during the close contact of the dance. Pincus often complained, however, that most of his female employees were dishonest and failed to render true accounts of their stealings.

Another and even more important source of income was developed by the girls in the Seattle and was their own particular racket; it was practically the only activity of which they were not supposed to share the proceeds with their employers. A woman employed in the dive was not permitted to leave the premises for purposes of prostitution, but if a man expressed a desire for her company in ways other than dancing, she would immediately promise so to arrange matters that she might spend the night with him, or rather what remained of the night after the Seattle had closed its doors, which was usually about three o'clock in the morning. She would point out, however, that there were great difficulties to overcome, and that they must proceed shrewdly and with caution. It was impossible, she would explain, for her to meet him anywhere or for him to wait for her at the back door of the resort, for her lover was extremely jealous and always walked home with her to make certain she didn't get into mischief. But after much discussion and many drinks she would evolve a plan whereby they might hope to circumvent the watchful sweetheart. She offered to sell, for a dollar or two dollars or whatever she thought the traffic would bear, a key to her room, so that the enamored visitor might join her there an hour or so after she had finished her work at the dance-hall. If he objected to thus buying a pig in a poke, she would indignantly retort that, after all, she didn't know him, and that if he failed to appear with the key she would have to employ a locksmith to make another. To a man befogged by bad liquor and confused by the joys of propinquity, all this sounded very reasonable. Nearly always he bought the key and carefully noted the address she gave him, which was usually a street number of a near-by tenement, but never that of the house where she actually lived. Some of the more popular girls sometimes sold as many as a dozen keys a night, at prices ranging from one to five dollars each, and for several hours after the Seattle had closed, furtive figures could be seen flitting through the streets searching hopelessly for doors which their keys would open. This lucrative scheme was practiced for more than a year, not only by the girls of the Seattle, but by those of other dives also. It was finally stopped by the police. They received too many complaints from honest householders who had been annoyed by drunken men trying to unlock their doors.

Pincus and Magee operated the Seattle until the early spring of 1908, when they sold the property to a syndicate headed by their manager, Billy Harrington, and thereafter confined their activities to brothels, in several of which they owned large interests. The names of Harrington's partners were not generally known until October, 1908, when the San Francisco *Call*, during one of its periodic crusades against Judge Carroll Cook, revealed that they were two officers of Judge Cook's branch of the Superior Court. Harrington and his associates changed the name of the resort to the Dash, and remodeled the interior, installing a row of curtained booths on either side of the dance-floor. They also discharged most of the dancing girls and in their places employed male degenerates who wore women's clothing. From one to three of these creatures were always to be found sitting in each of the booths, and for a dollar they would perform in a manner which may be imagined, but which may not be described. It was with good reason that the *Call* described the Dash as "one of the vilest saloons and dance halls ever maintained in San Francisco." The place was not very successful under the new régime, however, and was closed late in 1908, soon after Judge Cook had been defeated for re-election by the narrow margin of two thousand votes.

2

The most vicious dives of the new Barbary Coast were the wine dumps—dismal cellar dens in the alleys and along the waterfront which catered to the very dregs of Barbary Coast humanity, where the floors were covered with damp sawdust, where wine was sold for five cents a pint, and where the bars were rough boards laid atop kegs. They provided neither dancing nor entertainment—nothing but a few hard benches on which men and women sat and guzzled wine. And the wine, as often as not, was simply raw alcohol colored and flavored. These places were the particular rendezvous of the bums, the oldest and most hopeless of the street-walkers, the sneak-thieves and pickpockets, and the many Fagins who took street boys and girls under their wings and taught them to steal. Most of the wine dumps had been closed by the middle of 1913, principally because of the viciousness of their habitués—who, of course, were utterly without political or other influence—and the innumerable serious brawls which occurred in them. In one place known as the Morgue (no connection with the saloon of that name in the old Devil's Acre) the police averaged twenty-seven arrests a night over a period of almost a year.

The early traditions of the Barbary Coast were effectively maintained by the wine dumps, by the Seattle and similar establishments, and by the houses of prostitution; but as a whole the district underwent a radical change after the earthquake and fire. The decade that followed the rebuilding and reopening of the Barbary Coast was an era of glamour and spectacularity, of hullabaloo and ballyhoo, of bright lights and feverish gayety, of synthetic sin and imitation iniquity. Practically everything that occurred in the dives of this period was deliberately planned to startle and impress, and if possible to shock, the tourist and sightseer; in its last incarnation, particularly from about 1910 to the end of its existence, the Barbary Coast was a veritable slummers' paradise, although underneath there still flowed the same old current of vice and corruption which had been the life-blood of the quarter since the days of the Sydney Ducks. In earlier years visitors from the upper strata of society had been both infrequent and unwelcome, but virtually every dance-hall on the new Barbery Coast provided, as a special and very remunerative feature, a "slummers' balcony," which was filled each night by palpitant, wide-eyed spectators. They were firmly convinced that they were watching the underworld at its revels, and seeing life stripped to its elementals, and so they submitted meekly to exorbitant charges for admission and liquor. Beer was never less than a dollar a pint in the sightseeing galleries, and a highball, which might or might not contain a trace of whisky, was likewise a dollar, and sometimes even more. During this same period the maximum price of any mixed drink at the best bars in San Francisco was twenty-five cents, and of beer, except the finest imported brews, a dime. In the manner of the modern moving-picture cathedral, most of the better-known resorts on the Barbary Coast employed gaudily uniformed sidewalk barkers and doormen, who bellowed the glad tidings of glamour and excitement almost without cessation from early afternoon until long past midnight. They were usually fellows of little or no imagination, and their patter was fairly well standardized after this fashion:

"Right this way to the visitors' gallery, folks! Everybody happy! Everybody welcome! Everybody safe! The hottest show and the prettiest girls on the Coast! Watch 'em wiggle, gents; watch 'em wiggle! Don't talk about what you see in here, folks! It'll shock you, but it's worth seeing!"

While most of San Francisco's reputable citizens publicly bemoaned the iniquities of the Barbary Coast and performed lipservice in the many campaigns designed to eliminate its more objectionable features, secretly they were, for the most part, enormously proud of their city's reputation as the Paris of America and the wickedest town on the continent. A tour of the district, under proper police supervision, was usually a part of the itinerary of the distinguished visitor to San Francisco, and if through some oversight it wasn't, the distinguished visitor very frequently included it on his own account, for no area of similar size in the Western Hemisphere had been so widely publicized or was so universally known. And since comment upon the evils of the quarter was eagerly sought by the newspapers, few celebrities set foot in San Francisco without seeing it. Sarah Bernhardt always visited the Barbary Coast when she played in San Francisco on her frequent tours, and pleased local journalists immensely by declaring that she had found it more fascinatingly wicked than Montmartre. Anna Pavlowa, the famous dancer, often visited the dance-halls, and avowed that she had obtained many ideas for her own dance creations by watching the gyrations of the light-footed Barbary Coasters. And when John Masefield, now Poet Laureate of England, arrived in San Francisco some sixteen years ago, the first thing he said when he disembarked from a ferry-boat at Market Street was: "Take me to see the Barbary Coast."

Although prostitution and robbery remained the basic industries of the Barbary Coast, the resort features which brought thousands of sightseers into the district after the earthquake and fire were the dance-floors and the low variety shows. The latter usually consisted in skits, songs, and exhibition dancing, all carefully designed to shock, but not disgust. They were undeniably bawdy, coarse, and vulgar, for otherwise they would not have interested the slummers; but they were not nearly so obscene as the shows which were given as a matter of course in the old-time concert saloons. And, of course, in comparison with the peep-shows which were extremely popular features of San Francisco's brothels until the red-light district was abolished, they were as innocuous as so many Sunday-school tableaux. The *pièce de résistance* of a Barbary Coast variety program was the lewd cavorting of a hoochy-coochy artiste, or the Dance of the Seven Veils as interpreted by a fat and clumsy Salome dancer, who simply wiggled a muscle dance to semi-classical music. Occasionally a few of the veils were omitted, and the dancer squirmed and twisted in very scanty raiment indeed. For some curious reason, perhaps to show that her strength and agility were not confined entirely to her abdominal muscles, the Salome dancer almost invariably concluded her performance by gripping a chair between her teeth and swinging it about her head.

The variety shows, particularly those which included hoochy-coochy or Salome dancing, were very well liked, but it is doubtful if they alone could have made the Barbary Coast the extraor-

dinarily popular place that it became during the last ten years of its
existence. The principal attraction was dancing. The whole Barbary Coast was dance-crazy, and practically every dive of any
pretentiousness was a combination dance-hall and concert saloon,
offering both theatrical entertainment and an opportunity to trip
the light fantastic or to watch it being tripped. The number of
resorts which sprang up after the earthquake and fire and enjoyed
their comparatively brief flurries of success and prosperity was
really extraordinary—by 1910, four years after the disaster, there
were no fewer than three hundred saloons and dance-halls
crowded into six blocks, centering, of course, in Pacific Street,
which was more than ever intrenched in its position as the main
thoroughfare of the Barbary Coast. Throughout the quarter,
rentals soared to amazing heights; basement and street-level store-
rooms, which if rented to legitimate businesses would never have
brought more than thirty to a hundred dollars a month, were let
for ten times those amounts to be used as saloons and dance-halls
—one dive-operator paid nine hundred dollars a month on a ten-
year lease for a cellar about sixty feet long and thirty feet wide.
Many of these places were still in operation, though the names
of some had been changed and they were under different manage-
ments, when the Barbary Coast was finally closed in 1917.

MAE WEST AND JOHN RIDDELL:
A CORRESPONDENCE

By Corey Ford

1. J. R. to M. W.

At the time of the opening of this correspondence with the immortal Mae [the "Dream Girl of the ensuing letters], Miss West was appearing with Hal Clarendon's Stock Company at the old Gotham, where she had recently taken the town by storm with her performance of Little Eva in "Uncle Tom's Cabin." John Riddell, who was eight years old at the time, was living with his mother in lodgings at Wipple-cum-slink, The Chicester, Hants (now Central Park West) and often used to ride his bicycle in the Central Park Mall; and it is generally supposed that Miss West spied him first in this romantic manner. Although personally unacquainted, their correspondence began with a letter from her asking him "what he thought her chances were of learning to ride a bicycle." John Riddell replied at once with a conscientiously careful opinion of the possibilities; and the correspondence began in earnest.

Mrs. Siddons, who is referred to below, had made something of a reputation in London when she appeared in "The Fatal Marriage" at the Drury Lane some time previous (1782).—"Bike": evidently Riddell's colloquial term for his machine, an Iver-Johnson with carbide light and New Departure Coaster Brake, of which he was very proud.

24 June 1906
Wipple-cum-slink, W.

Dear Miss West,

I admit to an interest in bicycling, having lately tamed that steed myself with some proficiency; but I am at a loss, dear Lady, how I may impart to you all the subtleties involved in a performance of this feat. You must be aware that the Bike, like all art, depends primarily upon the principle of *revolution*, in which the machine overthrows its rider and sets up a democracy of its own. By a mechanical application of power, the pressure of the foot serves to turn a wheel in the rear of the bicycle, as a result of which the chain revolves around the sprocket and the bicycle moves forward, provided it was not facing backward at the time. But stay! I must not make this technical description any longer: you must be out of patience already. I really thought you magnificent in *Little Lord Fauntleroy*. You reminded me of Mrs. Siddons.

John Riddell

2. M. W. to J. R.

[*In this letter, stylistically forthright like all epistles from Miss West, it has been thought desirable to omit certain words and phrases, and a few whole sentences, which she embodied in her letter for the purpose of emphasis. Accustomed in her daily speech to express her exact meaning by certain delicate nuances of phrase familiar to her associates, it is clear that when she wrote she felt the need of some similar means of self-expression. If this emphatic language were reproduced here, however, the reader might feel that she suffered from a lack of that reserve usually attributed to the female sex; and it is in order to protect Miss West from such misconstruction that her phrases have not been reproduced save with the use of dashes, as G—d d—nn, —— of a ——, etc.*]

26 June 1906
Bushwick Ave., Brooklyn, W.

Dear Mr. Riddell,

Oh, you perfectly charming being. You are just a Duck! It was mostest kind of you to write me, dear Gentleman, and I must yet ask you to accept my bestest thanks for your splendid letter. Thank you. Thank you. *Thank* you for all your beautifulness. What do you say to picking me up at the theatre tonight and we'll take our bicycles to the Park and try them out together? Know what I mean?

Yours rather much,
Mae W.

3. J. R. to M. W.

[*That John Riddell did not take up Miss West's invitation to go bicycle-riding with her in the Park, after all, is apparent in the following letter.—Plato, who is mentioned below, was a Greek philosopher whose theories on love were regarded highly by Riddell.—Vesta Tilley: a vaudeville headliner of the period 1900-10, who had scored a success with the popular ballade "Come and Splash with Me."*]

7 July 1906

Dear Mae West,

Oh, dear! You've given me an attack of sentiment, and sentiment is a luxury like love. Love, dear Lady, is nothing but the passion for hate, because everything in life is real, except life. I know you will understand what I mean. I am your mental lover, you my Platonic mistress. Perhaps, sometimes, in the starlight—but no! I am getting idiotic again. Forgive me. I was in the eighth row of the balcony tonight when you came out between the acts of *For Their Children's Sake* and sang "Oceana Roll." It reminded me of Vesta Tilley in the flesh—but such flesh! If you will send me your photograph, I shall carry it always next my heart.

Thine,

J. R.

4. J. R. to M. W.

[*Miss West's reply unfortunately cannot be reproduced here; but it may be hinted briefly that Riddell's "mental lover" idea did not get over so big.—The photograph referred to evidently was taken while Miss West was appearing in her famous weight-lifting act at the old Palace (now the Palace).*

Marlowe: Julia Marlowe, who was appearing with E. H. Sothern in a Shakespearean repertory.]

9 July 1906

Dearest and everest,

Oh, why, *why* WHY did you send me that picture of yourself with your back turned? The pictures of you with your eyes in them are divine; it is like looking at the stars. But to turn your soul away from me and show me nothing but how beautiful the outlines of your cheek is, just to give me that lost feeling of fulfillment—oh, wretched Lady, some day you will provoke heaven too far, and then—stop! I must control myself. Forgive me.

Last night I saw you at the Colonial in your new dance, which you call the "shimmy." It is superb. You reminded me of Marlowe. My love, you *should* do Shakespeare.

John

5. M. W. to J. R.

[After the foregoing letter, there appears to be a conspicuous gap in the correspondence, during which Riddell and Mae West both followed their separate paths. Riddell secured a position of book-reviewer of "Vanity Fair," a magazine, where his criticisms soon won for him a large following, usually with shotguns. In the meantime, Miss West left the Keith Circuit, following the decline of the shimmy, and won new laurels in a Shubert revue, where she appeared as Cleopatra in a number called "Shakespeare's Garden of Love"—perhaps the direct outgrowth of Riddell's suggestion. The following letter was written from Welfare Island, where Miss West was spending a few days with friends following the abrupt closing of a play she wrote called "Sex."]

16 April 1927

Dear Riddy,

Oh, dear J. R., how does oo do? I've had a h—ll of a time, dear Gentleman, since last we wrote. (Oh, I forgot, I was not a-goin' to write you ever again, so there! *Can't* help it!) I hate this ole damp weather, and I am *lonely*. Won't you come over to see me tonight, I have so muchy-much to tell you. Now, my little minx, do not stand me up, 'cause Mama is expecting you, you big tramp. See?

I am,
Your Mazie

6. J. R. to M. W.

["Earl": apparently Earl Carroll, a theatrical producer, who wished to star Miss West. The "new play" which Riddell refers to is evidently "Diamond Lil."—Ada Rehan: an actress.

From the last sentence, incidentally, it is to be inferred that Riddell never took advantage of Miss West's invitation extended in the above letter.]

2 August 1928

My Dream Girl,

Last night I saw you in the new play. Without you, it would be a faintly amusing caricature of Chatham Square in the 'nineties —a rather tawdry melodrama. With you, it becomes important, curious, alive. You move with such a fascinating wiggle inside those dainty corsets; oh my Dear, never *never* NEVER let Earl take you out of them and star you in one of his tawdry revues. When you move those lovely great big round eyes of yours, I can scarcely keep from shouting: Ada Rehan! If I ever meet you, I shall tell you it is *Art*. All my love.

Riddy

7. M. W. to J. R.

["The show" is "Pleasure man," Miss West's current vehicle.]

22 September 1928

Dear Riddy,

O. K. about Art, big boy, but how's to get together some time? Won't you come around to my dressing-room tonight after the show? There's a jolly fire, and I've made some tea myself. Bless you, dear Brightness and snap into it.

I am,

YOUR MAISIE-WAISIE

8. *M. W. to J. R.*

[*Tony's: Tony Pastor's, now demolished.*]

23 September 1928

Dear Rid,

Oh, you dear little Darling, where the h—ll were you last night? I should sit alone in my dressing-room like a G—d d—mn fool, brewing tea. I's 'fraid oo forgot all about ickle me. Well, I'll forgive my dear little stupid Goose this time. Ring if you will meet me at Tony's tonight and tell me about Art. Don't forget, now, or mama will give you a poke on your teentsie-weentsie nose. Know what I mean, my great big beautifullest boudoir man?

Your Mae

9. *M. W. to J. R.*

3 July 1930

Dearie,

I'm here at my apartment, all alone, with my hair down. Come at once.

Passionately,

M.

10. *J. R. to M. W.*

[*The following letter, of which we present only a few brief excerpts, was evidently written by John Riddell while on a bicycle trip through Surrey (now Yonkers).—Effie: Miss Effie Simpkins (now Mrs. John Riddell).*]

7 July 1930

Oh, dear, dear, *dearest* Mae,

. . . I am so happy, and I know you will understand and be happy for me. These past few summer days Effie and I have biked through these beautiful hills together. I know she is not good enough for me, my Dear, but she *does* know how to ride a bicycle rather better than well, and I suppose I love her. At any rate, I think I shall let her marry me. What does your loving wisdom say to it?

J. R.

11. *M. W. to J. R.*

[This is what her "loving wisdom" said to it.]

9 July 1930

Listen, big boy, is hims by any chance trying to give his ickle Maisie-Waisie the run-around? Just what the h—ll is baby trying to pull off, anyhow? Does hims think him can't be had? Who is this Effie dame? If I ever catch you trying to stand me up, you lousy little ——
[The rest of this letter, through excessive heat, unfortunately caught fire and burned to a crisp.—Ed.]

12. *COHEN, O'BRIEN, LIPSCHITZ AND AUGEN-BRAUENER, ATTYS.-AT-LAW, TO J. R.*

[Here there appears to be another brief gap in the correspondence.]

16 August 1930

Dear Mr. Riddell,
Our client, Miss Mae West, has just turned over to us a collection of love-letters from you, representing a correspondence with her over a number of years. If you do not make a satisfactory settlement in exchange for these letters, we shall be forced to publish the entire contents at once.
Please let us know your terms at the earliest possible convenience.

Very truly yours,
COHEN, O'BRIEN, LIPSCHITZ
and AUGENBRAUENER

13. *J. R. to COHEN, O'BRIEN, LIPSCHITZ and AUGENBRAUENER, ATTYS.-AT-LAW*

19 August 1930

Dear Sirs,
My terms are ten percent of the royalties.

Very truly yours,
John Riddell

THE WORKS

By NATHAN ASCH

HE MET HER AT A PARTY. HE HAD COME LATE, AND IN THE KITCHEN there was an enormous and very drunken politician, boasting how his man had been elected senator and how he had the electoral votes of his state sewed up in his pocket. A tiny woman was perched on the kitchen stool yelling, "You can't use that kind of language in front of me!" Many people were leaving. He saw this girl standing alone in the passageway between the kitchen and the living room, her eyes shining brightly, expectantly, as if she had had one or two drinks and, not being used to drinking, thought something was about to happen. Their eyes met, and he felt stirred and a little sorry for her. He said to her, "Let's get out of here."

They drove across to Virginia, holding hands, and went to the Dance Barbecue; they watched sailors and girls; they stared down at the beer rings on the table while a girl near them accused another of having stolen five dollars. They discovered that both worked for the government, she as the secretary of an important administrator, he as a statistician. They left the Barbecue still holding hands. He drove very fast along the Potomac, through Alexandria, shimmering with white walls, past the woods lining the Mount Vernon Highway. As they were coming back, the sky turned to pink, the sun rose beyond the Monument; Washington shone with rooftops, was bright green with trees. She had a lovely profile. She withdrew her hand from his, looked at him with smiling, all-encompassing eyes, and shook her head. No, she didn't want any breakfast.

That afternoon, before leaving his office, he called her up. They had dinner together that night and afterward went to a movie. He found himself wondering how old she was and what he really thought of her. He still wondered the following evening, when he had dinner at her house. The girls she lived with were away for the night. There were silver candlesticks on the dining-room table, there was a uniformed maid, there was roast beef. She looked beautiful and young in the candlelight. She talked about her childhood: she had had a miserable, poverty-stricken time, with a mother determined her daughter would not have to suffer all her life, too. "My mother lived only to see me pass the Civil Service examination," she said. She spoke very little about the years since she had come to Washington; instead, she seemed to be under some compulsion to talk of the earlier years, of the father who had abandoned them, of her mother's illness, of the bedrooms with light housekeeping in Seattle, Portland, San Francisco, Los Angeles. She gave him coffee and brandy, and told him of a winter when she and her mother had subsisted almost solely on oranges. She had passed the examination, but while she was waiting for the appointment her mother had died, and her mother's share of the fare to Washington had been used instead for funeral expenses.

She asked him if he wanted her to play Gilbert and Sullivan, but he said no, not tonight. They sat for a long while holding hands, he thinking about his own uneventful childhood and she watching him.

Jerry, his chief in the research division, invited him to a picnic that Sunday, and he asked her did she want to come? She worried whether Jerry's wife would like her. She carried a large cardboard box from one of Washington's best caterers: she wore a ribbon around her hair, short socks, sneakers, and looked like a little girl. Jerry's wife liked her very much, insisted on sitting beside her, and the two began an intimate conversation that lasted until they got to Chesapeake Bay. Jerry's children stared at her. When he and Jerry went off to gather firewood, Jerry said, "That's a fine girl. I like her very much."

They had steaks roasted on charcoal, and *pâté-de-foie-gras* sandwiches from the caterer's box. The children ate up all the fancy cookies. Afterward he and she wandered off under a tree, and he fell asleep with his head on her lap. When he woke up it was getting dark, and when he looked up at her, her eyes were shining with tears.

The next morning, Jerry's wife called him. She said, "I like that girl. She's fine and serious." She invited the two of them to dinner. He said he was sorry, he had to go to New York. "Oh," she said, "Jerry hadn't told me." He said it wasn't on an office matter; Jerry didn't know.

Jerry said, "All right. If you want to go." The time off would be deducted from his annual leave. He went to New York, to the research foundation, his old office. Everybody was excited about the research fellowships to South America. When he asked the director if there was any chance of his being considered, he was told with a grin to keep on living off the government, out of the public trough.

He had dinner with his parents and told his mother he was going back to Washington that night. He went instead to a hotel; the next morning he took the subway to the Battery and slowly walked up Broadway. About noon he stopped in at a movie house and saw part of a feature. Twice he stopped to eat. In the evening he reached Van Cortlandt Park. He went to a drugstore and he called her up. She said, "Are you really calling from New York?" He said, "Yes. May I come to see you?" She said, "Please come."

It was too late to fly back. He arrived by train at an early morning hour, rushed the taxi through dark Washington streets. Her front door was open; by the time he reached it she appeared in the doorway, holding out her hand. When he took her in his arms she went limp all over.

She said, "We'll share everything, our thoughts and our hours. We'll become as one. We'll be so intertwined nobody will ever be able to tell us apart."

After that they seemed to be always together. He would call for her every evening and after dinner they would go for a drive, or they would return to her house and sit for hours listening to the radio. Weekends they went on picnics, they swam in hotel pools, they went cruising in Chesapeake Bay, they danced on the terrace at the edge of Rock Creek Park. She would telephone him every day at four; she had developed the habit of calling him just before he started checking the official figures for the day. She would say, "It's me." He would picture her, dark hair and very dark eyes, the receiver pressed tightly to her ear, her mouth half-open with eagerness. He would say, "Is it *really* you?" She would answer,

"Yes," and hang up. His assistant would notice his smile and smile back, and he would mentally shake his head to clear it and stare down hard at the checking list.

She took him to Maryland to her administrator's house. The servants greeted her affectionately, and when the administrator came down, he quickly walked up to her, took both her hands in his, and said, underlining each word, "*How are you?*" as if he hadn't seen her only two hours before. The three of them had dinner on the veranda, did not light the lights, but sat until very late. She remained silent, peering intently in the darkness from one man to the other while they talked.

She was a close friend of several women in diplomatic circles, and he began to receive invitations to embassy garden parties. He wore striped pants to these affairs and she wore lace and a floppy hat. There was music and there was champagne, and sometimes an important official would smilingly ask her, "Can you spare him for a moment?" and would take him aside to say, "I am very much interested in the work your office is doing. I hear you are the bright young man over there."

He saw none of his old friends except Jerry and his wife. But Jerry told him one day that at the end of this job he'd probably be sent on a job to South America, that there was strong pressure being exerted to have him sent there. Apparently some of his new acquaintances were taking an active interest in his welfare. He began to think of getting married and settling in the government service, and whenever she and he would pass a real-estate development they would stop and inspect the exhibition house.

One day he told her excitedly, "You know, down at the office we've at last collected enough data to tell what is happening. I think I'll start doing my report." She said, "That's wonderful. We'll only see each other twice a week." The next day she sent him an elaborate desk set by messenger. That night he said, "When you're not with me, just forget about me. Go out and have a good time." She said, "Do you think I could?"

He sat at home in a maze of figures, trying not to think of her. The telephone rang. She said, "I'm sorry. I feel your work isn't going very well. Can I help somehow?" He said, "I'm not working. I'm just wasting my time. Let's go driving instead."

They went for a drive through Virginia, headlights scanning the receding road, tall, ghostly trees flying back on both sides. She told him again about her unhappy childhood; in a voice that seemed not meant for him alone but that filled the entire car, she described her early life on the West Coast, her mother ill—trying to manage a Seattle rooming house, trying to hide her cough, while the man from the real-estate office had said, "If you can't collect the rent, we'll get somebody who can." She had then been a little girl of ten, but her mother had been too weak to climb stairs, and she had climbed them, knocked on doors, and demanded the room rent.

Before he said good night to her, he told her, "You know I would much rather spend the time with you, but I'm trying now to write a report. No one can help me. I'll have to fight it out alone. Please try not to call when we have no date." She looked like a little girl who was being punished and said in a whisper, "I promise. I won't."

The following night she called him, in what seemed almost an official voice, and told him that an invited guest had sent last-minute regrets to a diplomatic dinner and the hostess insisted that he fill in. She said, "I know how you feel, but you can't refuse." He said, "Of course I can't refuse."

She watched him from across the table through the dinner, even seemed to follow the movement of food to his mouth. Going home in the car, she kept silent, but just before they reached her home she said, "If you want, I won't see you for a week."

He took her in his arms and kissed her, and she burst into tears. He parked the car and consoled her for a long time, but she continued to weep and continued to insist she would not see him for a week.

The following evening all the figures fitted so well together that he became deeply absorbed. When he finally rose from his table it was too late to call her. He determined to send her flowers, but in the morning he forgot. Instead he called his office to say he was not coming in, and he worked at home through the day and all night. When he had finished, he was too excited to sleep. He took a shower and went to the office. He had decided to surprise her by unexpectedly taking her out to dinner.

When he went home to dress, there was a telegram from her: "I NEVER WANT TO SEE OR HEAR FROM YOU AGAIN." He tried to call her but was told she was too ill to come to the phone. When he arrived at her house she sent word she did not want to see him. He forced his way into her room and found her in bed, looking pale and old, with rings under her eyes. He begged her to forgive him, talked to her for a long time until she relaxed and closed her eyes to sleep.

The following evening she wore a white evening gown and red roses. Everyone in the restaurant stared at her, and when he told her she was beautiful, she said, "I'm beautiful for you. I love you." They danced until the orchestra stopped playing. She sat huddled against him in the car going back and she seemed not to breathe until they reached her house.

For several nights he tried to get ahead with his report. There were almost always phone calls and letters from her, and when there weren't, he could not concentrate for thinking of her. She had become very friendly with Jerry's wife and frequently visited at Jerry's. Finally he telephoned Jerry's wife one day and said, "Please talk to her. I love her, but she gives me too much of herself. There is too much emotion. She must learn to let me alone sometimes."

Jerry's wife said, "I think you ought to marry her."

He said, "I feel as if she were forcing me to at the point of a gun."

"What will probably happen," Jerry's wife said, "is that someday you will find her dead on your doorstep, a gun in her hand."

One evening a messenger brought him a thick envelope from her containing about forty pages in beautiful handwriting. The letter began, "Dearest, I can't sleep." It contained an analysis of herself, of him, and of their relationship. "We're on a turbulent stream, my darling, being pulled by a current and sucked by an undertow. We're amidst shoals and rocks, and I know you think we're about to strike at any moment and be wrecked. But, my love, I promise you, there is clear water ahead." Further along in the letter there were long paragraphs about her childhood, passages about her father. "I wish I could explain to you about my father. I remember particularly how I was always afraid that he would come home. Even now, when the bell rings and I'm not expecting anyone, I get cold at the thought that it might be he."

He put the half-read letter on his desk and went to bed. But he could not sleep. He lay a long time, then the black of night became a nightmare and he woke up cold with sweat. He rose and, still in the dark, he found the draft of the report he was working on. He held it in one hand. With the other he found her letter and threw it in the waste-basket. He dropped a lighted match after it, watched the flames consume the letter, and then he went back to bed and fell asleep.

Two weeks later, Jerry's wife called him and said, "You'd better go to see her. She is very sick." He went with a large box of flowers. When the nurse would not let him in, he felt relieved. He went to tell the florist to send her flowers daily and on the way he stopped off at a café for a drink.

The diplomatic circles forgot him and he dropped back into his old life. He went to several parties; he took a girl home. He rode up in the elevator at the bureau with Jerry's wife, and she cut him dead. Jerry spoke to him only on pressing business and never looked him in the eyes.

He began to feel bored with Washington, and he wondered whether he should resign and get a job in New York again. He heard she was going to Florida to recuperate and he telephoned to her to say goodbye. They found very little to talk about. She spoke mainly about her coming trip. She said, "Thank you for having found time to call me up."

After that he saw her only once more. Some time before he went back to New York, on a Saturday afternoon, he stopped his car at a red light on Connecticut Avenue. He saw her standing on the corner, waiting for the light to change. She was dressed in gray and she looked middle-aged. Their eyes met and with an effort he waved, and she waved back. In a moment the light turned to green and he drove away. He had gone a block or two before he thought that maybe he should have offered her a lift.

FAREWELL TO MUSCLE MOLLS

By Paul Gallico

FOR ALL HER OCCASIONAL BEAUTY AND UNQUESTIONED COURAGE, there has always been something faintly ridiculous about the big-time lady athletes. They never manage entirely to escape a vague hint of burlesque about the entire business. A generation ago they were funny in a mild way because they tried to play competitive games and at the same time retain their maidenly modesty. Today they manage to be amusing for exactly the opposite reason; they play with complete abandon and exposure, and as if that were not enough, the mores and morals of the times have made possible deliciously frank and biological discussions in the columns of the newspapers as to whether this or that famous woman athlete should be addressed as "Miss," "Mrs.," "Mr.," or "It."

Miss Helen Stephens, a big, rangy schoolgirl from Mississippi, out-galloped all the best women sprinters of the world in the hundred meters at the late Olympic Games in Berlin, including Poland's favorite, Stella Walsh. The Poles, with that sterling if peculiar sportsmanship for which Europe is famous, immediately accused Miss Stephens of being Mr. Stephens. There had been two cases, one in Czechoslovakia and one in England, where a masculine lady had, with the aid of a surgeon, succeeded in transforming herself into a not too feminine gentleman. The Poles thought they had spotted number three.

The situation was already full of laughter, but it remained for the awe-inspiring papas of the Amateur Athletic Union to supply the topper to it. Were they caught unprepared? They were not. They revealed solemnly that before being permitted to board the boat to uphold the honor of the U.S.A. as a member of its Olympic team the Olympic Committee had had La Stephens frisked for sex and had checked her in as one hundred per cent female. With no thought whatsoever for the feelings of the young lady in question, these findings were triumphantly if ungallantly aired in the press. The laugh which had previously been confined to the squawking Poles now rippled far and wide to include the A.A.U. and, I am afraid, lady athletes in general. Somehow there seems to be a rather far-reaching and complete criticism of the muscle moll *per se* when, immediately a lady succeeds in sprinting a hundred meters in 11.4 seconds, a world's record for girls, she is suspected of being a man. The men do the same distance in 10.3.

But laughter or no laughter, the girls have always made good copy and I am duly grateful. For the last time, a little sentimental and regretful, I take the reviewing stand and watch pass the parade of the lady athletes.

Here come the golf gals in their rough, tweedy clothes, with a sturdy stride, hips and shoulders a-swing. Their faces are weathered, their skin tanned and dried by sun and wind, and most of them have little tiny lines around the eyes from squinting down glaring fairways and measuring and calculating distances. Some of the huskier ones can wallop the ball 230 yards on the drive, but the woman's game is played on or around the greens. They are usually short on their second shots and have to rely upon chipping close to the hole for their pars. Listen closely and you will hear their marching song: "Meow. . . . Meow!" Golf is a funny game. If there is any larceny in a man, golf will bring it out. The game is a natural reagent for the cattiness that is in woman.

Next the tennis ladies, some in shorts, a garment that, anatomically, they were never meant to wear; smarter ones in short, graceful, pleated half-skirts. Yes, they have those eye lines too, from peering steadfastly across the net, awaiting service, and they have a little forward lean as they walk, stepping on the balls of their feet. Look at the shoulders on them, the forearms and the legs. Those legs! The quick stops and starts and the running do knot up the muscles and make them hard and lumpy and do something to the knees, too.

Ah, the beauty chorus of women in sport, the swimmers and divers. Those close-fitting black swim-suits! And see that high-tower diver with the yellow hair in the pure white bathing-suit. Powerful shoulders they all have, those water maidens, but their muscles are long, smooth, and flat. Some of the older ones are a little broad in the beam, a trifle hippy, but it makes them more buoyant. Too bad about those dogs. Refrain—all little swimmers have big feet. Never saw a good lady swimmer with small feet. There are some lovely faces in the ranks, though. A lot of them are merely children too. They catch them young. Somehow I am enormously tickled by the thought of a yellow-haired tadpole by the name of Mary Hoerger who at the age of eleven was national springboard champion, but who when she had attained the ripe and passé age of twelve suffered from an attack of nerves and failed even to place on the 1936 Olympic team. But at that, the event in Berlin turned out to be a triumph for veterans. It was won by a Marjorie Gestring, also of the United States, aged thirteen.

Oh, oh! The female track athletes, the runners, leapers, hurdlers, and throwers. Flat-chested, most of them with close-cropped hair. Not much on looks either. Most of them have hard faces. And those legs! Talk about your tennis girls, take a look at those sprinters. The track girls can wear those bias-cut shorts and shirts because they are not built or muscled like women, most of them. Only a man can wear a running-suit to advantage—or a woman constructed like a man.

Here is the minor sports division, the skaters, the fencers, the squash-players, the skiers, the field-hockey players, and the oars-women. What lovely legs and bodies those figure-skaters have! And how well those graceful skating-costumes show them off! Pity so many of those girl fencers *will* wear bloomers or knickers. But ski-clothes and flying-togs were made for women. There are those knotty muscles on the squash-players again. And what is it that could possibly want to make a girl sit in an eight-oared shell or barge and row?

The freaks bring up the rear guard. A pitiful crew, the female boxers, wrestlers, and ball-players. Most of them are toughies and exhibitionists. For the most part they have ugly bodies, hard faces, cheap minds. . . .

A strange, almost fantastic crew, all right, these muscle molls, especially the pretty ones. But sexless and unattractive, all of them? Not a bit of it. They have a definite glamour, these top-flight swimmers, divers, skaters, fencers, tennis-players, golfers, and fliers, a strong physical attraction.

As people, most of them are poor specimens, jealous, petty, spiteful, often bad-mannered, spoiled, frequently stupid, wretched sports, dull and self-centered, and yet withal gay and exciting, brave and absolutely game. They are, for that matter, gamer than most men, bear pain and discomfort better; and when they get their teeth into any kind of match, it is something to see.

The greatest girl or woman athlete that ever lived, certainly the greatest of our time, was an exceptional person as well as a great performer. She is Gertrude Ederle, the daughter of a German-American delicatessen-store proprietor, who on August 6, 1926, swam the English Channel from France to England, in 14 hours and 31 minutes, and was the first woman ever to accomplish this feat. She had made an attempt the year before and failed. She went back to it again and succeeded. No other woman athlete in any line of sport has ever come close to this performance as a demonstration of skill, stamina, courage, and indomitable will. Seven British girls have since swum the Channel, but none of them within an hour of Miss Ederle's time. And it must always be remembered that Trudy was the first. She softened it up for the others.

There is perhaps no athletic effort quite so useless and pointless as the swimming of the English Channel, and perhaps, too, no gesture in all sports equally gallant with the one made by this simple, brown-haired, round-faced storekeeper's daughter who learned her swimming in the tiny, tiled indoor pool of the Women's Swimming Association on the East Side. She made up her mind to do something that no girl had ever done before—beat the rip tides, cross-currents, and bruising, chopping waves of the world's stormiest, trickiest channel. It was also, I suspect, one of the few purely unselfish acts in the history of feminine sport. The girl wanted to do something for her Swimming Association—to make it famous.

And furthermore, she accomplished this feat alone. There were no cheering crowds to stimulate her, nothing but an accompanying tugboat carrying her sister, a few friends and newspaper reporters, and a hostile French captain who would have been glad to see the girl fail because she was an American. Her opponent was an insensate body of water that could be expected neither to tire nor to quit. Her opponent was also herself. The entire measure of difference between failure and success lay within herself. She had only to call out and she would have been lifted out of the water immediately.

Once, during the darkest hour, when the nasty, gray, choppy waves had battered her apparently to the limit of human endurance, when, for a time, for every yard she gained with her threshing crawl the tide and the cross-currents threw her back two, a friend on the escorting tug leaned over the side and asked her whether she wanted to quit. The girl rolled over on her side, lifted her face, quite blue with cold, out of the water, and called back: "What for?" She was just that simple and earnest. As long as she was conscious she would go on. She won her bitter fight, and paid for the winning of it. The battering she took about the head from the waves permanently affected her hearing.

Her backers implored her to return immediately. Instead she went to pay a visit to her grandmother in a little village in Germany. New York was sports mad at the time she accomplished her feat, and no woman in modern times was ever accorded the hero's welcome that this girl received when she finally did return from the other side. Thousands of harbor craft tied their whistles down when her liner came steaming up the bay, where she was met and taken off by the Mayor's Welcoming Committee boat, with Grover Whalen in charge, plug hat, gardenia, and all. She was paraded up Broadway then through miles of cheering crowds and showered from the canyon walls of the skyscrapers with Broadway confetti,—ticker tape and shredded telephone books and newspapers.

And yet of all the hundreds of girl athletes who have attained fame and publicity she was the only one I knew who remained completely unspoiled by publicity, adulation, and flattery. Her financial affairs upon her return to the United States were badly handled. She might have acquired a small fortune in personal appearances, indorsements, newspaper articles, and so on. The opportunities were wasted and lost, and besides, while she was in Germany, another woman swam the Channel, an English mother, and it took some of the edge off Trudy's performance. She was never bitter. She never complained. She was never rude or snobbish. She clung, almost pathetically, to the friends of the days before she was famous. She was never at any time anything but a simple, unassuming, wholly lovable person. She had become a professional as the result of her swim. She stuck to it and took a job as a swimming instructress and is working at it today. She never trades upon her past reputation or expects anything because of what she did. Deafness and other injuries suffered during her swimming career—she hurt her back and spent eight months in a plaster cast—have only sweetened her temper. There never has been a girl athlete like her.

The best all-around woman performer the country has ever known, was a hard-bitten, hawk-nosed, thin-mouthed little hoyden from Texas by the name of Mildred Didrikson, but her nickname was Babe. She was the sensation of the 1932 Olympic Games at Los Angeles, in which she won two events, the hurdle race and the javelin throw, and she should have won a third, the high jump, but was heckled out of it by officials who objected to her style. But in addition to being able to run, jump, and throw the javelin better than any other girl in the world at that time, Mildred could also play basketball, tennis, pool and billiards, swim, golf in the eighties, throw a baseball and a football, and also be pretty handy with her mitts when the occasion presented itself. Actually, there was no sport at which she could not perform better than average for a girl. She was the muscle moll to end all muscle molls, the complete girl athlete. Apparently she didn't have another thought in her head but sport. She was a tomboy who never wore make-up, who shingled her hair until it was as short as a boy's and never bothered to comb it, who didn't care about clothes and who despised silk underthings as being sissy. She had a boy's body, slim, straight, curveless, and she looked her best in a track suit. She hated women and loved to beat them. She was not, at that time, pretty. Her lips were thin and bloodless, with down showing on the upper one, and she had a prominent Adam's apple. She had good, clear, gray-green eyes, but she was what is commonly described at hatchet-faced. She looked and acted more like a boy than a girl, but she was in every respect a wholesome, normal female. She was as tough as rawhide leather. And yet, too, she was one of the loneliest and most appealing characters of all the more prominent girl athletes and perhaps one of the easiest to understand. I always thought that she became the greatest all-around athlete in the country simply because she would not or could not compete with women at their own and best game—man-snatching. It was an escape, a compensation. She would beat them at everything else they tried to do. And she did. You could see what was driving her in her intense dislike and contempt for all things feminine, rouge and powder, hairdressers, pretty clothes, silks and satins, and the women who made use of them. She lumped them all as sissy. Beyond her ability in sports she had no personal vanity whatsoever. And nothing pleased her so much as to walk up to a girl against whom she was scheduled to compete and state succinctly: "Ah'm gonna lick yuh tomorrow." And then deliver.

A curious but quite understandable change came over Babe Didrikson. Shortly after the Olympic Games in '32 she ran afoul of one of the trick amateur rules and was declared a professional. And as a professional she made considerable money touring the country, giving exhibitions. She acquired a manager and became even more of a celebrity than she had ever been before. And being a famous person suddenly, she began to attract men a little more. Ugly duckling that she was, she had acquired that strange and inexplicable glamour that apparently is a part of every great woman athlete.

And the last time I saw Mildred, the Texas Babe, she was an ugly duckling no longer. It was at the Men's National Open Golf Championship at Pittsburgh. The tomboy had vanished. Her hair had grown out and it had a stylish permanent wave. There was a touch of rouge on her cheeks and red at her lips. She wore an attractive sports ensemble and had a purse to match, with her initials on it. Inside the purse were compact and lipstick, tiny lace handkerchief and comb and all the rest of the first-aid kit to repair feminine ravages. I looked at her and grinned and she knew what I was grinning at. She said: "Yeah, and Ah got silk on underneath and Ah like it." She had come into her woman's birthright by a curiously devious route, but she had got there, which, I imagine, was more than she ever expected.

With but few exceptions, lady athletes are wretched sports. This is generally admitted throughout the sports world, even by the girls themselves, and cited as an example of just going to show. But the girls are not deliberately bad sports, nor can it be said that they do not know what good sportsmanship is. It is just that at all times they are women and no woman ever plays fair in any kind of competition against another woman if she can help it, and usually she cannot. It isn't instinctive with them, and above all it isn't practical. Man's competitive spirit derives from a desire to play, to be gregarious, to show off, perhaps to express himself. Woman's competitive instincts are rooted much deeper than that. They spring from the necessity to survive, to perpetuate herself. Women simply are psychologically unable to approach a contest of any kind from the same angle that a man does. Whether it happens to be golf, tennis, or squash makes no particular difference. It is still competition and the girls are not geared to take it. You can, with patience and training, teach some of them to lose with good grace, but you can never make them like it. It is quite true that nobody really likes to lose and that men as well as women often have to swallow something and set their faces into the prescribed cheerful masks of the good loser before they trot over to shake hands. But the ladies bear grudges afterwards, have alibis, and make remarks. No man ever takes a game as seriously as a woman does. And a man views his opponent with complete personal detachment. He represents a temporary problem and nothing more. A man will brood upon the forthcoming contest if it is of sufficient importance, but once it is over, win or lose, he forgets it, and the man against whom he has played is no longer an opponent, but simply another person to be liked or disliked for his social qualities. It is only an exceptional woman athlete who is able to be that impersonal about someone against whom she has played. The unspoken enmity between Helen Hull Jacobs and Helen Wills Moody is an interesting case in point. It is common knowledge that there is no love lost between them. For years Mrs. Moody barred Miss Jacobs's path to the championship and the fame that goes with it, such as it is. And for the same years Miss

Jacobs was Mrs. Moody's most dangerous rival. Sport and the love of both for the game of tennis have failed completely to bring them close together. Neither has been able to see in the other anything but a danger to ambition—in short, an enemy from whom no quarter was to be expected at any time. The girls don't forget and they don't forgive.

As has been suggested, women golfers seem to be the worst sports and the cattiest of all the strenuous sisters, but they are run neck and neck for honors by the figure-skaters, with tennis-players in third place. The girl swimmers seem to be the best-mannered and the best sportswomen of the lot. I have seen a girl swimmer awarded first place in a meet—it was an Olympic trial, and the place meant a lot—march up to the referee and heard her say: "I'm sorry, but I know I wasn't third. I saw Joan touch me out. I came in fourth." And she meant it. As much cannot be said for the male coaches of the female swimmers, and the mothers of the girls.

Unattractive girls are usually comparatively good sports. Pretty girls are not. This might be simply enough explained. An attractive woman hates to be made to look bad, and no one looks his or her best taking a licking at anything. The ugly ducklings, having taken to sport as an escape and to compensate for whatever it is they lack, sex appeal, charm, ready-made beauty, usually are too grateful to be up there in the championship flight to resent losing so much. The pretty ones go into high-pressure sports competi-tion because—because—well, I'm damned if I know why they do.

The figure-skaters in their lovely ballet costumes and the swim-mers in their bathing-suits manage to look attractive at all times, but there is no girl living who can manage to look anything but awful during the process of some strenuous game played on a hot day, particularly when she is tired, winded, perspiring, and losing. The tennis ladies bend over double, trying to catch their breaths and blow out of O-shaped mouths like netted fish. Their wet blouses cling damply and stickily to them, their faces get beet-red and glow like incandescent lamps. Their hair invariably escapes from the bandeau and looks frowsy.

If there is anything more dreadful æsthetically or more depress-ing than the fatigue-distorted face of a girl runner at the finish

line, I have never seen it unless it was a little lady I watched once
in a series of prizefights arranged for ambitious girl pugilists in a
New York taxi dance-hall. The girl had been rapped on her chin
a little harder than was good for her and she proceeded to come
all apart at the seams and stagger glassy-eyed, with sagging jaw
and wispy, drooping hair, like an old charwoman on a bender.
And then there were the two lady wrestlers who started out to
give a refined exhibition, forgot their lines, lost their tempers, and
went at it in real earnest, two viragos in a filthy brawl. And once,
too, I saw what was left of a girl after she had spattered her red
airplane and herself all over a potato patch during an air race. The
girl golfers should see themselves when they squat down on the
green and screw up their faces into a series of corrugations to
study a put, or when they waggle before a drive. They are imi-
tating men and they just look silly. Not that men ever were any
bargains æsthetically while at play and in the last stages of exhaus-
tion. But that doesn't alter the fact that women, because of their
sex, look twice as bad and ought to know better.

But courage? Not the courage it takes to accept a beating gracefully and finally, but physical courage and ability to overcome
pain and physical discomfort and carry on. Nothing can beat them
on two or four legs. When it comes to gameness they can look
any man in the eye—and very often pass him. I seem to remember
a girl diver in a springboard competition. The dive was being held
in water that was too shallow for the purpose. Before the start,
one of the men went off in a practice dive. The water began to
turn red before he came up, and when he did, one hand was
crimson where he had gashed it on a piece of broken bottle. The
girl diver was standing on the board waiting to do her practice
dive. The man swam in and was taken away for first aid. The girl
did her dive and so did the rest of them. I have seen a girl skater
in a mile race trip and fall on the first lap, gash her leg on a skate,
get up, set out after the pack, and win. There was the high-tower
diver who had hurt herself. A physician told her that if she did
another dive before allowing the injury time to heal, there was
every chance that she would break her neck. She thanked him
and then went on up the thirty-foot tower and took off because
it was in the middle of a competition and she couldn't think of

stopping. When you find a real fighter in a girl, it is something to see if only as an exhibition and demonstration of pure bulldog tenacity. Molla Mallory used to be like that. She would get her teeth into a tennis match and refuse to let go.

It is a pity, with all the effort, the publicity, and the acclaim, that actually, none of the girls can be taken seriously at their games, because, always excepting the amazing Miss Joyce Wethered, the English golf star, who could keep pace with the men and was the only woman I ever knew who could, they are at best second-rate imitations of the gentlemen. Miss Didrikson was unquestionably a great all-around girl athlete, the best in the world in her day, but any first-class high-school track man could easily have beaten her at any of her events. Mrs. Moody would be lucky to take two games from a player like Ellsworth Vines or Tilden. A man has swum a hundred yards in fifty-two seconds. A girl takes one minute and three seconds for the same distance, and so it goes. No matter how good they are, they can never be good enough, quite, to matter.

BEAT ME, POST-IMPRESSIONIST DADDY

By S. J. PERELMAN

ANY OF YOU KIDS SEEN SOMERSET MAUGHAM? I HAVEN'T RUN INTO him lately, but I'll bet those advertisements for "The Moon and Sixpence" put the roses in his cheeks. In case you've been spending the last couple of weeks underwater, the Messrs. Loew and Lewin have just transferred to the screen Mr. Maugham's novel of the ordeal of Charles Strickland, a character closely resembling Paul Gauguin. Faced with merchandising so spiritual a problem, the producers evidently recalled that Vincent van Gogh had been popularized as a man who mailed his ear to a friend, and decided to sell their boy on a similar basis. The leitmotiv of the campaign was a busty Polynesian hussy in a pitifully shrunken sarong, lolling on her back in considerable abandon and smelling a flower. Peering out of a palm tree above, mighty lak a chimp, was George Sanders in the best beard that money could buy. "I DON'T WANT LOVE! I hate it!" he was declaring petulantly. "It interferes with my work . . . and yet . . . *I'm only human!*" A second advertisement portrayed the painter in an equally disenchanted mood, over the caption "WOMEN ARE STRANGE LITTLE BEASTS! You can treat them like dogs (*he did!*)—beat them 'til your arm aches (*he did*) . . . and still they love you (*they did*). But in the end they'll get you and you are helpless in their hands."

Although Gauguin's journal, "Avant et Après," and his correspondence with D. de Montfreid are fairly blue in spots, he is not primarily remembered as passion's plaything, and these insinuations may confound the straitlaced. Now that Hollywood has thrown the ball into play, however, the following letters I recently unearthed in my bottom bureau drawer deserve careful scrutiny. They were written by the artist to my father's barber, who lived in the bureau between 1895 and 1897. Here and there I have taken

191

the liberty of translating the rather difficult argot into current idiom, for clarity.

MATAIÉA, JULY 17, 1896

DEAR MARCUS,

Well, my old, you must think I am a fine *pascudnick* indeed not to answer you before this, but man is born to trouble as the sparks fly upward and I am winging. The day after I wrote you, who should come mousing around but that little brunette, Tia, in her loose-leaf pareu, which it's enough to melt the umber on a man's palette. It so happened I was in the hut with this tall job from Papeete, dashing off a quick pastel. I told Tia to stop needling me, but she was inconsolable. Distraught, I asked what she required. "Poi," she responded. Poi is one thing I have never refused anybody yet, Marcus, so, brushing off this other head, I made with the poi. The instant we were alone, the pretty trickster revealed her design. "I'm a strange little beast!" she cried. "Beat me 'til your arm aches!" Me, a family man. *Figurez-vous*, Marcus, what could I do? I bounced her around a bit, knocked out several of her teeth, and invited her to withdraw, as I had to complete a gouache by five o'clock. *Dame!*—the next thing I knew, Miss Goody Two-shoes had sealed the door, swallowed the key [*clef*], and I was it.

As to the painting, it goes very slowly. Kindest thanks for your new calendar, which arrived in good condition. Personally, the model is somewhat skinny for my taste and there is too much drapery, but *tiens*, that is the bourgeois style. Tell me more about that youth, the son of your patron. The boy has genius, Marcus; I have an instinct for these things. Mark me well, he will yet be another Piero della Francesca.

I pinch your claws,

PAUL

MATAIÉA, NOVEMBER 12, 1896

DEAR MARCUS,

Life here becomes increasingly tiresome, my friend; the women refuse to let me alone. How I envy Vincent those days at Arles, with nothing between him and his muse but the solar spectrum.

I came to this miserable hole surfeited with civilization and its trinkets. One might as well be back in the Rue Vercingétorix. Last night I attended a native fête and, like a chump, neglected to close my door. Returning home about two with a charming person who insisted on seeing my frescoes, I found the wife of the Minister of Public Works concealed under the bed. The old story —I must beat her without further ado, treat her like a dog, else she will stop loving me. *Quelle bêtise!* My arms are so tired from flailing these cows that I can hardly mix my pigments. I sit down in a workingmen's café for an infusion; immediately I am surrounded by hordes of beauties begging me to maltreat them. I arise each morning determined to spend the day seriously. A pair of dark eyes at the window, a tender glance, and *pouf* [pouf] go my resolutions. After all, I'm only human.

I have a superb conception for a canvas which would be the very antithesis of Manet's "Olympia"—a native girl stretched on the sofa, regarding the onlooker with a mixture of fear and coquetry. At this rate I shall never finish it. Every sketch I begin ends the same. I pose the model on a divan, run my hand lightly over her back to enhance the sheen—*au fond* I am a painter of highlights—and *zut*, we are off at a tangent. For the time, merely to block in the masses, I am using a rolled-up unbrella in lieu of a girl. Actually, an ironic comment on your modern woman—all ribs and cloth. Where are those big, jolly, upholstered girls one used to see?

One fault only I find with your letters: there are too many lacunae. You say your patron's son was surprised embracing his governess. *Et alors?* What ensued? You leave too much to the imagination. Describe the scene with greater fidelity. Send photograph if possible. In any event, I must have a photo of the governess, preferably in her chemise, for a composition I am engaged on. It is an airy caprice in the manner of Watteau, quite unlike my current things—the startled governess blushing profusely, repulsing yet yielding to a diminutive satyr. I call it "Tickled Pink." Don't misunderstand, mon copain. This is simply relaxation, a change of pace from everything else I'm doing.

As ever,

PAUL

MATAIÉA, MAY 3, 1897

DEAR MARCUS,

Epochal news! I have arrived! After years of scorn and obloquy, after a lifetime of abuse from academicians and the kept press, I have at last attained official recognition! It came in the person of Mme. Dufresnoy, wife of the new Governor General, just as I was at the lowest ebb of despair. Reconstruct the scene for yourself: I was pacing moodily before my easel, alone, forgotten, attempting to wring some inspiration from the four or five scantily clad houris grouped on the dias. Suddenly, the sound of carriage wheels, and enter a vision of loveliness, a veritable Juno. What fluid rhythm, what vibrations . . . and yet a touch of that coarseness I find so piquant—I trembled like a schoolboy! But the real surprise was still to come. Housed in this ravishing exterior is no sordid Philistine but a delicate, subtle spirit attuned to mine; in a word, a connoisseur. Tales of my work have percolated through her flunkies and plenipotentiaries, and she must see it instanter. In a trice, the details are arranged—I am to bring my best canvasses to the executive mansion next Tuesday for inspection. Only one cloud mars my bliss. As the house is being plastered, the view is to be held in Madame's boudoir, a pitifully small room which I fear is hardly adequate to exhibit the larger oils. Perdition! . . . but we shall make the best of it. I am in a frenzy of preparation, varnishing pictures, borrowing pomade for my hair, a hundred distractions—I must fly.

I embrace you, my dear fellow,

PAUL

P.S. One passage puzzled me in your last letter. How could your patron's son have penetrated to the landlady's room without climbing up the air-shaft? Curb his exuberance, I implore you, and do not fail to send me a snapshot of the landlady.

MATAIÉA, MAY 19, 1897

DEAR MARCUS,

My decision is irrevocable: I am through with painting. I have a new mission, the extermination of the official class and particularly its wives. After that, the monastery.

The betrayal was complete, catastrophic. I waited on Mme. Dufresnoy afire with plans—a house in the Avenue Matignon, a summer palace on the Bosphorus, a villa at Chantilly. I am received by my benefactress in a filmy black peignoir, eyes sparkling with belladonna. The room is plunged in shadow; she prefers (sweet tyrant) to examine the canvases by artificial light. I shrug at her eccentricity, swallow a *fine à l'eau* as a digestive, launch into a short preamble about my work. *Basta!* Suddenly we are in Stygian darkness and I am held in a clasp of iron. "Madame," I entreat, "let us at least sit down and talk this thing over." *Enfin*, she reluctantly disposed herself in my lap and we had just arrived at a rationale when the door flew open and the Governor General rushed in. I could have demolished the big tub of tripes with my small finger, but he was escorted by a band of *apaches*, armed to the teeth. I acquitted myself handily, nevertheless, and outside a discolored eye and a trifling compound fracture, emerged an easy victor. Thanks to Madame's intercession, I was given the most spacious room in the lockup and the assignment of whitewashing the walls. It is not painting, but working with new textures is good artistic discipline.

Your letters, as always, remain my constant solace. If I may presume on our friendship, though, please to omit all further references to that miserable little brat, your patron's son. I am not interested in his grimy amours, nor anybody else's, for that matter. I have had enough of the whole god-damned subject.

Eternally,

P. GAUGUIN

BAREFOOTED . . . UP TO HER CHIN

By H. ALLEN SMITH

STIFF COMPETITION PREVAILS AMONG THE YOUNG WOMEN WHO specialize in public disrobing. A girl who is willing to rip off her clothing in front of a thousand concupiscent males, then bump things provokingly at those males before flitting into the wings needs more than a pretty face to get along.

She needs, to be sure, a striking figure and she needs to be clever, not only in the physical act of undressing, but in her relations outside the theater or outside the club where she works. It is a rare thing, indeed, to find a stripper who has more intelligence than a backing-off lathe. If they have any sense before they come into the trade it goes away. Generally speaking, these girls are hard, tough-talking babes, with the social consciousness of the black widow spider. It is necessary that they exhibit something in the nature of a brain in their dealings with the public, so they hire one—not a very good one, but a brain anyway. They hire a press agent, who thinks up gags to get the strippers' pictures in the papers, who promotes interviews and who shows them how to feign sanity.

The girls stop at nothing short of mopery to get in the papers, mopery being the old English misdemeanor of exposing one's self in front of a blind man on a public highway.

The wheels of national defense had no more than started turning last year when Margie Hart, one of the top strippers, burst into print. Margie announced that she was sending out five thousand alluring photographs of herself to members of the National Guard who were then in camp.

Margie's press agent thought up this master stroke, and it even got her mentioned in *Time* magazine. Explaining her burst of patriotic fervor in a telephone conversation, Margie said:

"After all, I want to do my bit. These pictures of myself will be sent only to single men. I think every soldier should have a sweetheart back home to think about and I'd just as soon they were thinking about me. I would not send these pictures to any married men, as the married men will have pictures of their wives to think about—or should anyway."

The stunt didn't cost Margie any five thousand photographs. One batch of fifty was sent to Major General William N. Haskell, sixty-two-year-old commander of the 27th Division, New York National Guard. Each picture bore the simple inscription, "To My Buddy, Margie Hart." The general looked the package over and asked: "Who is this Margie Hart?" Someone told him she was a stripper. Whereupon he fired the package right back at her.

Most people know that the most famous of all the nude performers, Sally Rand, is a smart girl. I have been calling on Sally periodically for years, interviewing her backstage in theaters and night clubs or in hotels where she happens to be living. Every time I talk to her she works the conversation around to her dramatic aspirations. Sally would give her left—well, let us say her left index finger—to become an important actress on the legitimate stage.

For all her reputation as a coolheaded businesswoman, Sally is high strung, nervous, inordinately proud of her fame and given to fits of anger in which she has been known to scream piercingly. These angry demonstrations usually have a natural climax when, no matter what the provocation, Sally cries out in a voice redolent of ham, "I'll sue!"

And for all her fame as a sharp bargainer, she has been taken in again and again. She once bought a boxcar full of elegant statuary which, the man told her, was produced by the great sculptors of ancient Italy. She wrapped and stored the pieces in a barn on her California property against the day when she might own a castle. Then she found out that the statues of cherubim and crusaders and whiskered saints had all been stolen from a Middle Western cemetery.

Once I had an evening appointment to see Sally backstage at the Casa Mañana. Somehow I happened to develop a technical interest in a bottle of scotch and missed the date. On the next evening I walked into her dressing room. She was in a fury.

"You are no gentleman!" she shouted, hitching up her girdle. "You can't do this to me. I won't stand for it. Not one minute. I'll *sue* you!"

In a little while she was sitting down and talking about a play in which she hoped to make a Broadway appearance within the next six months.

On another day I called on Sally in her rooms at the Park Central and found her nervously plucking hairpins from her blond tresses.

"Pardon me from here to there," she said, "while I take my hair down. I'm sorry you came in on me like this, with my face bare of make-up. I don't mind if you see any other part of me bare, but not my face."

She had just finished a long tour with her own company of forty-seven performers, including six girls who stood over six feet. Sally organized this troupe in Texas after playing a personal engagement with Billy Rose's show. She picked the performers, designed the scenery and costumes, wrote the dialogue and part of the music. She directed the dances nad other musical numbers, then booked the show from Florida to Canada.

She was telling me all about her own efficiency, when a tall girl came into the room. Sally introduced her as "my secretary, Miss Davis." Miss Davis sat down, and I asked her some things about herself.

"Well," she said, "I worked in New York before I went back to Texas on a visit. I was in the Elihu Root law office. It is a very dignified place. But I don't know what's come over me. I went back to Fort Worth and I met Sally, and the next thing I knew I was her secretary and traveling all over creation and back.

"One night Sally phoned me at the hotel. We had these six tall girls, and one of them was 'Stuttering Sam.' We called her that because she stuttered. She had a death in the family and had to go home, so Sally called me over to the theater, and the next thing you know she's got me in the dressing-room slapping make-up on me and putting me in a long dress. Then she shoved me out on the stage with the five other tall girls, and there I was. If I may say so, that is a hell of a hop from the Elihu Root law office."

"You're happy, dear, aren't you?" put in Sally.

"Oh Lord, yes!" breathed Miss Davis.

Then Sally began her lament.

"Here I am," she said. "I've been in and out of the theater since I was thirteen years old. All those years I have been aiming at one thing—to be a great dramatic actress. I want to do something nice and sympathetic. But they are going to make a loose woman out of me if it kills me. I am destined to be a slattern or a hussy on the stage whether I like it or not. Lord, how I'd love to play Mary of Scotland!"

She was leaving the next day, she explained, for New England to do a series of plays on the straw-hat circuit. Her first engagement would be at Skowhegan in *The Passing of the Third Floor Back*.

"I am a slattern," said Sally, "who changes to a sweet and lovely girl. After that I open at Ogunquit in *They Knew What They Wanted*. I start out in that play as a San Francisco waitress. I am a sort of hussy, but a wholesome and positive character. I never let anyone get messy with me, if you know what I mean, except one fellow. This happens after I marry the old man. The young fellow is a rat. He takes me out. Then I have a baby."

She said that her third and final engagement would be at Provincetown in *White Cargo*.

"In this one," she explained, "I am a native who makes all the white men go native, if you know what I mean. When I first come on the stage I say, 'I am Tondelayo,' and when I say it I swarm all over you."

She sat brooding for a while, and I asked her about the movies.

"The most money I ever got for a single fan dance," she said, "was in a movie. I finished the assignment in one day, and they handed me a check for twenty thousand dollars. That is very good money for a single dance. But I'd never do it again. I hate the movies. They are unfair. There are young actors and actresses out there whose genius is being smothered by the dopes who run the movie companies. They do not know real acting when they see it. When I got through that dance and realized what they had done to me I swore a big swear. I said I would never do it again—and I won't."

For twenty thousand dollars I, personally, would do a fan dance with a pair of wren feathers in Macy's window at high noon.

In the summer of 1940 Sally was back at the Park Central, this time heading a floor show at the Coconut Grove. I stopped in one Saturday midnight and sat through the show. There were acts with dogs and tootsies and acrobatic dancers and singers and at last came the big announcement—the great, the one and only, the terrific Sally Rand in her world-famous bubble dance.

There she stood, barefooted up to her chin. I hadn't seen her in a long time. She danced out toward me with the big balloon, spinning it in the air. Yes, she had changed. Her behind was beginning to bulge, and there was no compensating curve up above. The fiddles sang, and she danced on and on. At last she was back on the little stage. The music ceased, and she raised her arms to signal the end of her act.

There was no applause.

Occupational diseases in the profession of nakedness are intense jealousy and delusions of grandeur. A stripper usually hates all other strippers and says so with her mouth. And I have yet to meet a nudist performer who doesn't believe she is guilty of Art.

I talked to Faith Bacon in an office at Rockefeller Center one day just before she began an engagement in a Broadway night club. I asked her why she had filed a $375,000 suit against Sally Rand in California.

"Fan dancing is my baby," she replied, "and nobody is going to take credit as the originator of it, only over my dead body."

She was going to dance two new numbers at the night club—the "Bird of Paradise" and the "Dance of the Living Orchid." Whenever requested, she added, she would oblige with her old fan dance.

"It's always requested," she went on. "All three dances are done nude. I prefer to dance as nude as possible. I am going to see the authorities of this town and see if they won't make a concession in the name of Art. There should really be a committee to come around and pass on nude dances. After all, I am not dancing to be vulgar. I am one of three girls in this entire country who can dance on their toes barefooted.

"They have beautiful paintings of nude women, don't they? And they also have porniography." (Miss Bacon puts the letter *i* in it.) "So we should be able to put on a dance that is Art just as nude as we want to and keep it from being porniography. But," she added with a sigh, "I guess we are not that far advanced yet."

She recalled the celebrated case back in 1930 when she was arrested for performing a fan dance in Earl Carroll's *Vanities*.

"I was exonerated," she said. "I danced my dance before the grand jury, and they refused to indict me."

"You mean you danced nude with fans before the jury?" I asked.

"Oh no," she replied. "I didn't have my fans there, so I used newspapers folded up like fans."

"Do you remember which newspapers you used?"

She thought a moment. "Oh sure," she said. "I used your paper —the *World-Telegram*."

I had her. "Now, now, Miss Bacon," I said. "There was no such thing as the *World-Telegram* in 1930."

"What I mean was," she said, "I used the *World* and the *Telegram*. I had the *World* in one hand and the *Telegram* in the other."

That was nice going.

"Did you strip before the grand jury?"

"No, of course not, silly," she said. "I just raised up my skirts to show them how much was available to the public, if you get what I mean. They were nice and dignified about it.

"You see, as I said before, I thought this whole fan-dance business up. The law said that you could be nude on the stage if you were stationary. But if you were nude and started moving around, then it was against the law. There are aspects the public doesn't now about. I had the idea of the fans. I would conceal myself behind the fans while I was moving around and I would be stationary when I took the fans away so I wouldn't be violating any law. And whenever I took these fans away I was very careful not to move anything, knowing the law like I did. But the fools arrested me anyway."

I made inquiry about her early life, and the question angered her a little.

"I am a native of California," she said, "but I consider New York my home now. I came here when I was thirteen. I was going on fourteen when I opened in *Artists and Models* at the Winter Garden. I was doing a nude even then. I was quite voluptuous when I was going on fourteen. Perhaps"—she leaned back and gazed thoughtfully at the ceiling—"perhaps it was a shame that I got so famous when I was so young. Nowadays when people hear the name Faith Bacon they say, 'Faith Bacon! But, my dear!' They think back and remember me from years ago and they think I must be a droop by now. After all, I was only thirteen then. They think that I must be about thirty-six or more now when I'm really only twenty-five.

"I am not through by any means. My career has yet to reach its height. My ambition, you know, is to do a series of Sunday evening dance concerts with a symphony orchestra. I want to demonstrate my own technique. I'm a natural dancer, understand, and I never took a lesson in my life, yet I taught for two years at Carnegie Hall.

"In a night club, when I'm on the floor, I'm in a world apart from the people who are looking at me. I'm bathed in the soft colored lights. I'm in a world apart. I'm not conscious of the dopes sitting out there. It's something ethereal, if you get what I mean. If I was earthly about my work I'd be vulgar. I never bump or shake anything at anybody. If anything shakes it is a normal, natural thing and belongs there. You understand?"

I said I did but I didn't.

Gypsy Rose Lee was one of the major attractions at the 1940 World's Fair, and after it was announced that she would go into the *Streets of Paris* production I paid a call on her. She was living in a railroad flat on East Fifty-seventh Street, the guest of a woman friend, and when I walked in she waved a copy of *Time* magazine in my face.

"Did you see what this man Mencken said?" she demanded. I moved into the room, and behind me came Al Aumuller, the photographer. He was already scanning the premises for props.

Miss Lee turned to a paragraph in the magazine in which Henry L. Mencken was represented as having coined a word to describe a strip-tease artist. He suggested "ecdysiast"—a combining form of the Greek *ekdysis*, which means "getting out," and the zoological term, ecdysis, which means "the act of molting."

"Ecdysiast, he calls me!" cried Miss Lee, tossing her head. "Why, the man is an intellectual snob. He has been reading books. Dictionaries. We don't wear feathers and molt them off. He makes me think of the girl reporter out in Chicago who asked me if I used zippers when I stripped. Imagine. Zippers! Why, I'd catch my——"

"Have you ever," I interrupted, "read any of Mr. Mencken's works?"

"Certainly," she said. "I've read his stuff. In my youth. What does he know about stripping? I hope he comes out to the Fair this summer to see me toss 'em off and that he lets me know he's in the audience. I'll make his hair stand on end!"

At this point there was a wise-guy knock at the door. A wise-guy knock is one of those knocks that goes da-da-da-da-da, pause, da-da.

Miss Lee opened the door, and a man charged in. He seized her hand and kissed it, and then she introduced him as P. Tchelitchew (which she thoughtfully spelled out). In a quick behind-the-hand remark she described him as a very, very famous artist.

"Ah! Aha!" cried P. Tchelitchew in the time-honored manner of famous artists.

He is of Russian birth and tonal quality and he was engaged in designing the costume which Miss Lee would take off at the Fair. She remarked that the costume would cost about twenty-five hundred dollars, and I remarked that stripping off a twenty-five hundred dollar costume was like buying a diamond-encrusted baseball bat to kill a cockroach.

"I operate like that," explained Miss Lee airily.

Then she persuaded P. Tchelitchew to describe the costume and explain the dance as he had envisioned it. The dress was to be Edwardian.

"First," he said, "she takes off the top. Then she keeps take off down. Then she comes to pants. In the pants, pins is. The pins from the pants she takes out and throw to the poblic. Whoooooo! Then comes away the pants, and she is leave behind with only the nightshirt. She yawn sleepy. Then she go away. The poblic he cry out for more. She come back, this time in nightshirt, and she carry candle, Ah! Aha! The candle! The candle is light. She walk on the stage and she start the nightshirt to take off. Comes almost off the nightshirt, but not quite. She blow the candle. Poof! It is darkness, and nobody see what she got under."

"Marrrrrrvelous!" cried Miss Lee. "The candle! A stroke of genius! It was wonnnnnnderful!"

"Yes," agreed P. Tchelitchew. "Also the pins from the pants is wonderful."

I asked Miss Lee, when her ecstasy over the candle had died away, if she had seen much of the 1939 Fair.

"You know," she said, "I only got to the Fair one day last year. I went out with some friends from England, and we never got near the Midway. They took me to a place called the Buttery. Fancy *me* in a place called the Buttery!"

Al Aumuller had been taking random shots of Miss Lee through all these proceedings. He had been snooping around the apartment, too, and he had come upon a small kitchen. In the kitchen was an ancient bathtub.

"Miss Lee," he said, "I have got to get something original, some new kind of shot."

"I know," she said. "I know what you've been doing. You've been in that kitchen. I know what you want me to do. You want me to take off my clothes and get in that bathtub."

"Well," said Al, "it would make a nice picture."

"Nothing doing," said Gypsy Rose Lee. "I like to be accommodating, but you can't get me to do that. The picture would come out in the paper, and I would get my friend in trouble. Don't you know that it's against the tenement-house laws to have a bathtub in the kitchen?"

"Oh," said Al, "that's different."

A telephone call, to reach me, has to come through the city desk at the *World-Telegram*. One afternoon I was sitting looking at a picture of a Negro with two billiard balls and a golf ball in his mouth when someone yelled over:

"There's a dame wants you. Says her name's Hippeletta."

I took the call, and it was a nice voice.

"This is Hippolyta, the Queen of the Amazons. If you will come out to the World's Fair and look me up at the Amazon Village I will yield you my girdle."

"Yield me your what?" I asked.

"My girdle," she said. "Didn't you ever hear how Hippolyta consent to yield Hercules her girdle?"

"My initial is H," I said, "but it doesn't stand for Hercules."

Then a man's voice came on the wire. It was Jack Diamond, a former United Press writer turned press agent. He said he was handling the Amazon Village at the Fair and that the Queen of the Amazons would make a wonderful interview.

"Furthermore," said Jack, "it's educational. It wouldn't hurt you to get a little education."

I agreed and hopped a subway to the Fair. Jack Diamond met me and escorted me to the Amazon Village. We were just in time for a performance. It certainly was educational.

We stood back of heavy plate glass and looked through at the Amazons, who moved listlessly about their duties on a bare floor. They hurled the javelin, tossed the discus, shot arrows at a target which they never hit and engaged in combat with wooden swords.

The queen made a regal entrance in a little golden chariot, wearing a helmet and a yellow robe. Occasionally, when the chariot faced way, she would open this robe, revealing that she had forgotten to put on a petticoat or anything else.

"She knows we're out here," remarked Jack. "She's making it good."

As soon as the show was over we went outside, and pretty soon the queen arrived in street dress. She was a tremendous girl, six feet, two inches tall and weighing 180 pounds. She was perfectly proportioned and had a beautiful face. Jack introduced her to me as Miss Lois de Fee, and instead of a handshake or a curtsy she gave a grind and a little bump right there on the Midway.

The three of us retired to a restaurant to talk.

"Lots of celebrities come to the show because it's educational," said the queen. "I've seen Douglas Fairbanks, Burgess Meredith, Peter Arno, Franchot Tone, Woolworth Donahue, Joan Bennett, Harry Richman and Frederic March through the glass at one time or another. It doesn't bother me a bit when I see someone famous out there. I just give the old robe an extra flip, just like a drug-store man puts on an extra hump of ice cream for somebody he likes. Orson Welles has been in seven times that I counted."

While she was talking I suddenly remembered who she was. She was the girl who married the midget in Florida.

"What do you think of the men who press their noses up against that glass and ogle you when you open the robe?" I asked her.

"I won't tell you," she said, "because you couldn't print what I think of them. And the things they say!"

"Can you hear what they say?"

"I can't hear them but I'm a lip reader. I can tell every word they say. It's almost enough to make me blush, and I've been married six times. That includes the little fellow."

I asked her to enumerate her marriages.

"The first one," she said, "was a prize fighter who turned flier. Number two was a jockey, who now owns a haberdashery. Number three was a Montreal playboy. Four was a ham actor. Five was a half-portion—the midget. That was really just a stunt to get in the papers. We didn't—I mean, we were married at three o'clock in the afternoon in Miami, and the half pint took a plane for New York at seven o'clock that evening, and we didn't—— That is—— Oh hell! We didn't. I applied for an annulment the next day. My sixth husband was a playboy without money. I married him because I thought he had money, and he married me because he thought I had money. When we found out both of us were liars we almost killed each other."

"Do you plan to marry again?" I asked.

"Right now," she said, "I am engaged to two fellows and semi-engaged to one. I'm engaged to an oil man in Texas with two million dollars and I'm engaged to a boy in Italy who has more than that but I understand Mussolini won't let him take the money out of the country, so I think I'll forget him. I'm semiengaged to a boy from Detroit. I think I'll go out with him tonight."

"Don't you find it complicated to be engaged to two or three fellows at once?"

"Listen," she said, "don't you think there's enough of me to go around?"

She said that her Texas oil millionaire had been on the long-distance phone the night before. She calls him "Snooks." He seemed to be worried. He asked her how much clothing she had been wearing in her performances at the Fair. She told him:

"Why, Snooks, darling! You don't think I'm running around mother-naked, do you?"

Snooks seemed satisfied, she said, and trusting.

ENTRANCE FEE

By Alexander Woollcott

THIS, THEN, IS THE STORY OF COSETTE AND THE SAINT-CYRIEN, MUCH as they tell it (and these many years have been telling it) in the smoky popotes of the French army.

In the nineties, when one heard less ugly babel of alien tongues in the sidewalk cafés, the talk at the *apéritif* hour was sure to turn sooner or later on Cosette—Mlle. Cosette of the *Variétés*, who was regarded by common consent as the most desirable woman in France. She was no hedged-in royal courtesan, as her possessive fellow-citizens would point out with satisfaction, but a distributed du Barry, the *chère amie* of a republic.

Her origins were misty. Some said she had been born of fisher folk at Plonbazlanec on the Brittany coast. Others preferred the tale that she was the love-child of a famous actress by a very well-known king. In any case, she was now a national legend, and in her pre-eminence the still-bruised French people found in some curious way a balm for their wounded self-esteem. Her photographs, which usually showed her sitting piquantly on a café table, were cut from *L'Illustration* and pinned up in every barracks. Every French lad dreamed of her, and every right-minded French girl quite understood that her sweetheart was saying in effect, "Since I cannot hope to have Cosette, will you come to the river's edge at sundown?" Quite understood, and did not blame him.

Everyone had seen the pictures of Cosette's tiny, vine-hung villa at Saint-Cloud, with its high garden wall and its twittering aviary. And even those for whom that wall was hopelessly high took morbid pride in a persistent detail of the legend which said that no man was ever a guest there for the night who could not bring five thousand francs with him. This was in the nineties, mind you, when francs were francs, and men—by a coincidence then more dependable—were men.

The peasant blend of charm and thrift in Cosette filled the cadets at Saint-Cyr with a gentle melancholy. In their twilight hours of relaxation they talked it over, and all thought it a sorrowful thing that, so wretched is the soldier's pittance, not one of those who must some day direct the great *Revanche* would ever carry into battle a memory of the fairest woman in France. For what cadet could hope to raise five thousand francs? It was very sad. But, cried one of their number, his voice shaking, his eyes alight, there were a thousand students at Saint-Cyr, and not one among them so lacking in resources that he could not, if given time, manage to raise at least five francs.

That was how the Cosette Sweepstakes were started. There followed then all the anxious distraction of ways and means, with such Spartan exploits in self-denial, such Damon-and-Pythias borrowings, such flagrant letters of perjured appeal to unsuspecting aunts and godmothers, as Saint-Cyr had never known. But by the appointed time the last man had his, or somebody's, five francs.

The drawing of numbers was well under way when a perplexed instructor stumbled on the proceedings and reported his discovery to the Commandant. When the old General heard the story he was so profoundly moved that it was some time before he spoke.

"The lad who wins the lottery," he said at last, "will be the envy of his generation. But the lad who conceived the idea—ah, he, my friend, will some day be a Marshal of France!"

Then he fell to laughing at the thought of the starry-eyed youngster arriving at the stage door of the *Variétés* with nothing but his youth and his entrance fee. The innocent budget had made no provision for the trip to Paris, none for a carriage, a bouquet, perhaps a supper party. The Commandant said that he would wish to meet this margin of contingency from his own fatherly pocket.

"There will be extras," he said. "Let the young rascal who wins be sent to me before he leaves for Paris."

It was a cadet from the Vendée who reported to the Commandant next afternoon—very trim in his red breeches and blue tunic, his white gloves spotless, his white cockade jaunty, his heart in his mouth. The Commandant said no word to him, but put a little purse of gold *louis* in his hand, kissed him on both cheeks in benediction, and stood at his window, moist-eyed and chuckling, to watch until the white cockade disappeared down the avenue of trees.

The sunlight, latticed by the *jalousies*, was making a gay pattern on Cosette's carpet the next morning when she sat up and meditated on the day which stretched ahead of her. Her little cadet was cradled in a sweet, dreamless sleep, and it touched her rather to see how preposterously young he was. Indeed, it quite set her thinking of her early days, and how she had come up in the world. Then she began speculating on *his* early days, realized with a pang that he was still in the midst of them, and suddenly grew puzzled. Being a woman of action, she prodded him.

"Listen, my old one," she said, "how did a cadet at Saint-Cyr ever get hold of five thousand francs?"

Thus abruptly questioned, he lost his head and blurted out the tale of the sweepstakes. Perhaps he felt it could do no harm now, and anyway she listened so avidly, with such flattering little gasps of surprise and such sunny ripples of laughter, that he quite warmed to his story. When he came to the part about the Commandant, she rose and strode up and down, the lace of her peignoir fluttering behind her, tears in her violet eyes.

"Saint-Cyr has paid me the prettiest compliment I have ever known," she said, "and I am the proudest woman in France this day. But surely I must do my part. You shall go back and tell them all that Cosette is a woman of sentiment. When you are an old, old man in the Vendée you shall tell your grandchildren that once in your youth you knew the dearest favors in France, and they cost you not a sou. Not a sou."

At that she hauled open the little drawer where he had seen her lock up the lottery receipts the night before.

"Here," she said, with a lovely gesture. "I give you back your money."

And she handed him his five francs.

PART III

"To hold, as't were, the mirror up to nature."
                    —SHAKESPEARE: *Hamlet*

THE SHORT HAPPY LIFE OF
FRANCIS MACOMBER

By Ernest Hemingway

IT WAS NOW LUNCH TIME AND THEY WERE ALL SITTING UNDER THE
double green fly of the dining tent pretending that nothing had
happened.

"Will you have lime juice or lemon squash?" Macomber asked.

"I'll have a gimlet," Robert Wilson told him.

"I'll have a gimlet too. I need something," Macomber's wife
said.

"I suppose it's the thing to do," Macomber agreed. "Tell him
to make three gimlets."

The mess boy had started them already, lifting the bottles out
of the canvas cooling bags that sweated wet in the wind that blew
through the trees that shaded the tents.

"What had I ought to give them?" Macomber asked.

"A quid would be plenty," Wilson told him. "You don't want
to spoil them."

"Will the headman distribute it?"

"Absolutely."

Francis Macomber had, half an hour before, been carried to his
tent from the edge of the camp in triumph on the arms and
shoulders of the cook, the personal boys, the skinner and the
porters. The gun-bearers had taken no part in the demonstration.
When the native boys put him down at the door of his tent, he
had shaken all their hands, received their congratulations, and then
gone into the tent and sat on the bed until his wife came in. She
did not speak to him when she came in and he left the tent at
once to wash his face and hands in the portable wash basin outside
and go over to the dining tent to sit in a comfortable canvas chair
in the breeze and the shade.

"You've got your lion," Robert Wilson said to him, "and a damned fine one too."

Mrs. Macomber looked at Wilson quickly. She was an extremely handsome and well-kept woman of the beauty and social position which had, five years before, commanded five thousand dollars as the price of endorsing, with photographs, a beauty product which she had never used. She had been married to Francis Macomber for eleven years.

"He is a good lion, isn't he?" Macomber said. His wife looked at him now. She looked at both these men as though she had never seen them before.

One, Wilson, the white hunter, she knew she had never truly seen before. He was about middle height with sandy hair, a stubby mustache, a very red face and extremely cold blue eyes with faint white wrinkles at the corners that grooved merrily when he smiled. He smiled at her now and she looked away from his face at the way his shoulders sloped in the loose tunic he wore with the four big cartridges held in loops where the left breast pocket should have been, at his big brown hands, his old slacks, his very dirty boots and back to his red face again. She noticed where the baked red of his face stopped in a white line that marked the circle left by his Stetson hat that hung now from one of the pegs of the tent pole.

"Well, here's to the lion," Robert Wilson said. He smiled at her again and, not smiling, she looked curiously at her husband.

Francis Macomber was very tall, very well built if you did not mind that length of bone, dark, his hair cropped like an oarsman, rather thin-lipped, and was considered handsome. He was dressed in the same sort of safari clothes that Wilson wore except that his were new, he was thirty-five years old, kept himself very fit, was good at court games, had a number of big-game fishing records, and had just shown himself, very publicly, to be a coward.

"Here's to the lion," he said. "I can't ever thank you for what you did."

Margaret, his wife, looked away from him and back to Wilson.

"Let's not talk about the lion," she said.

Wilson looked over at her without smiling and now she smiled at him.

"It's been a very strange day," she said. "Hadn't you ought to put your hat on even under the canvas at noon? You told me that, you know."

"Might put it on," said Wilson.

"You know you have a very red face, Mr. Wilson," she told him and smiled again.

"Drink," said Wilson.

"I don't think so," she said. "Francis drinks a great deal, but his face is never red."

"It's red today," Macomber tried a joke.

"No," said Margaret. "It's mine that's red today. But Mr. Wilson's is always red."

"Must be racial," said Wilson. "I say, you wouldn't like to drop my beauty as a topic, would you?"

"I've just started on it."

"Let's chuck it," said Wilson.

"Conversation is going to be so difficult," Margaret said.

"Don't be silly, Margot," her husband said.

"No difficulty," Wilson said. "Got a damn fine lion."

Margot looked at them both and they both saw that she was going to cry. Wilson had seen it coming for a long time and he dreaded it. Macomber was past dreading it.

"I wish it hadn't happened. Oh, I wish it hadn't happened," she said and started for her tent. She made no noise of crying but they could see that her shoulders were shaking under the rose-colored, sun-proofed shirt she wore.

"Women upset," said Wilson to the tall man. "Amounts to nothing. Strain on the nerves and one thing'n another."

"No," said Macomber. "I suppose that I rate that for the rest of my life now."

"Nonsense. Let's have a spot of the giant killer," said Wilson. "Forget the whole thing. Nothing to it anyway."

"We might try," said Macomber. "I won't forget what you did for me though."

"Nothing," said Wilson. "All nonsense."

So they sat there in the shade where the camp was pitched under some wide-topped acacia trees with a boulder-strewn cliff behind them, and a stretch of grass that ran to the bank of a boulder-filled stream in front with forest beyond it, and drank their just-cool lime drinks and avoided one another's eyes while the boys set the table for lunch. Wilson could tell that the boys all knew about it now and when he saw Macomber's personal boy looking curiously at his master while he was putting dishes on the table he snapped at him in Swahili. The boy turned away with his face blank.

"What were you telling him?" Macomber asked.

"Nothing. Told him to look alive or I'd see he got about fifteen of the best."

"What's that? Lashes?"

"It's quite illegal," Wilson said. "You're supposed to fine them."

"Do you still have them whipped?"

"Oh, yes. They could raise a row if they chose to complain. But they don't. They prefer it to the fines."

"How strange!" said Macomber.

"Not strange, really," Wilson said. "Which would you rather do? Take a good birching or lose your pay?"

Then he felt embarrassed at asking it and before Macomber could answer he went on, "We all take a beating every day, you know, one way or another."

This was no better. "Good God," he thought. "I am a diplomat, aren't I?"

"Yes, we take a beating," said Macomber, still not looking at him. "I'm awfully sorry about that lion business. It doesn't have to go any further, does it? I mean no one will hear about it, will they?"

"You mean will I tell it at the Mathaiga Club?" Wilson looked at him now coldly. He had not expected this. So he's a bloody four-letter man as well as a bloody coward, he thought. I rather liked him too until today. But how is one to know about an American?

"No," said Wilson. "I'm a professional hunter. We never talk about our clients. You can be quite easy on that. It's supposed to be bad form to ask us not to talk though."

He had decided now that to break would be much easier. He would eat, then, by himself and could read a book with his meals. They would eat by themselves. He would see them through the safari on a very formal basis—what was it the French called it? Distinguished consideration—and it would be a damn sight easier than having to go through this emotional trash. He'd insult him and make a good clean break. Then he could read a book with his meals and he'd still be drinking their whisky. That was the phrase for it when a safari went bad. You ran into another white hunter and you asked, "How is everything going?" and he answered, "Oh, I'm still drinking their whisky," and you knew everything had gone to pot.

"I'm sorry," Macomber said and looked at him with his American face that would stay adolescent until it became middle-aged, and Wilson noted his crew-cropped hair, fine eyes only faintly shifty, good nose, thin lips and handsome jaw. "I'm sorry I didn't realize that. There are lots of things I don't know."

So what could he do, Wilson thought. He was all ready to break it off quickly and neatly and here the beggar was apologizing after he had just insulted him. He made one more attempt. "Don't worry about me talking," he said. "I have a living to make. You know in Africa no woman ever misses her lion and no white man ever bolts."

"I bolted like a rabbit," Macomber said.

Now what in hell were you going to do about a man who talked like that, Wilson wondered.

Wilson looked at Macomber with his flat, blue, machine-gunner's eyes and the other smiled back at him. He had a pleasant smile if you did not notice how the eyes showed when he was hurt.

"Maybe I can fix it up on buffalo," he said. "We're after them next, aren't we?"

"In the morning if you like," Wilson told him. Perhaps he had been wrong. This was certainly the way to take it. You most certainly could not tell a damned thing about an American. He was all for Macomber again. If you could forget the morning. But, of course, you couldn't. The morning had been about as bad as they come.

"Here comes the Memsahib," he said. She was walking over from her tent looking refreshed and cheerful and quite lovely. She had a very perfect oval face, so perfect that you expected her to be stupid. But she wasn't stupid, Wilson thought, no, not stupid.

"How is the beautiful red-faced Mr. Wilson? Are you feeling better, Francis, my pearl?"

"Oh, much," said Macomber.

"I've dropped the whole thing," she said, sitting down at the table. "What importance is there to whether Francis is any good at killing lions? That's not his trade. That's Mr. Wilson's trade. Mr. Wilson is really very impressive killing anything. You do kill anything, don't you?"

"Oh, anything," said Wilson. "Simply anything." They are, he thought, the hardest in the world; the hardest, the cruelest, the most predatory and the most attractive and their men have softened or gone to pieces nervously as they have hardened. Or is it that they pick men they can handle? They can't know that much at the age they marry, he thought. He was grateful that he had gone through his education on American women before now because this was a very attractive one.

"We're going after buff in the morning," he told her.

"I'm coming," she said.

"No, you're not."

"Oh, yes, I am. Mayn't I, Francis?"

"Why not stay in camp?"

"Not for anything," she said. "I wouldn't miss something like today for anything."

When she left, Wilson was thinking, when she went off to cry, she seemed a hell of a fine woman. She seemed to understand, to realize, to be hurt for him and for herself and to know how things really stood. She is away for twenty minutes and now she is back, simply enamelled in that American female cruelty. They are the damnedest women. Really the damnedest.

"We'll put on another show for you tomorrow," Francis Macomber said.

"You're not coming," Wilson said.

"You're very mistaken," she told him. "And I want *so* to see you perform again. You were lovely this morning. That is if blowing things' heads off is lovely."

"Here's the lunch," said Wilson. "You're very merry, aren't you?"

"Why not? I didn't come out here to be dull."

"Well, it hasn't been dull," Wilson said. He could see the boulders in the river and the high bank beyond with the trees and he remembered the morning.

"Oh, no," she said. "It's been charming. And tomorrow. You don't know how I look forward to tomorrow."

"That's eland he's offering you," Wilson said.

"They're the big cowy things that jump like hares, aren't they?"

"I suppose that describes them," Wilson said.

"It's very good meat," Macomber said.

"Did you shoot it, Francis?" she asked.

"Yes."

"They're not dangerous, are they?"

"Only if they fall on you," Wilson told her.

"I'm so glad."

"Why not let up on the bitchery just a little, Margot," Macomber said, cutting the eland steak and putting some mashed potato, gravy and carrot on the down-turned fork that tined through the piece of meat.

"I suppose I could," she said, "since you put it so prettily."

"Tonight we'll have champagne for the lion," Wilson said. "It's a bit too hot at noon."

"Oh, the lion," Margot said. "I'd forgotten the lion!"

So, Robert Wilson thought to himself, she *is* giving him a ride, isn't she? Or do you suppose that's her idea of putting up a good show? How should a woman act when she discovers her husband is a bloody coward? She's damn cruel but they're all cruel. They govern, of course, and to govern one has to be cruel sometimes. Still, I've seen enough of their damn terrorism.

"Have some more eland," he said to her politely.

That afternoon, late, Wilson and Macomber went out in the motor car with the native driver and the two gun-bearers. Mrs. Macomber stayed in the camp. It was too hot to go out, she said, and she was going with them in the early morning. As they drove off Wilson saw her standing under the big tree, looking pretty rather than beautiful in her faintly rosy khaki, her dark hair drawn back off her forehead and gathered in a knot low on her neck, her face as fresh, he thought, as though she were in England. She waved to them as the car went off through the swale of high grass and curved around through the trees into the small hills of orchard bush.

In the orchard bush they found a herd of impala, and leaving the car they stalked one old ram with long, wide-spread horns and Macomber killed it with a very creditible shot that knocked the buck down at a good two hundred yards and sent the herd off bounding wildly and leaping over one another's backs in long, leg-drawn-up leaps as unbelievable and as floating as those one makes sometimes in dreams.

"That was a good shot," Wilson said. "They're a small target."

"Is it a worth-while head?" Macomber asked.

"It's excellent," Wilson told him. "You shoot like that and you'll have no trouble."

"Do you think we'll find buffalo tomorrow?"

"There's a good chance of it. They feed out early in the morning and with luck we may catch them in the open."

"I'd like to clear away that lion business," Macomber said. "It's not very pleasant to have your wife see you do something like that."

I should think it would be even more unpleasant to do it, Wilson thought, wife or no wife, or to talk about it having done it. But he said, "I wouldn't think about that any more. Any one could be upset by his first lion. That's all over."

But that night after dinner and a whisky and soda by the fire before going to bed, as Francis Macomber lay on his cot with the mosquito bar over him and listened to the night noises it was not all over. It was neither all over nor was it beginning. It was there exactly as it happened with some parts of it indelibly emphasized and he was miserably ashamed at it. But more than shame he felt cold, hollow fear in him. The fear was still there like a cold slimy hollow in all the emptiness where once his confidence had been and it made him feel sick. It was still there with him now.

It had started the night before when he had wakened and heard the lion roaring somewhere up along the river. It was a deep sound and at the end there were sort of coughing grunts that made him seem just outside the tent, and when Francis Macomber woke in the night to hear it he was afraid. He could hear his wife breathing quietly, asleep. There was no one to tell he was afraid, nor to be afraid with him, and, lying alone, he did not know the Somali proverb that says a brave man is always frightened three times by a lion; when he first sees his track, when he first hears him roar and when he first confronts him. Then while they were eating breakfast by lantern light out in the dining tent, before the sun was up, the lion roared again and Francis thought he was just at the edge of camp.

"Sounds like an old-timer," Robert Wilson said, looking up from his kippers and coffee. "Listen to him cough."

"Is he very close?"

"A mile or so up the stream."

"Will we see him?"

"We'll have a look."

"Does his roaring carry that far? It sounds as though he were right in camp."

"Carries a hell of a long way," said Robert Wilson. "It's strange the way it carries. Hope he's a shootable cat. The boys said there was a very big one about here."

"If I get a shot, where should I hit him," Macomber asked, "to stop him?"

"In the shoulders," Wilson said. "In the neck if you can make it. Shoot for bone. Break him down."

"I hope I can place it properly," Macomber said.

"You shoot very well," Wilson told him. "Take your time. Make sure of him. The first one in is the one that counts."

"What range will it be?"

"Can't tell. Lion has something to say about that. Won't shoot unless it's close enough so you can make sure."

"At under a hundred yards?" Macomber asked.

Wilson looked at him quickly.

"Hundred's about right. Might have to take him a bit under. Shouldn't chance a shot at much over that. A hundred's a decent range. You can hit him wherever you want at that. Here comes the Memsahib."

"Good morning," she said. "Are we going after that lion?"

"As soon as you deal with your breakfast," Wilson said. "How are you feeling?"

"Marvelous," she said. "I'm very excited."

"I'll just go and see that everything is ready," Wilson went off. As he left the lion roared again.

"Noisy beggar," Wilson said. "We'll put a stop to that."

"What's the matter, Francis?" his wife asked him.

"Nothing," Macomber said.

"Yes, there is," she said. "What are you upset about?"

"Nothing," he said.

"Tell me," she looked at him. "Don't you feel well?"

"It's that damned roaring," he said. "It's been going on all night, you know."

"Why didn't you wake me," she said. "I'd love to have heard it."

"I've got to kill the damned thing," Macomber said, miserably.

"Well, that's what you're out here for, isn't it?"

"Yes. But I'm nervous. Hearing the thing roar gets on my nerves."

"Well then, as Wilson said, kill him and stop his roaring."

"Yes, darling," said Francis Macomber. "It sounds easy, doesn't it?"

"You're not afraid, are you?"

"Of course not. But I'm nervous from hearing him roar all night."

"You'll kill him marvellously," she said. "I know you will. I'm awfully anxious to see it."

"Finish your breakfast and we'll be starting."

"It's not light yet," she said. "This is a ridiculous hour."

Just then the lion roared in a deep-chested moaning, suddenly guttural, ascending vibration that seemed to shake the air and ended in a sigh and a heavy, deep-chested grunt.

"He sounds almost here," Macomber's wife said.

"My God," said Macomber. "I hate that damned noise."

"It's very impressive."

"Impressive. It's frightful."

Robert Wilson came up then carrying his short, ugly, shockingly big-bored .505 Gibbs and grinning.

"Come on," he said. "Your gun-bearer has your Springfield and the big gun. Everything's in the car. Have you solids?"

"Yes."

"I'm ready," Mrs. Macomber said.

"Must make him stop that racket," Wilson said. "You get in front. The Memsahib can sit back here with me."

They climbed into the motor car and, in the gray first daylight, moved off up the river through the trees. Macomber opened the breech of his rifle and saw he had metal-cased bullets, shut the bolt and put the rifle on safety. He saw his hand was trembling. He felt in his pocket for more cartridges and moved his fingers over the cartridges in the loops of his tunic front. He turned back to where Wilson sat in the rear seat of the doorless, box-bodied motor car beside his wife, them both grinning with excitement, and Wilson leaned forward and whispered,

"See the birds dropping. Means the old boy has left his kill."

On the far bank of the stream Macomber could see, above the trees, vultures circling and plummeting down.

"Chances are he'll come to drink along here," Wilson whispered. "Before he goes to lay up. Keep an eye out."

They were driving slowly along the high bank of the stream which here cut deeply to its boulder-filled bed, and they wound in and out through big trees as they drove. Macomber was watching the opposite bank when he felt Wilson take hold of his arm. The car stopped.

"There he is," he heard the whisper. "Ahead and to the right. Get out and take him. He's a marvellous lion."

Macomber saw the lion now. He was standing almost broadside, his great head up and turned toward them. The early morning breeze that blew toward them was just stirring his dark mane, and the lion looked huge, silhouetted on the rise of bank in the gray morning light, his shoulders heavy, his barrel of a body bulking smoothly.

"How far is he?" asked Macomber, raising his rifle.

"About seventy-five. Get out and take him."

"Why not shoot from where I am?"

"You don't shoot them from cars," he heard Wilson saying in his ear. "Get out. He's not going to stay there all day."

Macomber stepped out of the curved opening at the side of the front seat, onto the step and down onto the ground. The lion still stood looking majestically and coolly toward this object that his eyes only showed in silhouette, bulking like some super-rhino.

There was no man smell carried toward him and he watched the object, moving his great head a little from side to side. Then watching the object, not afraid, but hesitating before going down the bank to drink with such a thing opposite him, he saw a man figure detach itself from it and he turned his heavy head and swung away toward the cover of the trees as he heard a cracking crash and felt the slam of a .30–06 220-grain solid bullet that bit his flank and ripped in sudden hot scalding nausea through his stomach. He trotted, heavy, big-footed, swinging wounded full-bellied, through the trees toward the tall grass and cover, and the crash came again to go past him ripping the air apart. Then it crashed again and he felt the blow as it hit his lower ribs and ripped on through, blood sudden hot and frothy in his mouth, and he galloped toward the high grass where he could crouch and not be seen and make them bring the crashing thing close enough so he could make a rush and get the man that held it.

Macomber had not thought how the lion felt as he got out of the car. He only knew his hands were shaking and as he walked away from the car it was almost impossible for him to make his legs move. They were stiff in the thighs, but he could feel the muscles fluttering. He raised the rifle, sighted on the junction of the lion's head and shoulders and pulled the trigger. Nothing happened though he pulled until he thought his finger would break. Then he knew he had the safety on and as he lowered the rifle to move the safety over he moved another frozen pace forward, and the lion seeing his silhouette now clear of the silhouette of the car, turned and started off at a trot, and, as Macomber fired, he heard a whunk that mean that the bullet was home; but the lion kept on going. Macomber shot again and every one saw a bullet throw a spout of dirt beyond the trotting lion. He shot again, remembering to lower his aim, and they all heard the bullet hit, and the lion went into a gallop and was in the tall grass before he had the bolt pushed forward.

Macomber stood there feeling sick at his stomach, his hands that held the Springfield still cocked, shaking, and his wife and Robert Wilson were standing by him. Beside him too were the two gun-bearers chattering in Wakamba.

"I hit him," Macomber said. "I hit him twice."

"You gut-shot him and you hit him somewhere forward," Wilson said without enthusiasm. The gun-bearers looked very grave. They were silent now.

"You may have killed him," Wilson went on. "We'll have to wait a while before we go in to find out."

"What do you mean?"

"Let him get sick before we follow him up."

"Oh," said Macomber.

"He's a hell of a fine lion," Wilson said cheerfully. "He's gotten into a bad place though."

"Why is it bad?"

"Can't see him until you're on him."

"Oh," said Macomber.

"Come on," said Wilson. "The Memsahib can stay here in the car. We'll go to have a look at the blood spoor."

"Stay here, Margot," Macomber said to his wife. His mouth was very dry and it was hard for him to talk.

"Why?" she asked.

"Wilson says to."

"We're going to have a look," Wilson said. "You stay here. You can see even better from here."

"All right."

Wilson spoke in Swahili to the driver. He nodded and said, "Yes, Bwana."

Then they went down the steep bank and across the stream, climbing over and around the boulders and up the other bank, pulling up by some projecting roots, and along it until they found where the lion had been trotting when Macomber first shot. There was dark blood on the short grass that the gun-bearers pointed out with grass stems, and that ran away behind the river bank trees.

"What do we do?" asked Macomber.

"Not much choice," said Wilson. "We can't bring the car over. Bank's too steep. We'll let him stiffen up a bit and then you and I'll go in and have a look for him."

"Can't we set the grass on fire?" Macomber asked.

"Too green."

"Can't we send beaters?"

Wilson looked at him appraisingly. "Of course we can," he said. "But it's just a touch murderous. You see we know the lion's wounded. You can drive an unwounded lion—he'll move on ahead of a noise—but a wounded lion's going to charge. You can't see him until you're right on him. He'll make himself perfectly flat in cover you wouldn't think would hide a hare. You can't very well send boys in there to that sort of a show. Somebody bound to get mauled."

"What about the gun-bearers?"

"Oh, they'll go with us. It's their *shauri*. You see, they signed on for it. They don't look too happy though, do they?"

"I don't want to go in there," said Macomber. It was out before he knew he'd said it.

"Neither do I," said Wilson very cheerfully. "Really no choice though." Then, as an afterthought, he glanced at Macomber and saw suddenly how he was trembling and the pitiful look on his face.

"You don't have to go in, of course," he said. "That's what I'm hired for, you know. That's why I'm so expensive."

"You mean you'd go in by yourself? Why not leave him there?"

Robert Wilson, whose entire occupation had been with the lion and the problem he presented, and who had not been thinking about Macomber except to note that he was rather windy, suddenly felt as though he had opened the wrong door in a hotel and seen something shameful.

"What do you mean?"

"Why not just leave him?"

"You mean pretend to ourselves he hasn't been hit?"

"No. Just drop it."

"It isn't done."

"Why not?"

"For one thing, he's certain to be suffering. For another, some one else might run onto him."

"I see."

"But you don't have to have anything to do with it."

"I'd like to," Macomber said. "I'm just scared, you know."

"I'll go ahead when we go in," Wilson said, "with Kongoni tracking. You keep behind me and a little to one side. Chances are we'll hear him growl. If we see him we'll both shoot. Don't worry about anything. I'll keep you backed up. As a matter of fact, you know, perhaps you'd better not go. It might be much better. Why don't you go over and join the Memsahib while I just get it over with?"

"No, I want to go."

"All right," said Wilson. "But don't go in if you don't want to. This is my *shauri* now, you know."

"I want to go," said Macomber.

They sat under a tree and smoked.

"Want to go back and speak to the Memsahib while we're waiting?" Wilson asked.

"No."

"I'll just step back and tell her to be patient."

"Good," said Macomber. He sat there, sweating under his arms, his mouth dry, his stomach hollow feeling, wanting to find courage to tell Wilson to go on and finish off the lion without him. He could not know that Wilson was furious because he had not noticed the state he was in earlier and sent him back to his wife. While he sat there Wilson came up. "I have your big gun," he said. "Take it. We've given him time, I think. Come on."

Macomber took the big gun and Wilson said:

"Keep behind me and about five yards to the right and do exactly as I tell you." Then he spoke in Swahili to the two gun-bearers who looked the picture of gloom.

"Let's go," he said.

"Could I have a drink of water?" Macomber asked. Wilson spoke to the older gun-bearer, who wore a canteen on his belt, and the man unbuckled it, unscrewed the top and handed it to Macomber, who took it noticing how heavy it seemed and how hairy and shoddy the felt covering was in his hand. He raised it to drink and looked ahead at the high grass with the flat-topped trees behind it. A breeze was blowing toward them and the grass rippled gently in the wind. He looked at the gun-bearer and he could see the gun-bearer was suffering too with fear.

Thirty-five yards into the grass the big lion lay flattened out along the ground. His ears were back and his only movement was a slight twitching up and down of his long, black-tuffted tail. He had turned at bay as soon as he had reached this cover and he was sick with the wound through his full belly, and weakening with the wound through his lungs that brought a thin foamy red to his mouth each time he breathed. His flanks were wet and hot and flies were on the little openings the solid bullets had made in his tawny hide, and his big yellow eyes, narrowed with hate, looked straight ahead, only blinking when the pain came as he breathed, and his claws dug in the soft baked earth. All of him, pain, sickness, hatred and all of his remaining strength, was tightening into an absolute concentration for a rush. He could hear the men talking and he waited, gathering all of himself into this preparation for charge as soon as the men would come into the grass. As he heard their voices his tail stiffened to twitch up and down, and, as they came into the edge of the grass, he made a coughing grunt and charged.

Kongoni, the old gun-bearer, in the lead watching the blood spoor, Wilson watching the grass for any movement, his big gun ready, the second gun-bearer looking ahead and listening, Macomber close to Wilson, his rifle cocked, they had just moved into the grass when Macomber heard the blood-choked coughing grunt, and saw the swishing rush in the grass. The next thing he knew he was running; running wildly, in panic in the open, running toward the stream.

He heard the *ca-ra-wong!* of Wilson's big rifle, and again in a second crashing *carawong!* and turning saw the lion, horrible-looking now, with half his head seeming to be gone, crawling toward Wilson in the edge of the tall grass while the red-faced man worked the bolt on the short ugly rifle and aimed carefully as another blasting *carawong!* came from the muzzle, and the crawling, heavy, yellow bulk of the lion stiffened and the huge, mutilated head slid forward and Macomber, standing by himself in the clearing where he had run, holding a loaded rifle, while two black men and a white man looked back at him in contempt, knew the lion was dead. He came toward Wilson, his tallness all seeming a naked reproach, and Wilson looked at him and said:

"Want to take pictures?"

"No," he said.

That was all any one had said until they reached the motor car. Then Wilson had said:

"Hell of a fine lion. Boys will skin him out. We might as well stay here in the shade."

Macomber's wife had not looked at him nor he at her and he had sat by her in the back seat with Wilson sitting in the front seat. Once he had reached over and taken his wife's hand without looking at her and she had removed her hand from his. Looking across the stream to where the gun-bearers were skinning out the lion he could see that she had been able to see the whole thing. While they sat there his wife reached forward and put her hand on Wilson's shoulder. He turned and she had leaned forward over the low seat and kissed him on the mouth.

"Oh, I say," said Wilson, going redder than his natural baked color.

"Mr. Robert Wilson," she said. "The beautiful red-faced Mr. Robert Wilson."

Then she sat down beside Macomber again and looked away across the stream to where the lion lay, with uplifted, white-muscled, tendon-marked naked forearms, and white bloating belly, as the black men fleshed away the skin. Finally the gun-bearers brought the skin over, wet and heavy, and climbed in behind with it, rolling it up before they got in, and the motor car started. No one had said anything more until they were back in camp.

That was the story of the lion. Macomber did not know how the lion had felt before he started his rush, nor during it when the unbelievable smash of the .505 with a muzzle velocity of two tons had hit him in the mouth, nor what kept him coming after that, when the second ripping crash had smashed his hind quarters and he had come crawling on toward the crashing, blasting thing that had destroyed him. Wilson knew something about it and only expressed it by saying, "Damned fine lion," but Macomber did not know how Wilson felt about things either. He did not know how his wife felt except that she was through with him.

His wife had been through with him before but it never lasted. He was very wealthy, and would be much wealthier, and he knew she would not leave him ever now. That was one of the few things that he really knew. He knew about that, about motor cycles—

that was earliest—about motor cars, about duck-shooting, about fishing, trout, salmon and big-sea, about sex in books, many books, too many books, about all court games, about dogs, not much about horses, about hanging on to his money, about most of the other things his world dealt in, and about his wife not leaving him. His wife had been a great beauty and she was still a great beauty in Africa, but she was not a great enough beauty any more at home to be able to leave him and better herself and she knew it and he knew it. She had missed the chance to leave him and he knew it. If he had been better with women she would probably have started to worry about him getting another new, beautiful wife; but she knew too much about him to worry about him either. Also, he had always had a great tolerance which seemed the nicest thing about him if it were not the most sinister.

All in all they were known as a comparatively happily married couple, one of those whose disruption is often rumored but never occurs, and as the society columnist put it, they were adding more than a spice of *adventure* to their much envied and ever-enduring *Romance* by a *Safari* in what was known as *Darkest Africa* until the Martin Johnsons lighted it on so many silver screens where they were pursuing *Old Simba* the lion, the buffalo, *Tembo* the elephant and as well collecting specimens for the Museum of Natural History. This same columnist had reported them *on the verge* at least three times in the past and they had been. But they always made it up. They had a sound basis of union. Margot was too beautiful for Macomber to divorce her and Macomber had too much money for Margot ever to leave him.

It was now about three o'clock in the morning and Francis Macomber, who had been asleep a little while after he had stopped thinking about the lion, wakened and then slept again, woke suddenly, frightened in a dream of the bloody-headed lion standing over him, and listening while his heart pounded, he realized that his wife was not in the other cot in the tent. He lay awake with that knowledge for two hours.

At the end of that time his wife came into the tent, lifted her mosquito bar and crawled cozily into bed.

"Where have you been?" Macomber asked in the darkness.

"Hello," she said. "Are you awake?"

"Where have you been?"

"I just went out to get a breath of air."

"You did, like hell."

"What do you want me to say, darling?"

"Where have you been?"

"Out to get a breath of air."

"That's a new name for it. You *are* a bitch."

"Well, you're a coward."

"All right," he said. "What of it?"

"Nothing as far as I'm concerned. But please let's not talk, darling, because I'm very sleepy."

"You think that I'll take anything."

"I know you will, sweet."

"Well, I won't."

"Please, darling, let's not talk. I'm so very sleepy."

"There wasn't going to be any of that. You promised there wouldn't be."

"Well, there is now," she said sweetly.

"You said if we made this trip that there would be none of that. You promised."

"Yes, darling. That's the way I meant it to be. But the trip was spoiled yesterday. We don't have to talk about it, do we?"

"You don't wait long when you have an advantage, do you?"

"Please let's not talk. I'm so sleepy, darling."

"I'm going to talk."

"Don't mind me then, because I'm going to sleep." And she did.

At breakfast they were all three at the table before daylight and Francis Macomber found that, of all the many men that he had hated, he hated Robert Wilson the most.

"Sleep well?" Wilson asked in his throaty voice, filling a pipe.

"Did you?"

"Topping," the white hunter told him.

You bastard, thought Macomber, you insolent bastard.

So she woke him when she came in, Wilson thought, looking at them both with his flat, cold eyes. Well, why doesn't he keep his wife where she belongs? What does he think I am, a bloody plaster saint? Let him keep her where she belongs. It's his own fault.

"Do you think we'll find buffalo?" Margot asked, pushing away a dish of apricots.

"Chance of it," Wilson said and smiled at her. "Why don't you stay in camp?"

"Not for anything," she told him.

"Why not order her to stay in camp?" Wilson said to Macomber.

"You order her," said Macomber coldly.

"Let's not have any ordering, nor," turning to Macomber, "any silliness, Francis," Margot said quite pleasantly.

"Are you ready to start?" Macomber asked.

"Any time," Wilson told him. "Do you want the Memsahib to go?"

"Does it make any difference whether I do or not?"

The hell with it, thought Robert Wilson. The utter complete hell with it. So this is what it's going to be like. Well, this is what it's going to be like, then.

"Makes no difference," he said.

"You're sure you wouldn't like to stay in camp with her yourself and let me go out and hunt the buffalo?" Macomber asked.

"Can't do that," said Wilson. "Wouldn't talk rot if I were you."

"I'm not talking rot. I'm disgusted."

"Bad word, disgusted."

"Francis, will you please try to speak sensibly?" his wife said.

"I speak too damned sensibly," Macomber said. "Did you ever eat such filthy food?"

"Something wrong with the food?" asked Wilson quietly.

"No more than with everything else."

"I'd pull yourself together, laddybuck," Wilson said very quietly. "There's a boy waits at table that understands a little English."

"The hell with him."

Wilson stood up and puffing on his pipe strolled away, speaking a few words in Swahili to one of the gun-bearers who was standing waiting for him. Macomber and his wife sat on at the table. He was staring at his coffee cup.

"If you make a scene I'll leave you, darling," Margot said quietly.

"No, you won't."

"You can try it and see."

"You won't leave me."

"No," she said. "I won't leave you and you'll behave yourself."

"Behave myself? That's a way to talk. Behave myself."

"Yes. Behave yourself."

"Why don't *you* try behaving?"

"I've tried it so long. So very long."

"I hate that red-faced swine," Macomber said. "I loathe the sight of him."

"He's really *very* nice."

"Oh, *shut up*," Macomber almost shouted. Just then the car came up and stopped in front of the dining tent and the driver and the two gun-bearers got out. Wilson walked over and looked at the husband and wife sitting there at the table.

"Going shooting?" he asked.

"Yes," said Macomber, standing up. "Yes."

"Better bring a woolly. It will be cool in the car," Wilson said.

"I'll get my leather jacket," Margot said.

"The boy has it," Wilson told her. He climbed into the front with the driver and Francis Macomber and his wife sat, not speaking, in the back seat.

Hope the silly beggar doesn't take a notion to blow the back of my head off, Wilson thought to himself. Women *are* a nuisance on safari.

The car was grinding down to cross the river at a pebbly ford in the gray daylight and then climbed, angling up the steep bank, where Wilson had ordered a way shovelled out the day before so they could reach the parklike wooded rolling country on the far side.

It was a good morning, Wilson thought. There was a heavy dew and as the wheels went through the grass and low bushes he could smell the odor of the crushed fronds. It was an odor like verbena and he liked this early morning smell of the dew, the crushed bracken and the look of the tree trunks showing black through the early morning mist, as the car made its way through the untracked, parklike country. He had put the two in the back seat out of his mind now and was thinking about buffalo. The buffalo that he was after stayed in the daytime in a thick swamp where it was impossible to get a shot, but in the night they fed out into an open stretch of country and if he could come between them and their swamp with the car, Macomber would have a good chance at them in the open. He did not want to hunt buff with Macomber in thick cover. He did not want to hunt buff or anything else with Macomber at all, but he was a professional hunter and he had hunted with some rare ones in his time. If they got buff today there would only be rhino to come and the poor man would have gone through his dangerous game and things might pick up. He'd have nothing more to do with the woman and Macomber would get over that too. He must have gone through plenty of that before by the look of things. Poor beggar. He must have a way of getting over it. Well, it was the poor sod's own bloody fault.

He, Robert Wilson, carried a double size cot on safari to accommodate any windfalls he might receive. He had hunted for a certain clientele, the international, fast, sporting set, where the women did not feel they were getting their money's worth unless they had shared that cot with the white hunter. He despised them when he was away from them although he liked some of them well enough at the time, but he made his living by them; and their standards were his standards as long as they were hiring him.

They were his standards in all except the shooting. He had his own standards about the killing and they could live up to them or get some one else to hunt them. He knew, too, that they all respected him for this. This Macomber was an odd one though. Damned if he wasn't. Now the wife. Well, the wife. Yes, the wife. Hm, the wife. Well he'd dropped all that. He looked around at them. Macomber sat grim and furious. Margot smiled at him. She looked younger today, more innocent and fresher and not so professionally beautiful. What's in her heart God knows, Wilson thought. She hadn't talked much last night. At that it was a pleasure to see her.

The motor car climbed up a slight rise and went on through the trees and then out into a grassy prairie-like opening and kept in the shelter of the trees along the edge, the driver going slowly and Wilson looking carefully out across the prairie and all along its far side. He stopped the car and studied the opening with his field glasses. Then he motioned to the driver to go on and the car moved slowly along, the driver avoiding wart-hog holes and driving around the mud castles ants had built. Then, looking across the opening, Wilson suddenly turned and said,

"By God, there they are!"

And looking where he pointed, while the car jumped forward and Wilson spoke in rapid Swahili to the driver, Macomber saw three huge, black animals looking almost cylindrical in their long heaviness, like big black tank cars, moving at a gallop across the far edge of the open prairie. They moved at a stiff-necked, stiff bodied gallop and he could see the upswept wide black horns on their heads as they galloped heads out; the heads not moving.

"They're three old bulls," Wilson said. "We'll cut them off before they get to the swamp."

The car was going a wild forty-five miles an hour across the open and as Macomber watched, the buffalo got bigger and bigger until he could see the gray, hairless, scabby look of one huge bull and how his neck was a part of his shoulders and the shiny black of his horns as he galloped a little behind the others that were strung out in that steady plunging gait; and then, the car swaying as though it had just jumped a road, they drew up close and he could see the plunging hugeness of the bull, and the dust in his sparsely haired hide, the wide boss of horn and his outstretched, wide-nostrilled muzzle, and he was raising his rifle when Wilson shouted, "Not from the car, you fool!" and he had no fear, only hatred of Wilson, while the brakes clamped on and the car skidded, plowing sideways to an almost stop and Wilson was out on one side and he on the other, stumbling as his feet hit the still speeding-by of the earth, and then he was shooting at the bull as he moved away, hearing the bullets whunk into him, emptying his rifle at him as he moved steadily away, finally remembering to get his shots forward into the shoulder, and as he fumbled to re-load, he saw the bull was down. Down on his knees, his big head tossing, and seeing the other two still galloping he shot at the leader and hit him. He shot again and missed and he heard the *carawonging* roar as Wilson shot and saw the leading bull slide forward onto his nose.

"Get that other," Wilson said. "Now you're shooting!"

But the other bull was moving steadily at the same gallop and he missed, throwing a spout of dirt, and Wilson missed and the dust rose in a cloud and Wilson shouted, "Come on. He's too far!" and grabbed his arm and they were in the car again, Macomber and Wilson hanging on the sides and rocketing swayingly over the uneven ground, drawing up on the steady, plunging, heavy-necked, straight-moving gallop of the bull.

They were behind him and Macomber was filling his rifle, dropping shells onto the ground, jamming it, clearing the jam, then they were almost up with the bull when Wilson yelled "Stop," and the car skidded so that it almost swung over and Macomber fell forward onto his feet, slammed his bolt forward and fired as far forward as he could aim into the galloping, rounded black back, aimed and shot again, then again, then again, and the bullets, all of them hitting, had no effect on the buffalo that he could see. Then Wilson shot, the roar deafening him, and he could see the bull stagger. Macomber shot again, aiming carefully, and down he came, onto his knees.

"All right," Wilson said. "Nice work. That's the three."

Macomber felt a drunken elation.

"How many times did you shoot?" he asked.

"Just three," Wilson said. "You killed the first bull. The biggest one. I helped you finish the other two. Afraid they might have got into cover. You had them killed. I was just mopping up a little. You shot damn well."

"Let's go to the car," said Macomber. "I want a drink."

"Got to finish off that buff first," Wilson told him. The buffalo was on his knees and he jerked his head furiously and bellowed in pig-eyed, roaring rage as they came toward him.

"Watch he doesn't get up," Wilson said. Then, "Get a little broadside and take him in the neck just behind the ear."

Macomber aimed carefully at the center of the huge, jerking, rage-driven neck and shot. At the shot the head dropped forward.

"That does it," said Wilson. "Got the spine. They're a hell of a looking thing, aren't they?"

"Let's get the drink," said Macomber. In his life he had never felt so good.

In the car Macomber's wife sat very white faced. "You were marvellous, darling," she said to Macomber. "What a ride."

"Was it rough?" Wilson asked.

"It was frightful. I've never been more frightened in my life."

"Let's all have a drink," Macomber said.

"By all means," said Wilson. "Give it to the Memsahib." She drank the neat whisky from the flask and shuddered a little when she swallowed. She handed the flask to Macomber who handed it to Wilson.

"It was frightfully exciting," she said. "It's given me a dreadful headache. I didn't know you were allowed to shoot them from cars though."

"No one shot from cars," said Wilson coldly.

"I mean chase them from cars."

"Wouldn't ordinarily," Wilson said. "Seemed sporting enough to me though while we were doing it. Taking more chance driving that way across the plain full of holes and one thing and another than hunting on foot. Buffalo could have charged us each time we shot if he liked. Gave him every chance. Wouldn't mention it to any one though. It's illegal if that's what you mean."

"It seemed very unfair to me," Margot said, "chasing those big helpless things in a motor car."

"Did it?" said Wilson.

"What would happen if they heard about it in Nairobi?"

"I'd lose my license for one thing. Other unpleasantnesses," Wilson said, taking a drink from the flask. "I'd be out of business."

"Really?"

"Yes, really."

"Well," said Macomber, and he smiled for the first time all day. "Now she has something on you."

"You have such a pretty way of putting things, Francis," Margot Macomber said. Wilson looked at them both. If a four-letter man marries a five-letter woman, he was thinking, what number of letters would their children be? What he said was, "We lost a gun-bearer. Did you notice it?"

"My God no," Macomber said.

"Here he comes," Wilson said. "He's all right. He must have fallen off when we left the first bull."

Approaching them was the middle-aged gun-bearer, limping along in his knitted cap, khaki tunic, shorts and rubber sandals, gloomy-faced and disgusted looking. As he came up he called out to Wilson in Swahili and they all saw the change in the white hunter's face.

"What does he say?" asked Margot.

"He says the first bull got up and went into the bush," Wilson said with no expression in his voice.

"Oh," said Macomber blankly.

"Then it's going to be just like the lion," said Margot, full of anticipation.

"It's not going to be a damned bit like the lion," Wilson told her. "Did you want another drink, Macomber?"

"Thanks, yes," Macomber said. He expected the feeling he had had about the lion to come back but it did not. For the first time in his life he really felt wholly without fear. Instead of fear he had a feeling of definite elation.

"We'll go and have a look at the second bull," Wilson said. "I'll tell the driver to put the car in the shade."

"What are you going to do?" asked Margaret Macomber.

"Take a look at the buff," Wilson said.

"I'll come."

"Come along."

The three of them walked over to where the second buffalo bulked blackly in the open, head forward on the grass, the massive horns swung wide.

"He's a very good head," Wilson said. "That's close to a fifty-inch spread."

Macomber was looking at him with delight.

"He's hateful looking," said Margot. "Can't we go into the shade?"

"Of course," Wilson said. "Look," he said to Macomber, and pointed. "See that patch of bush?"

"Yes."

"That's where the first bull went in. The gun-bearer said when he fell off the bull was down. He was watching us helling along and the other two buff galloping. When he looked up there was the bull up and looking at him. Gun-bearer ran like hell and the bull went off slowly into that bush."

"Can we go in after him now?" asked Macomber eagerly.

Wilson looked at him appraisingly. Damned if this isn't a strange one, he thought. Yesterday he's scared sick and today he's a ruddy fire eater.

"No, we'll give him a while."

"Let's please go into the shade," Margot said. Her face was white and she looked ill.

They made their way to the car where it stood under a single, wide-spreading tree and all climbed in.

"Chances are he's dead in there," Wilson remarked. "After a little we'll have a look."

Macomber felt a wild unreasonable happiness that he had never known before.

"By God, that was a chase," he said. "I've never felt any such feeling. Wasn't it marvellous, Margot?"

"I hated it."

"Why?"

"I hated it," she said bitterly. "I loathed it."

"You know I don't think I'd ever be afraid of anything again," Macomber said to Wilson. "Something happened in me after we first saw the buff and started after him. Like a dam bursting. It was pure excitement."

"Cleans out your liver," said Wilson. "Damn funny things happen to people."

Macomber's face was shining. "You know something did happen to me," he said. "I feel absolutely different."

His wife said nothing and eyed him strangely. She was sitting far back in the seat and Macomber was sitting forward talking to Wilson who turned sideways talking over the back of the front seat.

"You know, I'd like to try another lion," Macomber said. "I'm really not afraid of them now. After all, what can they do to you?"

"That's it," said Wilson. "Worst one can do is kill you. How does it go? Shakespeare. Damned good. See if I can remember. Oh, damned good. Used to quote it to myself at one time. Let's see. 'By my troth, I care not; a man can die but once; we owe God a death and let it go which way it will he that dies this year is quit for the next.' Damned fine, eh?"

He was very embarrassed, having brought out this thing he had lived by, but he had seen men come of age before and it always moved him. It was not a matter of their twenty-first birthday.

It had taken a strange chance of hunting, a sudden precipitation into action without opportunity for worrying beforehand, to bring this about with Macomber, but regardless of how it had happened it had most certainly happened. Look at the beggar now, Wilson thought. It's that some of them stay little boys so long, Wilson thought. Sometimes all their lives. Their figures stay boyish when they're fifty. The great American boy-men. Damned strange people. But he liked this Macomber now. Damned strange fellow. Probably meant the end of cuckoldry too. Well, that would be a damned good thing. Damned good thing. Beggar had probably been afraid all his life. Don't know what started it. But over now. Hadn't had time to be afraid with the buff. That and being angry too. Motor car too. Motor cars made it familiar. Be a damn fire eater now. He'd seen it in the war work the same way. More of a change than any loss of virginity. Fear gone like an operation. Something else grew in its place. Main thing a man had. Made him into a man. Women knew it too. No bloody fear.

From the far corner of the seat Margaret Macomber looked at the two of them. There was no change in Wilson. She saw Wilson as she had seen him the day before when she had first realized what his great talent was. But she saw the change in Francis Macomber now.

"Do you have that feeling of happiness about what's going to happen?" Macomber asked, still exploring his new wealth.

"You're not supposed to mention it," Wilson said, looking in the other's face. "Much more fashionable to say you're scared. Mind you, you'll be scared too, plenty of times."

"But you *have* a feeling of happiness about action to come?"

"Yes," said Wilson. "There's that. Doesn't do to talk too much about all this. Talk the whole thing away. No pleasure in anything if you mouth it up too much."

"You're both talking rot," said Margot. "Just because you've chased some helpless animals in a motor car you talk like heroes."

"Sorry," said Wilson. "I have been gassing too much." She's worried about it already, he thought.

"If you don't know what we're talking about why not keep out of it?" Macomber asked his wife.

"You've gotten awfully brave, awfully suddenly," his wife said contemptuously, but her contempt was not secure. She was very afraid of something.

Macomber laughed, a very natural hearty laugh. "You know I *have*," he said. "I really have."

"Isn't it sort of late?" Margot said bitterly. Because she had done the best she could for many years back and the way they were together now was no one person's fault.

"Not for me," said Macomber.

Margot said nothing but sat back in the corner of the seat.

"Do you think we've given him time enough?" Macomber asked Wilson cheerfully.

"We might have a look," Wilson said. "Have you any solids left?"

"The gun-bearer has some."

Wilson called in Swahili and the older gun-bearer, who was skinning out one of the heads, straightened up, pulled a box of solids out of his pocket and brought them over to Macomber, who filled his magazine and put the remaining shells in his pocket.

"You might as well shoot the Springfield," Wilson said. "You're used to it. We'll leave the Mannlicher in the car with the Memsahib. Your gun-bearer can carry your heavy gun. I've this damned cannon. Now let me tell you about them." He had saved this until the last because he did not want to worry Macomber. "When a buff comes he comes with his head high and thrust straight out. The boss of the horns covers any sort of a brain shot. The only shot is straight into the nose. The only other shot is into his chest or, if you're to one side, into the neck or the shoulders. After they've been hit once they take a hell of a lot of killing. Don't try anything fancy. Take the easiest shot there is. They've finished skinning out that head now. Should we get started?"

He called to the gun-bearers, who came up wiping their hands, and the older one got into the back.

"I'll only take Kongoni," Wilson said. "The other can watch to keep the birds away."

As the car moved slowly across the open space toward the island of brushy trees that ran in a tongue of foliage along a dry water course that cut the open swale, Macomber felt his heart pounding and his mouth was dry again, but it was excitement, not fear.

"Here's where he went in," Wilson said. Then to the gun-bearer in Swahili, "Take the blood spoor."

The car was parallel to the patch of bush. Macomber, Wilson and the gun-bearer got down. Macomber, looking back, saw his wife, with the rifle by her side, looking at him. He waved to her and she did not wave back.

The brush was very thick ahead and the ground was dry. The middle-aged gun-bearer was sweating heavily and Wilson had his hat down over his eyes and his red neck showed just ahead of Macomber. Suddenly the gun-bearer said something in Swahili to Wilson and ran forward.

"He's dead in there," Wilson said. "Good work," and he turned to grip Macomber's hand and as they shook hands, grinning at each other, the gun-bearer shouted wildly and they saw him coming out of the bush sideways, fast as a crab, and the bull coming, nose out, mouth tight closed, blood dripping, massive head straight out, coming in a charge, his little pig eyes bloodshot as he looked at them. Wilson, who was ahead was kneeling shooting, and Macomber, as he fired, unhearing his shot in the roar of Wilson's gun, saw fragments like slate burst from the huge boss of the horns, and the head jerked, he shot again at the wide nostrils and saw the horns jolt again and fragments fly, and he did not see Wilson now and, aiming carefully, shot again with the buffalo's huge bulk almost on him and his rifle almost level with the on-coming head, nose out, and he could see the little wicked eyes and the head started to lower and he felt a sudden white-hot, blinding flash explode inside his head and that was all he ever felt.

Wilson had ducked to one side to get in a shoulder shot. Macomber had stood solid and shot for the nose, shooting a touch high each time and hitting the heavy horns, splintering and chipping them like hitting a slate roof, and Mrs. Macomber, in the car, had shot at the buffalo with the 6.5 Mannlicher as it seemed about to gore Macomber and had hit her husband about two inches up and a little to one side of the base of his skull.

Francis Macomber lay now, face down, not two yards from where the buffalo lay on his side and his wife knelt over him with Wilson beside her.

"I wouldn't turn him over," Wilson said.

The woman was crying hysterically.

"I'd get back in the car," Wilson said. "Where's the rifle?"

She shook her head, her face contorted. The gun-bearer picked up the rifle.

"Leave it as it is," said Wilson. Then, "Go get Abdulla so that he may witness the manner of the accident."

He knelt down, took a handkerchief from his pocket, and spread it over Francis Macomber's crew-cropped head where it lay. The blood sank into the dry, loose earth.

Wilson stood up and saw the buffalo on his side, his legs out, his thinly-haired belly crawling with ticks. "Hell of a good bull," his brain registered automatically. "A good fifty inches, or better. Better." He called to the driver and told him to spread a blanket over the body and stay by it. Then he walked over to the motor car where the woman sat crying in the corner.

"That was a pretty thing to do," he said in a toneless voice. "He *would* have left you too."

"Stop it," she said.

"Of course it's an accident," he said. "I know that."

"Stop it," she said.

"Don't worry," he said. "There will be a certain amount of unpleasantness but I will have some photographs taken that will be very useful at the inquest. There's the testimony of the gun-bearers and the driver too. You're perfectly all right."

"Stop it," she said.

"There's a hell of a lot to be done," he said. "And I'll have to send a truck off to the lake to wireless for a plane to take the three of us into Nairobi. Why didn't you poison him? That's what they do in England."

"Stop it. Stop it. Stop it," the woman cried.

Wilson looked at her with his flat blue eyes.

"I'm through now," he said. "I was a little angry. I'd begun to like your husband.

"Oh, please stop it," she said. "Please, please stop it."

"That's better," Wilson said. "Please is much better. Now I'll stop."

WELCOME TO THE CITY

By Irwin Shaw

AS HE DREW NEARER TO IT, ENDERS LOOKED UP AT HIS HOTEL through the black drizzle of the city that filled the streets with rain and soot and despair. A small red neon sign bloomed over the hotel entrance, spelling out CIRCUS HOTEL, REASONABLE, turning the drizzle falling profoundly around it into blood.

Enders sighed, shivered inside his raincoat, and walked slowly up the five steps to the entrance and went in. His nostrils curled, as they did each time he opened the door of the hotel, and his nose was hit by the ancient odor of ammonia and lysol and old linoleum and old beds and people who must depend on two bathrooms to the floor, and over the other odors the odor of age and sin, all at reasonable rates.

Wysocki was at the desk, in his gray suit with the markings of all the cafeteria soup in the city on it, and the pale face shaven down to a point where at any moment you half-expected to see the bone exposed, gleaming and green. Wysocki stood against the desk with the thirty-watt bulb shining down on his thinning hair and his navy-blue shirt and the solid orange tie, bright as hope in the dark hotel lobby, gravely reading the next morning's *Mirror,* his pale, hairy hands spread importantly, with delicate possessiveness, on the desk in front of him.

Josephine was sitting in one of the three lobby chairs, facing Wysocki. She wore a purple tailored suit with a ruffled waist, and open-toed red shoes, even though the streets outside were as damp and penetratingly cold as any marsh, and Enders could see the high red polish under her stockings, on her toenails. She sat there, not reading, not talking, her face carved out of powder and rouge under the blonde hair whose last surge of life had been strangled from it a dozen years before by peroxide and small-town hairdressers and curling irons that could have been used to primp the hair of General Sherman's granite horse.

"The English," Wysocki was saying, without looking up from his paper. "I wouldn't let them conduct a war for me for one million dollars in gilt-edged securities. Debaters and herring-fishermen," he said. "That's what they are."

"I thought Jews ate herring," Josephine said. Her voice scraped in the lobby, as though the Circus Hotel itself had suddenly broken into speech in its own voice, lysol and ammonia and rotting ancient wood finally put into sound.

"Jews eat herring," Wysocki said. "And the English eat herring."

Enders sighed again and walked up to the desk. In the chair near the stairway, he noticed, a girl was sitting, a pretty girl in a handsome green coat trimmed with lynx. He watched her obliquely as he talked to Wysocki, noticed that her legs were good and the expression cool, dignified, somehow hauntingly familiar.

"Hello, Wysocki," Enders said.

"Mr. Enders," Wysocki looked up pleasantly from the newspaper. "So you decided to come in out of the rain to your cozy little nest."

"Yes," said Enders, watching the girl.

"Did you know," Josephine asked, "that the English eat herring?"

"Yes," Enders said, digging into his mind for the face the girl reminded him of.

"That's what Wysocki said." Josephine shrugged. "I was living in happy ignorance."

Enders leaned over so that he could whisper into Wysocki's ear. "Who is she?" Enders asked.

Wysocki peered at the girl in the green coat, his eyes sly and guilty, as a thief might peer at a window at Tiffany's through which he intended to heave a brick later in the evening. "Zelinka," Wysocki whispered. "Her name's Bertha Zelinka. She checked in this afternoon. You could do worse, couldn't you?" He chuckled soundlessly, his bone-shaven face creasing without mirth, green and gleaming under the thirty-watt bulb.

"I've seen her some place," Enders whispered, looking at the girl over his shoulder. She sat remote, cold, her legs crossed beautifully under the green coat, looking under heavy lids at the scarred and battered clock over Wysocki's head. "I know that face," Enders said. "But from where?"

"She looks like Greta Garbo," Wysocki said. "That's where you know her from."

Enders stared at the girl in the green coat. She did look like Greta Garbo, the long pale face, the long eyes, the wide, firm mouth, the whole thing a mirror of passion and pain and deep Northern melancholy and bony, stubborn beauty. Suddenly Enders realized that he was a stranger in a strange city, a thousand miles from home, that it was raining out, that he had no girl, and that no one in this huge and wrangling seven-million town had ever said anything more tender to him than "Pass the mustard." And here, before him, solid as his hand, in a green coat with a lynx collar, sat a tall, melancholy girl who looked enough like Greta Garbo, pain and passion and beauty and understanding all mixed on the bony, pale face, to be her twin sister. His voice charged at his throat, leaping to say the first tender word in this rat-eaten, roach-claimed hotel lobby.

"Enders!" His name was spoken gaily, warmly. He turned from looking at Bertha Zelinka, wrenching his soul. "Mr. Enders, I was waiting for your appearance." It was Bishop, the owner of the hotel, a little fat gray-faced man with wet mustaches. He was rubbing his hands jovially now. "You were just the person I wanted to see tonight," he said.

"Thanks," said Enders.

"Wait!" Bishop's voice trilled. "Don't move an inch from the spot! I have a treat in store for you."

He darted back of the desk through the door into his office. Enders turned and looked at Bertha Zelinka, sitting there as calmly, as remotely, as Garbo herself.

"Observe!" Bishop darted out again from his office. "Look!" He held his hand high above his head. From it dangled a dead, wet chicken. "See what I've saved for you. I am willing to give you this chicken for sixty cents, Mr. Enders."

Enders looked politely at the chicken, hanging sadly in death from Bishop's proud hand.

"Thanks, Mr. Bishop," Enders said. "But I have no place to cook a chicken."

"Take it to your home," Bishop whirled the chicken lovingly, giving it a spruce and electric appearance of life, the wings spreading, the feathers ruffing. "Your mother would be delighted with this bird."

"My mother's in Davenport, Iowa," Enders said.

"You must have some relatives in the city." Bishop pushed it lovingly under his nose, spreading the limp wings for inspection. "They'll receive you with open arms with this chicken. This is a guaranteed Plymouth Rock chicken. Birds like this are exhibited in poultry shows from coast to coast. Sixty cents, Mr. Enders," Bishop said winningly. "Can you go wrong for sixty cents?"

Enders shook his head. "I have no relatives in the city," he said. "Thanks a lot, but I can't use it."

Bishop looked at him coldly. He shrugged. "I could've sold this chicken five times already," he said, "but I was saving it for you because you looked so pale. You gained my sympathy." He shrugged again, and holding the Plymouth Rock by the neck, he went into his office.

"Well," said Enders loudly, looking squarely at Bertha Zelinka. "I guess I'll turn in for the night."

"Want some company, Baby?" Josephine asked, in her voice the first note of hope she had allowed to sound there all evening.

"No, thank you," Enders said, embarrassedly, glad that Miss Zelinka wasn't looking at him at the moment.

"You certainly are a great ladies' man," Josephine said, her voice rasping through the lobby. "Don't you know you'll go crazy, you go so long without a woman? You been here two weeks, you haven't had a woman all that time. They face that problem in Sing Sing, the convicts climb on the walls."

Enders looked uneasily at Miss Zelinka. He didn't want a girl who looked like Greta Garbo to hear him mixed up in that kind of a conversation. "Good night," he said, and walked past Miss Zelinka, down the hallway to his own room, which was on the ground floor, at the bottom of an airwell, three dollars a week. He looked back regretfully. Miss Zelinka's legs were visible, jutting out, like a promise of poetry and flowers, past the grime and gloom of the hallway. Sadly he opened the door and went into his room, took off his hat and coat and fell on the bed. He could hear Josephine talking, as though the walls, the vermin, the old and wailing plumbing, the very rats hurrying on their gloomy errands between the floors, had at last found a voice.

"The papers are full of boys like him," Josephine was saying. "Turning the gas on and stuffing their heads into the oven. What a night! What a stinking whore of a night! They'll find plenty of bodies in the river tomorrow morning."

"Josephine," Wysocki's voice floated down the hallway. "You ought to learn to talk with more cheerfulness. You're ruining your business, Josephine. The wholesale butchers from Tenth Avenue, the slaughter-house workers, your whole regular clientele, they're all avoiding you. Should I tell you why?"

"Tell me why," Josephine said.

"Because you're gloomy!" Wysocki said. "Because you depress them with your talk. People like a woman to be cheerful. You can't expect to succeed in your line if you walk around like the last day of the world is beginning in two and three-quarter hours, Bulova watch time."

"The butchers from Tenth Avenue!" Josephine snarled. "Who wants them? I give them to you as a gift."

Enders lay on the bed, regretting that a proud and beautiful woman like Bertha Zelinka had to sit in one of the three chairs of the lobby of the Circus Hotel on a rainy night and listen to a conversation like that. He put on the light and picked up the book he was reading.

> I was neither at the hot gates
> Nor fought in the warm rain
> Nor knee deep in the salt marsh, heaving a cutlass,
> Bitten by flies, fought . . .

"What a night!" Josephine's voice scraped down the hallway. "The river will be stuffed with bodies in the morning."

Enders put down T. S. Eliot. It was hard to read T. S. Eliot in the Circus Hotel without a deep feeling of irony. Enders got up and looked around the doorpost, down the hall. The proud, poetic

legs were still there, lean, muscular, beautifully shaped, aristocratic, stemming down into slim ankles and narrow feet. Enders
leaned dreamily against the doorpost, regarding Miss Zelinka's
legs. Music played from a well-known orchestra in a night club
lit by orange lamps, where no dish cost less than a dollar seventy-
five, even tomato juice, and he danced with Bertha Zelinka, both
of them dressed beautifully, shiningly, and he made those deep,
long eyes, charged with Northern melancholy, crinkle with laughter, and later grow sober and reflective as he talked swiftly of
culture, of art, of poetry. " 'Nor fought in the warm rain,' in the
phrase of T. S. Eliot, a favorite of mine, 'nor knee deep in the
salt marsh . . . ' "

He walked quickly down the hallway, looking neither to right
nor left until he stopped at the desk. "Have there been any telephone calls for me today?" he asked Wysocki, carefully avoiding
looking at Miss Zelinka.

"No," said Wysocki. "Not a thing."

Enders turned and stared full at Miss Zelinka, trying with the
deep intensity of his glance, to get her to look at him, smile at
him . . .

"Heads like yours, my friend," Josephine said, "they find in
ovens."

Miss Zelinka sat passionless, expressionless, heedless, looking at a
point twenty-five feet over Wysocki's shoulder, patiently, but
coolly, in the attitude of a woman who is expecting a Lincoln to
drive up at any moment and a uniformed chauffeur to spring
from it and lead her fastidiously to the heavy, upholstered door,
rich with heavy hardware.

Enders walked slowly back to his room. He tried to read some
more. "April is the cruellest month . . . " He thumbed through
the book. "Here, said she, is your card, the drowned Phoenician
Sailor . . . " Enders put the book down. He couldn't read tonight. He went to the door and looked out. The legs, silk and
skin and firm muscle, were still there. Enders took a deep breath
and walked back toward the desk.

"Look," said Josephine, "the shuttle's back."

"I forgot to ask." He looked straight at Wysocki. "Is there any
mail for me?"

"No mail," said Wysocki.

"I'll tell you frankly, friend," Josephine said. "You should've stayed in Davenport, Iowa. That's my honest opinion. New York City will break you like a peanut shell."

"Nobody asked for your opinion," Wysocki said, noticing Enders peering uneasily at Miss Zelinka to see what impression Josephine's advice had made on her. "He's a nice boy, he's educated, he's going to go a long way. Leave him alone."

"I'm only giving him my honest opinion," Josephine said. "I've been in New York a dozen years. I see them begin and I see them wind up in the river."

"Will you, for Christ's sake, stop talking about the river?" Wysocki slammed his hand on the desk.

Gratefully, Enders noticed that Miss Zelinka was listening to the conversation, that her head tilted just a little, a shade went across her disdainful, beautiful eyes.

"I come from Fall River," Josephine said. "I should've stayed there. At least when you're dead in Fall River they bury you. Here they leave you walk around until your friends notice it. Why did I ever leave Fall River? I was attracted by the glamor of the Great White Way." She waved her red and white umbrella ironically, in salute to the city.

Enders noticed that a hint, a twitch of a smile, played at the corner of Miss Zelinka's mouth. He was glad that she'd heard Wysocki say he was educated, he was going to go a long way.

"If you'd like," he heard his voice boom out suddenly in the direction of Miss Zelinka, "if you'd like, if you're waiting for someone, you can wait in my room. It's not so noisy there."

"No, thank you," Miss Zelinka said, speaking curiously, her lips together, not showing her teeth. Her voice, behind the closed, beautiful lips, was deep and hoarse and moving, and Enders felt it grip at his throat like a cool, firm hand. He turned to Wysocki, determined now that he was not going back to his room.

"I was curious," he said. "Where did Bishop get that chicken he wants to sell me?"

Wysocki looked behind him carefully. "Don't buy those chickens, Enders," he said in a low voice. "I advise you as a good friend.

Bishop picks them up on Tenth Avenue, alongside the railroad tracks."

"What're they doing there?" Enders asked.

"The trains bring them in from the farms, from the country," Wysocki said. "The ones that died on the trip for one reason or another, the trainmen throw them off the cars and they're piled up alongside the tracks and Bishop picks out the ones that look as though they died most peaceful and he tries to sell them." Wysocki slid back to the office door, listened guiltily for a moment for Bishop, like a spy in the movies. "I advise you not to buy them. They're not the most nourishing articles of food in the world."

Enders smiled. "Bishop ought to be in Wall Street," he said. "With talent like that."

Miss Zelinka laughed. Feeling twice as tall as he had felt a moment before, Enders noticed that Miss Zelinka was laughing, quietly, and without opening her mouth, but true laughter. He laughed with her and their eyes met in friendly, understanding amusement.

"May I buy you a cup of coffee," hurled out of his throat, at Miss Zelinka's head, like a hand grenade.

The light of thought, consideration, appeared in the large gray eyes, while Enders waited. Then Miss Zelinka smiled. "All right," she said. She stood up, five feet six inches tall, graceful as a duchess.

"I'll be right back," Enders said, quickly. "Just have to get my coat."

He fled lightly down the hall toward his room.

"That's what keeps me poor," Josephine said. "Girls like that. What a night, what a dirty whore of a night!"

"I'm a dancer," Bertha Zelinka was saying two hours later, her coat off, in Enders' room, as she drank the whisky straight in one of the two water tumblers the room boasted. "Specialty dancing." She put the whisky down, suddenly sank beautifully to the floor in a split. "I'm as supple as a cat."

"I see," Enders said, his eyes furious with admiration for Miss Zelinka, full-breasted, flat-bellied, steel-thighed, supple as a cat, spread magnificently on the dirty carpet. It was more pleasant to look at her body, now that he had seen her eating, mouth opened to reveal the poor, poverty-stricken, ruined teeth jagged and sorrowful in her mouth. "That looks very hard to do."

"My name's been in lights," Miss Zelinka said, from the floor. "Please pass the whisky. From one end of the country to another. I've stopped show after show. I've got an uncanny sense of timing." She stood up, after taking another draught of her whisky, closing her eyes with a kind of harsh rapture as the Four Roses went down past the miserable teeth, down inside the powerful, long white throat. "I'm an actress, too, you know, Mr. Enders."

"I'm an actor," Enders said shyly, feeling the whisky beat in his blood, keeping his eyes fiercely and wonderingly on Miss Zelinka. "That's why I'm in New York. I'm an actor."

"You ought to be a good actor," Miss Zelinka said. "You got the face for it. It's refined." She poured herself another drink, watching the amber liquor pour into her glass with a brooding, intense expression on her face. "I had my name in lights from coast to coast. Don't you believe it?"

"I believe it," Enders said sincerely, noting that half the bottle was already gone.

"That's why I'm here now," she said. She walked beautifully around the small, flaky-walled room, her hands running sorrowfully over the warped bureau, the painted bedstead. "That's why I'm here now." Her voice was faraway and echoing, hoarse with whisky and regret. "I'm very much in demand, you know. I've stopped shows for ten minutes at a time. They wouldn't let me get off the stage. Musicals that cost one hundred and fifty thousand to ring the curtain up. That's why I'm here now," she said mysteriously, and drained her glass. She threw herself on the bed next to Enders, stared moodily through almost closed eyes, at the stained and beaten ceiling. "The Shuberts're putting on a musical. They want me for it. Rehearsals are on Fifty-second Street, so I thought I'd move close by for the time being." She sat up, silently reached for the bottle, poured with the fixed expression, brooding and infatuate, which she reserved for the distillers' product. Enders, too full for words, sitting on the same bed with a woman who looked like Greta Garbo, who had stopped musical

shows with specialty dancing from coast to coast, who got drunk
with the assured yet ferocious grace of a young society matron,
watched her every move, with hope, admiration, growing passion.

"You might ask," Miss Zelinka said, "what is a person like
myself doing in a rat-hole like this." She waited, but Enders
merely gulped silently at his whisky. She chuckled and patted
his hand. "You're a nice boy. Iowa, you said? You come from
Iowa?"

"Iowa."

"Corn," Miss Zelinka said. "That's what they grow in Iowa."
She nodded, having placed Iowa and Enders firmly in her mind.
"I passed through Iowa on my way to Hollywood." Half the
whisky in her glass disappeared.

"Have you acted in pictures?" Enders asked, impressed, sitting
on the same bed with a woman who had been in Hollywood.

Miss Zelinka laughed moodily. "Hollywood!" She finished her
drink. "Don't look for my footprints in front of Grauman's
Chinese." She reached fluently for the bottle.

"It seems to me," Enders said seriously, breathing deeply because Miss Zelinka was leaning across him for the moment. "It
seems to me you'd do very well. You're beautiful and you've got a
wonderful voice."

Miss Zelinka laughed again. "Look at me," she said.

Enders looked at her.

"Do I remind you of anybody?" Miss Zelinka asked.

Enders nodded.

Miss Zelinka drank moodily. "I look like Greta Garbo," she
said. "Nobody could deny that. I'm not being vain when I tell
you when I photograph you couldn't tell me apart from the
Swede." She sipped her whisky, ran it lovingly around in her
mouth, swallowed slowly. "A woman who looks like Greta Garbo
in Hollywood is like the fifth leg on a race horse. Do you understand what I mean?"

Enders nodded sympathetically.

"It's my private curse," Miss Zelinka said, tears looming in her
eyes like mist over the ocean. She jumped up, shaking her head,
walked lightly and dramatically around the room. "I have no
complaints," she said. "I've done very well. I live in a two-room

suite on the twentieth floor of a hotel on Seventy-fifth Street. Overlooking the park. All my trunks and bags are up there. I just took a few things with me, until the rehearsals are over. Seventy-fifth Street, on the East Side, is too far away; when you're rehearsing a musical comedy, you've got to be on tap twenty-four hours a day for the Shuberts. A very luxurious two-room suite in the Hotel Chalmers. It's very exclusive, but it's too far from Ffty-second Street." She poured some more whisky for herself, and Enders noticed that the bottle was almost empty. "Oh, yes," she said, crooning to the glass in her hand, "I've done very well. I've danced all over the country. In the most exclusive nightspots, I was the featured entertainment. I'm very greatly in demand." She sat down, close to him, her body moving gently and rhythmically as she spoke. "Seattle, Chicago, Los Angeles, Detroit." She gulped her whisky and her eyes clouded with a final, deep, vague mist and her voice suddenly got very throaty and hoarse. "Miami, Florida." She sat absolutely still and the cloud dissolved into tears and the tears coursed slowly down her face.

"What's the matter?" Enders asked anxiously. "Did I do something?"

Miss Zelinka threw the empty tumbler against the opposite wall. It broke heavily and sullenly, scattered over the carpet. She threw herself back on the bed, wept. "Miami, Florida," she sobbed. "Miami, Florida . . . "

Enders patted her shoulder consolingly.

"I danced in The Golden Horn in Miami, Florida," she cried. "It was a Turkish night club. Very exclusive."

"Why're you crying, darling?" Enders asked, feeling sorry for her, but elated, too, because he had said "darling."

"Every time I think of Miami, Florida," Miss Zelinka said, "I cry."

"Can I do anything to help?" Enders held her hand softly.

"It was January, 1936." Miss Zelinka's voice throbbed with old, hopeless, broken tragedy, forlorn as the story of a siege of a lost and ruined village. "I was dressed in Turkish garments: a brassiere, and veils around my legs and nothing around the middle. At the end of the dance I had to do a back-bend. I leaned back and touched the floor with my hands, with my hair falling down to the floor. There was a bald man. There was a convention of the Metal-Trades Union in Miami, Florida. He had on a badge. The whole night club was full of them." The tears and the anguish pulled at her face. "I'll remember that bald son of a bitch until the day I die. There was no music at that part of the dance. Drums and tambourines. He leaned over and put an olive in my navel and sprinkled it with salt." Miss Zelinka rolled suddenly over on her face and, clutching the bedspread, her shoulders heaving, burrowing into the grayish cotton. "It was a cartoon. He saw it in a cartoon in a magazine. It's funny in a magazine, but wait until it happens to you! The humiliation," she wept. "Every time I think of the humiliation I want to die. Miami, Florida."

Enders watched the bedspread stain with tears, mascara and rouge. With genuine sympathy, he put his arm around her. "I want to be treated with respect," Miss Zelinka wailed. "I was brought up in a good family, why shouldn't I be treated with respect? That fat, bald man, with the badge from the Metal-Trades Union Convention. He leaned over and put the olive in my navel like an egg in an egg cup and sprinkled salt like he was starting breakfast and everybody laughed and laughed, including the orchestra . . . " Her voice went wailing up the airwell, lost, despairing, full of an ancient and irreparable sorrow.

She sat up and threw her arms around Enders, digging her grief-torn head into his shoulder, clutching him with strong hands, both of them rocking back and forth like Jews praying, on the enameled bed that squeaked and wailed in the little room.

"Hold me tight," she wept, "hold me tight. I haven't got a two-room suite on East Seventy-fifth Street. I got no trunks in the Hotel Chalmers, hold me tight." Her hands dug into him and her tears and rouge and mascara stained his coat. "The Shuberts aren't giving me a job. Why do I lie, why do I always lie?" She lifted her head, kissed his throat fiercely. He shook at the soft, violent pressure, at the wetness of her lips and the tragic and exhilarating trickle of her tears under his chin, knowing that he was going to have this woman, this Bertha Zelinka. Lonely, far from home, on a rainy night, the city was pulling him in, making a place in its wild and ludicrous life for him. As he kissed her, this woman who looked like Greta Garbo, the century's dream of passion and tragedy and beauty, this woman whom he had met in a rat-tenanted lobby off Columbus Circle, among whores thinking of death and a Pole in an orange tie checking in each night's transients, age and sin, at reasonable rates, Enders felt suddenly at home, accounted for. The city had produced for him a great beauty, supple as a cat, full of lies and whisky and ancient shadowy victories, a woman with magnificent proud legs and deep stormy eyes who wept bitterly behind the frail, warped door because once, in 1936, a bald man from a Metal-Trades Union had put an olive in her navel. Enders held Bertha Zelinka's head in his two hands, looked intently at the bony, drunken, beautiful, tear-stained face. Bertha Zelinka peered longingly and sadly at him through half-closed classic lids, her mouth hanging softly open in passion and promise, her poor jagged teeth showing behind the long, heart-breaking lips. He kissed her, feeling deep within him, that in its own way, on this rainy night, the city had put out its hand in greeting, had called, in its own voice, wry and ironic, "Welcome, Citizen."

Gratefully, near tears, hating himself, his hands shaking exultantly, Enders bent to his knees and took the scraped, year-worn shoes, swollen with the streets' rain, from the long and handsome feet of Bertha Zelinka.

THE KNIFE

By Brendan Gill

MICHAEL THREW HIMSELF DOWN, LOCKED HIS HANDS OVER ONE OF his father's knees, and began, in a loud whisper, " 'Our Father, who art in heaven, hallowed be thy name, kingdom come, will be done, earth as it is in heaven, give us this day—' "

Carroll folded his newspaper. Michael should have been in bed an hour ago. "Take it easy, kid," he said. "Let's try it again, slow."

Michael repeated distinctly, " 'Our Father, who art in heaven, hallowed . . .' " The boy's pajamas, Carroll saw, were dirty at the cuffs; probably he had not brushed his teeth. " '. . . as we forgive them, who trespass against us'—what does 'trespass' mean, Dad?"

"Why, hurting anybody."

"Do I trespass anybody?"

"Not much, I guess. Finish it up."

Michael drew a breath. " 'And lead us not into temptation, but deliver us from evil. Amen.' "

"Now," his father said, brushing back Michael's tangled hair, "what about a good 'Hail Mary'?"

"All right," Michael said. " 'Hail, Mary, full of grace, the Lord is with thee, blessed art thou among women, and blessed is the fruit of thy womb, Jesus.' " Michael lifted his head to ask if a womb got fruit like a tree, but thought better of it. His father never answered questions seriously, the way his mother used to. Michael decided to wait and ask Mrs. Nolan. "Is Mrs. Nolan coming tomorrow?" he asked.

"She'll be here, all right," Carroll said. "I give you ten seconds to finish the prayer."

Michael grinned at the ultimatum. "I thought you wanted me to go slow. 'Holy Mary, Mother of God, pray for us sinners, now and at the hour of our death. Amen.' " He unlocked his fingers. "Will she?"

258

"Will she what?"

"Will she now and at the hour of our death, A-men?"

The words of Michael's prayer caught in Carroll's mind and stayed there, a long way beyond his smiling face. "Yes," he said, and set his pipe in the broken dish on the table beside him. He had not emptied the dish of ashes in two days. Mrs. Nolan would give him a piece of her mind tomorrow morning, as she did each week when she came in to give the apartment a general cleaning and to do the laundry.

"What good can she do?" Michael asked.

"Climb into bed, young ragamuffin," Carroll said sternly. "It's past nine."

"What *good* can she do?"

"She'll help you get anything you want. I suppose she'll help you climb up into heaven when the time comes. You know all about heaven, don't you?"

Michael felt himself on the defensive. "Of course."

"Well, then, get along with you."

But Michael had something difficult to say. "You mean she'll ask God for anything I want and He'll give it to her for me?"

"She's His mother."

Michael stood up and kissed his father carefully on the cheek. Then he walked from the room, and Carroll could hear his bare feet crossing the hall. The bed creaked as Michael lay down on it. Carroll opened the newspaper, read a paragraph, then dropped it in a white heap on the rug. He felt tired; perhaps tonight he might be able to get some sleep. He got up, clipped his suspenders from his shoulders, unknotted his tie, kicked off his shoes. He had learned to undress quickly in the last six months, since his wife had died.

His pajamas were hanging inside out in the bathroom, where he had left them that morning. When he had undressed he felt Michael's toothbrush with his thumb; it was dry. He should have explained to the child what happened to a person's teeth when he forgot to clean them every night and morning.

Carroll stared at his face in the mirror above the basin. He tried smiling. No one could honestly tell what a man was thinking by the way he smiled. Even Michael, who was like a puppy about sensing moods, could not tell. He entered the bedroom on tiptoe. Feeling the sheets bunched at the foot of the mattress, he remembered that he had made the beds in a hurry. The sheets felt fresh and cool only on Saturdays, when Mrs. Nolan changed them.

Michael was not asleep. "Dad?" he whispered.

"Go to sleep."

"I been asking Hail Mary for something."

"Tomorrow."

"No, I been asking her right now."

Carroll lay on his back with his hands over his eyes. "What've you been asking her for, Mickey?"

Michael hesitated. "I thought I'd better make it something easy first. To see what happened." He sat up in bed. "A jackknife."

A few blocks away the clock in the Metropolitan Life tower was striking ten. Michael was deep in the noisy middle of a dream. Carroll listened to his breathing. He tried matching his own breath to Michael's, to make sleep come, but it was no use. Every night Carroll pretended to himself he was just at the brink of falling off to sleep, but his eyes always widened with wakefulness in the dark. Now, as the clock stopped striking, Carroll got up and walked into the bathroom and dressed. Then he went into the living room, unlocked the outside door of the apartment, and then locked it again before he walked down the two flights of stairs to the sidewalk. Shops reached out of sight down both sides of Lexington Avenue. Carroll walked uptown as he always did. He stopped in front of each bright shop window, studying its contents for the fifth or sixth time. He knew by now the day on which each window was changed and by whom. Certain plaster models, certain fringed crêpe papers were old friends.

At the top of a long slope Carroll waited for the lights to change. On his left was a bar; on his right, across the street, a drugstore. Carroll waited a moment outside the bar. Between the slats of its cheap orange Venetian blinds be could see the gleaming mahogany counter, the stacked glasses, the barman slicing foam from a mug of beer. A man and a girl were sitting at a table by the window, a foot under Carroll's eyes. They did not seem to be speaking. The man's hands lay halfway across the table and the girl's black dress made her throat look soft and white. Carroll turned away and crossed the street to the drugstore. The owner, Sam Ramatsky, stood sniffing the night air under the painted sign bearing his name.

"Well, Mr. Carroll, nice night for March."

"Yes." Carroll wanted only to hear a voice. "How's business?" he asked.

"Can't complain." Sam grinned, shaking his head. "I take that back. It's *lousy*. I got to break myself of this old 'Can't complain.' I got to remember how serious it is. Business is lousy."

Carroll leaned back against Sam's window, which was crammed with hot-water bottles, perfumes, toys, and two cardboard girls in shorts and sandals. The girls had been there for two months. There was dust on their teeth and on their smooth brown legs. "You ought to brush their teeth, Sam," Carroll said, "and run your hand down their legs now and then."

"You walk a lot," Sam said. "I figure on you, ten or eleven, every night."

"I guess I do," Carroll said.

Sam patted his hard belly. "Nothing like exercise to keep a man in shape."

Carroll nodded impatiently. It was not Sam's voice he wanted to hear, after all. "Give me a milk shake, Sam."

They walked into the store. Carroll sat down on one of the round stools at the fountain and watched Sam pouring milk into the shaker. "Nothing like milk," Sam said, "keep a man's system clean." Carroll watched the hands of the electric clock above the door. Ten-forty-five. He could not go to bed before twelve. He glanced at the packed counters behind him. "Sell any jackknives, Sam?"

"Sure. I sell everything. That's what keeps me broke. Nothing like keeping a thing in stock to kill demand." Sam lifted a tray of jackknives from a counter, brought it over, and set it down on the fountain. "Beauties," Sam said. "Fifty cents up."

Carroll looked at several of them and finally picked up the biggest and shiniest one. "I'll take this one," he said.

"Such expensive taste! One buck."

Carroll paid for the milk shake and the knife, said "Good

night, Sam," and walked out into the street. In another hour and a half he should have walked six miles. By that time his body would be tired enough so that he could sleep. By that time, he hoped, no voice could rouse him.

It was morning when Carroll awoke. He lay with his face on his hands, listening to the sound of the March rain against the windows. He remembered suddenly the absurd song that everyone used to sing: "Though April showers may come your way, they bring the flowers that bloom in May." March rains brought you nothing. March rains only shut you in your room without any hope of escape.

Michael and Mrs. Nolan were talking together in the kitchen. Michael's voice was high with excitement. "Look at it, Mrs. Nolan, look at it! Isn't it beautiful?"

"It is that," Mrs. Nolan said in her deep voice. Carroll sat up in bed. It was too late to give Mrs. Nolan warning.

"Do you ask for things when you say your prayers, Mrs. Nolan?" Michael demanded.

"I do." A pan clattered to the floor. "I've seen many a nice clean sty I'd swap for this dirty kitchen," Mrs. Nolan said. "You live like a couple of savages from week to week. God love you."

"Do you always get what you ask for?" Michael said.

"It all depends. I sort of try to guess what the good Lord wants to give me, and I ask for that."

"That's how I got this knife," Michael said. "It's got a big blade and a little blade and a screwdriver and a thing to punch holes in leather with and a file."

"You must have said yourself a fine prayer," Mrs. Nolan said. There was no hint of surprise in her voice.

"It was only a 'Hail, Mary,'" Michael said, "but I did it very slow, the way Dad told me to." Michael was silent for a moment. "But I'm asking for the real thing tonight. The knife was just to see. Someone's going to be here when you come next week."

Mrs. Nolan made a clucking sound in her mouth. "Someone instead of me?"

"She was here with Dad and me before you came," Michael said, his voice thin with its burden, "and she's coming back."

"Michael!" Carroll shouted.

Michael ran to the doorway. The knife gleamed in his fist. "Look what I got," he said. "I was showing Mrs. Nolan."

"Come here," Carroll said. When Michael reached the edge of the bed Carroll bent over and fastened his arms behind the child's back. There was only one thing to say, and one way to say it, and that was fast. "I'm glad you like it," he said. "I bought it for you at Ramatsky's last night. The biggest and shiniest one he had."

DRESSING UP

By W. R. BURNETT

WHEN THE STORE MANAGER SAW BLUE AND HIS GIRL, BIRDY, COMING in the front door, he turned to Al, one of the clerks, and said:

"Look at this, Al. The stockyards're moving down town."

Al laughed, then he put on his best professional manner, clasped his hands in front of his stomach, inclined his head slightly, and walked up to Blue.

"What can I do for you, sir?"

Blue was short and stocky. His legs were thin, his waist small, but his shoulders were wide enough for a man six feet tall. His face was red and beefy, and his cheekbones were so prominent that they stuck out of his face. He looked up at Al.

"I'm buying an outfit, see," he said. "I'm gonna shed these rags and climb into something slick."

"Yes, sir," said Al. "How about one of our new spring models?"

"He wants a gray suit," said Birdy, adjusting her new fur neckpiece.

"Double-breasted," said Blue.

"Yes, sir," said Al.

"But fiirst I want some silk underwear," said Blue. "I'm dressing from the hide out."

The store manager came over and smiled.

"Take good care of this young man, won't you, Mr. Johnson?"

"Yes, sir," said Al.

"Warm, isn't it?" the store manager said to Birdy.

"Yeah, ain't it?" said Birdy, taking off her neckpiece and dangling it over her arm like the women in the advertisements."

The store manager walked to the back of the shop and talked to the cashier:

"There's a boy that's got a big hunk of money all of a sudden," he said, "and he's gonna lose it the same way."

264

"Yeah?" said the cashier. "Well, I wish my rich uncle that I haven't got would die. Take a look at that neckpiece his girl's wearing. He didn't get that for five dollars."

Al spread out the silk underwear on the counter, and Blue looked through it. Birdy held up a lavender shirt.

"Here you are, Blue. Here's what you ought to get."

"Say . . . !" said Blue.

"Yes, sir," said Al; "we're selling lots of that. Just had an order for a dozen suits for Mr. Hibschmann out in Lake Forest."

"That's where the swells come from," said Birdy.

Blue looked at the lavender shirt and the lavender shorts and said:

"All right. I'll take a dozen."

Al glanced up from his order book, caught the manager's eye, and winked. The manager came up to Blue, put his hand on his shoulder and said:

"My dear sir, since you seem to know real stuff when you see it, I'll let you in on something. We got a new shipment of cravats that we have only just begun to unpack. But if you'd like to look at them, I'll send down to the stockroom for them."

"Sure," said Blue.

"Thanks awfully," said Birdy.

"It's our very best stock. Handmade cravats of the best material obtainable."

"We want the best, don't we, Blue?" said Birdy.

"Sure," said Blue.

While the manager sent for the cravats, Blue bought a dozen silk shirts, some collars, a solid gold collar pin, some onyx cuff links, a set of military brushes, and two dozen pairs of socks. Al bent over his order book and wrote in the items swiftly, computing the possible amount of this windfall. In a few minutes a stock boy brought up the neckties and stood with his mouth open while Blue selected a dozen of the most expensive ties. The manager noticed him.

"Just leave the rest of the stock, please," he said, then he turned his back to Blue and hissed, "Get out of here!"

The stock boy went back to the basement, and the manager turned back to Blue, smiling.

"Those cravats retail at four dollars apiece," he said, "but because you're giving us such a nice order, I'll let you have them for three fifty."

"O.K.," said Blue.

"Them sure are swell ties, Blue," said Birdy, putting her arm through his. "Won't we be lit up, though?"

"Sure," said Blue.

When the accessories had been selected, Blue began to try on the suits Al brought him. Blue strode up and down in front of the big triple mirror, puffed out his chest, struck attitudes, and studied his profile, which he had never seen before except in one Bertillon picture. Al stayed at his elbow, offering suggestions, helping him with the set of a coat, telling him how wonderful he looked; and the manager stayed in the background, occasionally making a remark to Birdy, whom he addressed as "Madam."

Blue, after a long consultation with Birdy, selected two of the most expensive suits: a blue serge single-breasted and a gray double-breasted. Then he bought a gray felt hat at twelve dollars, a small sailor at eight, and a panama at eighteen.

"Well," said Blue, "I guess you guys got about as much of my jack as you're gonna get."

"How about shoes?" Al put in.

"By God, I forgot," said Blue. "Hey, Birdy, I forgot shoes. Aint that good? Look at this suitcase!"

He held up his foot. He was wearing big tan brogans, and there was a hole in the sole which went clear through the sock to the skin.

"Put your foot down, Blue," said Birdy. "Where do you think you're at?"

Blue bought a pair of tan oxfords, a pair of black oxfords, and a pair of white and tan sport shoes.

"Now we're done," said Blue. "I guess I ought to look pretty Boul' Mich' now."

Al totaled up the bill. Birdy and the manager had a long conversation about the weather; and Blue stood before the triple mirror studying his profile.

Al hesitated before he told Blue the amount of the bill. He called for the manager to O.K. it, then he said:

"Cash or charge, sir?"

Blue took out his billfold which was stuffed with big bills.

"Cash," he said. "How much?"

"Four hundred and sixty-five dollars," said Al.

Blue gave him five one-hundred-dollar bills.

"Now," said Blue, "I want you to get that gray suit fixed up right away so's I can put it on. I'm gonna dress from the hide out, and you guys can throw my old duds in the sewer."

"Yes, sir," said Al. "I'll get our tailor right away. We got a dressing-room on the second floor."

The cashier rang up the sale and gave the change to the manager.

"Are you going away for the summer?" asked the manager as he handed Blue his change.

"Yeah," said Blue; "me and the girl friend are gonna see New York. It'll be our first trip."

"That'll be nice," said the manager. "Are you in business for yourself?"

Blue glanced at Birdy, and she shook her head slightly.

"I'm in the oil business," said Blue. "I got some wells. I'm from Oklahoma."

"That's interesting," said the manager.

When they were leaving the café Blue took out his billfold and gave the doorman a five-dollar bill. The doorman's eyes popped but he managed to bow and smile.

"Yes, sir; yes, sir," he said. "Do you want a cab?"

"Yeah," said Blue, hanging on to Birdy, who was drunker than he was.

"Yeah, you're damn right we want a cab," said Birdy. "Do we look like the kind of people that walk?"

"That's right," said Blue.

"Yes, sir," said the doorman, and he went out into the middle of the street and blew his whistle.

Before the taxi came a small sedan drew up at the curb across the street, and two men got out.

"There he is," said one of them, pointing at Blue.

"Hello, Guido," shouted Blue. "Look at me, Aint I Boul' Mich'?"

Guido ran across the street, took Blue by the arm, shook him several times and said:

"You got to sober up, keed! Get it! You got to sober up. Somebody spilled something, see? Me and Bud's taking it on the lam. Saint Louis won't look bad to us."

"Yellow," said Blue.

"Sure," said Guido; "but I got a stake and I'm gonna spend some of it before I get bumped. Somebody wised Mike's boys. They're looking for Pascal right now."

"What the hell!" said Blue, laughing. "Look at me, Guido. Aint I Boul' Mich'? I got silk underwear under this suit. Look at Birdy."

"Look at me," said Birdy; "aint I Boul' Mich'?"

"Say," said Guido, "you better ditch that tommy and put in with us. We got room in the heap."

"Not me," said Blue. "I ain't scairt of Mike Bova. I'll bump him next."

"All right," said Guido; "you'll have a swell funeral."

"Guido," called the other man, "let that bum go."

"So long, Blue," said Guido.

"So long," said Blue.

"Bye, bye, Guido," said Birdy.

Guido crossed the street, got into the driver's seat, slammed the door, and the sedan moved off. The taxi was waiting, and the doorman helped Birdy and Blue into it.

"Good-night, sir," said the doorman.

Birdy was lying on the lounge flat on her back with her hands under her head and an empty drinking glass sitting upright on her stomach. Blue, in his shirtsleeves, his collar wilted and his tie untied, was sitting at the table reading a crumpled newspaper. There were three-inch headlines.

BOVA'S LIEUTENANT KILLED

SHOT DOWN AS HE LEFT

HIS OFFICE BY GUNMEN

"You hear me!" said Blue. "Funniest thing ever pulled. There I was waiting in a room across the stret trying to read a magazine, and Pascal was sitting with his head against the wall sleeping. 'Christ,' I says, 'there's Pete now.' He was coming out of his office. We wasn't looking for him for two hours yet. So I jist set there. Hell, I couldn't move, see, 'cause he come sudden, see, and I was figuring he wouldn't be out for two hours yet. 'Pascal,' I says, 'there's Pete now. But Pascal he jist opens his eyes like a fish and don't say nothing. Pete he stops and looks right up at the window where I'm sitting, see, and I wonder does this guy know something. Hell, I couldn't move. I wasn't ready, see? Well, so Pascal he slips and falls over and hits his head. This makes me laugh but still I couldn't move my trigger finger. Pete he holds out his hand like he's looking fo rain, then I let him have it. I don't know. It was funny. I jist let him have it without knowing it, see, and before, I couldn't pull that trigger when I wanted to. When the old Thompson starts to mark, Pascal gets up and yells, 'What you smoking for, you bum? It aint time yet.' Then he looks out the window and there's Pete on the sidewalk dead as yesterday's newspaper and an old woman is pointing up at us. We ditch the gun and beat it down the back stairs. That's all there was to it. There wasn't nobody in the alley, see, so we jist walked along slow, and pretty soon we come to a drugstore and went in to get some cigs 'cause we smoked all ours waiting for that guy to come out."

"Pour me a little drink, honey," said Birdy.

Blue got up, took a big flask out of his hip pocket, and poured Birdy another drink. Then he sat down, took out his billfold, and extracted a couple of railroad tickets.

"Look at them, old kid," he said. "When we ride, we ride. Twentieth Century to New York. That's us, kid; and won't we give 'em a treat over in Brooklyn! Say, them Easterners think we're still shooting Indians. Hell, Chi makes that place look like a Y. M. C. A. Yeah, I used to know Ruby Welch, and he was big stuff from Brooklyn; but what did he do when Guido started gunning for him? He got himself put in the can as a vag. Yeah, we ought to go big over in New York, kid. What they need over there is guts. We can give 'em that, kid. When somebody needs somebody for the No. 1 caper, Blue's the guy for the job. I was born with a rod in my cradle and I'm the best there is. Yeah, when the Big Boy wanted Pete bumped who did he call on first? Old Blue, yes, sir, old Blue."

Blue got up, turned on the gramophone, and started to dance with a chair.

"Hey," he said, "come on, let's dance, Birdy. We're big shots now, Birdy; let's dance. Look at me! If I had my coat on I'd look like the Prince of Wales. Boul' Mich', kid; that's us; Boul' Mich'. We'll knock their eyes out on Fifth Avenue, kid; yes, sir. Let's dance."

"I'm getting sick," said Birdy.

Blue went over and looked down at her. Her face was pale and drawn; there were blue circles under her eyes.

"Getting sick, Birdy?"

"Yeah. I can't stand it like I used to when I was with the Madam. Put me to bed, honey."

Blue picked Birdy up and carried her into the bedroom. Birdy began to hiccough.

"Gimme glass of water," she said.

"You don't want water," Blue said; "you want a nice big slug."

"No, gimme glass of water."

She lay down on the bed and, before Blue could bring her a glass of water, she was asleep. He stood looking down at her, then he went back into the living room, took a long pull at his flask, and picked up the crumpled newspaper. But he had read the account of the killing of Big Pete so many times that he knew it by heart. He sat staring at the paper, then he threw it on the floor and sat rolling a cigarette between his palms.

It had begun to get light. He heard a milk wagon passing the house. He got up and went over to the window. The houses were still dark, and far off down the street a string of lighted elevated cars ran along the horizon, but the sky was gray and in the east some of the clouds were turning yellow. It was quiet. Blue began to notice how quiet it was.

"Birdy," he called.

But he heard her snoring, and turned back to the table.

The telephone rang, but when he answered it there was nobody on the line.

"What's the idea?" he said.

He sat down at the table, took out his billfold, and counted his money; then he took out the railroad tickets and read everything printed on them. Again he noticed how quiet it was. He got up, put away his billfold, and went into the bedroom. Birdy was sleeping with her mouth open, flat on her back, with her arms spread out. Blue lay down beside her and tried to sleep, but he turned from side to side, and finally gave it up.

"I don't feel like sleeping," he thought. "I'm all het up about going East on the Century. Here I am, old Blue, riding the Century dressed up like John Barrymore and with a swell frail. Yeah, that's me. Boul' Mich' Blue."

He got up, put on his coat, and began to pose in front of the living-room mirror.

"Boul' Mich' Blue," he said.

Finally he sat down at the table and laid out a game of solitaire; but he had so many bad breaks with the cards that he began to cheat and then lost interest in the game.

"I know," he said, "what I need is food."

He got up and went to the refrigerator, but there wasn't anything in it except a few pieces of cold meat.

"Hell!" he said, "I guess I'll have to go down to Charley's."

He put on his new soft hat, but hesitated. If they was looking for Pascal, they was looking for him, too. Right now there wasn't nobody on the streets and it was a good time to bump a guy.

"Hell!" he said, buttoning his coat, "I got a streak of luck. It'll hold. Boul' Mich' Blue'll be on the Century to-morrow. Yeah bo! I aint scairt of no Mike Bova."

When Blue came out of the apartment house the sun was just coming up. The alley and areaways were still dark, but there was a pale yellow radiance in the streets. There was no one about; no sign of life. Not even a parked car.

"Hell!" said Blue; "safe as a tank-town."

A window across the street was raised, and Blue ducked without meaning to; but a fat woman put her head out of the window and stared into the street.

There was nobody in Charley's, not even a waiter. Behind the counter the big nickel coffee urns were sending up steam. Blue took out a fifty-cent piece and flung it on the counter. Wing, the counterman, looked in from the kitchen.

"Come on, Wing," said Blue, "snap it up."

"Didn't know you, kid," said Wing. "Aint you dressed up, though? Must've struck it."

"I sure did," said Blue. "Give me a combination and some muddy water."

"Muddy water, hell," said Wing. "I jist made that Java."

Blue leaned on the counter and stared at himself in the mirror, while Wing went back to make his sandwich.

"Hey, Wing," Blue shouted, "did you know I was going East on the Century?"

"Are, hunh?" Wing shouted back. "You're on the big time now, ain't you, kid?"

"That's the word," said Blue.

Blue turned to look out into the street. He saw a man passing, and stared at him. The man was small and had a slouch hat pulled down over his face. Blue thought he recognized him and slid his gun out of the holster under his armpit and put it in his coat pocket. The man passed without looking in.

"I got the jumps," said Blue. "It's that rotten gin."

Wing came in with the sandwich, drew Blue a cup of coffee, then leaned his elbows on the counter and watched Blue eat.

"Well," said Wing, "I see where they got Big Pete."

"Yeah," said Blue.

"I knew they was gonna," said Wing. "I got inside dope."

"Yeah?" said Blue.

"It was coming to him."

"Yeah."

Blue finished his sandwich, lighted a cigarette, and sipped his coffee. It was broad daylight now, and trucks had begun to pass the restaurant.

"Going East, are you, kid?" said Wing.

"Yeah," said Blue. "I got in on a big cut and I don't have to worry none for some time. I jist took my dame down and dressed her up this afternoon. Is she hot? Me, I got silk underwear on."

He unbuttoned his shirt and showed Wing his lavender underwear.

"You're sure a dressed-up boy," said Wing. "I bet you paid ten bucks for that hat you got on."

"Twelve," said Blue. "It was the best they had. I paid eighteen for a panama. You like this suit?"

"It's red hot," said Wing; then with a twinge of envy, "If I wasn't going straight maybe I could wear rags like that."

"How long's your parole got to run?"

"Plenty long. And I got the dicks down on me. They thought I'd stool for 'em in this ward. But that ain't my way."

"Why don't you make a break for Canada?"

"Yeah," said Wing, "and get jerked back to stir."

Blue finished his coffee, paid his check, and gave Wing a dollar bill. Wing turned the bill over and over.

"Say," he said, "give me another buck and I'll put you on to something hot at Arlington."

Blue laughed and tossed Wing a silver dollar.

"Never mind the tip," he said. "I know lots of better ways to lose my dough. Why don't you lay off the ponies, Wing? You can't beat that racket."

"I got the itch," said Wing.

Blue looked into the mirror and adjusted his hat to the proper angle.

"Well," he said, "I'm leaving you. I'll send you a postcard from the Big Burg, Wing."

Blue noticed that Wing had begun to get nervous; his face was twitching.

"Blue," said Wing, "for Christ's sake watch your step. I'm telling you straight, kid. One of Mike's boys was in here buzzing me about you jist 'fore she began to get light. I'm telling you straight, kid. It aint my fight and I wasn't gonna peep. But you're a right guy, Blue."

Blue rubbed his hand over his face, then he said:

"It was the Wolf. I seen him go past."

"Yeah," said Wing.

"Jesus!" said Blue, "which way'd I better go?"

"I'd put you upstairs . . ." Wing began.

"No use," said Blue. "The Wolf seen me."

Wing drew himself a cup of coffee and drank it at a gulp.

"If they knew I'd peeped they'd bump me sure," said Wing.

Blue stood staring at the counter, then he pulled his hat down over his eyes, and slipped his right hand into the pocket where the gun was.

"Well," he said, "the alley's no good. It's blind my way. The side street won't get me no place. So all I got's the front way. Hell!" he went on, puffing out his chest, "I got a streak of luck, Wing. It'll hold."

Wing drew himself another cup of coffee.

"Here's hoping," he said.

Blue went to the door and, putting his head out a little way, looked up and down. The street was deserted except for a truck which was coming toward him slowly. It was a Standard Oil truck.

"Wing," he said, "has any of Mike's boys got a hide-out anywhere around here?"

"Don't know of none."

"Well," said Blue, "here I go."

"So long," said Wing.

Blue stepped out of the restaurant, threw his shoulders back, and began to walk slowly toward Birdy's apartment. The Standard Oil truck passed him and went on. The street was quiet. At the end of the street he saw an elevated on its way toward the Loop.

"I wish I was on that baby," he said.

But the nearer he got to the apartment the surer he became that his luck would hold. Hell! it was the first break he'd had since he and Guido hijacked that big Detroit shipment. He had tickets on the Century. When a guy has tickets on the Century he uses them. And that wasn't all. He was a big shot now; the Big Boy had promised him a bonus; he had on silk underwear.

"Hell!" said Blue, "it ain't in the cards."

Across from Birdy's apartment he saw the same fat woman leaning out of the window. When he looked up she drew her head in hastily. Blue made a dash for the door, but across the street a Thompson gun began to spit. Blue stumbled, dropped his gun, and ran blindly out into the middle of the street; then he turned and ran blindly back toward the house. An iron fence caught him just below the belt and he doubled over it. Across the street a window was slammed.

WINTER DREAMS

By F. Scott Fitzgerald

SOME OF THE CADDIES WERE POOR AS SIN AND LIVED IN ONE-ROOM houses with a neurasthenic cow in the front yard, but Dexter Green's father owned the second best grocery-store in Black Bear —the best one was "The Hub," patronized by the wealthy people from Sherry Island—and Dexter caddied only for pocket-money.

In the fall when the days became crisp and gray, and the long Minnesota winter shut down like the white lid of a box, Dexter's skis moved over the snow that hid the fairways of the golf course. At these times the country gave him a feeling of profound melancholy—it offended him that the links should lie in enforced fallowness, haunted by ragged sparrows for the long season. It was dreary, too, that on the tees where the gay colors fluttered in summer there were now only the desolate sand-boxes knee-deep in crusted ice. When he crossed the hills the wind blew cold as misery, and if the sun was out he tramped with his eyes squinted up against the hard dimensionless glare.

In April the winter ceased abruptly. The snow ran down into Black Bear Lake scarcely tarrying for the early golfers to brave the season with red and black balls. Without elation, without an interval of moist glory, the cold was gone.

Dexter knew that there was something dismal about this Northern spring, just as he knew there was something gorgeous about the fall. Fall made him clinch his hands and tremble and repeat idiotic sentences to himself, and make brisk abrupt gestures of command to imaginary audiences and armies. October filled him with hope which November raised to a sort of ecstatic triumph, and in this mood the fleeting brilliant impressions of the summer at Sherry Island were ready grist to his mill. He became a golf champion and defeated Mr. T. A. Hedrick in a marvellous match play a hundred times over the fairways in his imagination, a match

275

each detail of which he changed about untiringly—sometimes he won with almost laughable ease, sometimes he came up magnificently from behind. Again, stepping from a Pierce-Arrow automobile, like Mr. Mortimer Jones, he strolled frigidly into the lounge of the Sherry Island Golf Club—or perhaps, surrounded by an admiring crowd, he gave an exhibition of fancy diving from the spring-board of the club raft. . . . Among those who watched him in open-mouthed wonder was Mr. Mortimer Jones.

And one day it came to pass that Mr. Jones—himself and not his ghost—came up to Dexter with tears in his eyes and said that Dexter was the — — best caddy in the club, and wouldn't he decide not to quit if Mr. Jones made it worth his while, because every other — — caddy in the club lost one ball a hole for him—regularly——

"No, sir," said Dexter decisively, "I don't want to caddy any more." Then, after a pause: "I'm too old."

"You're not more than fourteen. Why the devil did you decide just this morning that you wanted to quit? You promised that next week you'd go over to the State tournament with me."

"I decided I was too old."

Dexter handed in his "A Class" badge, collected what money was due him from the caddy master, and walked home to Black Bear Village.

"The best — — caddy I ever saw," shouted Mr. Mortimer Jones over a drink that afternoon. "Never lost a ball! Willing! Intelligent! Quiet! Honest! Grateful!"

The little girl who had done this was eleven—beautifully ugly as little girls are apt to be who are destined after a few years to be inexpressibly lovely and bring no end of misery to a great number of men. The spark, however, was perceptible. There was a general ungodliness in the way her lips twisted down at the corners when she smiled, and in the—Heaven help us!—in the almost passionate quality of her eyes. Vitality is born early in such women. It was utterly in evidence now, shining through her thin frame in a sort of glow.

She had come eagerly out on to the course at nine o'clock with a white linen nurse and five small new golf-clubs in a white canvas bag which the nurse was carrying. When Dexter first saw her she was standing by the caddy house, rather ill at ease and trying to conceal the fact by engaging her nurse in an obviously unnatural conversation graced by startling and irrevelant grimaces from herself.

"Well, it's certainly a nice day, Hilda," Dexter heard her say. She drew down the corners of her mouth, smiled, and glanced furtively around, her eyes in transit falling for an instant on Dexter.

Then to the nurse:

"Well, I guess there aren't very many people out here this morning, are there?"

The smile again—radiant, blatantly artificial—convincing.

"I don't know what we're supposed to do now," said the nurse, looking nowhere in particular.

"Oh, that's all right. I'll fix it up."

Dexter stood perfectly still, his mouth slightly ajar. He knew that if he moved forward a step his stare would be in her line of vision—if he moved backward he would lose his full view of her face. For a moment he had not realized how young she was. Now he remembered having seen her several times the year before—in bloomers.

Suddenly, involuntarily, he laughed, a short abrupt laugh—then, startled by himself, he turned and began to walk quickly away.

"Boy!"

Dexter stopped.

"Boy——"

Beyond question he was addressed. Not only that, but he was treated to that absurd smile, that preposterous smile—the memory of which at least a dozen men were to carry into middle age.

"Boy, do you know where the golf teacher is?"

"He's giving a lesson."

"Well, do you know where the caddy-master is?"

"He isn't here yet this morning."

"Oh." For a moment this baffled her. She stood alternately on her right and left foot.

"We'd like to get a caddy," said the nurse. "Mrs. Mortimer Jones sent us out to play golf, and we don't know how without we get a caddy."

Here she was stopped by an ominous glance from Miss Jones, followed immediately by the smile.

"There aren't any caddies here except me," said Dexter to the nurse, "and I got to stay here in charge until the caddy-master gets here."

"Oh."

Miss Jones and her retinue now withdrew, and at a proper distance from Dexter became involved in a heated conversation, which was concluded by Miss Jones taking one of the clubs and hitting it on the ground with violence. For further emphasis she raised it again and was about to bring it down smartly upon the nurse's bosom, when the nurse seized the club and twisted it from her hands.

"You damn little mean old *thing!*" cried Miss Jones wildly.

Another argument ensued. Realizing that the elements of the comedy were implied in the scene, Dexter several times began to laugh, but each time restrained the laugh before it reached audibility. He could not resist the monstrous conviction that the little girl was justified in beating the nurse.

The situation was resolved by the fortuitous appearance of the caddy-master, who was appealed to immediately by the nurse.

"Miss Jones is to have a little caddy, and this one says he can't go."

"Mr. McKenna said I was to wait here till you came," said Dexter quickly.

"Well, he's here now." Miss Jones smiled cheerfully at the caddy-master. Then she dropped her bag and set off at a haughty mince toward the first tee.

"Well?" The caddy-master turned to Dexter. "What you standing there like a dummy for? Go pick up the young lady's clubs."

"I don't think I'll go out to-day," said Dexter.

"You don't——"

"I think I'll quit."

The enormity of his decision frightened him. He was a favorite caddy, and the thirty dollars a month he earned through the summer were not to be made elsewhere around the lake. But he had received a strong emotional shock, and his perturbation required a violent and immediate outlet.

It is not so simple as that, either. As so frequently would be the case in the future, Dexter was unconsciously dictated to by his winter dreams.

II

Now, of course, the quality and the seasonability of these winter dreams varied, but the stuff of them remained. They persuaded Dexter several years later to pass up a business course at the State university—his father, prospering now, would have paid his way— for the precarious advantage of attending an older and more famous university in the East, where he was bothered by his scanty funds. But do not get the impression, because his winter dreams happened to be concerned at first with musings on the rich, that there was anything merely snobbish in the boy. He wanted not association with glittering things and glittering people—he wanted the glittering things themselves. Often he reached out for the best without knowing why he wanted it—and sometimes he ran up against the mysterious denials and prohibitions in which life indulges. It is with one of those denials and not with his career as a whole that this story deals.

He made money. It was rather amazing. After college he went to the city from which Black Bear Lake draws its wealthy patrons. When he was only twenty-three and had been there not quite two years, there were already people who liked to say: "Now *there's* a boy—" All about him rich men's sons were peddling bonds precariously, or investing patrimonies precariously, or plodding through the two dozen volumes of the "George Washington Commercial Course," but Dexter borrowed a thousand dollars on his college degree and his confident mouth, and bought a partnership in a laundry.

It was a small laundry when he went into it but Dexter made a specialty of learning how the English washed fine woollen golf-stockings without shrinking them, and within a year he was catering to the trade that wore knickerbockers. Men were insisting that their Shetland hose and sweaters go to his laundry just as they had insisted on a caddy who could find golf-balls. A little later he was doing their wives' lingerie as well—and running five branches in different parts of the city. Before he was twenty-seven he owned the largest string of laundries in his section of the country. It was then that he sold out and went to New York. But the part of his story that concerns us goes back to the days when he was making his first big success.

When he was twenty-three Mr. Hart—one of the gray-haired men who like to say "Now there's a boy"—gave him a guest card to the Sherry Island Golf Club for a week-end. So he signed his name one day on the register, and that afternoon played golf in a foursome with Mr. Hart and Mr. Sandwood and Mr. T. A. Hedrick. He did not consider it necessary to remark that he had once carried Mr. Hart's bag over this same links, and that he knew every trap and gully with his eyes shut—but he found himself glancing at the four caddies who trailed them, trying to catch a gleam or gesture that would remind him of himself, that would lessen the gap which lay between his present and his past.

It was a curious day, slashed abruptly with fleeting, familiar impressions. One minute he had the sense of being a trespasser— in the next he was impressed by the tremendous superiority he felt toward Mr. T. A. Hedrick, who was a bore and not even a good golfer any more.

Then, because of a ball Mr. Hart lost near the fifteenth green, an enormous thing happened. While they were searching the stiff grasses of the rough there was a clear call of "Fore!" from behind a hill in their rear. And as they all turned abruptly from their search a bright new ball sliced abruptly over the hill and caught Mr. T. A. Hedrick in the abdomen.

"By Gad!" cried Mr. T. A. Hedrick, "they ought to put some of these crazy women off the course. It's getting to be outrageous."

A head and a voice came up together over the hill:

"Do you mind if we go through?"

"You hit me in the stomach!" declared Mr. Hedrick wildly.

"Did I?" The girl approached the group of men. "I'm sorry. I yelled 'Fore!'"

Her glance fell casually on each of the men—then scanned the fairway for her ball.

"Did I bounce into the rough?"

It was impossible to determine whether this question was ingenuous or malicious. In a moment, however, she left no doubt, for as her partner came up over the hill she called cheerfully:

"Here I am! I'd have gone on the green except that I hit something."

As she took her stance for a short mashie shot, Dexter looked at her closely. She wore a blue gingham dress, rimmed at throat and shoulders with a white edging that accentuated her tan. The quality of exaggeration, of thinness, which had made her passionate eyes and down-turning mouth absurd at eleven, was gone now. She was arrestingly beautiful. The color in her cheeks was centred like the color in a picture—it was not a "high" color, but a sort of fluctuating and feverish warmth, so shaded that it seemed at any moment it would recede and disappear. This color and the mobility of her mouth gave a continued impression of flux, of intense life, of passionate vitality—balanced only partially by the sad luxury of her eyes.

She swung her mashie impatiently and without interest, pitching the ball into a sand-pit on the other side of the green. With a quick, insincere smile and a careless "Thank you!" she went on after it.

"That Judy Jones!" remarked Mr. Hedrick on the next tee, as they waited—some moments—for her to play on ahead. "All she needs is to be turned up and spanked for six months and then to be married off to an old-fashioned cavalry captain."

"My God, she's good-looking!" said Mr. Sandwood, who was just over thirty.

"Good-looking!" cried Mr. Hedrick contemptuously, "she always looks as if she wanted to be kissed! Turning those big cow-eyes on every calf in town!"

It was doubtful if Mr. Hedrick intended a reference to the maternal instinct.

"She'd play pretty good golf if she'd try," said Mr. Sandwood.

"She has no form," said Mr. Hedrick solemnly.

"She has a nice figure," said Mr. Sandwood.

"Better thank the Lord she doesn't drive a swifter ball," said Mr. Hart, winking at Dexter.

Later in the afternoon the sun went down with a riotous swirl of gold and varying blues and scarlets, and left the dry, rustling night of Western summer. Dexter watched from the veranda of the Golf Club, watched the even overlap of the waters in the little wind, silver molasses under the harvest-moon. Then the moon held a finger to her lips and the lake became a clear pool, pale and quiet. Dexter put on his bathing-suit and swam out to the farthest raft, where he stretched dripping on the wet canvas of the springboard.

There was a fish jumping and a star shining and the lights around the lake were gleaming. Over on a dark peninsula a piano was playing the songs of last summer and of summers before that —songs from "Chin-Chin" and "The Count of Luxemburg" and "The Chocolate Soldier"—and because the sound of a piano over a stretch of water had always seemed beautiful to Dexter he lay perfectly quiet and listened.

The tune the piano was playing at that moment had been gay and new five years before when Dexter was a sophomore at college. They had played it at a prom once when he could not afford the luxury of proms, and he had stood outside the gymnasium and listened. The sound of the tune precipitated in him a sort of ecstasy and it was with that ecstasy he viewed what happened to him now. It was a mood of intense appreciation, a sense that, for once, he was magnificently attune to life and that everything about him was radiating a brightness and a glamour he might never know again.

A low, pale oblong detached itself suddenly from the darkness of the Island, spitting forth the reverberate sound of a racing motor-boat. Two white streamers of cleft water rolled themselves out behind it and almost immediately the boat was beside him, drowning out the hot tinkle of the piano in the drone of its spray. Dexter raising himself on his arms was aware of a figure standing at the wheel, of two dark eyes regarding him over the lengthening space of water—then the boat had gone by and was sweeping in an immense and purposeless circle of spray round and round in the middle of the lake. With equal eccentricity one of the circles flattened out and headed back toward the raft.

"Who's that?" she called, shutting off her motor. She was so near now that Dexter could see her bathing-suit, which consisted apparently of pink rompers.

The nose of the boat bumped the raft, and as the latter tilted rakishly he was precipitated toward her. With different degrees of interest they recognized each other.

"Aren't you one of those men we played through this afternoon?" she demanded.

He was.

"Well, do you know how to drive a motor-boat? Because if you do I wish you'd drive this one so I can ride on the surf-board behind. My name is Judy Jones"—she favored him with an absurd smirk—rather, what tried to be a smirk, for, twist her mouth as she might, it was not grotesque, it was merely beautiful—"and I live in a house over there on the Island, and in that house there is a man waiting for me. When he drove up at the door I drove out of the dock because he says I'm his ideal."

There was a fish jumping and a star shining and the lights around the lake were gleaming. Dexter sat beside Judy Jones and she explained how her boat was driven. Then she was in the water, swimming to the floating surf-board with a sinuous crawl. Watching her was without effort to the eye, watching a branch waving or a sea-gull flying. Her arms, burned to butternut, moved sinuously among the dull platinum ripples, elbow appearing first, casting the forearm back with a cadence of falling water, then reaching out and down, stabbing a path ahead.

They moved out into the lake; turning, Dexter saw that she was kneeling on the low rear of the now uptilted surf-board.

"Go faster," she called, "fast as it'll go."

Obediently he jammed the lever forward and the white spray mounted at the bow. When he looked around again the girl was standing up on the rushing board, her arms spread wide, her eyes lifted toward the moon.

"It's awful cold," she shouted. "What's your name?"

He told her.

"Well, why don't you come to dinner to-morrow night?"

His heart turned over like the fly-wheel of the boat, and, for the second time, her casual whim gave a new direction to his life.

III

Next evening while he waited for her to come down-stairs, Dexter peopled the soft deep summer room and the sun-porch that opened from it with the men who had already loved Judy Jones. He knew the sort of men they were—the men who when he first went to college had entered from the great prep schools with graceful clothes and the deep tan of healthy summers. He had seen that, in one sense, he was better than these men. He was newer and stronger. Yet in acknowledging to himself that he wished his children to be like them he was admitting that he was but the rough, strong stuff from which they eternally sprang.

When the time had come for him to wear good clothes, he had known who were the best tailors in America, and the best tailors in America had made him the suit he wore this evening. He had acquired that particular reserve peculiar to his university, that set it off from other universities. He recognized the value to him of such a mannerism and he had adopted it; he knew that to be careless in dress and manner required more confidence than to be careful. But carelessness was for his children. His mother's name had been Krimslich. She was a Bohemian of the peasant class and she had talked broken English to the end of her days. Her son must keep to the set patterns.

At a little after seven Judy Jones came down-stairs. She wore a blue silk afternoon dress, and he was disappointed at first that she had not put on something more elaborate. This feeling was accentuated when, after a brief greeting, she went to the door of a butler's pantry and pushing it open called: "You can serve dinner, Martha." He had rather expected that a butler would announce dinner, that there would be a cocktail. Then he put these thoughts behind him as they sat down side by side on a lounge and looked at each other.

"Father and mother won't be here," she said thoughtfully.

He remembered the last time he had seen her father, and he was glad the parents were not to be here to-night—they might wonder who he was. He had been born in Keeble, a Minnesota village fifty miles farther north, and he always gave Keeble as his home instead of Black Bear Village. Country towns were well enough to come from if they weren't inconveniently in sight and used as footstools by fashionable lakes.

They talked of his university, which she had visited frequently during the past two years, and of the near-by city which supplied

Sherry Island with its patrons, and whither Dexter would return next day to his prospering laundries.

During dinner she slipped into a moody depression which gave Dexter a feeling of uneasiness. Whatever petulance she uttered in her throaty voice worried him. Whatever she smiled at—at him, at a chicken liver, at nothing—it disturbed him that her smile could have no root in mirth, or even in amusement. When the scarlet corners of her lips curved down, it was less a smile than an invitation to a kiss.

Then, after dinner, she led him out on the dark sun-porch and deliberately changed the atmosphere.

"Do you mind if I weep a little?" she said.

"I'm afraid I'm boring you," he responded quickly.

"You're not. I like you. But I've just had a terrible afternoon. There was a man I cared about, and this afternoon he told me out of a clear sky that he was poor as a church-mouse. He'd never even hinted it before. Does this sound horribly mundane?"

"Perhaps he was afraid to tell you."

"Suppose he was," she answered. "He didn't start right. You see, if I'd thought of him as poor—well, I've been mad about loads of poor men, and fully intended to marry them all. But in this case, I hadn't thought of him that way, and my interest in him wasn't strong enough to survive the shock. As if a girl calmly informed her fiancé that she was a widow. He might not object to widows, but——"

"Let's start right," she interrupted herself suddenly. "Who are you, anyhow?"

For a moment Dexter hesitated. Then:

"I'm nobody," he announced. "My career is largely a matter of futures."

"Are you poor?"

"No," he said frankly, "I'm probably making more money than any man my age in the Northwest. I know that's an obnoxious remark, but you advised me to start right."

There was a pause. Then she smiled and the corners of her mouth drooped and an almost imperceptible sway brought her closer to him, looking up into his eyes. A lump rose in Dexter's throat, and he waited breathless for the experiment, facing the unpredictable compound that would form mysteriously from the elements of their lips. Then he saw—she communicated her excitement to him, lavishly, deeply, with kisses that were not a promise but a fulfilment. They aroused in him not hunger demanding renewal but surfeit that would demand more surfeit . . . kisses that were like charity, creating want by holding back nothing at all.

It did not take him many hours to decide that he had wanted Judy Jones ever since he was a proud, desirous little boy.

IV

It began like that—and continued, with varying shades of intensity, on such a note right up to the dénouement. Dexter surrendered a part of himself to the most direct and unprincipled personality with which he had ever come in contact. Whatever Judy wanted, she went after with the full pressure of her charm. There was no divergence of method, no jockeying for position or premeditation of effects—there was a very little mental side to any of her affairs. She simply made men conscious to the highest degree of her physical loveliness. Dexter had no desire to change her. Her deficiencies were knit up with a passionate energy that transcended and justified them.

When, as Judy's head lay against his shoulder that first night, she whispered, "I don't know what's the matter with me. Last night I thought I was in love with a man and to-night I think I'm in love with you——" —it seemed to him a beautiful and romantic thing to say. It was the exquisite excitability that for the moment he controlled and owned. But a week later he was compelled to view this same quality in a different light. She took him in her roadster to a picnic supper, and after supper she disappeared, likewise in her roadster, with another man. Dexter became enormously upset and was scarcely able to be decently civil to the other people present. When she assured him that she had not kissed the other man, he knew she was lying—yet he was glad that she had taken the trouble to lie to him.

He was, as he found before the summer ended, one of a varying dozen who circulated about her. Each of them had at one time been favored above all others—about half of them still basked in the solace of occasional sentimental revivals. Whenever one showed signs of dropping out through long neglect, she granted him a brief honeyed hour, which encouraged him to tag along for a year or so longer. Judy made these forays upon the helpless and defeated without malice, indeed half conscious that there was anything mischievous in what she did.

When a new man came to town every one dropped out—dates were automatically cancelled.

The helpless part of trying to do anything about it was that she did it all herself. She was not a girl who could be "won" in the kinetic sense—she was proof against cleverness, she was proof against charm; if any of these assailed her too strongly she would immediately resolve the affair to a physical basis, and under the magic of her physical splendor the strong as well as the brilliant played her game and not their own. She was entertained only by the gratification of her desires and by the direct exercise of her own charm. Perhaps from so much youthful love, so many youthful lovers, she had come, in self-defense, to nourish herself wholly from within.

Succeeding Dexter's first exhilaration came restlessness and dissatisfaction. The helpless ecstasy of losing himself in her was opiate rather than tonic. It was fortunate for his work during the winter that those moments of ecstasy came infrequently. Early in their acquaintance it had seemed for a while that there was a deep and spontaneous mutual attraction—that first August, for example —three days of long evenings on her dusky veranda, of strange wan kisses through the late afternoon, in shadowy alcoves or behind the protecting trellises of the garden arbors, of mornings when she was fresh as a dream and almost shy at meeting him in the clarity of the rising day. There was all the ecstasy of an engagement about it, sharpened by his realization that there was no engagement. It was during those three days that, for the first time, he had asked her to marry him. She said "maybe some day," she said "kiss me," she said "I'd like to marry you," she said "I love you"—she said—nothing.

The three days were interrupted by the arrival of a New York man who visited at her house for half September. To Dexter's agony, rumor engaged them. The man was the son of the president of a great trust company. But at the end of a month it was reported that Judy was yawning. At a dance one night she sat all evening in a motor-boat with a local beau, while the New Yorker searched the club for her frantically. She told the local beau that she was bored with her visitor, and two days later he left. She was seen with him at the station, and it was reported that he looked very mournful indeed.

On this note the summer ended. Dexter was twenty-four, and he found himself increasingly in a position to do as he wished. He joined two clubs in the city and lived at one of them. Though he was by no means an integral part of the stag-lines at these clubs, he managed to be on hand at dances where Judy Jones was likely to appear. He could have gone out socially as much as he liked—he was an eligible young man, now, and popular with down-town fathers. His confessed devotion to Judy Jones had rather solidified his position. But he had no social aspirations and rather despised the dancing men who were always on tap for the Thursday or Saturday parties and who filled in at dinners with the younger married set. Already he was playing with the idea of going East to New York. He wanted to take Judy Jones with him. No disillusion as to the world in which she had grown up could cure his illusion as to her desirability.

Remember that—for only in the light of it can what he did for her be understood.

Eighteen months after he first met Judy Jones he became engaged to another girl. Her name was Irene Scheerer, and her father was one of the men who had always believed in Dexter. Irene was light-haired and sweet and honorable, and a little stout, and she had two suitors whom she pleasantly relinquished when Dexter formally asked her to marry him.

Summer, fall, winter, spring, another summer, another fall—so much he had given of his active life to the incorrigible lips of Judy Jones. She had treated him with interest, with encouragement, with malice, with indifference, with contempt. She had inflicted on him the innumerable little slights and indignities possible in such a case—as if in revenge for having ever cared for him at all. She had beckoned him and yawned at him and beckoned him again and he had responded often with bitterness and narrowed eyes. She had brought him ecstatic happiness and intolerable agony of spirit. She had caused him untold inconvenience and not a little trouble. She had insulted him, and she had ridden over him, and she had played his interest in her against his interest in his work—for fun. She had done everything to him except to criticise him—this she had not done—it seemed to him only because it might have sullied the utter indifference she manifested and sincerely felt toward him.

When autumn had come and gone again it occurred to him that he could not have Judy Jones. He had to beat this into his mind but he convinced himself at last. He lay awake at night for a while and argued it over. He told himself the trouble and the pain she had caused him, he enumerated her glaring deficiencies as a wife. Then he said to himself that he loved her, and after a while he fell asleep. For a week, lest he imagined her husky voice over the telephone or her eyes opposite him at lunch, he worked hard and late, and at night he went to his office and plotted out his years.

At the end of a week he went he went to a dance and cut in on her once. For almost the first time since they had met he did not ask her to sit out with him or tell her that she was lovely. It hurt him that she did not miss these things—that was all. He was not jealous when he saw that there was a new man to-night. He had been hardened against jealousy long before.

He stayed late at the dance. He sat for an hour with Irene Scheerer and talked about books and about music. He knew very little about either. But he was beginning to be master of his own time now, and he had a rather priggish notion that he—the young and already fabulously successful Dexter Green—should know more about such things.

That was in October, when he was twenty-five. In January, Dexter and Irene became engaged. It was to be announced in June, and they were to be married three months later.

The Minnesota winter prolonged itself interminably, and it was almost May when the winds came soft and the snow ran down into Black Bear Lake at last. For the first time in over a year Dexter was enjoying a certain tranquillity of spirit. Judy Jones had been in Florida, and afterward in Hot Springs, and somewhere she had been engaged, and somewhere she had broken it off. At first, when Dexter had definitely given her up, it had made him sad that people still linked them together and asked for news of her, but when he began to be placed at dinner next to Irene Scheerer people didn't ask him about her any more—they told him about her. He ceased to be an authority on her.

May at last. Dexter walked the streets at night when the darkness was damp as rain, wondering that so soon, with so little done, so much of ecstasy had gone from him. May one year back had been marked by Judy's poignant, unforgivable, yet forgiven turbulence—it had been one of those rare times when he fancied she had grown to care for him. That old penny's worth of happiness he had spent for this bushel of content. He knew that Irene would be no more than a curtain spread behind him, a hand moving among gleaming tea-cups, a voice calling to children . . . fire and loveliness were gone, the magic of nights and the wonder of the varying hours and seasons . . . slender lips, down-turning, dropping to his lips and bearing him up into a heaven of eyes. . . . The thing was deep in him. He was too strong and alive for it to die lightly.

In the middle of May when the weather balanced for a few days on the thin bridge that led to deep summer he turned in one night at Irene's house. Their engagement was to be announced in a week now—no one would be surprised at it. And to-night they would sit together on the lounge at the University Club and look on for an hour at the dancers. It gave him a sense of solidity to go with her—she was so sturdily popular, so intensely "great."

He mounted the steps of the brownstone house and stepped inside.

"Irene," he called.

Mrs. Scheerer came out of the living-room to meet him.

"Dexter," she said, "Irene's gone up-stairs with a splitting headache. She wanted to go with you but I made her go to bed."

"Nothing serious, I——"

"Oh, no. She's going to play golf with you in the morning. You can spare her for just one night, can't you, Dexter?"

Her smile was kind. She and Dexter liked each other. In the living-room he talked for a moment before he said good-night.

Returning to the University Club, where he had rooms, he stood in the doorway for a moment and watched the dancers. He leaned against the doorpost, nodded at a man or two—yawned.

"Hello, darling."

The familiar voice at his elbow startled him. Judy Jones had left a man and crossed the room to him—Judy Jones, a slender enamelled doll in cloth of gold: gold in a band at her head, gold in two slipper points at her dress's hem. The fragile glow of her face seemed to blossom as she smiled at him. A breeze of warmth and light blew through the room. His hands in the pockets of his dinner-jacket tightened spasmodically. He was filled with a sudden excitement.

"When did you get back?" he asked casually.

"Come here and I'll tell you about it."

She turned and he followed her. She had been away—he could have wept at the wonder of her return. She had passed through enchanted streets, doing things that were like provocative music. All mysterious happenings, all fresh and quickening hopes, had gone away with her, come back with her now.

She turned in the door.

"Have you a car here? If you haven't, I have."

"I have a coupé."

In then, with a rustle of golden cloth. He slammed the door. Into so many cars she had stepped—like this—like that—her back against the leather, so—her elbow resting on the door—waiting. She would have been soiled long since had there been anything to soil her—except herself—but this was her own self outpouring.

With an effort he forced himself to start the car and back into the street. This was nothing, he must remember. She had done this before, and he had put her behind him, as he would have crossed a bad account from his books.

He drove slowly down-town and, affecting abstraction, traversed the deserted streets of the business section, peopled here and there where a movie was giving out its crowd or where consumptive or pugilistic youth lounged in front of pool halls. The clink of glasses and the slap of hands on the bars issued from saloons, cloisters of glazed glass and dirty yellow light.

She was watching him closely and the silence was embarrassing, yet in this crisis he could find no casual word with which to profane the hour. At a convenient turning he began to zigzag back toward the University Club.

"Have you missed me?" she asked suddenly.

"Everybody missed you."

He wondered if she knew of Irene Scheerer. She had been back only a day—her absence had been almost contemporaneous with his engagement.

"What a remark!" Judy laughed sadly—without sadness. She looked at him searchingly. He became absorbed in the dashboard.

"You're handsomer than you used to be," she said thoughtfully. "Dexter, you have the most rememberable eyes."

He could have laughed at this, but he did not laugh. It was the sort of thing that was said to sophomores. Yet it stabbed at him.

"I'm awfully tired of everything, darling." She called every one darling, endowing the endearment with careless, individual comraderie. "I wish you'd marry me."

The directness of this confused him. He should have told her now that he was going to marry another girl, but he could not tell her. He could as easily have sworn that he had never loved her.

"I think we'd get along," she continued, on the same note, "unless probably you've forgotten me and fallen in love with another girl."

Her confidence was obviously enormous. She had said, in effect, that she found such a thing impossible to believe, that if it were true he had merely committed a childish indiscretion—and probably to show off. She would forgive him, because it was not a matter of any moment but rather something to be brushed aside lightly.

"Of course you could never love anybody but me," she continued, "I like the way you love me. Oh, Dexter, have you forgotten last year?"

"No, I haven't forgotten."

"Neither have I!"

Was she sincerely moved—or was she carried along by the wave of her own acting?

"I wish we could be like that again," she said, and he forced himself to answer:

"I don't think we can."

"I suppose not. . . . I hear you're giving Irene Scheerer a violent rush."

There was not the faintest emphasis on the name, yet Dexter was suddenly ashamed.

"Oh, take me home," cried Judy suddenly; "I don't want to go back to that idiotic dance—with those children."

Then, as he turned up the street that led to the residence district, Judy began to cry quietly to herself. He had never seen her cry before.

The dark street lightened, the dwellings of the rich loomed up around them, he stopped his coupé in front of the great white bulk of the Mortimer Joneses house, somnolent, gorgeous, drenched with the splendor of the damp moonlight. Its solidity startled him. The strong walls, the steel of the girders, the breadth and beam and pomp of it were there only to bring out the contrast with the young beauty beside him. It was sturdy to accentuate her slightness—as if to show what a breeze could be generated by a butterfly's wing.

He sat perfectly quiet, his nerves in wild clamor, afraid that if he moved he would find her irresistibly in his arms. Two tears had rolled down her wet face and trembled on her upper lip.

"I'm more beautiful than anybody else," she said brokenly, "why can't I be happy?" Her moist eyes tore at his stability—her mouth turned slowly downward with an exquisite sadness: "I'd like to marry you if you'll have me, Dexter. I suppose you think I'm not worth having, but I'll be so beautiful for you, Dexter."

A million phrases of anger, pride, passion, hatred, tenderness fought on his lips. Then a perfect wave of emotion washed over him, carrying off with it a sediment of wisdom, of convention, of doubt, of honor. This was his girl who was speaking, his own, his beautiful, his pride.

"Won't you come in?" He heard her draw in her breath sharply.

Waiting.

"All right," his voice was trembling, "I'll come in."

V

It was strange that neither when it was over nor a long time afterward did he regret that night. Looking at it from the perspective of ten years, the fact that Judy's flare for him endured just one month seemed of little importance. Nor did it matter that by his yielding he subjected himself to a deeper agony in the end and gave serious hurt to Irene Scheerer and to Irene's parents, who had befriended him. There was nothing sufficiently pictorial about Irene's grief to stamp itself on his mind.

Dexter was at bottom hard-minded. The attitude of the city on his action was of no importance to him, not because he was going to leave the city, but because any outside attitude on the situation seemed superficial. He was completely indifferent to popular opinion. Nor, when he had seen that it was no use, that he did not possess in himself the power to move fundamentally or to hold Judy Jones, did he bear any malice toward her. He loved her, and he would love her until the day he was too old for loving —but he could not have her. So he tasted the deep pain that is reserved only for the strong, just as he had tasted for a little while the deep happiness.

Even the ultimate falsity of the grounds upon which Judy terminated the engagement that she did not want to "take him away" from Irene—Judy, who had wanted nothing else—did not revolt him. He was beyond any revulsion or any amusement.

He went East in February with the intention of selling out his laundries and settling in New York—but the war came to America in March and changed his plans. He returned to the West, handed over the management of the business to his partner, and went into the first officers' training-camp in late April. He was one of those young thousands who greeted the war with a certain amount of relief, welcoming the liberation from webs of tangled emotion.

VI

This story is not his biography, remember, although things creep into it which have nothing to do with those dreams he had when he was young. We are almost done with them and with him

now. There is only one more incident to be related here, and it
happens seven years farther on.

It took place in New York, where he had done well—so well
that there were no barriers too high for him. He was thirty-two
years old, and, except for one flying trip immediately after the
war, he had not been West in seven years. A man named Devlin
from Detroit came into his office to see him in a business way,
and then and there this incident occurred, and closed out, so to
speak, this particular side of his life.

"So you're from the Middle West," said the man Devlin with
careless curiosity. "That's funny—I thought men like you were
probably born and raised on Wall Street. You know—wife of one
of my best friends in Detroit came from your city. I was an usher
at the wedding."

Dexter waited with no apprehension of what was coming.

"Judy Simms," said Devlin with no particular interest; "Judy
Jones she was once."

"Yes, I knew her." A dull impatience spread over him. He had
heard, of course, that she was married—perhaps deliberately he had
heard no more.

"Awfully nice girl," brooded Devlin meaninglessly, "I'm sort
of sorry for her."

"Why?" Something in Dexter was alert, receptive, at once.

"Oh, Lud Simms has gone to pieces in a way. I don't mean he
ill-uses her, but he drinks and runs around——"

"Doesn't she run around?"

"No. Stays at home with her kids."

"Oh."

"She's a little too old for him," said Devlin.

"Too old!" cried Dexter. "Why, man, she's only twenty-seven."

He was possessed with a wild notion of rushing out into the
streets and taking a train to Detroit. He rose to his feet spasmodically.

"I guess you're busy," Devlin apologized quickly. "I didn't
realize——"

"No, I'm not busy," said Dexter, steadying his voice. "I'm not
busy at all. Not busy at all. Did you say she was—twenty-seven?
No, I said she was twenty-seven."

"Yes, you did," agreed Devlin dryly.

"Go on, then. Go on."

"What do you mean?"

"About Judy Jones."

Devlin looked at him helplessly.

"Well, that's—I told you all there is to it. He treats her like the devil. Oh, they're not going to get divorced or anything. When he's particularly outrageous she forgives him. In fact, I'm inclined to think she loves him. She was a pretty girl when she first came to Detroit."

A pretty girl! The phrase struck Dexter as ludicrous.

"Isn't she—a pretty girl, any more?"

"Oh, she's all right."

"Look here," said Dexter, sitting down suddenly, "I don't understand. You say she was a 'pretty girl' and now you say she's 'al right.' I don't understand what you mean—Judy Jones wasn't a pretty girl, at all. She was a great beauty. Why, I knew her, I knew her. She was——"

Devlin laughed pleasantly.

"I'm not trying to start a row," he said. "I think Judy's a nice girl and I like her. I can't understand how a man like Lud Simms could fall madly in love with her, but he did." Then he added: "Most of the women like her."

Dexter looked closely at Devlin, thinking wildly that there must be a reason for this, some insensitivity in the man or some private malice.

"Lots of women fade just like *that*," Devlin snapped his fingers. "You must have seen it happen. Perhaps I've forgotten how pretty she was at her wedding. I've seen her so much since then, you see. She has nice eyes."

A sort of dulness settled down upon Dexter. For the first time in his life he felt like getting very drunk. He knew that he was laughing loudly at something Devlin had said, but he did not know what it was or why it was funny. When, in a few minutes, Devlin went he lay down on his lounge and looked out the window at the New York sky-line into which the sun was sinking in dull lovely shades of pink and gold.

He had thought that having nothing else to lose he was invulnerable at last—but he knew that he had just lost something more, as surely as if he had married Judy Jones and seen her fade away before his eyes.

The dream was gone. Something had been taken from him. In a sort of panic he pushed the palms of his hands into his eyes and tried to bring up a picture of the waters lapping on Sherry Island and the moonlit veranda, and gingham on the golf-links and the dry sun and the gold color of her neck's soft down. And her mouth damp to his kisses and her eyes plaintive with melancholy and her freshness like new fine linen in the morning. Why, these things were no longer in the world! They had existed and they existed no longer.

For the first time in years the tears were streaming down his face. But they were for himself now. He did not care about mouth and eyes and moving hands. He wanted to care, and he could not care. For he had gone away and he could never go back any more. The gates were closed, the sun was gone down, and there was no beauty but the gray beauty of steel that withstands all time. Even the grief he could have borne was left behind in the country of illusion, of youth, of the richness of life, where his winter dreams had flourished.

"Long ago," he said, "long ago, there was something in me, but now that thing is gone. Now that thing is gone, that thing is gone. I cannot cry. I cannot care. That thing will come back no more."

THE SOBBIN' WOMEN

By STEPHEN VINCENT BENÉT

ᴛHEY CAME OVER THE PASS ONE DAY IN ONE BIG WAGON—ALL TEN of them—man and woman and hired girl and seven big boy children, from the nine-year-old who walked by the team to the baby in arms. Or so the story runs—it was in the early days of settlement and the town had never heard of the Sobbin' Women then. But it opened its eyes one day, and there were the Pontipees.

They were there but they didn't stay long—just time enough to buy meal and get a new shoe for the lead horse. You couldn't call them unsociable, exactly—they seemed to be sociable enough among themselves. But you could tell, somehow, from the look of them, that they weren't going to settle on ground other people had cleared. They were all high-colored and dark-haired—handsome with a wilderness handsomeness—and when you got them all together, they looked more like a tribe or a nation than an ordinary family. I don't know how they gave folks that feeling, but they did. Yes, even the baby, when the town women tried to handle him. He was a fine, healthy baby, but they said it was like trying to pet a young raccoon.

Well, that was all there was to it, at the start. They paid for what they bought in good money and drove on up into Sobbin' Women Valley—only it wasn't called Sobbin' Women Valley then. And pretty soon, there was smoke from a chimney there that hadn't been there before. But you know what town gossip is when it gets started. The Pontipees were willing enough to let other folks alone—in fact, that was what they wanted. But, because it was what they wanted, the town couldn't see why they wanted it. Towns get that way, sometimes.

So, it was mostly cross questions and crooked answers when the Pontipees came into town, to trade off their pelts and such and buy at the store. There wasn't much actual trouble—not after two loafers at the tavern made fun of Pa Pontipee's fur cap and Pa Pontipee stretched them both before you could say "Jack Robinson." But there wasn't a neighborly feeling—yes, you could say that. The women would tell their children about the terrible Pontipees and the men would wag their heads. And when they came in to church—which they did once a year—there'd be a sort of rustle in the congregation, though they always took a back pew and listened perfectly respectful. But the minister never seemed to be able to preach as good a sermon as usual that Sunday—and naturally, he blamed the Pontipees for that. Till, finally, they got to be a sort of legend in the community—the wild folks who lived up the valley like bears in the woods—and, indeed, some said they turned into bears in the winter time, which just shows you what people will say. And, though the boys were well set up, they might as well have been deaf-mutes for all the notice the town-girls took of them—except to squeak and run to the other side of the road when the Pontipees came marching along.

While, as for the Pontipees—nobody knew what they made of it all, for they weren't much on talking. If one of them said "It's a fine day" and another admitted it was, that was conversation that would last them a long while. Besides, they had work enough and to spare, in their own valley, to keep them busy; and, if Ma Pontipee would have liked more society, she never let on. She did her duty by the boys and tried to give them some manners, in spite of their backwoods raising; and that was enough for any woman to do.

But things never stand still in this world, and soon enough, the boys weren't boys any more, they were men. And when the fall of a tree took Pa Pontipee, his wife didn't linger long after him. There was a terrible fuss about the funerals too—for the Pontipee boys got the minister, but they wouldn't let the burials take place in town. They said Pa and Ma wouldn't feel comfortable, all crowded up among strangers in the churchyard, so they laid them to rest in the Valley where they'd lived, and the town found that queerer than ever. But there's worse places to lie than looking out over the fields you've cleared.

After that, though, the town thought some of the boys, at least, would move in from the Valley and get more sociable. They figured they'd have to—they figured with their Pa and Ma gone, the boys would fight amongst themselves—they figured a dozen things. But none of the things they figured happened at all. The Pontipee boys stayed out in the Valley, and when they came to the town, they walked through it as proud as Lucifer, and when they came to the church, they put just the same money in the collection-plate they had when Ma and Pa Pontipee were alive. Some thought it was because they were stupid to count, but I don't think it was that.

They went on just the same, as I say, but things didn't go quite the same for them. For one thing, the hired girl couldn't keep the place the way Ma Pontipee kept it. And besides, she was getting old herself. Well, pretty soon, she up and died. They gave her as good a funeral as they knew how—she'd always been part of the family. But, after that, though the farm went ahead as well as ever, things in the house began to go from bad to worse.

Menlike, they didn't notice what was wrong at first, except there was a lot of dust around and things didn't get put away. But, after each one of them had tried to week of cooking for the others and all the others had cursed out the one who was cooking something proper, they decided something had to be done about it. It took them a long time to decide that—they were slow thinkers as well as slow talkers, the Pontipees. But, when they decided about a thing, it got done.

"The flapjacks are greasy again," said Harry Pontipee, one evening—Harry was the oldest. "You know what we've got to get, brothers? We've got to get a woman to take care of this place. I can lay a tree within two inches of where I want it to fall. I can shoot the eye out of a grey squirrel in a treetop. I can do all a man should do. But I can't cook and make it taste human."

"You're right, brother," said Hob Pontipee—Hob was the youngest. "I can tan deerskin better than an Injun squaw. I can wrastle underholt and overholt and throw any man in this county. I can play on a boxwood fiddle—but I can't sweep dust so it stays swept. It takes a woman to do that, for there seems to be a trick about it. We've got to get a woman."

Then they all joined in saying what they could do—and it was plenty—but they couldn't cook and they couldn't dust and they couldn't make a house comfortable because that was woman's business, and there seemed to be a trick about it. So they had to get a woman to keep house for them. But where were they going to get her?

"We could get a hired girl, maybe," said Hosea Pontipee—the middle one—but, even as he spoke, there wasn't much hope in his voice.

"That hired girl we had was the last one left in the East," said Harry Pontipee. "Some may have growed up, since her time, but I don't want to go back across the Pass on the chance of an out-and-out miracle."

"Well then," said Hob Pontipee, practical, "there's just one thing to do. One of us has to get married. And I think it ought to be Harry—he's the eldest."

Well, that remark nearly caused a break-up in the family. Harry kicked like a cow in fly-time at the bare idea of getting married, and tried to put it on to Halbert, who was next in line. And Halbert passed it on to Harvey, but Harvey said women was snares and delusions, or so he'd heard, and he wouldn't have a strange woman around him for a brand-new plow.

So it went on down to Hob and he wouldn't hear of it—and it wasn't till a couple of chairs had been broken and Hob had a black eye that the ruckus quieted at all. But, gradually, they came to see that one of 'em would have to get married, as a matter of family duty, or they'd all be eating spoiled flapjacks for the rest of their lives. Only then the question came up as to who it was to be, and that started a bigger disturbance than ever.

Finally, they agreed that the only fair way was drawing straws. So Hob held the straws and they drew—and, sure enough, Harry got the long one. Sick enough he looked about it—but there it was. The others started congratulating him and making jokes—especially Hob.

"You'll have to slick up, tomorrow," said Hob, glad it wasn't him. "You'll have to cut your hair and brush your clothes and act pretty, if you're going to be a bridegroom!"

Next morning they got him down and cut his hair and put bear's grease on it and dressed him up in the best clothes they had and sent him into town to look for a wife.

It was all right when he started out from the Valley. He even took a look at himself in a spring and was kind of surprised at the young man who looked back at him. But the nearer he got to town, the queerer and tremblier he felt, and the less able to go about doing what he'd promised.

He tried to remember how it had been when his Pa and Ma had been courting. But, naturally, as he hadn't been born then, he didn't know. Then he tried to think of various girls in the village, but the more he thought of them, the more they mixed in his mind—till, finally, all he could think of was a high, wild bank of rhododendron flowers that mixed and shimmered and laughed at you the closer you came to it.

"Oh, Lordy! It's a heavy responsibility to lay on a man!" he said and mopped his forehead with his sleeve.

Finally, however, he made up his mind. "I'll ask the first woman I see, pretty or ugly!" he said to himself, with the perspiration fairly rolling down his face, though it was a cold March day. And he gave his horse a lick.

But, when he got into town, the first woman he saw was the storekeeper's wife. The second he saw was a little girl in a pinafore —and the third was the minister's daughter. He was all set up to speak to her—but she squeaked and ran to the other side of the street as soon as she saw him and left him standing there with his hat in his hand. That sort of took the courage out of him.

"By the whiskers of Moses!" he said to himself, "this marryin' job is a harder job than I bargained for. I guess I'll go over to the tavern and get me a drink—maybe that will put some ideas in my head."

It was there he saw her—feeding the chickens out in the poultry-yard. Her name was Milly and she was a bound girl, as they had it in those days. Next door to a slave she was, for all she'd come of good stock and had some education. She was young and thin, with a sharp little thoughtful face and ragged clothes, but she walked as straight as an Indian as she went about the yard. Harry Pontipee couldn't have said if she were pretty or plain, but, as he watched her through the window, feeding the chickens, something seemed to tell him that he might have better luck with her than he'd had with the others.

Well, he drank his drink and went out.

"Hello, girl," he said, in one of those big voices men use when they're pretending not to be embarrassed.

She looked up at him straight. "Hello, backwoodsman!" she said, friendly enough. She didn't look a bit scared of him and that put him off.

"It's a nice morning," said Harry, louder, trying to lead up to his point.

"It is for some," said the girl, perfectly polite but going on feeding the chickens.

Harry swallowed hard at that. "It'd be a nice morning to get married, they tell me," he said, with the perspiration breaking out all over him again. He'd meant to say something else, but when it came to the point, he couldn't.

Well, she didn't say anything to that so he had to start all over again.

"My name's Harry Pontipee," he said. "I've got a good farm up in the Valley."

"Have you?" said the girl.

"Yes," he said. "It's a right good farm. And some folks seem to think I'd make a good husband."

"Do they?" said the girl. I guess she was smiling by now but Harry couldn't see it—she had her head turned.

"Yes they do," said Harry, kind of desperate, his voice getting louder and louder. "What do you think about it?"

"I couldn't tell on such short acquaintance," said the girl.

"Will you marry me and find out?" said Harry, in a perfect bellow, shaking all over.

"Yes, I will, if you don't ask me quite so loud," she said, very prim—and even Harry could see she was smiling now.

Well, they made a queer pair when they went up to the minister—the girl still in her chicken-feed clothes, for she didn't have any others, and Harry in his backwoods finery. He'd had to buy out her time from the innkeeper for twelve beaver pelts and a hunting knife.

But when the wedding service was over, "Well, we're married," said Harry, with great relief. "And now we'll be going home."

"Oh, no we won't," said she. "We're going to the store first and buy me some cloth for a decent dress—for landless I may be and dowryless I may be, but I'm a married woman now, and what's fit for a chickengirl isn't fit for a married woman."

In a sort of daze, he saw her lay out the price of twelve more beaver pelts in cloth and woman's fixings, and beat down the storekeeper on the price, too.

He only asked her a question about one thing—a little pair of slippers she bought. They were fancy slippers, with embroidery on them. "I thought you had a pair of shoes," he said. She turned to him, with a cocky sort of look on her face. "Silly," she said. "How could anyone tell your wife had pretty feet in the shoes I had?"

Well, he thought that over, and, after a while, something in the way she said it and the cocky look on her face made him feel pleased, and he began to laugh. He wasn't used to laughing in front of a girl, but he could see it might have its points.

Then they rode back to the Valley, her riding pillion, with her bundles in the saddlebags. And all the way back, she was trying him and testing him and trying to find out, by one little remark or another, just what kind of a man he was. She was a spunky little girl, and she had more education than she let on. And long ago, she'd made up her mind to get out of being a bound girl the first way that offered. But, all the same, marrying Harry Pontipee was a leap in the dark.

But the more she tried and tested Harry, the better bargain she seemed to think she'd made. And that took courage to admit—for the way was a wild one and a lonesome, and, naturally, she'd heard stories of Pontipee Valley. She couldn't quite believe they lived with bears, up there, but she didn't know.

And finally, they came to the house, and there were dark things moving outside it. "Bears!" thought Milly, kind of hopeless, and her heart went into her throat, but she didn't let on.

"W-what's that, Harry dear?" she said, holding on tight.

"Oh, that's just my brothers," said Harry, kind of careless, and with that those six hungry six-footers moved into the light.

"Oh!" said Milly, "you didnt' tell me you had six brothers." But her voice wasn't reproachful, just sort of soft and quiet.

"I guess it was the wedding kind of knocked it out of my

mind," said Harry. "But, there—you'll see enough of 'em anyhow, because we all live together."

"Oh," said Milly again, kind of soft. "I see." And the brothers came up, one by one, and shook hands. They'd intended to cut quite a few jokes on Harry if he did come home with a wife, but, somehow, when they looked at Milly, they forgot about that.

Well, they brought her into the house. It was a handsome house, for the times, with genuine windowglass. But Milly rubbed her finger along a window sill and saw it come off black and then she wrote her name in the dust on the mantelpiece.

"What a lovely big house!" she said, coughing a little with the dust she'd raised.

"It's mebbe a little dusty now," said Harry. "But now you're here——"

"Yes," said Milly and passed on to the kitchen. Well, the kitchen was certainly a sight. But Milly didn't seem to notice.

Presently, "What a great big jar of flapjack batter!" she said. "And what a big tub of salt pork!"

"That's for tonight," said Harry. "Me and my brothers is hearty eaters. We haven't been eating so well since we had to cook for ourselves, but now you're here——"

"Yes," said Milly and passed on to the laundry. The laundry was half full of huckaback shirts and such that needed washing—piles and piles of them.

"What a lot of wash!" said Milly.

"That's so," said Harry, kind of pleased. "Me and my brothers is kind of hard on our clothes—all seven of us—so there's lots of washing and mending, but now you're here——"

"Yes," said Milly, swallowing a little. "And now all you men clear out of my kitchen while I get supper. Clear out!" she said, smiling at them, though she didn't feel much like smiling.

I don't know what she said to herself when they'd left her alone. I know what a man would have said and I guess she said that, too. I know she thought at least once of the money in her stocking and how far it was back to town. And then her eye happened to fall on that great big jar of flapjack batter—and, all of a sudden the whole think struck her as funny, and she laughed till she cried.

But then she found a clean handkerchief and blew her nose and straightened her hair and set about her work.

Those boys hadn't had a supper like that in months and they treated it respectful. And Milly didn't say a word to them about manners then, though, later on, she said plenty. She just sat and watched them, with a curious light in her eyes.

When it was over finally, and they were stuffed, "Mrs. Harry," said Howard. "You're a wonder, Mrs. Harry!" and "You're sure a wonder, Mrs. Harry!" chorused all the rest of them, down to Hob. She could see they meant it, too.

"Thanks," she said, very polite and gracious. "Thank you, Howard, and you, Hosea, and all my brothers."

At the end of three months, there wasn't one of those boys that wouldn't have laid down his life for Milly, and, as for Harry, he just worshipped the ground she walked on. With all that work to do, naturally, she got thinner and thinner and peakeder and peakeder, but she didn't complain. She knew what she wanted and how she was going to get it—and she waited her chance.

Finally, Harry noticed how thin she was getting and he spoke to her about it.

"Can't you ever sit down and rest, Milly?" he said one day, watching her fly around the kitchen, doing six things at once.

But she just laughed at him and said, "I'm cooking for you and your six brothers, and that makes work, you know."

Well, he thought that over, inside him, but he didn't say anything, then. But he came up to her in the laundry another time, and when she was dusting the house another time—she was looking peakeder each day—and asked her if she couldn't rest a spell. The last time, he brought his fist down on the table with a bang.

"This has got to stop!" he said. "Me and my six brothers is wearing you to skin and bone with our victuals and our shirts and the dust we track in the house, and I won't have it no more! It's got to stop!"

"Well, Harry," she said, sort of quiet, "if it's got to stop, it's got to—and pretty soon, Harry. Because, I'm expecting, and a woman that's expecting can't work like a woman in her usual health."

Well, after he got his sense back, after hearing that, he called the whole family into consultation that evening and put it to them plain. They'd do anything for Milly by then.

She led the conversation where she wanted it to go, though she didn't seem to, and finally they decided it was up to Halbert, the second oldest, to get married, so his wife could take some of the work off Milly's hands. So next day, Halbert spruced up and went to town to look for a wife. But when he came home, he was alone and all dejected.

"They won't have me," he said, very mournful. "They won't none of 'em have me—and I asked fourteen of 'em."

"Why, what's the matter?" said Milly.

"Well," said Halbert, "it seems they've heard about the seven of us and the lot of victuals we eat and the wash and all—and they say only a fool would marry into a family like that and they don't see how you stand it, Milly."

"Oh, that's what they say, is it?" said Milly, with her eyes as bright as candles. "Well, your turn next, Harvey."

So Harvey tried it and Hosea tried it and all of them tried it. But none of them had any luck. And then, finally, Milly let loose at them, good and proper.

"You great big lumps of men!" she said, with the cocky look on her face. "There's more ways of killing a cat than choking it with cream. If they won't marry you after you've asked 'em— why don't you marry 'em first and ask 'em afterwards?"

"But how can we do that?" said Harvey, who was the stupidest.

"Well," said Milly—and here's where her education came in that I've made such a point of—"I read in a history book once about a bunch of people called Romans who were just in your fix." And she went on to tell them about the Romans—how they were settled in a country that was unfriendly to them, just like the Pontipees, and how they all needed wives, just like the Ponti-pees, and how, when they couldn't get them in the ordinary way from the other people of the country who were called the Sobbin's or the Sabbin's or some such name, they raided the Sobbin' town one night and carried off a lot of the Sobbin' women and married them.

"And, if you can't do as well for yourselves as a lot of old dead

Romans," she ended, "you're no brothers of mine and you can cook your own suppers the rest of your lives."

They all sat around dumbfounded for a while. Finally Hob spoke up.

"That sounds all right, in history," he said, "but this is different. Supposing these women just cry and pine away when we've carried them off—supposing that?"

"Listen to me," said Milly. "I know what I'm talking about. Every one of those girls is crazy to get married—and there's not half enough men in town to go round. They think a lot of you boys, too, for I've heard them talk about you; but they're scared of your being backwoodsmen, and scared of the work, and each one is scared of being the first to leave the others. I'll answer for them, once you've married them. Is there anybody around here who can marry people, except the regular minister?"

"There's a sort of hedge-parson just come to town," said Hob. "I reckon he can tie a knot as tight as any preacher in the county."

"All right," said Milly. "That settles it."

It was the evening of the big sociable that it happened. They held it once a year, around Thanksgiving time, and those who had rifles and weapons left them at the door. The Pontipee boys had never attended before—so there was a good deal of stir when they marched in, all seven of them, with Milly in the middle. The brothers were shaved and clean and dressed up spick and span and Milly never looked better, in a dress she'd made out of store cloth and her embroidered slippers.

There was quite a bit of giggling from the town girls, as the Pontipees entered, and a buzz around the hall, but then the fiddler struck up and people began to dance and play games and enjoy themselves, and pretty soon they forgot the Pontipees were there at all, except that the Pontipee boys acted very polite to everybody—Milly'd taught 'em that—and, I guess, before the evening was over, some of the town girls were wondering why they'd turned down boys like that just because they lived in the backwoods.

But they didn't get much chance to think about it, at that. Because, just as they were all going to sit down to supper—"Ready, boys?" called Milly, in a voice that cut through all the talk and commotion. Everybody turned to look at her. And then there was a gasp and a cry, for "Ready!" chorused the six bachelor Ponti-pees; and suddenly, each one had one hand on a rifle and the other holding a girl, while Harry and Milly trained a couple more rifles on the rest of the community to keep them quiet. It happened so sudden, half the folks didn't even know it was happening—till the Pontipee boys had their girls outside in the street, and the big doors locked and bolted behind them.

Then there was Cain to raise for fair in the meeting-hall, and people started to beat and kick at the doors—but they built solid, in those days. There wasn't any use in trying to shoot the locks off, because the Pontipee boys had tied up the guard over the weapons and dumped him and them outside in a shed.

It wasn't till pretty near dawn that the doors gave way—and when they did, the townspeople took one look outside and groaned. For it was snowing, lickety split, till you couldn't see your hand before your face—and when it snows, in our part of the country, it certainly snows. The blizzard didn't let up for four days, either, and by that time, the pass through the hills to Pontipee Valley was blocked solid, and nothing to do but wait for Spring and the thaw.

And, meanwhile, Milly had her work cut out for her. It wasn't an easy job, convoying three sleigh-loads full of hysterics all that long, cold ride. But she let them hysteric away, and, by the time they got to the Pontipee house, the stolen brides were so tuckered out that they'd quieted down a good deal.

Still, at first, they swore they wouldn't take bite or sup till they were restored to their grieving families. But Milly had some tea ready for them, in a jiffy—and a woman will usually take tea, no matter how mad she is. Well, Milly let them get warm and a little cozy, and then, when they were on their second cups, she made her little speech.

"Ladies," she said, "this affair makes me mighty sad—to see fine girls like you stole away by a lot of uncouth backwoodsmen. And I'd never have lent a hand to it if I'd known the truth of the matter. But, you and me, we'll turn the tables on them yet. You can't get back to your families till the blizzard lets up, but, while you've got to stay here, I'll see you're treated respectful. And just

to prove that"—and she took a bunch of keys from her pocket—
"I'll lock this house up tight, with us inside it; and, as for those
backwoods Pontipees, they can sleep and eat in the stable with the
livestock. That'll teach them they can't fool us!"

Well, that little speech—and the tea—cheered the girls up quite
a bit. And by the time Milly showed them to their rooms—nice-
looking rooms, too—and let them bolt themselves in, they were
pretty well convinced that Milly was their friend.

So a week or so went by like that—the girls keeping house for
themselves and never seeing hide nor hair of a Pontipee.

At first, it was a regular picnic for the girls. They allowed as
how they'd always wanted to live without any men around, and,
now they were, it was even better than they'd thought. And Milly
agreed with them as hard as she could agree. She made them little
speeches about the worthlessness of men in general and husbands
in particular that would have raised the hair off any man's head.
And, at first, the other girls listened to her and chimed in, and
then they listened, but you could see they were being polite. And,
by the end of the week, it was awful hard for her to get a real
audience.

So, when she began to catch them looking out of windows
when they should have been dusting, and peeking from behind
curtains to try and get a sight of the terrible Pontipees, she knew
it was time for the next step. For things got duller and duller in
the house and little spats and quarrels began to break out among
the girls. So, one afternoon, she suggested, tactfully, just to break
the monotony, that they all go up and rummage in the garret.

They rummaged around and had quite a bit of fun, until finally
the minister's daughter opened a long box and gave a little squeal
of joy.

"What a lovely wedding-dress—whose was it?" she said, and
pulled out the long white veil and the dress itself, while the rest
stood round and admired.

"Oh, shucks, that's just an old wedding-dress those backwoodsmen made me make when they thought you were going to marry.
'em," said Milly, in a very disgusted voice. "Put it back!" but the
girls weren't paying attention.

"Will it fit me, I wonder?" said the minister's daughter.

"It's bad luck, trying on wedding-dresses, if you're not going to have a wedding!" said Milly. "Let's go downstairs and have tea." But the minister's daughter was stepping out of her regular clothes already. The other girls helped fix her up—and then they oh-ed and ah-ed, for, I must say, she made a handsome-looking bride.

"That Pontipee boy named Hob's got curly hair," said the minister's daughter, trailing out her veil. "I always did have a liking for curly hair."

"Hob's not nearly as good-looking as Halbert," said the lawyer's niece, quite voilent, and another one said, "Handsome is as handsome does—the one they call Harvey isn't so handsome, maybe, but he certainly has nice eyes."

"There's something about a man around the house that brisks things up remarkable," said a fourth one. "Not that I want to get married, but Howard's a nice name, even if Pontipee is hitched to it and——"

"Girls, girls—are you crazy, girls?" said Milly, shocked and horrified. But the minute she started to reprove them, they all turned on her, most ungratefully, and there was a regular revolt. So, at last, she had to give in and admit that there were five more wedding-dresses in the garret—and that if anybody was thinking of getting married, there just happened to be a hedge-parson, spending the winter with the Pontipees. But one thing she was firm about.

"Get married if you like," she said. "I can't stop you. But I'm responsible for you to your families—and, after the ceremony's ended, your husbands go back to the stable and stay there, till I know your families approve of them." She looked very fierce about it, and she made them promise. The hedge-parson married them all—all six in their wedding dresses—and then the boys went back to the stable. And, at dinner that night, the minister's daughter burst out crying.

"I hate men just as much as ever!" she wailed. "But it's terrible to be lawful married to a man you can't even see, except now and then out of a window!"

So Milly saw she had to make some new rules and she did. Three afternoons a week, the boys were allowed to call on their new wives, and once in a while, for a great treat, they could stay to supper. But, always with Milly to chaperon.

Well, at first, the husbands and wives were mighty stiff and formal with each other, but, gradually, they got better and better acquainted. Till, pretty soon, the minister's daughter was letting Hob hold her hand, when she thought Milly wasn't looking, and the lawyer's niece was asking permission to sew a button on Halbert's coat—and there was a general atmosphere of courting around the Pontipee place that'd make an old bachelor sick.

Milly took it all in but she never stopped chaperoning.

Well, finally, it was one day along in January. Milly woke up in the morning—and she knew she was near her time. But, first thing in the morning, as always, she reached underneath her pillow for her keys—and then she smiled. For somebody must have stolen them while she was sleeping—and when she got up, and went to the window in her wrapper, the door of the house was wide open. And there was Hob and his wife, helping each other shovel snow from the doorstep, and Halbert and his wife were throwing snowballs at Harvey and his, and Howard was kissing the doctor's eldest behind the kitchen door. "Praise be!" said Milly. "I can have my baby in peace"—and she went down to congratulate them all.

Only then, there were the families and relatives still to fix. But Milly had a plan for that—she had plans for everything. When they stole the girls away, they left a letter she drew up, signed by all the boys and expressing all the honorable intentions you could put a name to. But she was afraid that wouldn't cool down the townspeople much, even when they thought it over, and it didn't.

One day when the first thaws had come and Milly's baby was about six weeks old, Hob came running in from his lookout post.

"They're coming, Milly!" he said. "The whole dum town! They's got rifles and scythes and ropes and they look mighty wild and bloodthirsty! What'll we do?"

"Do?" said Milly, perfectly calm. "You get the boys together and keep out of sight—and tell the girls to come here. For it's women's work, now, that'll save us, if anything will."

When she got the girls together, she gave them their orders. I

guess they were a bit white-faced, but they obeyed. Then she
looked out of the window—and there was the town, marching up
the road, slow and steady. She'd have liked it better if they'd
shouted or cried, but they didn't shout nor cry. The minister was
in the lead, with his lips shut, and a six foot rifle in his hand, and
his face like an iron mask.

She saw them come up to the gate of the Pontipee place. The
gate was wide open and nobody there to hinder. She could see
them take that in—and the little waver in the crowd. Because that
made them feel queer.

Then they caught themselves and came tramping along toward
the house, the minister still in the lead. Milly caught her breath, for
they still looked awful mad. She knew what they'd expect when
they got near the house—every window barred and every door
bolted and red-hot bullets spitting through the loop-holes in the
walls.

But the windows were open—you could see white curtains in
them; there were plants on some of the sills. The door of the house
stood ajar and Milly's cat was asleep on the doorstone, there in
the sun.

They stood outside that door for quite a little bit, just milling
around and staring. It was very quiet; they could hear their own
breath breathe and their own hearts knock. Finally the minister
brushed his face, as if he were brushing a cobweb away from it,
and he gripped his gun and went up on the porch and knocked
at the open door. He'd intended to stomp up those steps like a
charge of cavalry, but he walked soft, instead. He couldn't have
told you why.

He knocked once and he knocked again—and then Milly was
standing in the door, with her baby in her arms.

Somebody at the back of the crowd dropped the scythe he was
carrying, and another one coughed in his hand.

"You're just in time to christen my child, your reverence," said
Milly. "Have you brought that rifle to help you christen my
child?"

The minister's eyes dropped, after a minute, and he lowered his
rifle but he still held it in the crook of his arm.

"Your child?" he said, and his voice was as low as Milly's, but there was a fierceness in it. "What about my child?"

"Listen!" said Milly, raising her hand, and the whole crowd fell dead still. Then from somewhere in the house came the hum of a spinning-wheel, low and steady, and a woman's voice, humming with the wheel.

"That's your child you hear, your reverence," said Milly. "Does she sound hurt, your reverence, or does she sound content?"

The minister hesitated for a moment and the crowd fell dead still again. Then they all heard the hum of the wheel and the hum of the woman's voice, humming back and forth to each other, as they did their work in the world.

"She sounds content—heaven help me!" said the minister, and a twist went over his face. But there was a sudden outburst of cries and questions from the others. "My child, what about my child?" "Where's Mary?" "Is Susy safe?"

"Listen!" said Milly again, and they all fell silent once more. And, from somewhere, there came the splash of a churn and the voice of a woman talking to the butter to make it come; and the rattling of pans in a kitchen and a woman singing at her work; and the slap of clothes on a laundry board and the little clatter a woman makes setting table.

"There's your children," said Milly. "Hear 'em? Don't they sound all right? And—dinner will be ready in about half an hour—and you're all staying, I hope."

Then the daughters came out and their folks rushed to them; and, after all the crying and conniptions were over, Milly introduced the parents to their sons-in-law.

THE TUXEDOS

By JEROME WEIDMAN

EVER SINCE THE TIME, SOME TEN YEARS AGO, WHEN I WORKED FOR Mr. Brunschweig on Canal Street, I have been peculiarly sensitive to the half-hour of the day that comes between five-thirty and six o'clock in the late afternoon. Mr. Brunschweig was an excellent boss, as bosses go, except for one lamentable defect: he was a minute-pincher. He carried two large pocket watches and spent a good part of each day comparing them with each other and with the huge Seth Thomas on the wall. I am certain that he was a little terrified by the inexorableness of time and that his sensitivity to it was a direct result of the way he earned his living. Mr. Brunschweig rented tuxedos.

The tuxedo-renting business, as I knew it, was distinguished by two cardinal rules. First, the suits had to be made of the toughest and heaviest materials available. And second, it was necessary to deliver them as close to the moment of wearing as possible and even more imperative to pick them up as soon after they were taken off as the wearer would permit. Mr. Brunschweig's timing in this respect was so good and I was so nimble as a delivery boy that while many of his customers cursed him roundly for having delayed them in getting to a wedding, not one of them could say with honesty that he had worn a Brunschweig tuxedo to more than one affair for the price of a single renting.

My relations with Mr. Brunschweig were amicable if somewhat exhausting, but every day, as the hands of the clock crept around to half-past five, a definite tension would come into the atmosphere. My quitting time was six o'clock. As a general rule, Mr. Brunschweig arranged deliveries in such fashion that the last one carried me up to, or past, that hour. We had an understanding to the effect that if I took out a delivery at any time after five-thirty and could not get to my destination until six o'clock or a few min-

315

utes before, I did not have to return to the Canal Street store that
night and was at liberty to go directly home. However, the possibility of his only employee departing for home five or ten minutes
ahead of quitting time was so disturbing to Mr. Brunschweig that
very often he would detain me in the store before I went out on
my final delivery, talking about the weather or discussing the baseball scores, just to make sure that I could not possibly complete the
delivery before six o'clock.

Strangely enough, I did not resent these obvious subterfuges,
because I sensed that Mr. Brunschweig was a little ashamed of
them. What I did resent was that unconsciously I was being forced
into practices I didn't approve of to combat him.

For instance, I would instinctively stall on any delivery after
five-fifteen to make certain that I would not get back to the store
in time to make another delivery before quitting. Or I would rush
through a four-o'clock delivery to make sure that there would be
ample time for still another one before six o'clock. In either case
it was very unsettling, and scarcely a day went by that I didn't
have a struggle with my conscience or the clock.

There were times, of course, when my energy overcame my
caution. One day, in an industrious mood, I returned from an
uptown delivery at twenty minutes to six. It had been a long
trip and I could have stretched it for another twenty minutes with
ease, but I had temporarily forgotten Mr. Brunschweig's vice and
I did not realize my mistake until I came into the store. He was
boxing an unusually large order, and I could tell from his cheery
greeting that this one would carry me well past six o'clock. I was
about to dismiss the occurrence as simply another occasion on
which I had been outmaneuvered by Mr. Brunschweig when I
saw that he had stacked six boxes, one on top of the other.

"Is that *one* delivery?" I asked in amazement.

The average delivery weighed well over ten pounds and consisted of a tuxedo, a shirt, a tie, studs, and a pair of patent-leather
pumps, packed neatly into a heavy cardboard box. Two or three
of these boxes were a load. Six of them were an incredible amount.

"Yeah," he said cheerfully. "Italian wedding. It all goes to one
family. I'll give you a help to the subway."

I should have been grateful to him for this offer, I suppose, since it was an unusual move, but all I could think of was the prospect of juggling sixty pounds of tuxedos through the subway in the rush hour.

"Where's it going?" I asked.

"Brooklyn," he said. "It's just over the bridge. Won't take you long."

The boxes weighed so much I could scarcely raise them from the floor.

"Here," he said. "You take the hats. I'll take the suits till we get to the train."

I hadn't even thought about top hats. They were not very heavy, but they were the most perishable items in Mr. Brunschweig's stock and consequently were always packed with great care in individual boxes.

"We gotta hurry," Mr. Brunschweig said, handing me a slip of paper with an address on it. "It's the bride's family and I promised them early. Name is Lasquadro."

He took the lashed tuxedo boxes and I took the pile of hatboxes, tied one on top of another so that they resembled a small steamship funnel. In the street we paused for a moment while he locked the store, and then we started off down Canal Street to the subway station.

The only satisfactory recollection I have of that evening is the brief memory of Mr. Brunschweig tottering along in front of me under the weight of six boxes of tuxedos and accessories. The rest was a nightmare. I remember being on the subway platform, between my two huge bundles, trying to get into train after train. I had to let seven or eight go by before I could wedge my way into one of them. Then I remember standing, perspiring and exhausted, outside the subway station in Brooklyn, looking at the two bundles and realizing that I could carry them no further. It had grown quite dark and I began to be worried, too, about being late with the delivery. Finally I worked out a plan. I dragged the tuxedos along the ground for a short distance, then went back for the hats, dragged them up to the tuxedos, and then repeated the process. It was an effective method but an extremely slow one. Though the address Mr. Brunschweig had given me was only three blocks from the Brooklyn subway station, it was almost twenty

minutes later that I stopped, breathless, in front of the correct
house number.

The street was deserted and dark; the house was a two-story
brownstone affair and only the basement windows showed lights
from behind drawn shades. As I wiped the perspiration from my
face and tried to think of an excuse for being so late, I heard noises
coming from the basement. Figures kept passing the windows
quickly and the sound of scuffling and angry voices reached me
clearly. I was frightened and spent another precious minute trying
to puzzle out a way of leaving my bundles without having to face
the people inside the house.

Then, in a burst of nervous courage, I tumbled the bulky bundles down the steps that led to the basement door and knocked
gently. There was no answer. The angry noises inside continued,
and I knocked again. Still no answer. Then I discovered a push
button on the wall beside the door, jabbed at it hastily, and a bell
pealed shrilly somewhere inside the house. At once the door was
pulled open and a small young man in shirtsleeves, with a tight,
dark, scowling face, shot his head out and glared at me.

"What the hella *you* want?" he demanded harshly.

"The—the tuxedos," I said awkwardly. "I brought the tuxedos."

The young man turned his head and yelled at someone in the
room behind him. "He brought the tuxedos! You hear that? He
brought the tuxedos!"

He laughed unpleasantly and a man's voice replied from inside
the room. "Tell him he knows what he can do with them!"

The young man in front of me reached for the door and started
to slam it shut. The thought that I might have to drag those two
bundles back to Canal Street that night was enough to make me
forget my fright. I braced my shoulder against the door and held
it open.

"I have to leave these here," I said quickly. "I have to—I have
to get the receipt signed."

The little dark face glared at me and the hand on the door drew
back threateningly. "Aah," he started to say, and then stopped.
"O.K., O.K., come on. Bring 'em in and beat it."

He dragged the bundles in and the door swung shut behind me.
As I began to fumble in my pocket for the receipt book, I stole a

scared look at the scene in the room. It was a large, shabbily furnished living room, with a new radio in one corner, a huge potted rubber plant in another, and embroidered mottoes on the wall. A pretty, dark-haired girl in a white wedding gown was sitting at a table in the middle of the room. Five men, all in vests and shirt-sleeves and all looking as if they must be brothers of the young man who had opened the door for me, were standing over her. One of the men held the girl and was twisting her arm behind her, and she was sobbing violently. A tiny old woman, with white hair in a knot at the back of her head and wearing a black alpaca apron, hovered on the outskirts of the group around the table, jabbering shrilly in Italian. The young man who had let me in joined his brothers. Nobody paid any attention to me.

"Come on," one of the men said, leaning over the girl. "What's his address? Give us that address!"

The girl shook her head and the man who was holding her arm gave it another twist. She screamed and dropped her head forward. Another man pushed his face down close to hers.

"Come on!" he yelled. "Give it to us. We're doing this for the family, ain't we? What's his address?"

The girl shook her head again; the little old lady chattered away. One of the brothers reached over and slapped the girl's face.

"Where was he when he called up?" he said. "Come on, tell us. We ain't gonna hurt him. We'll just murder the louse, that's all. Where was he?"

She didn't answer.

"Come on, you damn fool," the man who held her arm said. "Talk! You want him to go spreading it to the whole world he walked out on you an hour before the wedding?" He shook her angrily. "Where was he when he called up? Where does he live? We'll fix him so he won't talk. What's his address?"

The girl did not answer. He started to shake her again, then he saw me standing near the door. "Get that guy out of here," he said. The brother who had let me in came across the room in three steps and grabbed my shoulder. "Come on, kid," he said. "Beat it!"

I lifted my reecipt book in front of his face. "The receipt," I said. "I must get my receipt signed. I can't leave the—" He snatched the book from me and fumbled in his vest pocket for a pencil. He couldn't find one. I held my own out to him and he scribbled his name in my receipt book.

"O.K., kid," he said sharply. "Outside!" and he shoved the receipt book and pencil at me. I took them and started toward the door. Suddenly the little old lady grabbed my arm and pulled me back.

"What the hellsa matter?" the young man asked angrily.

She gestured violently toward me and poured a stream of Italian at him.

"All right, all right," he said, and reached into his pocket, pulled out a coin, and tossed the tip to me. I caught it and turned toward the door again.

"Thanks," I said quickly. But before I could open the door the old lady was on me. She clawed at my hand until I opened it so she could see the coin. It was a quarter. She swung around to the young man and clutched his coat.

"What the hellsa matter now?" he cried. "I gave him the tip, didn't I?"

Again she started talking in Italian, pointing at the bundle of tuxedos and tapping off the boxes with her finger—one, two, three, four, five, six. She waved six fingers in his face and yelled at him. He bit his lip, dug into his pocket again, and slapped some more coins into my palm. At once the little old lady seized my hand again. Now there were two quarters, a dime, and a nickel in it. She counted them quickly, snatched up the nickel, and counted again. Sixty cents remained. Another glance at the tuxedos and another glance at the two quarters and dime in my hand. Six tuxedos. Sixty cents. She nodded sharply to herself. Now it was all right.

"Give us that address!" shouted one of the brothers. There was the sound of a slap and the girl screamed again. "Where was he when he called up?"

The little old lady pulled open the door, pushed me out roughly, and slammed it shut behind me.

RED

By W. Somerset Maugham

THE SKIPPER THRUST HIS HAND INTO ONE OF HIS TROUSERS POCKETS and with difficulty—for they were not at the sides but in front, and he was a portly man—pulled out a large silver watch. He looked at it and then looked again at the declining sun.

The Kanaka at the wheel gave him a glance, but did not speak. The skipper's eyes rested on the island they were approaching. A white line of foam marked the reef. He knew there was an opening large enough to get his ship through, and when they came a little nearer he counted on seeing it.

They had nearly an hour of daylight still before them. In the lagoon the water was deep and they could anchor comfortably. The chief of the village which he could already see among the coconut trees was a friend of the mate and it would be pleasant to go ashore for the night.

The mate came forward at that minute, and the skipper turned to him.

"We'll take a bottle of booze along with us and get some girls in to dance," he said.

"I don't see the opening," said the mate.

He was a Kanaka, a handsome swarthy fellow, with somewhat the look of a later Roman emperor, inclined to stoutness; but his face was fine and clean-cut.

"I'm dead sure there's one right here," said the captain, looking through his glasses. "I can't understand why I can't pick it up. Send one of the boys up the mast to have a look."

The mate called one of the crew and gave him the order. The captain watched the Kanaka climb and waited for him to speak. But the Kanaka shouted down that he could see nothing but the unbroken line of foam. The captain spoke Samoan like a native, and he cursed him freely.

"Shall he stay up there?" asked the mate.

"What the hell good does that do?" answered the captain. "The blame' fool can't see worth a cent. You bet your sweet life I'd find the opening if I was up there."

He looked at the slender mast with anger. It was all very well for a native who had been used to climbing up coconut trees all his life. He was fat and heavy.

"Come down," he shouted. "You're no more use than a dead dog. We'll just have to go along the reef till we find the opening."

It was a seventy-ton schooner with paraffin auxiliary, and it ran, when there was no head-wind, between four and five knots. It was a bedraggled object: it had been painted white a very long time ago, but it was now dirty, dingy and mottled. It smelled strongly of paraffin and of the copra which was its usual cargo.

They were within a hundred feet of the reef now, and the captain told the steersman to run along it till they came to the opening. But when they had gone a couple of miles he realized that they had missed it. He went about and slowly worked back again. The white foam of the reef continued without interruption, and now the sun was setting. With a curse at the stupidity of the crew the skipper resigned himself to waiting till next morning.

"Put her about," he said. "I can't anchor here."

They went out to sea a little and presently it was quite dark. They anchored. When the sail was furled the ship began to roll a great deal. They said in Apia that one day she would roll right over; and the owner, a German-American who managed one of the largest stores, said no money was big enough to induce him to go out in her.

The cook, a Chinese in white trousers, very dirty and ragged, and a thin white tunic, came to say that supper was ready, and when the skipper went into the cabin he found the engineer already seated at table. The engineer was a long lean man with a scraggy neck. He was dressed in blue overalls and a sleeveless jersey which showed his thin arms tattooed from elbow to wrist.

"Hell, having to spend the night outside," said the skipper.

The engineer did not answer, and they ate in silence.

The cabin was lighted by a dim oil-lamp. When they had eaten the canned apricots with which the meal finished, the Chink brought them a cup of tea. The skipper lighted a cigar and went on the upper deck. The island now was only a darker mass against the night. The stars were very bright. The only sound was the ceaseless breaking of the surf.

The skipper sank into a deck-chair and smoked idly. Presently three or four members of the crew came up and sat down. One of them had a banjo and another a concertina. They began to play, and one of them sang. The native song sounded strange on these instruments.

Then, to the singing, a couple began to dance. It was a barbaric dance, savage and primeval, rapid, with quick movements of the hands and feet and contortions of the body; it was sensual, sexual even, but sexual without passion. It was very animal, direct, weird without mystery; natural, in short, and one might almost say childlike.

At last they grew tired. They stretched themselves on the deck and slept, and all was silent. The skipper lifted himself heavily out of his chair and clambered down the companionway. He went into his cabin and got out of his clothes. He climbed into his bunk and lay there. He panted a little in the heat of the night.

But next morning, when the dawn crept over the tranquil sea, the opening in the reef which had eluded them the night before was seen a little to the east of where they lay. The schooner entered the lagoon. There was not a ripple on the surface of the water. Deep down among the coral rocks you saw little colored fish swim.

When he had anchored his ship the skipper ate his breakfast and went on deck. The sun shone from an unclouded sky, but in the early morning the air was grateful and cool. It was Sunday, and there was a feeling of quietness, a silence as though Nature were at rest, which gave him a peculiar sense of comfort. He sat looking at the wooded coast and felt lazy and well at ease.

Presently a slow smile moved his lips and he threw the stump of his cigar into the water.

"I guess I'll go ashore," he said. "Get the boat out."

He climbed stiffly down the ladder and was rowed to a little cove. The coconut trees came down to the water's edge, not in rows, but spaced out with an ordered formality. They were like a ballet of spinsters, elderly but flippant, standing in affected attitudes with the simpering graces of a bygone age.

He sauntered idly through them, along a path that could be just seen winding its tortuous way, and it led him presently to a broad creek. There was a bridge across it, but a bridge constructed of single trunks of coconut trees, a dozen of them, placed end to end and supported where they met by a forked branch driven into the bed of the creek. You walked on a smooth round surface, narrow and slippery, and there was no support for the hand. To cross such a bridge required sure feet and a stout heart.

The skipper hesitated. But he saw on the other side, nestling among the trees, a white man's house; he made up his mind and, rather gingerly, began to walk.

He watched his feet carefully, and where one trunk joined on to the next and there was a difference of level, he tottered a little. It was with a gasp of relief that he reached the last tree and finally set his feet on the firm ground of the other side. He had been so intent on the difficult crossing that he never noticed any one was watching him, and it was with surprise that he heard himself spoken to.

"It takes a bit of nerve to cross these bridges when you're not used to them."

He looked up and saw a man standing in front of him. He had evidently come out of the house which the captain had seen.

"I saw you hesitate," the man continued, with a smile on his lips, "and I was watching to see you fall in."

"Not on your life," said the captain, who had now recovered confidence.

"I've fallen in myself before now. I remember one evening I came back from shooting, and I fell in, gun and all. Now I get a boy to carry my gun for me."

He was a man no longer young, with a small beard, now somewhat gray, and a thin face. He was dressed in a singlet without arms, and a pair of duck trousers. He wore neither shoes nor socks. He spoke English with a slight accent.

"Are you Neilson?" asked the skipper.

"I am."

"I've heard about you. I thought you lived somewhere around here."

The skipper followed his host into the little bungalow and sat down heavily in the chair which the other motioned him to take. While Neilson went to fetch whisky and glasses he took a look round the room.

It filled him with amazement. He had never seen so many books. The shelves reached from floor to ceiling on all four walls, and they were closely packed. There was a grand piano littered with music, and a large table on which books and magazines lay in disorder.

The room made him feel embarrassed. He remembered that Neilson was a queer fellow. No one knew very much about him, although he had been in the islands for so many years, but those who knew him agreed that he was queer.

"You've got one big heap of books here," he said, when Neilson returned.

"They do no harm," answered Neilson with a smile.

"Have you read them all?" asked the skipper.

"Most of them."

"I'm a bit of a reader myself. I have *The Saturday Evening Post* sent me regler."

Neilson poured his visitor a good stiff glass of whisky and gave him a cigar. The skipper volunteered a little information.

"I got in last night, but I couldn't find the opening, so I had to anchor outside. I never been this run before, but my people had some stuff they wanted to bring over here. Gray, d'you know him?"

"Yes, he's got a store a little way along."

"Well, there was a lot of canned stuff that he wanted over, an' he's got some copra. They thought I might just as well come over as lie idle at Apia. I run between Apia and Pago-Pago mostly; but they've got smallpox there just now, and there's nothing stirring."

He took a drink of his whisky and lighted a cigar. He was a taciturn man, but there was something in Neilson that made him nervous, and his nervousness made him talk. The Swede was looking at him with large dark eyes in which there was an expression of faint amusement.

"This is a tidy little place you've got here."

"I've done my best with it."

"You must do pretty well with your trees. They look fine. With copra at the price it is now. I had a bit of a plantation myself once; in Upoli it was but I had to sell it."

He looked round the room again, where all those books gave him a feeling of something incomprehensible and hostile.

"I guess you must find it a bit lonesome here, though," he said.

"I've got used to it. I've been here for twenty-five years."

Now the captain could think of nothing more to say, and he smoked in silence. Neilson had apparently no wish to break it. He looked at his guest with a meditative eye. He was a tall man, more than six feet high, and very stout. His face was red and blotchy, with a network of little purple veins on the cheeks, and his features were sunk into its fatness. His eyes were bloodshot. His neck was buried in rolls of fat. But for a fringe of long curly hair, nearly white, at the back of his head he was quite bald; and that immense shiny surface of forehead, which might have given him a false look of intelligence, on the contrary gave him one of peculiar imbecility. He wore a blue flannel shirt, open at the neck and showing his fat chest covered with a mat of reddish hair, and a very old pair of blue serge trousers.

He sat in his chair in a heavy ungainly attitude, his great belly thrust forward and his fat legs uncrossed. All elasticity had gone from his limbs. Neilson wondered idly what sort of man he had been in his youth. It was almost impossible to imagine that this creature of vast bulk had ever been a boy who ran about.

The skipper finished his whisky, and Neilson pushed the bottle toward him.

"Help yourself."

The skipper leaned forward and with his great hand seized it.

"And how come you in these parts yourself?" he said.

"Oh, I came out to the islands for my health. My lungs were bad and they said I hadn't a year to live. You see they were wrong."

"I mean, how come you to settle down right here?"

"I am a sentimentalist."

"Oh!"

Neilson knew that the skipper had not an idea what he meant, and he looked at him with an ironical twinkle in his dark eyes. Perhaps just because the skipper was so gross and dull a man, the whim seized him to talk further.

"You were too busy keeping your balance to notice, when you crossed the bridge, but this spot is generally considered rather pretty."

"It's a cute little house you've got here."

"Ah, that wasn't here when I first came. There was a native hut, with its beehive roof and its pillars, overshadowed by a great tree with red flowers; and the croton bushes, their leaves yellow and red and golden, made a pied fence around it. And then all about were the coconut trees, as fanciful as women, and as vain. They stood at the water's edge and spent all day looking at their reflections.

"I was a young man then—good heavens! it's a quarter of a century ago—and I wanted to enjoy all the loveliness of the world in the short time allotted to me before I passed into the darkness. I thought it was the most beautiful spot I had ever seen. The first time I saw it I had a catch at my heart, and I was afraid I was going to cry. I wasn't more than twenty-five, and though I put the best face I could on it, I didn't want to die. And somehow it seemed to me that the very beauty of this place made it easier for me to accept my fate. I felt when I came here that all my past life had fallen away, Stockholm and its University, and then Bonn; it all seemed the life of somebody else, as though now at last I had achieved the reality which our doctors of philosophy—I am one myself, you know—had discussed so much. 'A year,' I cried to myself. 'I have a year. I will spend it here, and then I am content to die.'

"We are foolish and sentimental and melodramatic at twenty-five; but if we weren't, perhaps we should be less wise at fifty.

"Now drink, my friend. Don't let the nonsense I talk interfere with you."

He waved his thin hand toward a bottle, and the skipper finished what remained in his glass.

"You ain't drinking nothin'," he said, reaching for the whisky.

"I am of sober habit," smiled the Swede. "I intoxicated myself in ways which I fancy are more subtle. But perhaps that is only vanity. Anyhow, the effects are more lasting and the results less deleterious."

"They say there's a deal of cocaine taken in the States now," said the captain.

Neilson chuckled.

"But I do not see a white man often," he continued, "and for once I don't think a drop of whisky can do me any harm."

He poured himself out a little, added some soda and took a sip.

"And presently I found out why the spot had such an unearthly loveliness. Here love had tarried for a moment, like a migrant bird that happens on a ship in mid-ocean and for a little while folds its tired wings. The fragrance of a beautiful passion hovered over it like the fragrance of a thorn in May in the meadows of my home. It seems to me that the places where men have loved or suffered keep about them always some faint aroma of something that has not wholly died. It is as though they had acquired a spiritual significance which mysteriously affects those who pass. I wish I could make myself clear." He smiled a little. "Though I can not imagine that if I did you would understand."

He paused.

"I think this place was beautiful because here I had been loved beautifully." And now he shrugged his shoulders. "But perhaps it is only that my esthetic sense is gratified by the happy conjunction of young love and a suitable setting."

Even a man less thick-witted than the skipper might have been forgiven if he were bewildered by Neilson's words. For he seemed faintly to laugh at what he said. It was as though he spoke from emotion which his intellect found ridiculous. He said himself that he was a sentimentalist, and when sentimentality is joined with skepticism there is often the devil to pay. He was silent for an instant, and looked at the captain with eyes in which there was a sudden perplexity.

"You know, I can't help thinking that I've seen you before somewhere or other," he said.

"I couldn't say as I remember you," returned the skipper.

"I have a curious feeling as though your face were familiar to me. It's been puzzling me for some time. But I can't situate my recollection in any place or at any time."

The skipper massively shrugged his heavy shoulders.

"It's thirty years since I first come to the islands. A man can't figure on remembering all the folk he meets in a while like that."

The Swede shook his head.

"You know how one sometimes has the feeling that a place one has never been to before is strangely familiar. That's how I seem to see you." He gave a whimsical smile. "Perhaps, perhaps you were the master of a galley in Ancient Rome and I was a slave at the oar. Thirty years you have been here?"

"Every bit of thirty years."

"I wonder if you knew a man called Red?"

"Red?"

"That is the only name I've ever known him by. I never knew him personally. I never even set eyes on him. And yet I seem to see him more clearly than many men, my brothers, for instance, with whom I passed my daily life for many years. He lives in my imagination with the distinctness of a Palo Malatesta or a Romeo. But I dare say you have never read Dante or Shakespeare?"

"I can't say as I have," said the captain.

Neilson, smoking a cigar, leaned back in his chair and looked vacantly at the ring of smoke which floated in the still air. A smile played on his lips, but his eyes were grave.

Then he looked at the captain. There was in his gross obesity something extraordinarily repellent. He had the plethoric self-satisfaction of the very fat. It was an outrage. It set Neilson's nerves on edge. But the contrast between the man before him and the man he had in mind was pleasant.

"It appears that Red was the most comely thing you ever saw. I've talked to quite a number of people who knew him in those days, white men, and they all agree that the first time you saw him his beauty just took your breath away. They called him Red on account of his flaming hair. It had a natural wave and he wore it long. It must have been of that wonderful color that the pre-Raphaelites raved over. I don't think he was vain of it, he was much too ingenuous for that; but no one could have blamed him if he had been.

"He was tall, six feet and an inch or two—in the native house that used to stand here was the mark of his height cut with a knife on the central trunk that supported the roof—and he was made like a Greek god, broad in the shoulders and thin in the flanks; he was like Apollo, with just that soft roundness which Praxiteles gave him, and that suave feminine grace which has in it something troubling and mysterious. His skin was dazzling white, milky, like satin; his skin was like a woman's."

"I had a kind of white skin myself when I was a kiddie," said the skipper, with a twinkle in his bloodshot eyes.

But Neilson paid no attention to him. He was telling his story now, and interruption made him impatient.

"And his face was just as beautiful as his body. He had large blue eyes, very dark, so that some say they were black, and unlike most red-haired people he had dark eyebrows and long dark lashes. His features were perfectly regular and his mouth was like a scarlet wound. He was twenty."

On these words the Swede stopped with a certain sense of the dramatic. He took a sip of whisky.

"He was unique. There never was any one more beautiful. There was no more reason for him than for a wonderful blossom to flower on a wild plant. He was a happy accident of Nature.

"One day he landed at that cove into which you must have put this morning. He was an American sailor, and he had deserted from a man-of-war in Apia. He had induced some good-humored native to give him a passage on a cutter that happened to be sailing from Apia to Saforo, and he had been put ashore here in a dugout.

"I do not know why he deserted. Perhaps life on a man-of-war, with its restrictions, irked him; perhaps he was in trouble; and perhaps it was the South Seas and these romantic islands that got into his bones. Every now and then they take a man strangely, and he finds himself like a fly in a spider's web. It may be that there was a softness of fiber in him, and these green hills with their soft airs, this blue sea, took the Northern strength from him as Delilah took the Nazarite's. Anyhow, he wanted to hide himself, and he thought he would be safe in this secluded nook till his ship had sailed from Samoa.

"There was a native hut at the cove, and as he stood there, wondering where exactly he should turn his steps, a young girl came out and invited him to enter. He knew scarcely two words of the native tongue, and she as little English. But he understood well enough what her smiles meant, and her pretty gestures, and he followed her. He sat down on a mat and she gave him slices of pineapple to eat.

"I can speak of Red only from hearsay, but I saw the girl three years after he first met her, and she was scarcely nineteen then. You can not imagine how exquisite she was. She had the passionate grace of the hibiscus and the rich color. She was rather tall, slim with the delicate features of her race, and large eyes like pools of still water under the palm trees; her hair, black and curling, fell down her back, and she wore a wreath of scented flowers. Her hands were lovely. They were so small, so exquisitely formed, they gave your heart-strings a wrench.

"And in those days she laughed easily. Her smile was so delightful that it made your knees shake. Her skin was like a field of ripe corn on a summer day.

"Good heavens! How can I describe her? She was too beautiful to be real.

"And these two young things, she was sixteen and he was twenty, fell in love with each other at first sight. That is the real love, not the love that comes from sympathy, common interests or intellectual community, but love pure and simple. That is the love that Adam felt for Eve when he awoke and found her in the Garden gazing at him with dewy eyes. That is the love that draws the beasts to one another, and the gods. That is the love that makes the world a miracle. That is the love which gives life its pregnant meaning. You have never heard of the wise cynical French duke who said that with two lovers there is always one who loves and one who lets himself be loved; it is a bitter truth to which most of us have to resign ourselves. But now and then there are two who love and two who let themselves be loved. Then one might fancy that the sun stands still, as it stood when Joshua prayed to the God of Israel.

"And even now after all these years, when I think of these two, so young, so fair, so simple, and of their love, I feel a pang. It tears my heart, just as my heart is torn when on certain nights I watch the full moon shining on the lagoon from an unclouded sky. There is always pain in the contemplation of perfect beauty.

"They were children. She was good and sweet and kind. I know nothing of him, and I like to think that then, at all events, he was ingenuous and frank. I like to think that his soul was as comely as his body. But I dare say he had no more soul than the creatures of the woods and forests who made pipes from reeds and bathed in the mountain streams when the world was young, and you might catch sight of little fauns galloping through the glade on the back of a bearded centaur. A soul is a troublesome possession, and when made developed it he lost the Garden of Eden.

"Well, when Red came to the island it had recently been visited by one of those epidemics which the white man has brought to the South Seas, and one-third of the inhabitants had died. It seems that the girl had lost all her near kin and she lived in the house of distant cousins. This household consisted of two ancient crones, bowed and wrinkled, two younger women and a man and a boy.

"For a few days he stayed there. But perhaps he felt himself too near the shore, with the possibility that he might fall in with white men who would reveal his hiding-place; perhaps the lovers could not bear that the company of others should rob them for an instant of the delight of being together. One morning they set out, the pair of them, with the few things that belonged to the girl, and walked along a grassy path under the coconuts, till they came to the creek you see. They had to cross the bridge you crossed, and the girl laughed gleefully because he was afraid. She held his hand till they came to the end of the first tree, and then his courage failed him and he had to go back. He was obliged to take off all his clothes before he could risk it, and she carried them over for him on her head.

"They settled down in the empty hut that stood here. Whether she had any rights over it land tenure is a complicated business in the lands, or whether the owner had died during the epidemic, I do not know; but anyhow, no one questioned them, and they took possession. Their furniture consisted of a couple of grass-mats on which they slept, a fragment of looking-glass and a bowl or two. In this pleasant land that is enough to start housekeeping on.

"They say that happy people have no history, and certainly a happy love has none. They did nothing all day long, and yet the days seemed all too short.

"The girl had a native name, but Red called her Sally. He picked up the easy language very quickly, and he used to lie on the mat for hours while she chattered gaily to him. He was a silent fellow, and perhaps his mind was lethargic. He smoked incessantly the cigarettes which she made him out of the native tobacco and pandanus leaf, and he watched her while with deft fingers she made grass-mats.

"Often natives would come in and tell long stories of the old days when the island was disturbed by tribal wars. Sometimes he would go fishing on the reef, and bring home a basketful of colored fish. Sometimes at night he would go out with a lantern to catch lobster. There were plaintains round the hut, and Sally would roast them for their frugal meal. She knew how to make delicious messes from coconuts, and the bread-fruit tree by the side of the creek gave them its fruit. On feast-days they killed a little pig and cooked it on hot stones. They bathed together in the creek; and in the evening they went down to the lagoon and paddled about in a dugout, with its great outrigger.

"The sea was deep blue, wine-colored at sundown, like the sea of Homeric Greece; but in the lagoon the color had an infinite variety, aquamarine and amethyst and emerald, and the setting sun turned it for a short moment to liquid gold. Then there was the color of the coral, brown, white, pink, red, purple; and the shapes it took were marvelous. It was like a magic garden, and the hurrying fish were like butterflies. It strangely lacked reality. Among the coral were pools with a floor of white sand, and here, where the water was dazzling clear, it was very good to bathe.

"Then, cool and happy, they wandered back in the gloaming over the soft grass road to the creek, walking hand in hand, and now the mynah birds filled the coconut trees with their clamor. And then the night, with that great sky shining with gold, that seemed to stretch more widely than the skies of Europe, and the soft airs that blew gently through the open hut, the long night again was all too short.

"She was sixteen and he was barely twenty. The dawn crept in among the wooden pillars of the hut and looked at those lovely children sleeping in each other's arms. The sun hid behind the great tattered leaves of the plaintains so that it might not disturb them, and then, with playing malice, shot a golden ray, like the out-stretched paw of a Persian cat, on their faces. They opened their sleepy eyes and they smiled to welcome another day.

"The weeks lengthened into months, and a year passed. They seemed to love each other as—I hesitate to say passionately, for passion has in it always a shade of sadness, a touch of bitterness or anguish, but as whole-heartedly, as simply and naturally, as on that first day on which, meeting, they had recognized that a god was in them.

"If you had asked them, I have no doubt that they would have thought it impossible to suppose their love could ever cease. Do we not know that the essential element of love is a belief in its own eternity? And yet perhaps in Red there was already a very little seed, unknown to himself and unsuspected by the girl, of the natives from the cove told them that some way down the coast at the anchorage was a British whaling-ship.

"'Gee!' he said. 'I wonder if I could make a trade of some nuts and plaintains for a pound or two of tobacco?'

"The pandanus cigarettes that Sally made him with untiring hands were strong and pleasant enough to smoke, but they left him unsatisfied; and he yearned on a sudden for real tobacco, hard, rank and pungent. He had not smoked a pipe for many months. His mouth watered at the thought of it.

"One would have thought some premonition of harm would have made Sally seek to dissuade him; but love possessed her so completely that it never occurred to her any power on earth could take him from her. They went up into the hills together and gath-ered a great basket of wild oranges, green, but sweet and juicy; and they picked plaintains around the hut, and coconuts from their trees, and bread-fruit and mangoes, and they carried them down to the cove. They loaded the unstable canoe with them, and Red and the native boy who had brought them the news of the ship paddled along outside the reef.

"It was the last time she ever saw him.

"Next day the boy came back alone. He was all in tears. This is the story he told. When, after their long paddle, they reached the ship and Red hailed it, a white man looked over the side and told them to come on board. They took the fruit they had brought with them and Red piled it up on the deck. The white man and he began to talk, and they seemed to come to some agreement. One of them went below and brought up tobacco. Red took some at once and lighted a pipe. The boy imitated the zest with which he blew a great cloud of smoke from his mouth. Then they said something to him and he went into the cabin.

"Through the open door the boy, watching curiously, saw a bottle brought out, and glasses. Red drank and smoked. They seemed to ask him something, for he shook his head and laughed. The man, the first man who had spoken to them, laughed too, and he filled Red's glass once more. They went on talking and drinking, and presently, growing tired of watching a sight that which would in time have grown to weariness. For one day one meant nothing to him, the boy curled himself up on the deck and slept.

"He was awakened by a kick; and, jumping to his feet, he saw that the ship was slowly sailing out of the lagoon. He caught sight of Red seated at the table, with his head resting heavily on his arms, fast asleep. He made a movement toward him, intending to wake him, but a rough hand seized his arm, and a man, with a scowl and words which he did not understand, pointed to the side. He shouted to Red, but in a moment he was seized and flung overboard. Helpless, he swam round to his canoe, which was drifting a little way off, and pushed it on to the reef. He climbed in and, sobbing all the way, paddled back to shore.

"What had happened was obvious enough. The whaler, by desertion or sickness was short of hands, and the captain, when Red came aboard, had asked him to sign on, on his refusal, he had made him drunk and kidnaped him.

"Sally was beside herself with grief. For three days, she screamed and cried. The natives did what they could to comfort her, but she would not be comforted. She would not eat. And then, exhausted, she sank into a sullen apathy.

"She spent long days at the cove, watching the lagoon, in the vain hope that Red somehow or other would manage to escape. She sat on the white sand, hour after hour, with the tears running down her cheeks, and at night dragged herself wearily back across the creek to the little hut where she had been happy. The people with whom she had lived before Red came to the island wished her to return to them, but she would not; she was convinced that Red would come back, and she wanted him to find her where he had left her. Four months later she was delivered of a still-born child, and the old woman who had come to help her through her confinement remained with her in the hut.

"All joy was taken from her life. If her anguish with time became less intolerable, it was replaced by a settled melancholy. You would not have thought that among these people, whose emotions, though so violent, are very transient, a woman could be found capable of so enduring a passion. She never lost the profound conviction that sooner or later Red would come back. She watched for him, and every time some one crossed this slender little bridge of coconut trees she looked. It might at last be he."

Neilson stopped talking and gave a faint sigh.

"And what happened to her in the end?" asked the skipper.

Neilson smiled bitterly.

"Oh, three years afterward she took up with another white man."

The skipper gave a fat cynical chuckle.

"That's generally what happens to them," he said.

The Swede shot him a look at hatred. He did not know why that gross obese man excited in him so violent a repulsion. But his thoughts wandered, and he found his mind filled with memories of the past.

He went back five-and-twenty years. It was when he first came to the island, weary of Apia, with its heavy drinking, its gambling and coarse sensuality, a sick man, trying to resign himself to the loss of the career which had fired his imagination with ambitious thought. He set behind him resolutely all his hopes of making a great name for himself, and strove to content himself with the few poor months of careful life which was all that he could count on.

He was boarding with a half-caste trader who had a store a couple of miles along the coast at the edge of a native village; and one day, wandering aimlessly along the grassy paths of the coconut groves, he had come upon the hut in which Sally lived. The beauty of the spot had filled him with a rapture so great that it was almost painful, and then he had seen Sally.

She was the loveliest creature he had ever seen, and the sadness in those dark magnificent eyes of hers affected him strangely. The Kanakas were a handsome race, and beauty was not rare among them; but it was the beauty of shapely animals. It was empty. But those tragic eyes were dark with mystery, and you felt in them the bitter complexity of the groping human soul. The trader told him the story and it moved him.

"Do you think he'll ever come back?" asked Neilson.

"No fear. Why, it'll be a couple of years before the ship is paid off, and by then he'll have forgotten all about her. I bet he was pretty mad when he woke up and found he'd been shanghaied, and I shouldn't wonder but he wanted to fight somebody. But he'd got to grin and bear it, and I guess in a month he was thinking it the best thing that had ever happened to him that he got away from the island."

But Neilson could not get the story out of his head. Perhaps because he was sick and weakly, the radiant health of Red appealed to his imagination. Himself an ugly man, insignificant of appearance, he prized very highly comeliness in others.

He had never been passionately in love, and certainly he had never been passionately loved. The mutual attraction of those two young things gave him a singular delight. It had the ineffable beauty of the Absolute.

He went again to the little hut by the creek. He had a gift for languages and an energetic mind, accustomed to work, and he had already given much time to the study of the local tongue. Old habit was strong in him, and he was gathering together material for a paper on the Samoan speech.

The old crone who shared the hut with Sally invited him to come in and sit down. She gave him kava to drink and cigarettes to smoke. She was glad to have some one chat with, and while she talked he looked at Sally. She reminded him of the Psyche in the museum of Naples. Her features had the same clear purity of line, and though she had borne a child she had still a virginal aspect.

It was not till he had seen her two or three times that he induced her to speak. Then it was only to ask him if he had seen in Apia a man called Red. Two years had passed since his disappearance, but it was plain that she still thought of him incessantly.

It did not take Neilson long to discovered that he was in love with her. It was only by an effort of will now that he prevented himself from going every day to the creek, and when he was not with Sally his thoughts were.

At first, looking upon himself as a dying man, he asked only to look at her, and occasionally hear her speak, and his love gave him a wonderful happiness. He exulted in its purity. He wanted nothing from her but the opportunity to weave around her graceful person a web of beautiful fancies.

But the open air, the equable temperature, the rest, the simple fare, began to have an unexpected effect on his health. His temperature did not soar at night to such alarming heights, he coughed less and began to put on weight; six months passed without his having a hemorrhage; and on a sudden he saw the possibility that he might live. He had studied his disease carefully, and the hope dawned upon him that with care he might arrest its course.

It exhilarated him to look forward once more to the future. He made plans. It was evident that any active life was out of the question; but he could live on the islands, and the small income he had, insufficient elsewhere would be ample to keep him. He would grow coconuts; that would give him an occupation; and he would send for his books and a piano; but his quick mind saw that in all this he was merely trying to conceal from himself the desire which obsessed him.

He wanted Sally. He loved not only her beauty, but that dim soul which he divined behind her suffering eyes. He would intoxicate her with his passion. In the end he would make her forget. And in an ecstasy of surrender he fancied himself giving her, too, the happiness which he had thought never to know again, but had now so miraculously achieved.

He asked her to live with him. She refused. He had expected that, and did not let it depress him, for he was sure that sooner or later she would yield. His love was irresistible.

He told the old woman of his wishes, and found, somewhat to his surprise, that she and the neighbors, long aware of them, were strongly urging Sally to accept his offer. After all every native was glad to keep house for a white man, and Neilson, according to the standards of the island, was a rich one.

The trader with whom he boarded went to her and told her not to be a fool; such an opportunity would not come again, and after so long she could not still believe that Red would ever return.

The girl's resistance only increased Neilson's desire, and what had been a very pure love now became an agonizing passion. He was determined that nothing should stand in his way. He gave Sally no peace. At last, worn out by his persistence and the persuasions, by turns pleading and angry of every one around her, she consented.

But the day after, when, exultant, he went to see her, he found that in the night she had burned down the hut in which she and Red had lived together. The old crone ran toward him full of angry abuse of Sally, but he waved her aside; it did not matter, they would build a bungalow on the place where the hut had stood. A European house would really be more convenient if he wanted to bring out a piano and a vast number of books.

And so the little wooden house was built in which he had now lived for many years, and Sally became his wife.

But after the first few weeks of rapture, during which he was satisfied with what she gave him, he had known little happiness. She had yielded to him, through weariness, but she had only yielded what she set no store on. The soul which he had dimly glimpsed escaped him. He knew that she cared nothing for him. She still loved Red, and all the time she was waiting for his return. At a sign from him, Neilson knew that, notwithstanding his love, his tenderness, his sympathy, his generosity, she would leave him without a moment's hesitation. She would never give a thought to his distress.

Anguish seized him, and he battered at that impenetrable self of hers which sullenly resisted him. His love became bitter. He tried to melt her heart with kindness, but it remained as hard as before; he reigned indifference, but she did not notice it. Sometimes he lost his temper and abused her, and then she wept silently. Sometimes he thought she was nothing but a fraud, and that soul simply an invention of his own, and that he could not get into the sanctuary of her heart because there was no sanctuary there. His love became a prison from which he longed to escape, but he had not the strength merely to open the door—that was all it needed—and walk out into the open air. It was torture, and at last he became numb and hopeless.

In the end the fire burned itself out, and when he saw her eyes rest for an instant on the slender bridge, it was no longer rage that filled his heart, but impatience. For many years now they had lived together, bound by the ties of habit and convenience, and it was with a smile that he looked back on his old passion. She was an old woman, for the women on the islands age quickly, and if he had no love for her any more he had tolerance. She left him alone. He was contented with his piano and his books.

His thoughts led him to a desire for words.

"When I look back now and reflect on that brief passionate love of Red and Sally, I think that perhaps they should thank the ruthless fate that separated them when their love seemed still to be at its height. They suffered, but they suffered in beauty. They were spared the real tragedy of love."

"I don't know exactly as I get you," said the skipper.

"The tragedy of love is not death or separation. How long do you think it would have been before one or other of them ceased to care? Oh, it is dreadfully bitter to look at a woman whom you have loved with all your heart and soul, so that you felt you could not bear to let her out of your sight, and realize that you would not mind if you never saw her again. The tragedy of love is indifference."

But while he was speaking a very extraordinary thing happened. Though he had been addressing the skipper he had not been talking to him; he had been putting his thoughts into words for himself, and with his eyes fixed on the man in front of him. But now an image presented itself to them, an image not of the man he saw, but of another man. It was as though he were looking into one of those distorting mirrors that make you extraordinarily squat or outrageously elongate; but here exactly the opposite took place, and in the obese, ugly old man he caught the shadowy glimpse of a stripling.

He gave him now a quick searching scrutiny. Why had a haphazard stroll brought him just to this place?

A sudden tremor of his heart made him slightly breathless. An absurd suspicion seized him. What had happened to him was impossible, and yet it might be a fact.

"What is your name?" he asked abruptly.

The skipper's face puckered and he gave a cunning chuckle. He looked then malicious and horribly vulgar.

"It's such a damned long time since I heard it that I almost forgot it myself; but for thirty years now in the islands they've always called me Red."

His huge form shook as he gave a low, almost silent laugh. It was obscene. Neilson shuddered. Red was hugely amused, and from his bloodshot eyes tears ran down his cheeks.

Neilson gave a gasp, for at that moment a woman came in. She was a native, a woman of somewhat commanding presence, stout without being corpulent, dark, for the natives grow darker with age, with very gray hair. She wore a black Mother Hubbard, and its thinness showed her heavy breasts. The moment had come.

She made an observation to Neilson about some household matter and he answered. He wondered if his voice sounded as unnatural to her as it did to himself. She gave the man who was sitting in the chair by the window an indifference glance, and went out of the room. The moment had come and gone.

Neilson for a moment could not speak. He was strangely shaken. Then he said:

"I'd be very glad if you'd stay and have a bit of dinner with me. Pot luck."

"I don't think I will," said Red. "I must go after this fellow Gray. I'll give him his stuff and then I'll get away. I want to be back in Apia to-morrow."

"I'll send a boy along with you to show you the way."

"That'll be fine."

Red heaved himself out of his chair, while the Swede called one of the boys who worked on the plantation. He told him where the skipper wanted to go, and the boy stepped along the bridge. Red prepared to follow him.

"Don't fall in," said Neilson.

"Not on your life."

Neilson watched him make his way across, and when he had disappeared among the coconuts he looked still. Then he sank heavily in his chair. Was that the man who had prevented him from being happy? Was that the man whom Sally had loved all these years and for whom she had waited so desperately? It was grotesque. A sudden fury seized him so that he had an instinct to spring up and smash everything around him. He had been cheated. They had seen each other at last and had not known it. He began to laugh mirthlessly, and his laughter grew till it became hysterical. The gods had played him a cruel trick. And he was old now.

At last Sally came in to tell him dinner was ready. He sat down in front of her and tried to eat. He wondered what she would say if he told her now that the fat old man sitting in the chair was the lover whom she remembered still with the passionate abandonment of her youth. Years ago, when he hated her because she made him so unhappy, he would have been glad to tell her. He wanted to hurt her then as she hurt him, because his hatred was only love. But now he did not care. He shrugged his shoulders listlessly.

"What did that man want?" she asked presently.

He did not answer at once. She was old, too, a fat old native woman. He wondered why he had ever loved her so madly. He had laid at her feet all the treasures of his soul, and she had cared nothing for them.

Waste, what waste!

And now, when he looked at her, he felt only contempt. His patience was at last exhausted. He answered her question.

"He's the captain of a schooner. He's come from Apia."

"Yes."

"He brought me news from home. My eldest brother is very ill and I must go back."

"Will you be gone long?"

He shrugged his shoulders.

ON THE WAGON

By JOSEPH MITCHELL

IT HAD BEEN SIX WEEKS, BUT MIKE COULDN'T GET USED TO IT. "A month and a half," he said, "and I've just got started. Sooner or later I'll get used to it. I got to get used to it."

Half past five was quitting time in the office, and that was the hardest part of the day. He would walk it off. He would leave as if in a hurry to get home, and then walk eighteen blocks to his furnished room. He would wash up and go over to a diner on Third Avenue. While he ate, he would try to look preoccupied. Mike was embarrassed by his loneliness; he didn't want anybody, not even a counterman in a diner, to guess that he was lonesome. Like many lonesome people, he felt there was something shameful about it. Some nights after dinner he couldn't force himself to go back to his furnished room, and he would go for a ride on the Third Avenue "L." It would please him to see the four enormous, beautifully polished copper kettles in the windows of Ruppert's brewery, and it would please him to smell the wet hops, a lovely smell that blew into the car as it rattled past. He would get off the "L" at the Hanover Square station, light a cigarette, and walk back and forth on the cement plaza in front of the Cotton Exchange. He found it comforting to walk there in the dark and listen to the whistles of the tugs in the East River. The best job he ever had had been in a coffee warehouse a block from Hanover Square. That had been four years ago, and since then he had lost three other jobs, all because of drinking. After a while he would leave the plaza and get back on the "L." And all the way uptown he would stare down into the street, watching for the cheerful, flickering neons over the entrances of barrooms. "Six weeks on the wagon," he would say. "Six weeks and not even a beer!" Whenever the "L" got on his nerves, he would get out and walk until he was so tired he could sleep. Sometimes, walking at night,

343

he saw things that made him feel better because they took his mind off himself—a street fight, an automobile wreck, a boat unloading dripping bushels of mackerel at a Fulton Market pier. He seldom stopped to look at such things, however; his purpose in walking was to tire himself out.

The hardest part of the day for Mike, certainly, was the moment he put on his coat and hat and left the wholesale drug company where, for three weeks, he had been assistant bookkeeper. But lunchtime was almost as bad. The others in the office, even Miss O'Brien, the fussy file clerk, ate across the street in the bar and grill, but he always went up the street to the coffeepot. After work, Mr. Schmidt, the bookkeeper, and Clancy, the head shipping clerk, would go across the street for beers. Once Mr. Schmidt, getting into his coat, turned to Mike and said, "I never see you across the street, Thompson. Why don't you drop in and have a beer with me and Clancy?" Mike said, "My liver isn't all it should be," and Mr. Schmidt had said, "That's tough. Take care of yourself." There was nothing wrong with Mike's liver. Mike loathed the coffeepot, but he was afraid to go across the street. He would make up his mind to have lunch in the bar and grill with the others and then he would get to thinking, and he would say to himself, "I better go up to the coffeepot. Like Betty said, unless I stay on the wagon I'll never be able to hold down a job. I'm thirty-nine and I'm not getting any younger. I had an awful time getting this job and I got to hold on to it."

He dreaded Sunday. The Sunday which marked the beginning of his seventh week on the wagon was cold and clear. He spent the afternoon in his furnished room, reading a newspaper. Late in the day he pulled his chair to the window and sat there. Acres of tenement roofs stretched out beneath his window; on one roof a pigeon-keeper was waving a bamboo pole and frightening his birds aloft. Each time they were driven off their coop the birds flew into the air, wheeled around, and settled immediately a couple of roofs away on chimneys decorated with the yellow-paint signs of the New York Frame & Picture Co. They perched on the chimneys a few tentative moments and then flew back to their coop and were driven aloft again. Mike was amused by the game. After a while the pigeon-keeper locked the birds in their coop, took a paper bag out of his pocket, and tossed some corn into each pen. Then he left the roof, and Mike felt deserted. While he sat at the window, leaning forward, with his elbows on the sill, it became dark and he began to feel bad. He had slept little the night before. A hot bath had done no good and aspirin had made him even more shaky. He had been too jittery and too lonesome to sleep. Staring out over the dark roofs, he tried to get control of himself, but it was no use. He began to cry. He took off his glasses and rubbed his eyes. His eyes were strained by sleeplessness and the tears made them smart. Mike had got so he talked to himself. "I cry as easy as an old maid in the dark at a movie," he said. "I got to hold on to myself somehow." He walked up and down in the shabby room. When he could bear it no longer he stretched out on the bed, face downward. After a while he sat up. He reached into a pocket of his coat, which hung on the back of a chair, and got his cigarettes. He sat on the edge of the bed, smoking in the dark. When he had finished the cigarette he put on his coat, got his hat, and felt in the dark for the doorknob. He didn't want to turn on the light and see, on the bureau, the photograph of Betty. As he walked downstairs, Mike thought, "I can't blame her much for leaving me. I can't blame anybody but myself." On the street he felt that people looked away when they saw his strained face.

He walked down the street, hunting for a new place to eat. For six weeks he had eaten in places that did not sell liquor—diners, coffeepots, cafeterias, and chow-mein joints. He was hungry. After he had sent the weekly money order to Betty Saturday afternoon and paid the rent on the furnished room, he had fourteen dollars left. In the old days he had spent twice that on a Saturday night, making a round of barrooms, and had thought nothing of it. "I'm sick of the junky grub in those cafeterias," he said. "I'm going someplace and get a decent meal." He stared into the neon-lit window of a bar and grill. There was a row of booths parallel with the bar. The place was not crowded. He could eat in peace. Mike went in. He ordered a steak. An old man and a young man were standing at the bar, hunched over beers. The old man was quiet, but the young man hummed a song. He would hum a few moments, absent-mindedly, and then he would break out into a verse.

" 'Oh,' " he sang, " 'the wheel flew off the hearse, and the coffin rolled out in the road. The widow got out of her carriage and she said—' "

The bartender came out of the kitchen and gave the young man a stern look; he quit singing in the middle of the verse.

"Don't look at me like that," the young man said, frowning at the bartender. "I know I'm a nuisance. I know I'm a no-good bum. No good to myself, no good to nobody. Day I was born, I wish they'd dropped me in a tub, like I was a cat. Let me have a beer. 'Oh, the wheel flew off the hearse, and the coffin rolled out in the road.' What's the matter with you? Did you have a stroke? Let's have that beer."

"Keep your pants on," said the bartender.

"None of your lip," said the young man. "Let's have that beer."

"I think he wants a beer," said the old man, not looking up.

The bartender took the empty glass and went reluctantly to the spigot.

"I never saw a man could drink so much beer," he said angrily. "It ain't human."

"I drink so much beer," said the young man, winking at his companion, "because I'm afraid if I was to drink whiskey, it would make me drunk. They say whiskey makes you drunk. I sure wouldn't want that to happen to me."

The old man snickered.

Eating his steak and potatoes, Mike felt at ease. The atmosphere of the barroom, the bickering of the men at the bar, the beer smell comforted him. It was a small barroom, a neighborhood joint. Over the bar was a poster advertising a Monster Bingo Party at the Catholic church around the corner. When he had finished his coffee, Mike got up and walked over to the bar and stood there. The bartender was out in the kitchen. Mike stood at the bar, one foot on the rail, with his right hand in a pocket of his trousers. He rubbed coins together in his pocket and his palm was sweating. Suddenly he realized he hadn't left a tip for the waitress. He went back to the table and put fifteen cents beside his coffee cup. Then the bartender came out and Mike handed him his check and a dollar bill. "Eighty-fi' cents," said the bartender, ringing up Mike's bill. He gave Mike his change and Mike put on his overcoat and started for the door. He glanced at the clock on the wall; it was eight-thirty. He remembered the furnished room with the unshaded electric light hanging from the middle of the splotched ceiling and his heart sank, and he thought, "I just can't stand it any longer." At the door he paused. He turned and walked over to the cigarette machine. "Six weeks," Mike thought, "and not even a beer." Opening the package of cigarettes, he walked back to the bar. The bartender came and stood it front of him.

"What'll it be?" he asked.

Mike stared nervously at the bottles behind the bar and noticed a blue Bromo-Seltzer bottle, upended in its rack.

"Fix me a Bromo," Mike said.

The bartender mixed the Bromo in two beer glasses. Mike drank the violently bubbling mixture.

"Good for what ails you," the bartender said, smiling.

The young man looked at Mike.

"You got a hangover, too?" he asked.

"Well, not exactly," Mike said.

"I got a hangover would kill a horse, damn near," said the young man.

"Hell," said the old man, "you don't know what a hangover is."

The young man grunted.

"Once I had a job in a liquor store," said the old man. "Some mornings I'd come in with a hangover and I'd have to stand there all days with thousands of bottles of the stuff staring me in the face. I'd have to say, 'Yes, sir, that's an A-1 grade of Scotch. Best we have in stock,' when just to look at it made me rock back on my heels. It was worse than a bartender with a hangover, because he can sneak a drink to brace himself, but I worked in that store six months and I never saw a cork pulled out of a bottle."

"Geez," said the young man.

"Talk about a hangover," said the old man, hunched over his beer. "You don't know what a hangover is."

Mike laughed. He thought, "A beer or two won't hurt me. A couple of beers, and I'll go home. I'll have a couple of beers and maybe I can get some sleep. I got to get some sleep. A man can't live without sleep." The bartender saw Mike looking at the rack of bottles behind the bar.

"You want something?" he asked.

Mike heard himself say, "A beer."

The bartender spanked the foam off the beer with his black paddle. Then he held the glass under the spigot an instant longer. He set the glass in front of Mike and Mike put a dime on the wet bar.

"First in six weeks," said Mike. "I been on the wagon six weeks now."

The bartender did not seem impressed.

"It don't hurt nobody to leave the stuff alone for a while," he said. "Once I was on the wagon eight months."

"Yeah?" said Mike.

"Yeah," said the bartender. "I was in a hospital."

They both laughed.

"St. Vincent's," said the bartender. "Auto accident."

Mike took a deep drink of the beer. In a little while the old man and the young man finished their beers and walked toward the door. "Pleasant dreams," the bartender called out, and took their glasses away. Left alone, Mike suddenly felt desolate. He finished his beer and lit a cigarette. He had made up his mind to leave when two women came in and sat down on bar stools at the end of the bar, next to the cigarette machine. They knew the bartender. "How's it, Tommy?" said one. "Never better," said the bartender. "What'll it be, two Manhattans?" "How'd you guess?" asked the woman, smiling. Mike felt cheerful again. When he had finished with the women, the bartender looked at Mike's empty glass.

"Fill her up?" he asked.

"Fill her up," said Mike.

A man came in with a *Daily News*. He stood at the bar and looked through a comic strip in the back of the paper. He did not order, but the bartender automatically placed a bottle of rye, a whiskey glass, and a glass of water on the bar in front of him. When he finished the comic strip, the man laughed.

"Hey, Tommy," he called to the bartender, "don't miss Moon Mullins. Kayo certainly pulled a fast one on Lord Plushbottom."

Mike smiled. On his way home he would pick up the *News* and see what had happened to Lord Plushbottom. He would get a *News* and a *Mirror* and read himself to sleep. His glass was empty again.

"I tell you," he said to the bartender, "let's have a rye this time. Beer chaser."

"O.K.," said the bartender. "Rye and a small beer."

He placed the bottle of rye in front of Mike.

"It looks the same," said Mike, filling his glass.

THERE'S NO FUTURE IN IT

By H. E. BATES

THE NIGHTS HE WAS NOT FLYING THEY WOULD DRIVE BACK LATE to the station, using her car. The flare-path would be laid; the lights on the hangars would shine like red stars in the winter darkness above the flat land. Sometimes the searchlights would be up, throwing a blue-white fire that fell widely like moonlight on the dark trees and hedges and on the winding road. They would sit in the car and, holding each other, talk for a long time. Frost on the very coldest nights would form like a silver collar on the glass of the windscreen and sometimes, on very still nights, he would wind down the window of the car and listen for a moment or two to the silence outside. She would lean her head on his shoulder and look upwards into the dark sky and then, listening too, hear the sound of the bombers coming home.

It did not seem to matter much that they were never likely to be married. He was rather small and compact, with fresh grey eyes that he sometimes did not seem able to focus correctly. He had thirty-one operational trips to his credit, and all that seemed to matter was that he should continue coming back.

The morning afterwards, perhaps, he would ring the office. He would say simply: "Hello, dear, tonight." She would try to remain calm, and later, perhaps, if operations were scrubbed, he would ring her again and she would find herself trembling as she put down the telephone, all her pretence of calmness gone.

She knew generally that he would be briefed in the early afternoon. He would take off about three o'clock or a little later and, according to the target, come back somewhere between eight and ten. It would often be too late to ring her after interrogation, but going to bed she would try to lie awake for the sound of the telephone. Sometimes she would fall asleep with the light still burning and would wake up in the small hours of the morning, bewildered and startled, not knowing where she was. Twice she fell half asleep and did not hear the telephone. Downstairs her father heard it, but after answering it, did not come to tell her who it was.

Her father was a rather big, grey-haired man with cheeks like loose pink rubber. He rolled his own cigarettes and it seemed to her that she never saw him without a newspaper. He rolled the cigarettes very badly—the tobacco fell wastefully on his clothes. The war had developed in him the latent qualities of the amateur strategist, and he always discussed the war while waving an untidy, wasteful cigarette. "We ought to have cut the Tripoli road long ago. Long ago. You have only to look at the map. The same with the bombing of Berlin. What's gone wrong? Why aren't we over there more? Why aren't we over there night after night? Striking early and often is the decisive factor. You'd suppose it wouldn't escape our people."

"Perhaps it's the weather," she would say.

"Weather? There's another thing that beats me. Argue on simple lines, draw some absolutely logical conclusion which ought to be apparent to the merest child, and you always get the same answer. The weather! I don't doubt the weather is sometimes bad. But far from always, far from always. It's too often a convenient excuse—like the workman blaming his tools."

"Nevertheless it nearly always is the weather."

"Oh? Then what about last night? Clear moonlight like day. And was there a single operation? A couple of bombers over Brest."

"You talk as if Brest were a seaside resort."

"Look at the weather again tonight. Magnificent. And in the morning what shall we hear? The same old story again, I suppose. A handful of bombers over Brest. Or nothing at all."

"It's probably the most heavily defended place in Europe," she said. "It's just plain hell."

"Kitty, Kitty," her mother said. She looked up from her knitting, always khaki, and looked down again.

"Also I think you may find that tonight has been a big thing."

"Oh! You know, do you?"

"No. Not exactly. I've an idea, that's all."

"Ah! Your pilot friend."

She did not speak.

"You haven't brought him in lately."

"No, dear," her mother said.

"They spend most of their time out," her father said. "Some-where."

Her mother spoke without looking up from her knitting.

"Were you at the Red Lion last week?" her mother said. "We heard you were there. Drinking with Air Force officers."

"I was."

"Is that the kind of place to be?" her father said.

"Drinking," her mother said. "It's not nice. Do you think so?"

"I want to be wherever he is."

"Even there? Couldn't you give him up?" her mother said. "He struck me as being older than he said. Do you know much about him? You are only twenty. It's all so terribly unsure. Perhaps he is married. Do you know?"

She did not answer.

"He looks older than twenty-four," her mother said. "Experienced. His eyes look old."

She got up, calmly enraged, definite. "He has done things that make him old," she said, and went out of the room.

The following night they drove back late to the station. With the moon rising and the searchlights up, the road shone misty white between the dark hedges. The evening lay behind them, as always, simply secure; a few rounds of light ale at the Red Lion, the boys coming in group by group, the rounds growing, the crews mixing, sergeants with squadron leaders, gunners with nagigators, warm broad Canadian voices mingled with English; and then the drive home, the blue lighting of the searchlights, and the moonlight throwing into relief the black winter trees, the hangars lit by red stars, the huge solitary dispersed aircraft in the fields; and lastly the silence after the car had stopped beyond the gate of the station.

"Was it a good trip, darling?"

He did not answer.

"Bad?"

"Pretty bad."

"Did you have trouble?"

"The usual. Ten tenths most of the way and then some hellish flak."

She thought of her father. She saw him in an armchair, rolling the cigarettes, waving a newspaper. "Always the weather!"

"I'm sorry I couldn't ring," he said. "It was late when we got in for interrogation. I didn't want to wake you."

"I was awake," she said.

They sat still, not speaking. She thought again of her father.

"Tell me about the trip."

"Nothing to tell. Routine stuff."

She did not like the sound of his voice, tired and guarded; the feeling that part of him was deliberately withheld.

"I can tell when you have trouble."

"What trouble? No trouble at all."

"Why have you got your hand in your pocket?" she said. "You've had it there all the time."

"All right," he said.

He began suddenly to tell her something about the trip. Though she had heard so much of it before, the awful significance of it was not lessened. He told her about the weather; ten tenths, a bad storm soon after they turned for home, a spot of ice. "They put up a hell's own flak at us. Just routine stuff, only a bloody sight worse. And they hit my hand. Took the skin off, that's all." He kept it in his pocket.

She knew that he was not telling everything, that he never did, perhaps never would. Routine stuff, hellish flak, a spot of ice; the same words, the same repeated demand on courage, on fear if you like, the same holding back. She thought once more of her father: the world of the newspaper, the protest, the old indignations. To contrast it with the world of flak and ice, the long darkness of endurance, the spell of cold and strain thirty-one times repeated, was so difficult and angrily confusing that she said only: "Does your hand hurt? Can I do anything for you?"

"Thanks, darling, I'm O.K."

She remembered something.

"What time did interrogation finish? Why were you so late?"

"It wasn't so late. Not so very late."

"If it wasn't so late, why didn't you ring me?"

"I didn't want to wake you."

"Tell me what happened," she said.

He looked beyond the car window and said: "We got a bit shot up. Just one of those things."

"Bad?"

"Bad enough. A lump of flak blew a hole as big as a cartwheel in the starboard wing and the transmitter was u.s. Shaky landing. But why pick on me? It happens every day."

"Not to you."

"It happens," he said.

"You hate it, don't you?" she said.

"Hate what?" he said.

"You hate going, don't you, time after time? The same place. The same job. The same everything. I know you hate it."

"I hate it like hell," he said. He looked beyond the car window again. The diffused lighting of the searchlights and the cloudy moon shone on the misted windscreen. The trees were black against it. "But I hate what they're doing even more. That's what I really hate. What they do to me isn't half of what I mean doing to them. Not half. Not a quarter. Not a hundredth part. Is there anything wrong about hatred?"

She was thinking of her father, fussy with indignation, and she did not answer.

"It's good honest downright emotion, isn't it?" he said.

"Yes.

"Sometimes I think we want more of it," he said. "God, sometimes I think we do."

"When at last she drove back from the station it was later than she thought. But at the house, to her surprise, her father and mother were still up. Her mother looked up from her knitting and her father looked at his watch.

"Either my watch is fast or it's ten past twelve."

She did not speak.

"Even the Red Lion closes at ten."

"It so happens I haven't been there."

Her father coughed heavily. "Does your pilot friend realize that we sit here waiting?"

She did not answer.

"We have a right to be considered."

She stood slowly taking off her gloves.

"You'll agree that he owes us something, won't you?"

She stood thinking of the long flight in the darkness, the hellish flak, the hole in the wing, the shell through the fuselage, the shaky landing; routine stuff; easy, nothing to tell, something done again and again. Her mind became unsteady with hatred. She looked at her mother. The clean prejudiced hands were motionless on the knitting. Her father with the evening newspaper folded between his fingers stood with his back to the dying fire.

"Is he married?" her mother asked.

"Does it matter?" she said.

Her father crackled the newspaper.

"My dear child, my dear child! Does it matter? I ask you. What about the future? Is there any future in that?"

"No," she said; "there's no future in it."

She wanted to go on speaking, but her thoughts were disrupted and dispersed in the corners of her mind and she could not gather them together. She wanted to say why there was no future. She wanted to tell them about the flak, the darkness, and the bitter cold, about the way the tracer bullets came in at you so slowly that you could watch them until suddenly they hurled with red frenzy past your face, about the hatred and the monotony and the courage that was greater because it was rarefied by terror. She wanted to tell them that if there was any future it lay through this.

She went out of the room and went upstairs instead. She felt stifled by the warmth of the room downstairs and, not putting on the light, she opened the window and stood looking out. The air was bright with frost, and the coldness struck with a momentary shock on her face and hands.

She stood there for a long time, looking out. The moon was going down beyond the houses. The searchlights were no longer up beyond the town. The sky was clear and calm, and, as if there were no war and as it might be in the future, if there were a future, there was no sounds of wings.

BIG BLONDE

By Dorothy Parker

HAZEL MORSE WAS A LARGE, FAIR WOMAN OF THE TYPE THAT incites some men when they use the word "blonde" to click their tongues and wag their heads roguishly. She prided herself upon her small feet and suffered for her vanity, boxing them in snub-toed, high-heeled slippers of the shortest bearable size. The curious things about her were her hands, strange terminations to the flabby white arms splattered with pale tan spots—long, quivering hands with deep and convex nails. She should not have disfigured them with little jewels.

She was not a woman given to recollections. At her middle thirties, her old days were a blurred and flickering sequence, an imperfect film, dealing with the actions of strangers.

In her twenties, after the deferred death of a hazy widowed mother, she had been employed as a model in a wholesale dress establishment—it was still the day of the big woman, and she was then prettily colored and erect and high-breasted. Her job was not onerous, and she met numbers of men and spent numbers of evenings with them, laughing at their jokes and telling them she loved their neckties. Men liked her, and she took it for granted that the liking of many men was a desirable thing. Popularity seemed to her to be worth all the work that had to be put into its achievement. Men liked you because you were fun, and when they liked you they took you out, and there you were. So, and successfully, she was fun. She was a good sport. Men liked a good sport.

No other form of diversion, simpler or more complicated, drew her attention. She never pondered if she might not be better occupied doing something else. Her ideas, or, better, her acceptances, ran right along with those of the other substantially built blondes in whom she found her friends.

When she had been working in the dress establishment some years she met Herbie Morse. He was thin, quick, attractive, with shifting lines about his shiny, brown eyes and a habit of fiercely biting at the skin around his finger nails. He drank largely; she found that entertaining. Her habitual greeting to him was an allusion to his state of the previous night.

"Oh, what a peach you had," she used to say, through her easy laugh. "I thought I'd die, the way you kept asking the waiter to dance with you."

She liked him immediately upon their meeting. She was enormously amused at his fast, slurred sentences, his interpolations of apt phrases from vaudeville acts and comic strips; she thrilled at the feel of his lean arm tucked firm beneath the sleeve of her coat; she wanted to touch the wet, flat surface of his hair. He was as promptly drawn to her. They were married six weeks after they had met.

She was delighted at the idea of being a bride; coquetted with it, played upon it. Other offers of marriage she had had, and not a few of them, but it happened that they were all from stout, serious men who had visited the dress establishment as buyers; men from Des Moines and Houston and Chicago and, in her phrase, even funnier places. There was always something immensely comic to her in the thought of living elsewhere than New York. She could not regard as serious proposals that she share a western residence.

She wanted to be married. She was nearing thirty now, and she did not take the years well. She spread and softened, and her darkening hair turned her to inexpert dabblings with peroxide. There were times when she had little flashes of fear about her job. And she had had a couple of thousand evenings of being a good sport among her male acquaintances. She had come to be more conscientious than spontaneous about it.

Herbie earned enough, and they took a little apartment far uptown. There was a Mission-furnished dining-room with a hanging central light globed in liver-colored glass; in the living-room were an "overstuffed suite," a Boston fern, and a reproduction of the Henner "Magdalene" with the red hair and the blue draperies; the bedroom was in gray enamel and old rose, with Herbie's photograph on Hazel's dressing-table and Hazel's likeness on Herbie's chest of drawers.

She cooked—and she was a good cook—and marketed and chatted with the delivery boys and the colored laundress. She loved the flat, she loved her life, she loved Herbie. In the first months of their marriage, she gave him all the passion she was ever to know.

She had not realized how tired she was. It was a delight, a new game, a holiday, to give up being a good sport. If her head ached or her arches throbbed, she complained piteously, babyishly. If her mood was quiet, she did not talk. If tears came to her eyes, she let them fall.

She fell readily into the habit of tears during the first year of her marriage. Even in her good sport days, she had been known to weep lavishly and disinterestedly on occasion. Her behavior at the theater was a standing joke. She could weep at anything in a play—tiny garments, love both unrequited and mutual, seduction, purity, faithful servitors, wedlock, the triangle.

"There goes Haze," her friends would say, watching her. "She's off again."

Wedded and relaxed, she poured her tears freely. To her who had laughed so much, crying was delicious. All sorrows became her sorrows; she was Tenderness. She would cry long and softly over newspaper accounts of kidnaped babies, deserted wives, unemployed men, strayed cats, heroic dogs. Even when the paper was no longer before her, her mind revolved upon these things and the drops slipped rhythmically over her plump cheeks.

"Honestly," she would say to Herbie, "all the sadness there is in the world when you stop to think about it!"

"Yeah," Herbie would say.

She missed nobody. The old crowd, the people who had brought her and Herbie together, dropped from their lives, lingeringly at first. When she thought of this at all, it was only to consider it fitting. This was marriage. This was peace.

But the thing was that Herbie was not amused.

For a time, he had enjoyed being alone with her. He found the voluntary isolation novel and sweet. Then it palled with a ferocious suddenness. It was as if one night, sitting with her in the steam-heated living-room, he would ask no more; and the next night he was through and done with the whole thing.

He became annoyed by her misty melancholies. At first, when he came home to find her softly tired and moody, he kissed her neck and patted her shoulder and begged her to tell her Herbie what was wrong. She loved that. But time slid by, and he found that there was never anything really, personally, the matter.

"Ah, for God's sake," he would say. "Crabbing again. All right, sit here and crab your head off. I'm going out."

And he would slam out of the flat and come back late and drunk.

She was completely bewildered by what hapened to their marriage. First they were lovers; and then, it seemed without transition, they were enemies. She never understood it.

There were longer and longer intervals between his leaving his office and his arrival at the apartment. She went through agonies of picturing him run over and bleeding, dead and covered with a sheet. Then she lost her fears for his safety and grew sullen and wounded. When a person wanted to be with a person, he came as soon as possible. She desperately wanted him to want to be with her; her own hours only marked the time till he would come. It was often nearly nine o'clock before he came home to dinner. Always he had had many drinks, and their effect would die in him, leaving him loud and querulous and bristling for affronts.

He was too nervous, he said, to sit and do nothing for an evening. He boasted, probably not in all truth, that he had never read a book in his life.

"What am I expected to do—sit around this dump on my tail all night?" he would ask, rhetorically. And again he would slam out.

She did not know what to do. She could not manage him. She could not meet him.

She fought him furiously. A terrific domesticity had come upon her, and she would bite and scratch to guard it. She wanted what she called "a nice home." She wanted a sober, tender husband, prompt at dinner, punctual at work. She wanted sweet, comforting evenings. The idea of intimacy with other men was terrible to her; the thought that Herbie might be seeking entertainment in other women set her frantic.

It seemed to her that almost everything she read—novels from the drug-store lending library, magazine stories, women's pages in the papers—dealt with wives who lost their husband's love. She could bear those, at that, better than accounts of neat, companionable marriages and living happily ever after.

She was frightened. Several times when Herbie came home in the evening, he found her determinedly dressed—she had had to alter those of her clothes that were not new, to make them fasten—and rouged.

"Let's go wild tonight, what do you say?" she would hail him. "A person's got lots of time to hang around and do nothing when they're dead."

So they would go out, to chop houses and the less expensive cabarets. But it turned out badly. She could no longer find amusement in watching Herbie drink. She could not laugh at his whimsicalities, she was so tensely counting his indulgencies. And she was unable to keep back her remonstrances—"Ah, come on, Herb, you've had enough, haven't you? You'll feel something terrible in the morning."

He would be immediately enraged. All right, crab; crab, crab, crab, crab, that was all she ever did. What a lousy sport *she* was! There would be scenes, and one or the other of them would rise and stalk out in fury.

She could not recall the definite day that she started drinking, herself. There was nothing separate about her days. Like drops upon a window-pane, they ran together and trickled away. She had been married six months; then a year; then three years.

She had never needed to drink, formerly. She could sit for most of a night at a table where the others were imbibing earnestly and never droop in looks or spirits, nor be bored by the doings of those about her. If she took a cocktail, it was so unusual as to cause twenty minutes or so of jocular comment. But now anguish was in her. Frequently, after a quarrel, Herbie would stay out for the night, and she could not learn from him where the time had been spent. Her heart felt tight and sore in her breast, and her mind turned like an electric fan.

She hated the taste of liquor. Gin, plain or in mixtures, made her promptly sick. After experiment, she found that Scotch whisky was best for her. She took it without water, because that was the quickest way to its effect.

Herbie pressed it on her. He was glad to see her drink. They both felt it might restore her high spirits, and their good times together might again be possible.

" 'Atta girl," he would approve her. "Let's see you get boiled, baby."

But it brought them no nearer. When she drank with him, there would be a little while of gaiety and then, strangely without beginning, they would be in a wild quarrel. They would wake in the morning not sure what it had all been about, foggy as to what had been said and done, but each deeply injured and bitterly resentful. There would be days of vengeful silence.

There had been a time when they had made up their quarrels, usually in bed. There would be kisses and little names and assurances of fresh starts. . . . "Oh, it's going to be great now, Herb. We'll have swell times. I was a crab. I guess I must have been tired. But everything's going to be swell. You'll see."

Now there were no gentle reconciliations. They resumed friendly relations only in the brief magnanimity caused by liquor, before more liquor drew them into new battles. The scenes became more violent. There were shouted invectives and pushes, and sometimes sharp slaps. Once she had a black eye. Herbie was horrified next day at sight of it. He did not go to work; he followed her about, suggesting remedies and heaping dark blame on himself. But after they had had a few drinks—"to pull themselves together" —she made so many wistful references to her bruise that he shouted at her and rushed out and was gone for two days.

Each time he left the place in a rage, he threatened never to come back. She did not believe him, nor did she consider separation. Somewhere in her head or her heart was the lazy, nebulous hope that things would change and she and Herbie settle suddenly into soothing married life. Here were her home, her furniture, her husband, her station. She summoned no alternatives.

She could no longer bustle and potter. She had no more vicarious tears; the hot drops she shed were for herself. She walked ceaselessly about the rooms, her thoughts running mechanically round and round Herbie. In those days began the hatred of being alone that she was never to overcome. You could be by yourself when things were all right, but when you were blue you got the howling horrors.

She commenced drinking alone, little, short drinks all through the day. It was only with Herbie that alcohol made her nervous and quick in offense. Alone, it blurred sharp things for her. She lived in a haze of it. Her life took on a dream-like quality. Nothing was astonishing.

A Mrs. Martin moved into the flat across the hall. She was a great blonde woman of forty, a promise in looks of what Mrs. Morse was to be. They made acquaintance, quickly became inseparable. Mrs. Morse spent her days in the opposite apartment. They drank together, to brace themselves after the drinks of the night before.

She never confided her troubles about Herbie to Mrs. Martin. The subject was too bewildering to her to find comfort in talk. She let it be assumed that her husband's business kept him much away. It was not regarded as important; husbands, as such, played but shadowy parts in Mrs. Martin's circle.

Mrs. Martin had no visible spouse; you were left to decide for yourself whether he was or was not dead. She had an admirer, Joe, who came to see her almost nightly. Often he brought several friends with him—"The Boys," they were called. The Boys were big, red, good-humored men, perhaps forty-five, perhaps fifty. Mrs. Morse was glad of invitations to join the parties—Herbie was scarcely ever at home at night now. If he did come home, she did not visit Mrs. Martin. An evening alone with Herbie meant inevitably a quarrel, yet she would stay with him. There was always her thin and wordless idea that, maybe, this night, things would begin to be all right.

The Boys brought plenty of liquor along with them whenever they came to Mrs. Martin's. Drinking with them, Mrs. Morse became lively and good-natured and audacious. She was quickly popular. When she had drunk enough to cloud her most recent battle with Herbie, she was excited by their approbation. Crab, was she? Rotten sport, was she? Well, there were some that thought different.

Ed was one of The Boys. He lived in Utica—had "his own business" there, was the awed report—but he came to New York almost every week. He was married. He showed Mrs. Morse the then current photographs of Junior and Sister, and she praised them abundantly and sincerely. Soon it was accepted by the others that Ed was her particular friend.

He staked her when they all played poker; sat next her and occasionally rubbed his knee against hers during the game. She was rather lucky. Frequently she went home with a twenty-dollar bill or a ten-dollar bill or a handful of crumpled dollars. She was glad of them. Herbie was getting, in her words, something awful about money. To ask him for it brought an instant row.

"What the hell do you do with it?" he would say. "Shoot it all on Scotch?"

"I try to run this house half-way decent," she would retort. "Never thought of that, did you? Oh, no, his lordship couldn't be bothered with that."

Again, she could not find a definite day, to fix the beginning of Ed's proprietorship. It became his custom to kiss her on the mouth when he came in, as well as for farewell, and he gave her little quick kisses of approval all through the evening. She liked this rather more than she disliked it. She never thought of his kisses when she was not with him.

He would run his hand lingeringly over her back and shoulders.

"Some dizzy blonde, eh?" he would say. "Some doll."

One afternoon she came home from Mrs. Martin's to find Herbie in the bedroom. He had been away for several nights, evidently on a prolonged drinking bout. His face was gray; his hands jerked as if they were on wires. On the bed were two old suitcases, packed high. Only her photograph remained on his bureau, and the wide doors of his closet disclosed nothing but coathangers.

"I'm blowing," he said. "I'm through with the whole works. I got a job in Detroit."

She sat down on the edge of the bed. She had drunk much the

night before, and the four Scotches she had had with Mrs. Martin had only increased her fogginess.

"Good job?" she said.

"Oh, yeah," he said. "Looks all right."

He closed a suitcase with difficulty, swearing at it in whispers.

"There's some dough in the bank," he said. "The bank book's in your top drawer. You can have the furniture and stuff."

He looked at her, and his forehead twitched.

"God damn it, I'm through, I'm telling you," he cried. "I'm through."

"All right, all right," she said. "I heard you, didn't I?"

She saw him as if he were at one end of a cannon and she at the other. Her head was beginning to ache bumpingly, and her voice had a dreary, tiresome tone. She could not have raised it.

"Like a drink before you go?" she asked.

Again he looked at her, and a corner of his mouth jerked up.

"Cockeyed again for a change, aren't you?" he said. "That's nice. Sure, get a couple of shots, will you?"

She went to the pantry, mixed him a stiff highball, poured herself a couple of inches of whisky and drank it. Then she gave herself another portion and brought the glasses into the bedroom. He had strapped both suitcases and had put on his hat and overcoat.

He took his highball.

"Well," he said, and he gave a sudden, uncertain laugh. "Here's mud in your eye."

"Mud in your eye," she said.

They drank. He put down his glass and took up the heavy suitcases.

"Got to get a train around six," he said.

She followed him down the hall. There was a song, a song that Mrs. Martin played doggedly on the phonograph, running loudly through her mind. She had never liked the thing.

> "Night and daytime,
> Always playtime.
> Ain't we got fun?"

At the door he put down the bags and faced her.

"Well," he said. "Well, take care of yourself. You'll be all right, will you?"

"Oh, sure," she said.

He opened the door, then came back to her, holding out his hand.

" 'By, Haze," he said. "Good luck to you."

She took his hand and shook it.

"Pardon my wet glove," she said.

When the door had closed behind him, she went back to the pantry.

She was flushed and lively when she went in to Mrs. Martin's that evening. The Boys were there, Ed among them. He was glad to be in town, frisky and loud and full of jokes. But she spoke quietly to him for a minute.

"Herbie blew today," she said. "Going to live out west."

"That so?" he said. He looked at her and played with the fountain pen clipped to his waistcoat pocket.

"Think he's gone for good, do you?" he asked.

"Yeah," she said. "I know he is. I know. Yeah."

"You going to live on across the hall just the same?" he said. "Know what you're going to do?"

"Gee, I don't know," she said. "I don't give much of a damn."

"Oh, come on, that's no way to talk," he told her. "What you need—you need a little snifter. How about it?"

"Yeah," she said. "Just straight."

She won forty-three dollars at poker. When the game broke up, Ed took her back to her apartment.

"Got a little kiss for me?" he asked.

He wrapped her in his big arms and kissed her violently. She was entirely passive. He held her away and looked at her.

"Little tight, honey?" he asked anxiously. "Not going to be sick, are you?"

"Me?" she said. "I'm swell."

II

When Ed left in the morning, he took her photograph with
him. He said he wanted her picture to look at, up in Utica. "You
can have that one on the bureau," she said.

She put Herbie's picture in a drawer, out of her sight. When
she could look at it, she meant to tear it up. She was fairly successful in keeping her mind from racing around him. Whisky
slowed it for her. She was almost peaceful, in her mist.

She accepted her relationship with Ed without question or
enthusiasm. When he was away, she seldom thought definitely of
him. He was good to her; he gave her frequent presents and a
regular allowance. She was even able to save. She did not plan
ahead of any day, but her wants were few, and you might as
well put money in the bank as have it lying around.

When the lease of her apartment neared its end, it was Ed who
suggested moving. His friendship with Mrs. Martin and Joe had
become strained over a dispute at poker; a feud was impending.

"Let's get the hell out of here," Ed said. "What I want you to
have is a place near the Grand Central. Make it easier for me."

So she took a little flat in the Forties. A colored maid came in
every day to clean and to make coffee for her—she was "through
with that housekeeping stuff," she said, and Ed, twenty years
married to a passionately domestic woman, admired this romantic
uselessness and felt doubly a man of the world in abetting it.

The coffee was all she had until she went out to dinner, but
alcohol kept her fat. Prohibition she regarded only as a basis for
jokes. You could always get all you wanted. She was never noticeably drunk and seldom nearly sober. It required a larger daily
allowance to keep her misty-minded. Too little, and she was ach-
ingly melancholy.

Ed brought her to Jimmy's. He was proud, with the pride of
the transient who would be mistaken for a native, in his knowledge
of small, recent restaurants occupying the lower floors of shabby
brownstone houses; places where, upon mentioning the name of
an habitué friend, might be obtained strange whisky and fresh gin
in many of their ramifications. Jimmy's place was the favorite of
his acquaintants.

There, through Ed, Mrs. Morse met many men and women, formed quick friendships. The men often took her out when Ed was in Utica. He was proud of her popularity.

She fell into the habit of going to Jimmy's alone when she had no engagement. She was certain to meet some people she knew, and join them. It was a club for her friends, both men and women.

The women at Jimmy's looked remarkably alike, and this was curious, for, through feuds, removals, and opportunities of more profitable contacts, the personnel of the group changed constantly. Yet always the newcomers resembled those whom they replaced. They were all big women and stout, broad of shoulder and abundantly breasted, with faces thickly clothed in soft, high-colored flesh. They laughed loud and often, showing opaque and lusterless teeth like squares of crockery. There was about them the health of the big, yet a slight, unwholesome suggestion of stubborn preservation. They might have been thirty-six or forty-five or anywhere between.

They composed their titles of their own first names with their husbands' surnames—Mrs. Florence Miller, Mrs. Vera Riley, Mrs. Lilian Block. This gave at the same time the solidity of marriage and the glamor of freedom. Yet only one or two were actually divorced. Most of them never referred to their dimmed spouses; some, a shorter time separated, described them in terms of great biological interest. Several were mothers, each of an only child— a boy at school somewhere, or a girl being cared for by a grandmother. Often, well on toward morning, there would be displays of kodak portraits and of tears.

They were comfortable women, cordial and friendly and irrepressibly matronly. Theirs was the quality of ease. Become fatalistic, especially about money matters, they were unworried. Whenever their funds dropped alarmingly, a new donor appeared; this had always happened. The aim of each was to have one man, permanently, to pay all her bills, in return for which she would have immediately given up other admirers and probably would have become exceedingly fond of him; for the affections of all of them were, by now, unexacting, tranquil, and easily arranged. This end, however, grew increasingly difficult yearly. Mrs. Morse was regarded as fortunate.

Ed had a good year, increased her allowance and gave her a sealskin coat. But she had to be careful of her moods with him. He insisted upon gaiety. He would not listen to admissions of aches or weariness.

"Hey, listen," he would say, "I got worries of my own, and plenty. Nobody wants to hear other people's troubles, sweetie. What you got to do, you got to be a sport and forget it. See? Well, slip us a little smile, then. That's my girl."

She never had enough interest to quarrel with him as she had with Herbie, but she wanted the privilege of occasional admitted sadness. It was strange. The other women she saw did not have to fight their moods. There was Mrs. Florence Miller who got regular crying jags, and the men sought only to cheer and comfort her. The others spent whole evenings in grieved recitals of worries and ills; their escorts paid them deep sympathy. But she was instantly undesirable when she was low in spirits. Once, in Jimmy's, when she could not make herself lively, Ed had walked out and left her.

"Why the hell don't you stay home and not go spoiling everybody's evening?" he had roared.

Even her slightest acquaintances seemed irritated if she were not conspicuously light-hearted.

"What's the matter with you, anyway?" they would say. "Be your age, why don't you? Have a little drink and snap out of it."

When her relationship with Ed had continued nearly three years, he moved to Florida to live. He hated leaving her; he gave her a large check and some shares of a sound stock, and his pale eyes were wet when he said good-by. She did not miss him. He came to New York infrequently, perhaps two or three times a year, and hurried directly from the train to see her. She was always pleased to have him come and never sorry to see him go.

Charley, an acquaintance of Ed's that she had met at Jimmy's, had long admired her. He had always made opportunities of touching her and leaning close to talk to her. He asked repeatedly of all their friends if they had ever heard such a fine laugh as she had. After Ed left, Charley became the main figure in her life. She classified him and spoke of him as "not so bad." There was nearly a year of Charley; then she divided her time between him and

Sydney, another frequenter of Jimmy's; then Charley slipped away altogether.

Sydney was a little, brightly dressed, clever Jew. She was perhaps nearer contentment with him. He amused her always; her laughter was not forced.

He admired her completely. Her softness and size delighted him. And he thought she was great, he often told her, because she kept gay and lively when she was drunk.

"Once I had a gal," he said, "used to try and throw herself out of the window every time she got a can on. Jee-*zuss*," he added, feelingly.

Then Sydney married a rich and watchful bride, and then there was Billy. No—after Sydney came Ferd, then Billy. In her haze, she never recalled how men entered her life and left it. There were no surprises. She had no thrill at their advent, nor woe at their departure. She seemed to be always able to attract men. There was never another as rich as Ed, but they were all generous to her, in their means.

Once she had news of Herbie. She met Mrs. Martin dining at Jimmy's, and the old friendship was vigorously renewed. The still admiring Joe, while on a business trip, had seen Herbie. He had settled in Chicago, he looked fine, he was living with some woman —seemed to be crazy about her. Mrs. Morse had been drinking vastly that day. She took the news with mild interest, as one hearing of the sex peccadilloes of somebody whose name is, after a moment's groping, familiar.

"Must be damn near seven years since I saw him," she commented. "Gee. Seven years."

More and more, her days lost their individuality. She never knew dates, nor was sure of the day of the week.

"My God, that was a year ago!" she would exclaim, when an event was recalled in conversation.

She was tired so much of the time. Tired and blue. Almost everything could give her the blues. Those old horses she saw on Sixth Avenue—struggling and slipping along the car-tracks, or standing at the curb, their heads dropped level with their worn knees. The tightly stored tears would squeeze from her eyes as she teetered past on her aching feet in the stubby, champagne-colored slippers.

The thought of death came and stayed with her and lent her a sort of drowsy cheer. It would be nice, nice and restful, to be dead.

There was no settled, shocked moment when she first thought of killing herself; it seemed to her as if the idea had always been with her. She pounced upon all the accounts of suicides in the newspapers. There was an epidemic of self-killings—or maybe it was just that she searched for the stories of them so eagerly that she found many. To read of them roused reassurance in her; she felt a cozy solidarity with the big company of the voluntary dead.

She slept, aided by whisky, till deep into the afternoons, then lay abed, a bottle and glass at her hand, until it was time to dress and go out for dinner. She was beginning to feel toward alcohol a little puzzled distrust, as toward an old friend who has refused a simple favor. Whisky could still soothe her for most of the time, but there were sudden, inexplicable moments when the cloud fell treacherously away from her, and she was sawed by the sorrow and bewilderment and nuisance of all living. She played voluptuously with the thought of cool, sleepy retreat. She had never been troubled by religious belief and no vision of an after-life intimidated her. She dreamed by day of never again putting on tight shoes, or never having to laugh and listen and admire, of never more being a good sport. Never.

But how would you do it? It make her sick to think of jumping from heights. She could not stand a gun. At the theater, if one of the actors drew a revolver, she crammed her fingers into her ears and could not even look at the stage until after the shot had been fired. There was no gas in her flat. She looked long at the bright blue veins in her slim wrists—a cut with a razor blade, and there you'd be. But it would hurt, hurt like hell, and there would be blood to see. Poison—something tasteless and quick and painless—was the thing. But they wouldn't sell it to you in drug-stores, because of the law.

She had few other thoughts.

There was a new man now—Art. He was short and fat and exacting and hard on her patience when he was drunk. But there had been only occasionals for some time before him, and she was glad of a little stability. Too, Art must be away for weeks at a stretch, selling silks, and that was restful. She was convincingly gay with him, though the effort shook her.

"The best sport in the world," he would murmur, deep in her neck. "The best sport in the world."

One night, when he had taken her to Jimmy's, she went into the dressing-room with Mrs. Florence Miller. There, while designing curly mouths on their faces with lip-rouge, they compared experiences of insomnia.

"Honestly," Mrs. Morse said, "I wouldn't close an eye if I didn't go to bed full of Scotch. I lie there and toss and turn and toss and turn. Blue! Does a person get blue lying awake that way!"

"Say, listen, Hazel," Mrs. Miller said, impressively, "I'm telling you I'd be awake for a year if I didn't take veronal. That stuff makes you sleep like a fool."

"Isn't it poison, or something?" Mrs. Morse asked.

"Oh, you take too much and you're out for the count," said Mrs. Miller. "I just take five grains—they come in tablets. I'd be scared to fool around with it. But five grains, and you cork off pretty."

"Can you get it anywhere?" Mrs. Morse felt superbly Machiavellian.

"Get all you want in Jersey," said Mrs. Miller. "They won't give it to you here without you have a doctor's prescription. Finished? We'd better go back and see what the boys are doing."

That night, Art left Mrs. Morse at the door of her apartment; his mother was in town. Mrs. Morse was still sober, and it happened that there was no whisky left in her cupboard. She lay in bed, looking up at the blank ceiling.

She rose early, for her, and went to New Jersey. She had never taken the tube, and did not understand it. So she went to the Pennsylvania Station and bought a railroad ticket to Newark. She thought of nothing in particular on the trip out. She looked at the uninspired hats of the women about her and gazed through the smeared window at the flat, gritty scene.

In Newark, in the first drug-store she came to, she asked for a tin of talcum powder, a nailbrush, and a box of veronal tablets.

The powder and the brush were to make the hypnotic seem also a casual need. The clerk was entirely unconcerned. "We only keep them in bottles," he said, and wrapped up for her a little glass vial containing ten white tablets, stacked one on another.

She went to another drug-store and bought a face-cloth, an orange-wood stick, and a bottle of veronal tablets. The clerk was also uninterested.

"Well, I guess I got enough to kill an ox," she thought, and went back to the station.

At home, she put the little vials in the drawer of her dressing-table and stood looking at them with a dreamy tenderness.

"There they are, God bless them," she said, and she kissed her finger-tips and touched each bottle.

The colored maid was busy in the living-room.

"Hey, Nettie," Mrs. Morse called. "Be an angel, will you? Run around to Jimmy's and get me a quart of Scotch."

She hummed while she awaited the girl's return.

During the next few days, whisky ministered to her as tenderly as it had done when she first turned to its aid. Alone, she was soothed and vague, at Jimmy's she was the gayest of the groups. Art was delighted with her.

Then, one night, she had an appointment to meet Art at Jimmy's for an early dinner. He was to leave afterward on a business excursion, to be away for a week. Mrs. Morse had been drinking all the afternoon; while she dressed to go out, she felt herself rising pleasurably from drowsiness to high spirits. But as she came out into the street the effects of the whisky deserted her completely, and she was filled with a slow, grinding wretchedness so horrible that she stood swaying on the pavement, unable for a moment to move forward. It was a gray night with spurts of mean, thin snow, and the streets shone with dark ice. As she slowly crossed Sixth Avenue, consciously dragging one foot past the other, a big, scarred horse pulling a rickety express-wagon crashed to his knees before her. The driver swore and screamed and lashed the beast insanely, bringing the whip back over his shoulder for every blow, while the horse struggled to get a footing on the slippery asphalt. A group gathered and watched with interest.

Art was waiting, when Mrs. Morse reached Jimmy's.

"What's the matter with you, for God's sake?" was his greeting to her.

"I saw a horse," she said. "Gee, I—a person feels sorry for horses. I—it isn't just horses. Everything's kind of terrible, isn't it? I can't help getting sunk."

"Ah, sunk, me eye," he said. "What's the idea of all the belly-aching? What have you got to be sunk about?"

"I can't help it," she said.

"Ah, help it, me eye," he said. "Pull yourself together, will you? Come on and sit down, and take that face off you."

She drank industriously and she tried hard, but she could not overcome her melancholy. Others joined them and commented on her gloom, and she could do no more for them than smile weakly. She made little dabs at her eyes with her handkerchief, trying to time her movements so they would be unnoticed, but several times Art caught her and scowled and shifted impatiently in his chair.

When it was time for him to go to his train, she said she would leave, too, and go home.

"And not a bad idea, either," he said. "See if you can't sleep yourself out of it. I'll see you Thursday. For God's sake, try and cheer up by then, will you?"

"Yeah," she said. "I will."

In her bedroom, she undressed with a tense speed wholly unlike her usual slow uncertainty. She put on her nightgown, took off her hair-net and passed the comb quickly through her dry, vari-colored hair. Then she took the two little vials from the drawer and carried them into the bathroom. The splintering misery had gone from her, and she felt the quick excitement of one who is about to receive an anticipated gift.

She uncorked the vials, filled a glass with water and stood before the mirror, a tablet between her fingers. Suddenly she bowed graciously to her reflection, and raised the glass to it.

"Well, here's mud in your eye," she said.

The tablets were unpleasant to take, dry and powdery and sticking obstinately half-way down her throat. It took her a long time to swallow all twenty of them. She stood watching her reflection with deep, impersonal interest, studying the movements of the gulping throat. Once more she spoke aloud.

"For God's sake, try and cheer up by Thursday, will you?" she said. "Well, you know what he can do. He and the whole lot of them."

She had no idea how quickly to expect the effect from the veronal. When she had taken the last tablet, she stood uncertainly, wondering, still with a courteous, vicarious interest, if death would strike her down then and there. She felt in no way strange, save for a slight stirring of sickness from the effect of swallowing the tablets, nor did her reflected face look at all different. It would not be immediate, then; it might even take an hour or so.

She stretched her arms high and gave a vast yawn.

"Guess I'll go to bed," she said. "Gee, I'm nearly dead."

That struck her as comic, and she turned out the bathroom light and went in and laid herself down in her bed, chuckling softly all the time.

"Gee, I'm nearly dead," she quoted. "That's a hot one!"

III

Nettie, the colored maid, came in late the next afternoon to clean the apartment, and found Mrs. Morse in her bed. But then, that was not unusual. Usually, though, the sounds of cleaning waked her, and she did not like to wake up. Nettie, an agreeable girl, had learned to move softly about her work,

But when she had done the living-room and stolen in to tidy the little square bedroom, she could not avoid a tiny clatter as she arranged the objects on the dressing-table. Instinctively, she glanced over her shoulder at the sleeper, and without warning a sickly uneasiness crept over her. She came to the bed and stared down at the woman lying there.

Mrs. Morse lay on her back, one flabby, white arm flung up, the wrist against her forehead. Her stiff hair hung untenderly along her face. The bed covers were pushed down, exposing a deep square of soft neck and a pink nightgown, its fabric worn uneven by many launderings; her great breasts, freed from their tight confiner, sagged beneath her arm-pits. Now and then she made knotted, snoring sounds, and from the corner of her opened mouth to the blurred turn of her jaw ran a lane of crusted spittle.

"Mis' Morse," Nettie called. "Oh, Mis' Morse! It's terrible late."

Mrs. Morse made no move.

"Mis' Morse," said Nettie. "Look, Mis' Morse. How'm I goin' get this bed made?"

Panic sprang upon the girl. She shook the woman's hot shoulder. "Ah, wake up, will yuh?" she whined. "Ah, please wake up."

Suddenly the girl turned and ran out in the hall to the elevator door, keeping her thumb firm on the black, shiny button until the elderly car and its Negro attendant stood before her. She poured a jumble of words over the boy, and led him back to the apartment. He tiptoed creakingly in to the bedside; first gingerly, then so lustily that he left marks in the soft flesh, he prodded the unconscious woman.

"Hey, there!" he cried, and listened intently, as for an echo.

"Jeez. Out like a light," he commented.

At his interest in the spectacle, Nettie's panic left her. Importance was big in both of them. They talked in quick, unfinished whispers, and it was the boy's suggestion that he fetch the young doctor who lived on the ground floor. Nettie hurried along with him. They looked forward to the limelit moment of breaking their news of something untoward, something pleasurably unpleasant. Mrs. Morse had become the medium of drama. With no ill wish to her, they hoped that her state was serious, that she would not let them down by being awake and normal on their return. A little fear of this determined them to make the most, to the doctor, of her present condition. "Matter of life and death," returned to Nettie from her thin store of reading. She considered startling the doctor with the phrase.

The doctor was in and none too pleased at interruption. He wore a yellow and blue striped dressing-gown, and he was lying on his sofa, laughing with a dark girl, her face scaly with inexpensive powder, who perched on the arm. Half-empty highball glasses stood beside them, and her coat and hat were neatly hung up with the comfortable implication of a long stay.

Always something, the doctor grumbled. Couldn't let anybody

alone after a hard day. But he put some bottles and instruments into a case, changed his dressing-gown for his coat and started out with the Negroes.

"Snap it up there, big boy," the girl called after him. "Don't be all night."

The doctor strode loudly into Mrs. Morse's flat and on to the bedroom, Nettie and the boy right behind him. Mrs. Morse had not moved; her sleep was as deep, but soundless, now. The doctor looked sharply at her, then plunged his thumbs into the lidded pits above her eyeballs and threw his weight upon them. A high, sickening cry broke from Nettie.

"Look like he tryin' to push her right on th'ough the bed," said the boy. He chuckled.

Mrs. Morse gave no sign under the pressure. Abruptly the doctor abandoned it, and with one quick movement swept the covers down to the foot of the bed. With another he flung her nightgown back and lifted the thick, white legs, cross-hatched with blocks of tiny, iris-colored veins. He pinched them repeatedly, with long, cruel nips, back of the knees. She did not awaken.

"What's she been drinking?" he asked Nettie, over his shoulder.

With the certain celerity of one who knows just where to lay hands on a thing, Nettie went into the bathroom, bound for the cupboard where Mrs. Morse kept her whisky. But she stopped at the sight of the two vials, with their red and white labels, lying before the mirror. She brought them to the doctor.

"Oh, for the Lord Almighty's sweet sake!" he said. He dropped Mrs. Morse's legs, and pushed them impatiently across the bed. "What did she want to go taking that tripe for? Rotten yellow trick, that's what a thing like that is. Now we'll have to pump her out, and all that stuff. Nuisance, a thing like that is; that's what it amounts to. Here, George, take me down in the elevator. You wait here, maid. She won't do anything."

"She won't die on me, will she?" cried Nettie.

"No," said the doctor. "God, no. You couldn't kill her with an ax."

IV

After two days, Mrs. Morse came back to consciousness, dazed at first, then with a comprehension that brought with it the slow, saturated wretchedness.

"Oh, Lord, oh, Lord," she moaned, and tears for herself and her life striped her cheeks.

Nettie came in at the sound. For two days she had done the ugly, incessant tasks in the nursing of the unconscious, for two nights she had caught broken bits of sleep on the living-room couch. She looked coldly at the big, blown woman in the bed.

"What you been tryin' to do, Mis' Morse?" she said. "What kine o' work is that, takin' all that stuff?"

"Oh, Lord," moaned Mrs. Morse, again, and she tried to cover her eyes with her arms. But the joints felt stiff and brittle, and she cried out at their ache.

"Tha's no way to ack, takin' them pills," said Nettie. "You can thank you' stars you heah at all. How you feel now?"

"Oh, I feel great," said Mrs. Morse. "Swell, I feel."

Her hot, painful tears fell as if they would never stop.

"Tha's no way to take on, cryin' like that," Nettie said. "After what you done. The doctor, he says he could have you arrested, doin' a thing like that. He was fit to be tied, here."

"Why couldn't he let me alone?" wailed Mrs. Morse. "Why the hell couldn't he have?"

"Tha's terr'ble, Mis' Morse, swearin' an' talkin' like that," said Nettie, "after what people done for you. Here I ain' had no sleep at all for two nights, an' had to give up goin' out to my other ladies!"

"Oh, I'm sorry, Nettie," she said. "You're a peach. I'm sorry I've given you so much trouble. I couldn't help it. I just got sunk. Didn't you ever feel like doing it? When everything looks just lousy to you?"

"I wouldn't think o' no such thing," declared Nettie. "You got to cheer up. Tha's what you got to do. Everybody's got their troubles."

"Yeah," said Mrs. Morse. "I know."

"Come a pretty picture card for you," Nettie said. "Maybe that will cheer you up."

She handed Mrs. Morse a post-card. Mrs. Morse had to cover one eye with her hand, in order to read the message; her eyes were not yet focusing correctly.

It was from Art. On the back of a view of the Detroit Athletic Club he had written: "Greeting and salutations. Hope you have lost that gloom. Cheer up and don't take any rubber nickels. See you on Thursday."

She dropped the card to the floor. Misery crushed her as if she were between great smooth stones. There passed before her a slow, slow pageant of days spent lying in her flat, of evenings at Jimmy's being a good sport, making herself laugh and coo at Art and other Arts; she saw a long parade of weary horses and shivering beggars and all beaten, driven, stumbling things. Her feet throbbed as if she had crammed them into the stubby champagne-colored slippers. Her heart seemed to swell and harden.

"Nettie," she cried, "for heaven's sake pour me a drink, will you?"

The maid looked doubtful.

"Now you know, Mis' Morse," she said, "you been near daid. I don' know if the doctor he let you drink nothin' yet."

"Oh, never mind him," she said. "You get me one, and bring in the bottle. Take one yourself."

"Well," said Nettie.

She poured them each a drink, deferentially leaving hers in the bathroom to be taken in solitude, and brought Mrs. Morse's glass in to her.

Mrs. Morse looked into the liquor and shuddered back from its odor. Maybe it would help. Maybe, when you had been knocked cold for a few days, your very first drink would give you a lift. Maybe whisky would be her friend again. She prayed without addressing a God, without knowing a God. Oh, please, please, let her be able to get drunk, please keep her always drunk.

She lifted the glass.

"Thanks, Nettie," she said. "Here's mud in your eye."

The maid giggled. "Tha's the way, Mis' Morse," she said. "You cheer up, now."

"Yeah," said Mrs. Morse. "Sure.

HELEN, I LOVE YOU

By James Farrell

"you got a goofy look," dick buckford said. "yeh," dan said.

The two boys stood in front of one of the small graystone houses in the 5700 block on Indiana Avenue, glaring at each other.

Dan didn't know what to say. He glanced aside at the hopeless, rainy autumn day. His eyes roved over the damp street, the withered grass and mud by the sidewalk across the street, the three-story apartment buildings, and at the sky which dumped down top-heavily behind the buildings.

"Yeah, you're goofy! You're goofy!" Dick sneered.

"Then so are you," Dan countered.

"Am I?" Dick challenged.

"Yes!" Dan answered with determination.

"Am I goofy?"

"If you say I am, then you're a goof, too!"

Dan hoped nothing would happen. He knew how, if he lost a fight when he was still new in the neighborhood, everybody would start taking picks on him, bullying him, making a dope out of him, and kidding him all the time because he had been licked. He hoped that he wouldn't be forced into a fight with Dick, who was about ten pounds heavier than he was. But he pretended that he was fighting Dick, beating hell out of him. He pretended that he slugged Dick in the face, and saw the blood spurt from his big nose. He slugged Dick, until Dick was bloody and winded and said quits, and a crowd of guys and girls watching the fight cheered and said that Dan was certainly a fine fighter, and then he pretended that Helen Scanlan came up to him and told him she was so glad.

But he'd already had his chance with her. She had seemed to like him, but he'd been too damn bashful. Once, he could have held her hand and kissed her, and they could have gone over to the park, and kissed some more, if he only hadn't been so bashful. She had even said that she liked him.

They were standing right in front of the parlor window of the Scanlan house. He thought again of himself slamming Dick around, with Helen in the window watching him. Red-haired Helen Scanlan, he loved her. He said to himself: Helen, I love you!

"Why don't you pull in your ears? Huh," said Dick.

"Aw, freeze your teeth and give your tongue a sleigh-ride," Dan said.

He wished Dick would go away, because he wanted to walk around alone, and maybe go over to the park, where it would be all quiet except for the wind, and where the leaves would be wet and yellow, and it would be easy to think of Helen. He could walk around, and think and be a little happy-sad, and think about Helen. And here was Dick before him, and Dick was supposed to be one of the best scrappers in the neighborhood, and he seemed to want to pick a fight, and right here, too, outside of Helen's window. And maybe Dick would win, with Helen there to watch it all.

Dan wanted Dick to go away. He told himself that he loved Helen. He told himself that he was awfully in love with curly, red-haired Helen. He remembered last summer, when he had peddled bills for half a dollar, putting them in mail boxes all over the neighborhood. The day after, they had gone riding on the tail-gate of hump-backed George's grocery wagon, and it had been fun, himself and Helen sitting there on the back of the wagon, holding hands as they bounced through the alleys, and while they waited for George to deliver his orders. And he had spent all his money on her. He told himself that he loved her.

He remembered how, after riding on the wagon, he had gone home, and they had bawled him out because he had worn out the soles on his shoes delivering the bills, and then had gone and spent the money so foolishly, with nothing to show for it. There had been a big scrap, and he had answered them back, and got so sore that he had bawled like a cry baby. Afterwards, he'd sat in the parlor, crying and cursing, because he was sore. He'd had such a swell time that afternoon, too. And the family just hadn't understood it at all. And then Helen had come around, because all the kids in the neighborhood used to come around to his front steps at night to play and talk. Somebody had called to tell him she was there. He hadn't known what he was doing, and he'd answered that he didn't care if she was there or not.

After that Helen hadn't paid any attention to him.

He told himself: Helen, I love you!

II

"If I was as goofy as you, I'd do something about it," Dick said.

"Yeh. Well, I ain't got nothing on you."

"No? Well, look at it, your stockings are falling down. You can't even keep your stockings up," said Dick.

"Well, you're sniffin' and don't even know enough to blow your nose."

"Don't talk to me like that!" Dick said.

"Well, don't talk to me like that, either!"

"I ain't afraid of you!" Dick said.

"And I ain't afraid of you, either!" said Dan.

"Wanna fight?" asked Dick.

"If you do, I do!" said Dan.

"Well, start something," said Dick.

"You start something," said Dan.

"But maybe you won't, because you're yellow," said Dick.

"No, I ain't, neither. I ain't afraid of you."

Dick smiled sarcastically at Dan.

"I don't know whether to kiss you or kill you," he said with exaggerated sweetness.

"Yeh, you heard Red Kelly make that crack, and you're just copying it from him. You ain't funny," Dan said.

"That's all you know about it! Well, I made it up and Red heard me say it. That's where he got it. How do you like that?"

"Tie your bull in somebody else's alley," Dan said.

Dick tried to out-stare Dan. Dan frowned back at him.

"And today in school, when Sister Cyrilla called on you, you didn't even know enough how to divide fractions. You're goofy," Dick said.

"Well, if I'm goofy, I don't know what you ain't," Dan said.

Dan again pretended that they were fighting, and that he was kicking the hell out of Dick with Helen watching. And he remembered how last summer when he had gotten those hats advertising Cracker Jack, he had given one to her. He had felt good that day, because she had worn the hat he gave her. And every night they had all played tin-tin, or run-sheep-run, or chase-one-chase-all, or eeny-meeny-miny-mo. He had just moved around then, and he had thought that it was such a good neighborhood, and now, if Dick went picking a fight with him and beat him, well, he just wouldn't be able to show his face any more and would just about have to sneak down alleys and everything.

But if he beat Dick up and Helen saw him, he would be her hero, and he would be one of the leaders of their gang, and then maybe she would like him again, and twice as much, and everything would be all so swell, just like it was at the end of the stories he sometimes read in The Saturday Evening Post.

Last summer, too, he had read Penrod, and he had thought of Helen because she was like Marjorie Jones in the book, only more so, and prettier, and nicer, and she had nicer hair, because the book said Marjorie Jones's hair was black, and Helen's was red, and red hair was nicer than black hair.

"One thing I wouldn't be called is yellow," Dick sneered.

"I ain't yellow," Dan said.

"I wouldn't be yellow," Dick said.

"And I wouldn't be a sniffer, and not have enough sense to blow my nose," said Dan.

"Who's a sniffer?" demanded Dick.

"Well, why don't you blow your nose?"

"Why doncha not be so goofy?" demanded Dick.

"I ain't no goofier than you."

"If I was as goofy as you, I'd quit living," Dick said.

"Yeh, and if I was like you, I'd drown myself."

"You better do it then, because you're goofier than anybody I know," Dick said.

"Yeh?"

"Yeh!"

"Yeh!"

"And let me tell you, I ain't afraid of nobody like you," Dick said.

"I ain't, neither. Just start something, and see!"

"I would, only I don't wanna get my hands dirty, picking on a goof. If you wasn't afraid of me, you wouldn't stand there, letting me say you're goofy."

"Well, I'm here saying you're just as goofy."

"I couldn't be like you."

"And I couldn't be as dumb as you," Dan said.

"You're so goofy, I wouldn't be seen with you."

"Don't then!" said Dan.

"I ain't! I was here first!"

"I live on this street."

"I lived in this neighborhood longer than you," said Wick.

"I live on this street, and you can beat it if you don't like it."

"You're so goofy you belong in the Kankakee nut house. Your whole family's goofy. My old man says I shouldn't have nothing to do with you because of all the goofiness in your family.

"Well, my old man and my uncle don't think nothing of your old man," Dan said.

"Well, don't let my old man hear them sayin' it, because if he does, he's liable to bat their snoots off," said Dick.

"Let him try! My old man ain't afraid of nothing!"

"Yeh? Don't never think so. My old man could take your old man on blindfolded."

"Yeh? My old man could trim your old man with his little finger, and it's cut off," said Dan.

"Say, if my old man's hands were tied behind his back, and he said 'Boo,' your old man would take to his heels lickety-split down the streets."

"Let him start something and see, then!"

"If he ever does, I'd feel sorry for your old man," said Dick.

"You don't need to be."

"My old man's strong, and he says I take after him, and when I grow up, I'll be like him, a lineman climbing telephone poles for the telephone company," said Dick.

"Yeh?" said Dan.

"Yeh!" said Dick.

"Yeh?" said Dan.

"Baloney," said Dick.

"Bouswah," said Dan.

"B.S., said Dick.

They sneered toughly at one another.

"That for you!" Dick said, snapping his fingers in Dan's face.

"That for you!" Dan said, screwing up his lips and twitching his nose.

"If this is the street you live on, I won't hang around it no more, because it smells just as bad as you do," said Dick.

"That's because you're on it."

"I'm going, because I don't want nobody to know that I'm even acquainted with anyone as goofy as you."

"Good riddance to bad rubbage," said Dan.

"If you weren't such a clown, I'd break you with my little finger!" said Dick.

"And I'd blow you over with my breath!" said Dan.

III

Dan watched Dick walk away, without looking back. He sat on the iron fence around the grass plot, feeling good because he had proven to himself that he wasn't afraid of Dick. He said to himself:

Helen, I love you!

He sat through slow, oblivious minutes. He arose and decided to take a walk. Wishing that he could see Helen, he strolled down to Fifty-eighth Street, and bought five cents' worth of candy. He returned and sat on the iron fence in front of her house, and for about twenty-five minutes he nibbled at his candy, hoping that she would come along, wondering where she was, wishing he could give her some of his candy. He told himself:

Helen, I love you!

He thought of how he had held her hand that day on the grocery wagon. He imagined her watching him while he cleaned the stuffings out of Dick Buckford.

The day was sad. He wished that it had some sun. The day wouldn't be sad, though, if she came along and talked to him.

He walked over to Washington Park. It was lonely, and he didn't see anybody in the park. The wind kept beating against the trees and bushes, and sometimes, when he listened closely, it seemed to him like an unhappy person, crying. He walked on and on, wetting his feet, but he didn't care. He stopped to stand by the lagoon. There were small waves on it, and it looked dark, and black, and mean. He said to himself:

Helen, I love you!

He continued gazing at the lagoon. Then, he strolled on.

"Yes, if Dick had started something, he would have cleaned the guts out of him. Dick would have rushed him, and he would have biffed Dick, giving him a pretty shiner. Dick would have rushed him again and he would have biffed Dick a second time, and Dick would have had a bloody nose. He would have stood back and led with a left to the solar plexus, and Dick would have doubled up, and he would have smashed Dick with a right, and Dick would have fallen down with another black eye. Dick would have yelled quit, and Helen, who would have been watching it all, would have yelled for him, and maybe she would have said:

Dan, I want to be your girl.

He walked. He looked all around him in the park stretching away in wet, darkened, dying grass, with shadows falling down over it. The light was going out of the sky, and he said good-bye to Mr. Day. He felt all alone, and thought how nice it would be if he only had someone to talk to. Maybe Helen. Maybe himself and Helen walking in the wet grass. Maybe some man would try to kidnap her. The man would run away with her under his arm crying for help. And he would pick up a rock and fling at the guy, and it would smack the guy in the skull, and he would drop down unconscious, but Helen wouldn't be hurt. And he would rush up, hit the guy with another rock so that he would be out colder than if he had been hit by Ruby Bob Fitzsimmons in his prime. Police would come, and he would have his picture in the papers, and he would be a real hero, and Helen would say to him:

Dan, I love you, and I'll always love you.

He walked. It was almost dark, and the wind sounds seemed worse than the voices of ghosts. He wished he wasn't so all alone. He had strange feelings. He wondered what he ought to do, and it seemed like there were people behind every tree. The park was too lonely to be in, and he decided that he'd better go home. And it was getting to be supper time.

The wind was awfully sad. There wasn't any moon or stars in the sky yet.

He didn't know what he was afraid of, but he was awfully afraid.

And it would have been so nice, and so different, if he was only with Helen. She would be afraid, too, and he would be protecting her.

He started back toward home, thinking what he would have done to Dick if Dick had really started a fight. Yes, sir, he would have made Dick sorry.

Helen, I love you!

DEAD MAN

By James M. Cain

I

HE FELT THE TRAIN CHECK, KNEW WHAT IT MEANT. IN A MOMENT, from up toward the engine, came the chant of the railroad detective: "Rise and shine, boys, rise and shine." The hoboes began dropping off. He could hear them out there in the dark, cursing as the train went by. That was what they always did on these freights: let the hoboes climb on in the yards, making no effort to dislodge them there; for that would have meant a foolish game of hide-and-seek between two or three detectives and two or three hundred hoboes, with the hoboes swarming on as fast as the detectives put them off. What they did was let the hoboes alone until the train was several miles under way; then they pulled down to a speed slow enough for men to drop off, but too fast for them to climb back on. Then the detective went down the line, brushing them off, like caterpillars from a twig. In two minutes they would all be ditched, a crowd of bitter men in a lonely spot; but they always cursed, always seemed surprised.

He crouched in the coal gondola and waited. He hadn't boarded a flat or a refrigerator with the others, back in the Los Angeles yards, tempting though this comfort was. He wasn't long on the road, and he still didn't like to mix with the other hoboes, admit he was one of them. Also, he couldn't shake off a notion that he was sharper than they were, that playing a lone hand he might think of some magnificent trick that would defeat the detective, and thus, even at this ignoble trade, give him a sense of accomplishment, of being good at it. He had slipped into the gond not in spite of its harshness, but because of it; it was black, and would give him a chance to hide, and the detective, not expecting him there, might pass him by. He was nineteen years old, and was

387

proud of the nickname they had given him in the poolroom back home. They called him Lucky.

"Rise and shine, boys, rise and shine."

Three dropped off the tank car ahead, and the detective climbed into the gond. The flashlight shot around, and Lucky held his breath. He had curled into one of the three chutes for unloading coal. The trick worked. These chutes were dangerous, for if you stepped into one and the bottom dropped, it would dump you under the train. The detective took no chances. He first shot the flash, then held on to the side while he climbed over the chutes. When he came to the last one, where Lucky lay, he shot the flash, but carelessly, and not squarely into the hole, so that he saw nothing. Stepping over, he went on, climbed to the box car behind, and resumed his chant; there were more curses, more feet sliding on ballast on the roadbed outside. Soon the train picked up speed. That meant the detective had reached the caboose, that all the hoboes were cleared.

Lucky stood up, looked around. There was nothing to see, except hot-dog stands along the highway, but it was pleasant to poke your head up, let the wind whip your hair, and reflect how you had outwitted the detective. When the click of the rails slowed and station lights showed ahead, he squatted down again, dropped his feet into the chute. As soon as lights flashed alongside, he braced against the opposite side of the chute: that was one thing he had learned, the crazy way they shot the brakes on these freights. When the train jerked to a shrieking stop, he was ready, and didn't get slammed. The bell tolled, the engine pulled away, there was an interval of silence. That meant they had cut the train, and would be picking up more cars. Soon they would be going on.

"Ah-ha! Hiding out on me, hey?"

The flashlight shot down from the box car. Lucky jumped, seized the side of the gond, scrambled up, vaulted. When he hit the roadbed, his ankles stung from the impact, and he staggered for footing. The detective was on him, grappling. He broke away, ran down the track, past the caboose, into the dark. The detective followed, but he was a big man and began to lose ground. Lucky was clear, when all of a sudden his foot drove against a switch bar and he went flat on his face, panting from the hysteria of shock.

The detective didn't grapple this time. He let go with a barrage of kicks.

"Hide out on me, will you? Treat you right, give you a break, and you hide out on me. I'll learn you to hide out on me."

Lucky tried to get up, couldn't. He was jerked to his feet, rushed up the track on the run. He pulled back, but couldn't get set. He sat down, dug in with his sliding heels. The detective kicked and jerked, in fury. Lucky clawed for something to hold on to, his hand caught the rail. The detective stamped on it. He pulled it back in pain, clawed again. This time his fingers closed on a spike, sticking an inch or two out of the tie. The detective jerked, the spike pulled out of the hole, and Lucky resumed his unwilling run.

"Lemme go! Why don't you lemme go?"

"Come on! Hide out on me, will you? I'll learn you to hide out on Larry Nott!"

"Lemme go! Lemme—"

Lucky pulled back, braced with his heels, got himself stopped. Then his whole body coiled like a spring and let go in one convulsive, passionate lunge. The spike, still in his hand, came down on the detective's head, and he felt it crush. He stood there, looking down at something dark and formless, lying across the rails.

II

Hurrying down the track, he became aware of the spike, gave it a toss, heard it splash in the ditch. Soon he realized that his steps on the ties were being telegraphed by the listening rail, and he plunged across the ditch to the highway. There he resumed his rapid walk, trying not to run. But every time a car overtook him his heels lifted queerly, and his breath first stopped, then came in gasps as he listened for the car to stop. He came to a crossroads, turned quickly to his right. He let himself run here, for the road wasn't lighted as the main highway was, and there weren't many cars. The running tired him, but it eased the sick feeling in his stomach. He came to a sign that told him Los Angeles was 17 miles, and to his left. He turned, walked, ran, stooped down sometimes, panting, to rest. After a while, it came to him why he had to get to Los Angeles, and so soon. The soup kitchen opened at seven o'clock. He had to be there, in that same soup kitchen where he had had supper, so it would look as though he had never been away.

When the lights went off, and it came broad daylight with the suddenness of Southern California, he was in the city, and a clock told him it was ten minutes after five. He thought he had time. He pressed on, exhausted but never relaxing his rapid, half-shuffling walk.

It was ten minutes to seven when he got to the soup kitchen, and he quickly walked past it. He wanted to be clear at the end of the line, so he could have a word with Shorty, the man who dished out the soup, without impatient shoves from behind, and growls to keep moving.

Shorty remembered him. "Still here, hey?"

"Still here."

"Three in a row for you. Holy smoke, they ought to be collecting for you by the month."

"Thought you'd be off."

"Who, me?"

"Sunday, ain't it?"

"Sunday? Wake up. This is Saturday."

"Saturday? You're kidding."

"Kidding my eye, this is Saturday, and a big day in this town, too."

"One day looks like another to me."

"Not this one. Parade."

"Yeah?"

"Shriners. You get that free."

"Well, that's my name, Lucky."

"My name's Shorty, but I'm over six feet."

"Nothing like that with me. I really got luck."

"You sure?"

"Like, for instance, getting a hunk of meat."

"I didn't give you no meat."

"Ain't you going to?"

"Shove your plate over quick. Don't let nobody see you."

"Thanks."

"Okay, Lucky. Don't miss the parade."

"I won't."

He sat at the rough table with the others, dipped his bread in the soup, tried to eat, but his throat kept contracting from excitement and he made slow work of it. He had what he wanted from Shorty. He had fixed the day, and not only the day but the date, for it would be the same date as the big Shriners' parade. He had fixed his name, with a little gag. Shorty wouldn't forget him. His throat relaxed, and he wolfed the piece of meat.

Near the soup kitchen he saw signs: "Lincoln Park Pharmacy," "Lincoln Park Cafeteria."

"Which way is the park, Buddy?" If it was a big park, he might find a thicket where he could lie down, rest his aching legs.

"Straight down, you'll see it."

There was a fence around it, but he found a gate, opened it, slipped in. Ahead of him was a thicket, but the ground was wet from a stream that ran through it. He crossed a small bridge, followed a path. He came to a stable, peeped in. It was empty, but the floor was thickly covered with new hay. He went in, made for a dark corner, burrowed under the hay, closed his eyes. For a few moments everything slipped away, except warmth, relaxation, ease. But then something began to drill into the back of his mind: Where did he spend last night? Where would he tell them he spent last night? He tried to think, but nothing would come to him. He would have said that he spent it where he spent the night before, but he hadn't spent it in Los Angeles. He had spent it in Santa Barbara, and come down in the morning on a truck. He had never spent a night in Los Angeles. He didn't know the places. He had no answers to the questions that were now pounding at him like sledge-hammers:

"What's that? Where you say you was?"

"In a flophouse."

"Which flophouse?"

"I didn't pay no attention which flophouse. It was just a flophouse."

"Where was this flophouse at?"

"I don't know where it was at. I never been to Los Angeles before. I don't know the names of no streets."

"What this flophouse look like?"

"Looked like a flophouse."

"Come on, don't give us no gags. What this flophouse look like? Ain't you got eyes, can't you say what this here place looked like? What's the matter, can't you talk?"

Something gripped his arm, and he felt himself being lifted. Something of terrible strength had hold of him, and he was going straight up in the air. He squirmed to get loose, then was plopped on his feet and released. He turned, terrified.

An elephant was standing there, exploring his clothes with its trunk. He knew then that he had been asleep. But when he backed away, he bumped into another elephant. He slipped between the two elephants, slithered past a third to the door, which was open about a foot. Out in the sunlight, he made his way back across the little bridge, saw what he hadn't noticed before: pens with deer in them, and ostriches, and mountain sheep, that told him he had stumbled into a zoo. It was after four o'clock, so he must have slept a long time in the hay. Back on the street, he felt a sobbing laugh rise in his throat. *That* was where he had spent the night. "In the elephant house at Lincoln Park."

"*What?*"

"That's right. In the elephant house."

"What you giving us? A stall?"

"It ain't no stall. I was in the elephant house."

"With them elephants?"

"That's right."

"How you get in there?"

"Just went in. The door was open."

"Just went in there, seen the elephants, and bedded down with them?"

"I thought they was horses."

"You thought them elephants was horses?"

"It was dark. I dug in under the hay. I never knowed they was elephants till morning."

"How come you went in this place?"

"I left the soup kitchen, and in a couple of minutes I came to the park. I went in there, looking for some grass to lie down on.

Then I come to this here place, looked to me like a stable, I peeped in, seen the hay, and hit it."

"And you wasn't scared of them elephants?"

"It was dark, I tell you, and I could hear them eating the hay, but I thought they was horses. I was tired, and I wanted some place to sleep."

"Then what?"

"Then when it got light, and I seen they was elephants, I run out of there and beat it."

"Couldn't you tell them elephants by the smell?"

"I never noticed no smell."

"How many elephants was there?"

"Three."

III

He brushed wisps of hay off his denims. They had been fairly new, but now they were black with the grime of the coal gond. Suddenly his heart stopped, a suffocating feeling swept over him. The questions started again, hammered at him, beat into his brain.

"Where that coal dust come from?"

"I don't know. The freights, I guess."

"Don't you know it aint no coal ever shipped into this part of the state? Don't you know that here all they burn is gas? Don't you know it aint only been but one coal car shipped in here in six months, and that came in by a misread train order? Don't you know that car was part of that train this here detective was riding that got killed? *Don't you know that?* Come on, out with it,

WHERE THAT COAL DUST COME FROM?"

Getting rid of the denims instantly became an obsession. He felt that people were looking at him on the street, spying the coal dust, waiting till he got by, then running into drugstores to phone the police that he had just passed by. It was like those dreams he sometimes had, where he was walking through crowds naked, except that this was no dream, and he wasn't naked, he was wearing these denims, these tell-tale denims with coal dust all over them. He clenched his hands, had a moment of terrible concentration, headed into a filling station.

"Hello."

"Hello."

"What's the chances on a job?"

"No chances."

"Why not?"

"Don't need anybody."

"That's not the only reason."

"There's about forty-two other reasons, one of them is I can't even make a living myself, but it's all the reason that concerns you. Here's a dime, kid. Better luck somewhere else."

"I don't want your dime. I want a job. If the clothes were better, that might help, mightn't it?"

"If the clothes were good enough for Clark Gable in the swell gambling house scene, that wouldn't help a bit. Not a bit. I just don't need anybody, that's all."

"Suppose I got better clothes. Would you talk to me?"

"Talk to you anytime, but I don't need anybody."

"I'll be back when I get the clothes."

"Just taking a walk for nothing."

"What's your name?"

"Hook's my name. Oscar Hook."

"Thanks, Mr. Hook. But I'm coming back. I just got a idea I can talk myself into a job. I'm some talker."

"You're all of that, kid. But don't waste your time. I don't need anybody."

"Okay. Just the same, I'll be back."

He headed for the center of town, asked the way to the cheap clothing stores. At Los Angeles and Temple, after an hour's trudge, he came to a succession of small stores in a Mexican quarter that were what he wanted. He went into one. The storekeeper was a Mexican, and two or three other Mexicans were standing around, smoking.

"Mister, will you trust me for a pair of white pants and a shirt?"

"No trust. Hey, scram."

"Look. I can have a job Monday morning if I can show up in that outfit. White pants and a white shirt. That's all."

"No trust. What you think this is, anyway?"

"Well, I got to get that outfit somewhere. If I get that, they'll let me go to work Monday. I'll pay you soon as I get paid off Saturday night."

"No trust. Sell for cash."

He stood there. The Mexicans stood there, smoked, looked out at the street. Presently one of them looked at him. "What kind of job, hey? What you mean, got to have white pants a white shirt a hold a job?"

"Filling station. They got a rule you got to have white clothes before you can work there."

"Oh. Sure. Filling station."

After a while the storekeeper spoke. "Ha! Is a joke. Job in filling station, must have a white pants, white shirt. Ha! Is a joke."

"What else would I want them for? Holy smoke, these are better for the road, ain't they? Say, a guy don't want white pants to ride freights, does he?"

"What filling station? Tell me that?"

"Guy name of Hook, Oscar Hook, got a Acme station, Main near Twentieth. You don't believe me, call him up."

"You go to work there, hey?"

"I'm *supposed* to go to work. I *told* him I'd get the white pants and white shirt, somehow. Well—if I don't get them I don't go to work."

"Why you come to me, hey?"

"Where else would I go? If it's not you, it's another guy down the street. No place else I can dig up the stuff over Sunday, is there?"

"Oh."

He stood around. They all stood around. Then once again the storekeeper looked up. "What size you wear, hey?"

He had a wash at a tap in the back yard, then changed there, between piled-up boxes and crates. The storekeeper gave him a white shirt, white pants, necktie, a suit of thick underwear, and a pair of shoes to replace his badly-worn brogans. "Is pretty cold, night-time, now. A thick underwear feel better."

"Okay. Much obliged."

"Can roll this other stuff up."

"I don't want it. Can you throw it away for me?"

"Is pretty dirty."

"Plenty dirty."

"You no want?"

"No."

His heart leaped as the storekeeper dropped the whole pile into a rubbish brazier and touched a match to some papers at the bottom of it. In a few minutes, the denims and everything else he had worn were ashes.

He followed the storekeeper inside. "Okay, here is a bill. I put all a stuff on a bill, no charge you more than anybody else. Is six dollar ninety-eight cents, then is a service charge one dollar."

All of them laughed. He took the "service charge" to be a gyp overcharge to cover the trust. He nodded. "Okay on the service charge."

The storekeeper hesitated. "Well, six ninety-eight. We no make a service charge."

"Thanks."

"See you keep a white pants clean till Monday morning."

"I'll do that. See you Saturday night."

"*Adios.*"

Out in the street, he stuck his hand in his pocket, felt something, pulled it out. It was a $1 bill. Then he understood about the "service charge," and why the Mexicans had laughed. He went back, kissed the $1 bill, waved a cheery salute into the store. They all waved back.

He rode a streetcar down to Mr. Hook's, got turned down for the job, rode a streetcar back. In his mind, he tried to check over everything. He had an alibi, fantastic and plausible. So far as he could recall, nobody on the train had seen him, not even the other hoboes, for he had stood apart from them in the yards, and had done nothing to attract the attention of any of them. The denims were burned, and he had a story to account for the whites. It even looked pretty good, this thing with Mr. Hook, for anybody who had committed a murder would be most unlikely to make a serious effort to land a job.

But the questions lurked there, ready to spring at him, check and recheck as he would. He saw a sign, "5-Course Dinner, 35

Cents." He still had ninety cents, and went in, ordered steak and fried potatoes, the hungry man's dream of heaven. He ate, put a ten-cent tip under the plate. He ordered cigarettes, lit one, inhaled. He got up to go. A newspaper was lying on the table.

He froze as he saw the headline:

L. R. NOTT, R. R. MAN, KILLED

IV

On the street, he bought a paper, tried to open it under a street light, couldn't, tucked it under his arm. He found Highway 101, caught a hay truck bound for San Francisco. Going out Sunset Boulevard, it unexpectedly pulled over to the curb and stopped. He looked warily around. Down a side-street, about a block away, were the two red lights of a police station. He was tightening to jump and run, but the driver wasn't looking at the lights. "I told them bums that air hose was leaking. They set you nuts. Supposed to keep the stuff in shape and all they ever do is sit around and play blackjack."

The driver fished a roll of tape from his pocket and got out. Lucky sat where he was a few minutes, then climbed down, walked to the glare of the headlights, opened his paper. There it was:

L. R. NOTT, R. R. MAN, KILLED

The decapitated body of L. R. Nott, 1327 De Soto Street, a detective assigned to a northbound freight, was found early this morning on the track near San Fernando station. It is believed he lost his balance while the train was shunting cars at the San Fernando siding and fell beneath the wheels. Funeral services will be held tomorrow from the De Soto Street Methodist Church.

Mr. Nott is survived by a widow, formerly Miss Elsie Snowden of Mannerheim, and a son, L. R. Nott, Jr., 5.

He stared at it, refolded the paper, tucked it under his arm, walked back to where the driver was tapping the air hose. He was clear, and he knew it. "Boy, do they call you Lucky? Is your name Lucky? I'll say it is."

He leaned against the trailer, let his eye wander down the street. He saw the two red lights of the police station—glowing. He looked away quickly. A queer feeling began to stir inside him. He wished the driver would hurry up.

Presently he went back to the headlights again, found the notice, reread it. He recognized that feeling now; it was the old Sunday-night feeling that he used to have back home, when the bells would ring and he would have to stop playing hide in the twilight, go to church, and hear about the necessity for being saved. It shot through his mind, the time he had played hookey from church, and hid in the livery stable; and how lonely he had felt, because there was nobody to play hide with; and how he had sneaked into church, and stood in the rear to listen to the necessity for being saved.

His eyes twitched back to the red lights and slowly, shakily, but unswervingly he found himself walking toward them.

"I want to give myself up."

"Yeah, I know, you're wanted for grand larceny in Hackensack, New Jersey."

"No, I—"

"We quit giving them rides when the New Deal come in. Beat it."

"I killed a man."

"You—? . . . When was it you done this?"

"Last night."

"Where?"

"Near here. San Fernando. It was like this—"

"Hey, wait till I get a card . . . Okay, what's your name?"

"Ben Fuller."

"No middle name?"

"They call me Lucky."

"Lucky like in good luck?"

"Yes, sir. . . . Lucky like in good luck."

SEVENTY THOUSAND ASSYRIANS

By William Saroyan

I HADN'T HAD A HAIRCUT IN FORTY DAYS AND FORTY NIGHTS, AND I was beginning to look like several violinists out of work. You know the look: genius gone to pot, and ready to join the Communist Party. We barbarians from Asia Minor are hairy people: when we need a haircut, we *need* a haircut. It was so bad, I had outgrown my only hat. (I am writing a very serious story, perhaps one of the most serious I shall ever write. That is why I am being flippant. Readers of Sherwood Anderson will begin to understand what I am saying after a while; they will know that my laughter is rather sad.) I was a young man in need of a haircut, so I went down to Third Street (San Francisco), to the Barber College, for a fifteen-cent haircut.

Third Street, below Howard, is a district; think of the Bowery in New York, Main Street in Los Angeles: think of old men and boys, out of work, hanging around, smoking Bull Durham, talking about the government, waiting for something to turn up, simply waiting. It was a Monday morning in August and a lot of the tramps had come to the shop to brighten up a bit. The Japanese boy who was working over the free chair had a waiting list of eleven; all the other chairs were occupied. I sat down and began to wait. Outside, as Hemingway (*The Sun Also Rises; Farewell to Arms; Death in the Afternoon; Winner Take Nothing*) would say, haircuts were four bits. I had twenty cents and a half-pack of Bull Durham. I rolled a cigarette, handed the pack to one of my contemporaries who looked in need of nicotine, and inhaled the dry smoke, thinking of America, what was going on politically, economically, spiritually. My contemporary was a boy of sixteen. He looked Iowa; splendid potentially, a solid American, but down, greatly down in the mouth. Little sleep, no change of clothes for several days, a little fear, etc. I wanted very much to know his

399

name. A writer is always wanting to get the reality of faces and figures. Iowa said, "I just got in from Salinas. No work in the lettuce fields. Going north now, to Portland; try to ship out." I wanted to tell him how it was with me: rejected story from *Scribner's*, rejected essay from *The Yale Review*, no money for decent cigarettes, worn shoes, old shirts, but I was afraid to make something of my own troubles. A writer's troubles are always boring, a bit unreal. People are apt to feel, *Well, who asked you to write in the first place?* A man must pretend not to be a writer. I said, "Good luck, north." Iowa shook his head. "I know better. Give it a try, anyway. Nothing to lose." Fine boy, hope he isn't dead, hope he hasn't frozen, mighty cold these days (December, 1933), I hope he hasn't gone down; he deserved to live. Iowa, I hope you got work in Portland; I hope you are earning money; I hope you have rented a clean room with a warm bed in it; I hope you are sleeping nights, eating regularly, walking along like a human being, being happy. Iowa, my good wishes are with you. I have said a number of prayers for you. (All the same, I think he is dead by this time. It was in him the day I saw him, the low malicious face of the beast, and at the same time all the theatres in America were showing, over and over again, an animated film-cartoon in which there was a song called "Who's Afraid of the Big Bad Wolf?", and that's what it amounts to; people with money laughing at the death that is crawling slyly into boys like young Iowa, pretending that it isn't there, laughing in warm theatres. I have prayed for Iowa, and I consider myself a coward. By this time he must be dead, and I am sitting in a small room, talking about him, only talking.)

I began to watch the Japanese boy who was learning to become a barber. He was shaving an old tramp who had a horrible face, one of those faces that emerge from years and years of evasive living, years of being unsettled, of not belonging anywhere, of owning nothing, and the Japanese boy was holding his nose back (his own nose) so that he would not smell the old tramp. A trivial point in a story, a bit of data with no place in a work of art, nevertheless, I put it down. A young writer is always afraid some significant fact may escape him. He is always wanting to put in everything he sees. I wanted to know the name of the Japanese boy. I am profoundly interested in names. I have found that those that are unknown are the most genuine. Take a big name like Andrew Mellon. I was watching the Japanese boy very closely. I wanted to understand from the way he was keeping his sense of smell away from the mouth and nostrils of the old man what he was thinking, how he was feeling. Years ago, when I was seventeen, I pruned vines in my uncle's vineyard, north of Sanger, in the San Joaquin Valley, and there were several Japanese working with me, Yoshio Enomoto, Hideo Suzuki, Katsumi Sujimoto, and one or two others. These Japanese taught me a few simple phrases, *hello, how are you, fine day, isn't it, good-bye,* and so on. I said in Japanese to the barber student, "How are you?" He said in Japanese, "Very well, thank you." Then, in impeccable English, "Do you speak Japanese? Have you lived in Japan?" I said, "Unfortunately, no. I am able to speak only one or two words. I used to work with Yoshio Enomoto, Hideo Suzuki, Katsumi Sujimoto; do you know them?" He went on with his work, thinking of the names. He seemed to be whispering, "Enomoto, Suzuki, Sujimoto." He said, "Suzuki. Small man?" I said, "Yes." He said, "I know him. He lives in San Jose now. He is married now."

I want you to know that I am deeply interested in what people remember. A young writer goes out to places and talks to people. He tries to find out what they remember. I am not using great material for a short story. Nothing is going to happen in this work. I am not fabricating a fancy plot. I am not creating memorable characters. I am not using a slick style of writing. I am not building up a fine atmosphere. I have no desire to sell this story or any story to *The Saturday Evening Post* or to *Cosmopolitan* or to *Harper's.* I am not trying to compete with the great writers of short stories, men like Sinclair Lewis and Joseph Hergesheimer and Zane Grey, men who really know how to write, how to make up stories that will sell. Rich men, men who understand all the rules about plot and character and style and atmosphere and all that stuff. I have no desire for fame. I am not out to win the Pulitzer Prize or the Nobel Prize or any other prize. I am out here in the far West, in San Francisco, in a small room on Carl Street, writing a letter to common people, telling them in simple language things they already know. I am merely making a record, so if I wander around a little, it is because I am in no hurry and because I do not know the rules. If I have any desire at all, it is to show the brotherhood of man. This is a big statement and it sounds a little precious. Generally a man is ashamed to make such a statement. He is afraid sophisticated people will laugh at him. But I don't mind. I'm asking sophisticated people to laugh. That is what sophistication is for. I do not believe in races. I do not believe in governments. I see life as one life at one time, so many millions simultaneously, all over the earth. Babies who have not yet been taught to speak any language are the only race of the earth, the race of man: all the rest is pretense, what we call civilization, hatred, fear, desire for strength. . . . But a baby is a baby. And the way they cry, there you have the brotherhood of man, babies crying. We grow up and we learn the words of a language and we see the universe through the language we know, we do not see it through all languages or through no language at all, through silence, or example, and we isolate ourselves in the language we know. Over here we isolate ourselves in English, or American as Mencken calls it. All the eternal things, in our words. If I want to do anything, I want to speak a more universal language. The heart of man, the unwritten part of man, that which is eternal and common to all races.

Now I am beginning to feel guilty and incompetent. I have used all this language and I am beginning to feel that I have said nothing. This is what drives a young writer out of his head, this feeling that nothing is being said. Any ordinary journalist would have been able to put the whole business into a three-word caption. Man is man, he would have said. Something clever, with any number of implications. But I want to use language that will create a single implication. I want the meaning to be precise, and perhaps that is why the language is so imprecise. I am walking around my subject, the impression I want to make, and I am trying to see it from all angles, so that I will have a whole picture, a picture of wholeness. It is the heart of man that I am trying to imply in this work.

Let me try again: I hadn't had a haircut in a long time and I was beginning to look seedy, so I went down to the Barber College on Third Street, and I sat in a chair. I said, "Leave it full in the back. I have a narrow head and if you do not leave it full in the back, I will go out of this place looking like a horse. Take as much as you like off the top. No lotion, no water, comb it dry." Reading makes a full man, writing a precise one, as you see. This is what happened. It doesn't make much of a story, and the reason is that I have left out the barber, the young man who gave me the haircut.

He was tall, he had a dark serious face, thick lips, on the verge of smiling but melancholy, thick lashes, sad eyes, a large nose. I saw his name on the card that was pasted on the mirror, Theodore Badal. A good name, genuine, a good young man, genuine. Theodore Badal began to work on my head. A good barber never speaks until he has been spoken to, no matter how full his heart may be.

"That name," I said, "Badal. Are you an Armenian?" I am an Armenian. I have mentioned this before. People look at me and begin to wonder, so I come right and tell them. "I am an Armenian," I say. Or they read something I have written and begin to wonder, so I let them know. "I am an Armenian," I say. It is a meaningless remark, but they expect me to say it, so I do. I have no idea what it is like to be an Armenian or what it is like to be an Englishman or a Japanese or anything else. I have a faint idea what it is like to be alive. This is the only thing that interests me greatly. This and tennis. I hope some day to write a great philosophical work on tennis, something on the order of *Death in the Afternoon*, but I am aware that I am not yet ready to undertake such a work. I feel that the cultivation of tennis on a large scale among the peoples of the earth will do much to annihilate racial differences, prejudices, hatred, etc. Just as soon as I have perfected my drive and my lob, I hope to begin my outline of this great work. (It may seem to some sophisticated people that I am trying to make fun of Hemingway. I am not. *Death in the Afternoon* is a pretty sound piece of prose. I could never object to it as prose. I cannot even object to it as philosophy. I think it is finer philosophy than that of Will Durant and Walter Pitkin. Even when Hemingway is a fool, he is at least an accurate fool. He tells you what actually takes place and he doesn't allow the speed of an occurrence to make his exposition of it hasty. This is a lot. It is some sort of advancement for literature. To relate leisurely the nature and meaning of that which is very brief in duration.)

"Are you an Armenian?" I asked.

We are a small people and whenever one of us meets another, it is an event. We are always looking around for someone to talk to in our language. Our most ambitious political party estimates that there are nearly two million of us living on the earth, but most of us don't think so. Most of us sit down and take a pencil and a piece of paper and we take one section of the world at a time and imagine how many Armenians at the most are likely to be living in that section and we put the highest number on the paper, and then we go on to another section, India, Russia, Soviet Armenia, Egypt, Italy, Germany, France, America, South America, Australia, and so on, and after we add up our most hopeful figures the total comes to something a little less than a million. Then we start to think how big our families are, how high our birthrate and how low our death-rate (except in times of war when massacres increase the death-rate), and we begin to imagine how rapidly we will increase if we are left alone a quarter of a century, and we feel pretty happy. We always leave out earthquakes, wars, massacres, famines, etc., and it is a mistake. I remember the Near East Relief drives in my home town. My uncle used to be our orator and he used to make a whole auditorium full of Armenians weep. He was an attorney and he was a great orator. Well, at first the trouble was war. Our people were being destroyed by the enemy. Those who hadn't been killed were homeless and they were starving, *our own flesh and blood*, my uncle said, and we all wept. And we gathered money and sent it to our people in the old country. Then after the war, when I was a bigger boy, we had another Near East Relief drive and my uncle stood on the stage of the Civic Auditorium of my home town and he said, "Thank God this time it is not the enemy, but an earthquake. God has made us suffer. We have worshipped Him through trial and tribulation, through suffering and disease and torture and horror and (my uncle began to weep, began to sob) through the madness of despair, and now he has done this thing, and still we praise Him, still we worship Him. We do not understand the ways of God." And after the drive I went to my uncle and I said, "Did you mean what you said about God?" And he said, "That was oratory. We've got to raise money. What God? It is nonsense." "And when you cried?" I asked, and my uncle said, "That was real. I could not help it. I had to cry. Why, for God's sake, why must we go through all this God damn hell? What have we done to deserve all this torture? Man won't let us alone. God won't let us alone. Have we done something? Aren't we supposed to be pious people? What is our sin? I am disgusted with God. I am sick of man. The only reason I am willing to get up and talk is that I don't dare keep my mouth shut. I can't bear the thought of more of our people dying. Jesus Christ, have we done something?"

I asked Theodore Badal if he was an Armenian.

He said, "I am an Assyrian."

Well, it was something. They, the Assyrians, came from our part of the world, they had noses like our noses, eyes like our eyes, hearts like our hearts. They had a different language. When they spoke we couldn't understand them, but they were a lot like us. It wasn't quite as pleasing as it would have been if Badal had been an Armenian, but it was something.

"I am an Armenian," I said. "I used to know some Assyrian boys in my home town, Joseph Sargis, Nito Elia, Tony Saleh. Do you know any of them?"

"Joseph Sargis, I know him," said Badal. "The others I do not know. We lived in New York until five years ago, then we came out west to Turlock. Then we moved up to San Francisco."

"Nito Elia," I said, "is a Captain in the Salvation Army." (I don't want anyone to imagine that I am making anything up, or that I am trying to be funny.) "Tony Saleh," I said, "was killed eight years ago. He was riding a horse and he was thrown and the horse began to run. Tony couldn't get himself free, he was caught by a leg, and the horse ran around and around for a half hour and then stopped, and when they went up to Tony he was dead. He was fourteen at the time. I used to go to school with him. Tony was a very clever boy, very good at arithmetic."

We began to talk about the Assyrian language and the Armenian language, about the old world, conditions over there, and so on. I was getting a fifteen-cent haircut and I was doing my best to learn something at the same time, to acquire some new truth, some new appreciation of the wonder of life, the dignity of man. (Man has great dignity, do not imagine that he has not.)

Badal said, "I cannot read Assyrian. I was born in the old country, but I want to get over it."

He sounded tired, not physically but spiritually.

"Why?" I said. "Why do you want to get over it?"

"Well," he laughed, "simply because everything is washed up over there." I am repeating his words precisely, putting in nothing of my own. "We were a great people once," he went on. "But that was yesterday, the day before yesterday. Now we are a topic in ancient history. We had a great civilization. They're still admiring it. Now I am in America learning how to cut hair. We're washed up as a race, we're through, it's all over, why should I learn to read the language? We have no writers, we have no news—well, there is a little news: once in a while the English encourage the Arabs to massacre us, that is all. It's an old story, we know all about it. The news comes over to us through the Associated Press, anyway."

These remarks were very painful to me, an Armenian. I had always felt badly about my own people being destroyed. I had never heard an Assyrian speaking in English about such things. I felt great love for this young fellow. Don't get me wrong. There is a tendency these days to think in terms of pansies whenever a man says that he has affection for man. I think now that I have affection for all people, even for the enemies of Armenia, whom I have so tactfully not named. Everyone knows who they are. I have nothing against any of them because I think of them as one man living one life at a time, and I know, I am positive, that one man at a time is incapable of the monstrosities performed by mobs. My objection is to mobs only.

"Well," I said, "it is much the same with us. We, too, are old. We still have our church. We still have a few writers, Aharonian, Isahakian, a few others, but it is much the same."

"Yes," said the barber, "I know. We went in for the wrong things. We went in for the simple things, peace and quiet and families. We didn't go in for machinery and conquest and militarism. We didn't go in for diplomacy and deceit and the invention of machine-guns and poison gases. Well, there is no use in being disappointed. We had our day, I suppose."

"We are hopeful," I said. "There is no Armenian living who does not still dream of an independent Armenia."

"Dream?" said Badal. "Well, that is something Assyrians cannot even dream any more. Why, do you know how many of us are left on earth?"

"Two or three millions," I suggested.

"Seventy thousand," said Badal. "That is all. Seventy thousand Assyrians in the world, and the Arabs are still killing us. They killed seventy of us in a little uprising last month. There was a small paragraph in the paper. Seventy more of us destroyed. We'll be wiped out before long. My brother is married to an American girl and he has a son. There is no more hope. We are trying to forget Assyria. My father still reads a paper that comes from New York, but he is an old man. He will be dead soon."

Then his voice changed, he ceased speaking as an Assyrian and began to speak as a barber: "Have I taken enough off the top?" he asked.

The rest of the story is pointless. I said *so long* to the young Assyrian and left the shop. I walked across town, four miles, to my room on Carl Street. I thought about the whole business: Assyria and this Assyrian, Theodore Badal, learning to be a barber, the sadness of his voice, the hopelessness of his attitude. This was months ago, in August, but ever since I have been thinking about Assyria, and I have been wanting to say something about Theodore Badal, a son of an ancient race, himself youthful and alert, yet hopeless. Seventy thousand Assyrians, a mere seventy thousand of that great people, and all the others quiet in death and all the greatness crumbled and ignored, and a young man in America learning to be a barber, and a young man lamenting bitterly the course of history.

Why don't I make up plots and write beautiful love stories that can be made into motion pictures? Why don't I let these unimportant and boring matters go hang? Why don't I try to please the American reading public?

Well, I am an Armenian. Michael Arlen is an Armenian, too. He is pleasing the public. I have great admiration for him, and I think he has perfected a very fine style of writing and all that, but I don't want to write about the people he likes to write about. Those people were dead to begin with. You take Iowa and the Japanese boy and Theodore Badal, the Assyrian; well, they may go down physically, like Iowa, to death, or spiritually, like Badal, to death, but they are of the stuff that is eternal in man and it is this stuff that interests me. You don't find them in bright places, making witty remarks about sex and trivial remarks about art. You find them where I found them, and they will be there forever, the races of man, the part of man, of Assyria as much as of England, that cannot be destroyed, the part that massacre does not destroy, the part that earthquake and war and famine and madness and everything else cannot destroy.

This work is in tribute to Iowa, to Japan, to Assyria, to Armenia, to the race of man everywhere, to the dignity of that race, the brotherhood of things alive. I am not expecting Paramount Pictures to film this work. I am thinking of seventy thousand Assyrians, one at a time, alive, a great race. I am thinking of Theodore Badal, himself seventy thousand Assyrians and seventy million Assyrians, himself Assyria, and man, standing in a barber shop, in San Francisco, in 1933, and being, still, himself, the whole race.

THE LOVE NEST

By RING LARDNER

"I'LL TELL YOU WHAT I'M GOING TO DO WITH YOU, MR. BARTLETT,"
said the great man. "I'm going to take you right out to my home
and have you meet the wife and family; stay to dinner and all
night. We've got plenty of room and extra pajamas, if you don't
mind them silk. I mean that'll give you a chance to see us just as
we are. I mean you can get more that way than if you sat here a
whole week, asking me questions."

"But I don't want to put you to a lot of trouble," said Bartlett.

"Trouble!" The great man laughed. "There's no trouble about
it. I've got a house that's like a hotel. I mean a big house with lots
of servants. But anyway I'm always glad to do anything I can for
a writing man, especially a man that works for Ralph Doane. I'm
very fond of Ralph. I mean I like him personally besides being a
great editor. I mean I've known him for years and when there's
anything I can do for him, I'm glad to do it. I mean it'll be a
pleasure to have you. So if you want to notify your family——"

"I haven't any family," said Bartlett.

"Well, I'm sorry for you! And I bet when you see mine, you'll
wish you had one of your own. But I'm glad you can come and
we'll start now so as to get there before the kiddies are put away
for the night. I mean I want you to be sure and see the kiddies.
I've got three."

"I've seen their pictures," said Bartlett. "You must be very
proud of them. They're all girls, aren't they?"

"Yes, sir; three girls. I wouldn't have a boy. I mean I always
wanted girls. I mean girls have a lot more zip to them. I mean
they're a lot zippier. But let's go! The Rolls is downstairs and if
we start now we'll get there before dark. I mean I want you to
see the place while it's still daylight."

The great man—Lou Gregg, president of Modern Pictures, Inc.

—escorted his visitor from the magnificent office by a private door
and down a private stairway to the avenue, where the glittering
car with its glittering chauffeur waited.

"My wife was in town today." said Gregg as they glided northward, "and I hoped we could ride out together, but she called up
about two and asked would I mind if she went on home in the
Pierce. She was through with her shopping and she hates to be
away from the house and the kiddies any longer than she can help.
Celia's a great home girl. You'd never know she was the same girl
now as the girl I married seven years ago. I mean she's different.
I mean she's not the same. I mean her marriage and being a
mother has developed her. Did you ever see her? I mean in
pictures?"

"I think I did once," replied Bartlett. "Didn't she play the
young sister in 'The Cad'?"

"Yes, with Harold Hodgson and Marie Blythe."

"I thought I'd seen her. I remember her as very pretty and
vivacious."

"She certainly was! And she is yet! I mean she's even prettier,
but of course she ain't a kid, though she looks it. I mean she was
only seventeen in that picture and that was ten years ago. I mean
she's twenty-seven years old now. But I never met a girl with as
much zip as she had in those days. It's remarkable how marriage
changes them. I mean nobody would ever thought Celia Sayles
would turn out ot be a sit-by-the-fire. I mean she still likes a good
time, but her home and kiddies come first. I mean her home and
kiddies come first."

"I see what you mean," said Bartlett.

An hour's drive brought them to Ardsley-on-Hudson and the
great man's home.

"A wonderful place!" Bartlett exclaimed with a heroic sem-
blance of enthusiasm as the car turned in at an *arc de triomphe* of
a gateway and approached a white house that might have been
mistaken for the Yale Bowl.

"It ought to be!" said Gregg. "I mean I've spent enough on it.
I mean these things cost money."

He indicated with a gesture the huge house and Urbanesque
landscaping.

"But no amount of money is too much to spend on home. I mean it's a good investment if it tends to make your family proud and satisfied with their home. I mean every nickel I've spent here is like so much insurance; it insures me of a happy wife and family. And what more can a man ask!"

Bartlett didn't know, but the topic was forgotten in the business of leaving the resplendent Rolls and entering the even more resplendent reception hall.

"Forbes will take your things," said Gregg. "And, Forbes, you may tell Dennis that Mr. Bartlett will spend the night." He faced the wide stairway and raised his voice. "Sweetheart!" he called.

From above came the reply in contralto: "Hello, sweetheart!"

"Come down, sweetheart. I've brought you a visitor."

"All right, sweetheart, in just a minute."

Gregg led Bartlett into a living-room that was five laps to the mile and suggestive of an Atlantic City auction sale.

"Sit here," said the host, pointing to a balloon-stuffed easy chair, "and I'll see if we can get a drink. I've got some real old Bourbon that I'd like you to try. You know I come from Chicago and I always liked Bourbon better than Scotch. I mean I always preferred it to Scotch. Forbes," he addressed the servant, "we want a drink. You'll find a full bottle of that Bourbon in the cupboard."

"It's only half full, sir," said Forbes.

"Half full! That's funny! I mean I opened it last night and just took one drink. I mean it ought to be full."

"It's only half full," repeated Forbes, and went to fetch it.

"I'll have to investigate," Gregg told his guest. "I mean this ain't the first time lately that some of my good stuff has disappeared. When you keep so many servants, it's hard to get all honest ones. But here's Celia!"

Bartlett rose to greet the striking brunette who at this moment made an entrance so Delsarte as to be almost painful. With never a glance at him, she minced across the room to her husband and took a half interest in a convincing kiss.

"Well, sweetheart," she said when it was at last over.

"This is Mr. Bartlett, sweetheart," said her husband. "Mr. Bartlett, meet Mrs. Gregg."

Bartlett shook his hostess's proffered two fingers.

"I'm so pleased!" said Celia in a voice reminiscent of Miss Claire's imitation of Miss Barrymore.

"Mr. Bartlett," Gregg went on, "is with Mankind, Ralph Doane's magazine. He is going to write me up; I mean us."

"No, you mean you," said Celia. "I'm sure the public is not interested in great men's wives."

"I am sure you are mistaken, Mrs. Gregg," said Bartlett politely. "In this case at least. You are worth writing up aside from being a great man's wife."

"I'm afraid you're a flatterer, Mr. Bartlett," she returned. "I have been out of the limelight so long that I doubt if anybody remembers me. I'm no longer an artist; merely a happy wife and mother."

"And I claim, sweetheart," said Gregg, "that it takes an artist to be that."

"Oh, no, sweetheart," said Celia. "Not when they have you for a husband!"

The exchange of hosannahs was interrupted by the arrival of Forbes with the tray.

"Will you take yours straight or in a high-ball?" Gregg inquired of his guest. "Personally I like good whisky straight. I mean mixing it with water spoils the flavor. I mean whisky like this, it seems like a crime to mix it with water."

"I'll have mine straight," said Bartlett, who would have preferred a high-ball.

While the drinks were being prepared, he observed his hostess more closely and thought how much more charming she would be if she had used finesse in improving on nature. Her cheeks, her mouth, her eyes, and lashes had been, he guessed, far above the average in beauty before she had begun experimenting with them. And her experiments had been clumsy. She was handsome in spite of her efforts to be handsomer.

"Listen, sweetheart," said her husband. "One of the servants has been helping himself to this Bourbon. I mean it was a full bottle last night and I only had one little drink out of it. And now it's less than half full. Who do you suppose has been at it?"

"How do I know, sweetheart? Maybe the groceryman or the iceman or somebody."

"But you and I and Forbes are the only ones that have a key. I mean it was locked up."

"Maybe you forgot to lock it."

"I never do. Well, anyway, Bartlett, here's a go!"

"Doesn't Mrs. Gregg indulge?" asked Bartlett.

"Only a cocktail before dinner," said Celia. "Lou objects to me drinking whisky, and I don't like it much anyway."

"I don't object to you drinking whisky, sweetheart. I just object to your drinking to excess. I mean I think it coarsens a woman to drink. I mean it makes them coarse."

"Well, there's no argument, sweetheart. As I say, I don't care whether I have it or not."

"It certainly is great Bou:bon!" said Bartlett, smacking his lips and putting his glass back on the tray.

"You bet it is!" Gregg agreed. "I mean you can't buy that kind of stuff any more. I mean it's real stuff. You help yourself when you want another. Mr. Bartlett is going to stay all night, sweetheart. I told him he could get a whole lot more of a line on us that way than just interviewing me in the office. I mean I'm tongue-tied when it comes to talking about my work and my success. I mean it's better to see me out here as I am, in my home, with my family. I mean my home life speaks for itself without me saying a word."

"But, sweetheart," said his wife, "what about Mr. Latham?"

"Gosh! I forgot all about him! I must phone and see if I can call it off. That's terrible! You see," he explained to Bartlett, "I made a date to go up to Tarrytown tonight, to K. L. Latham's, the sugar people. We're going to talk over the new club. We're going to have a golf club that will make the rest of them look like a toy. I mean a real golf club! They want me to kind of run it. And I was to go up there tonight and talk it over. I'll phone and see if I can postpone it."

"Oh, don't postpone it on my account!" urged Bartlett. "I can come out again some other time, or I can see you in town."

"I don't see how you *can* postpone it, sweetheart," said Celia.

"Didn't he say old Mr. King was coming over from White Plains? They'll be mad at you if you don't go."

"I'm afraid they would resent it, sweetheart. Well, I'll tell you. You can entertain Mr. Bartlett and I'll go up there right after dinner and come back as soon as I can. And Bartlett and I can talk when I get back. I mean we can talk when I get back. How is that?"

"That suits me," said Bartlett.

"I'll be as entertaining as I can," said Celia, "but I'm afraid that isn't very entertaining. However, if I'm too much of a bore, there's plenty to read."

"No danger of my being bored," said Bartlett.

"Well, that's all fixed then," said the relieved host. "I hope you'll excuse me running away. But I don't see how I can get out of it. I mean with old King coming over from White Plains. I mean he's an old man. But listen, sweetheart—where are the kiddies? Mr. Bartlett wants to see them."

"Yes, indeed!" agreed the visitor.

"Of course you'd say so!" Celia said. "But we *are* proud of them! I suppose all parents are the same. They all think their own children are the only children in the world. Isn't that so, Mr. Bartlett? Oh haven't you any children?"

"I'm sorry to say I'm not married."

"Oh, you poor thing! We pity him, don't we, sweetheart? But why aren't you, Mr. Bartlett? Don't tell me you're a woman hater!"

"Not now, anyway," said the gallant Bartlett.

"Do you get that, sweetheart? He's paying you a pretty compliment."

"I heard it, sweetheart. And now I'm sure he's a flatterer. But I must hurry and get the children before Hortense puts them to bed."

"Well," said Gregg when his wife had left the room, "would you say she's changed?"

"A little, and for the better. She's more than fulfilled her early promise."

"I think so," said Gregg. "I mean I think she was a beautiful girl and now she's an even more beautiful woman. I mean wife-

hood and maternity have given her a kind of a—well, you know—
I mean a kind of a pose. I mean a pose. How about another
drink?"

They were emptying their glasses when Celia returned with
two of her little girls.

"The baby's in bed and I was afraid to ask Hortense to get her
up again. But you'll see her in the morning. This is Norma and
this is Grace. Girls, this is Mr. Bartlett."

The girls received this news calmly.

"Well, girls," said Bartlett.

"What do you think of them, Bartlett?" demanded their father.
"I mean what do you think of them?"

"They're great!" replied the guest with creditable warmth.

"I mean aren't they pretty?"

"I should say they are!"

"There, girls! Why don't you thank Mr. Bartlett?"

"Thanks," murmured Norma.

"How old are you, Norma?" asked Bartlett.

"Six," said Norma.

"Well," said Bartlett. "And how old is Grace?"

"Four," replied Norma.

"Four," said Bartlett. "And how old is baby sister?"

"One and a half," answered Norma.

"Well," said Bartlett.

As this seemed to be final, "Come, girls," said their mother.
"Kiss daddy good night and I'll take you back to Hortense."

"I'll take them," said Gregg. "I'm going up-stairs anyway. And
you can show Bartlett around. I mean before it gets any darker."

"Good night, girls," said Bartlett, and the children murmured
a good night.

"I'll come and see you before you're asleep," Celia told them.
And after Gregg had led them out, "Do you really think they're
pretty?" she asked Bartlett.

"I certainly do. Especially Norma. She's the image of you,"
said Bartlett.

"She looks a little like I used to," Celia admitted. "But I hope
she doesn't look like me now. I'm too old looking."

"You look remarkably young!" said Bartlett. "No one would believe you were the mother of three children."

"Oh, Mr. Bartlett! But I mustn't forget I'm to 'show you around.' Lou is so proud of our home!"

"And with reason," said Bartlett.

"It *is* so wonderful! I call it our love nest. Quite a big nest, don't you think? Mother says it's too big to be cosy; she says she can't think of it as a home. But I always say a place is whatever one makes of it. A woman can be happy in a tent if they love each other. And miserable in a royal palace without love. Don't you think so, Mr. Bartlett?"

"Yes, indeed."

"Is this really such wonderful Bourbon? I think I'll take just a sip of it and see what it's like. It can't hurt me if it's so good. Do you think so, Mr. Bartlett?"

"I don't believe so."

"Well then, I'm going to taste it and if it hurts me it's your fault."

Celia poured a whisky glass two-thirds full and drained it at a gulp.

"It *is* good, isn't it?" she said. "Of course I'm not much of a judge as I don't care for whisky and Lou won't let me drink it. But he's raved so about this Bourbon that I did want to see what it was like. You won't tell on me, will you, Mr. Bartlett?"

"Not I!"

"I wonder how it would be in a high-ball. Let's you and I have just one. But I'm forgetting I'm supposed to show you the place. We won't have time to drink a high-ball and see the place too before Lou comes down. Are you so crazy to see the place?"

"Not very."

"Well, then, what do you say if we have a high-ball? And it'll be a secret between you and I."

They drank in silence and Celia pressed a button by the door.

"You may take the bottle and tray," she told Forbes. "And now," she said to Bartlett, "we'll go out on the porch and see as much as we can see. You'll have to guess the rest."

Gregg, having changed his shirt and collar, joined them.

"Well," he said to Bartlett, "have you seen everything?"

"I guess I have, Mr. Gregg," lied the guest readily. "It's a wonderful place!"

"We like it. I mean it suits us. I mean it's my idea of a real home. And Celia calls it her love nest."

"So she told me," said Bartlett.

"She'll always be sentimental," said her husband.

He put his hand on her shoulder, but she drew away.

"I must run up and dress," she said.

"Dress!" exclaimed Bartlett, who had been dazzled by her flowered green chiffon.

"Oh, I'm not going to really dress," she said. "But I couldn't wear this thing for dinner!"

"Perhaps you'd like to clean up a little, Bartlett," said Gregg. "I mean Forbes will show you your room if you want to go up."

"It might be best," said Bartlett.

Celia, in a black lace dinner gown, was rather quiet during the elaborate meal. Three or four times when Gregg addressed her, she seemed to be thinking of something else and had to ask, "What did you say, sweetheart?" Her face was red and Bartlett imagined that she had "sneaked" a drink or two besides the two helpings of Bourbon and the cocktail that had preceded dinner.

"Well, I'll leave you," said Gregg when they were in the living-room once more. "I mean the sooner I get started, the sooner I'll be back. Sweetheart, try and keep your guest awake and don't let him die of thirst. *Au revoir*, Bartlett. I'm sorry, but it can't be helped. There's a fresh bottle of the Bourbon, so go to it. I mean help yourself. It's too bad you have to drink alone."

"It *is* too bad, Mr. Bartlett," said Celia when Gregg had gone.

"What's too bad?" asked Bartlett.

"That you have to drink alone. I feel like I wasn't being a good hostess to let you do it. In fact, I refuse to let you do it. I'll join you in just a little wee sip."

"But it's so soon after dinner!"

"It's never too soon! I'm going to have a drink myself and if you don't join me, your're a quitter."

She mixed two life-sized high-balls and handed one to her guest.

"Now we'll turn on the radio and see if we can't stir things up.

There! No, no! Who cares about the old baseball! Now! This is better! Let's dance."

"I'm sorry, Mrs. Gregg, but I don't dance."

"Well, you're an old cheese! To make me dance alone! 'All alone, yes, I'm all alone.'"

There was no affectation in her voice now and Bartlett was amazed at her unlabored grace as she glided around the big room.

"But it's no fun alone," she complained. "Let's shut the damn thing off and talk."

"I love to watch you dance," said Bartlett.

"Yes, but I'm no Pavlowa," said Celia as she silenced the radio. "And besides, it's time for a drink."

"I've still got more than half of mine."

"Well, you had that wine at dinner, so I'll have to catch up with you."

She poured herself another high-ball and went at the task of "catching up."

"The trouble with you, Mr.—now isn't that a scream! I can't think of your name."

"Bartlett."

"The trouble with you, Barker—do you know what's the trouble with you? You're too sober. See? You're too damn sober! That's the whole trouble, see? If you weren't so sober, we'd be better off. See? What I can't understand is how you can be so sober and me so high."

"You're not used to it."

"Not used to it! That's the cat's pajamas! Say, I'm like this half the time, see? If I wasn't, I'd die!"

"What does your husband say?"

"He don't say because he don't know. See, Barker? There's nights when he's out and there's a few nights when I'm out myself. And there's other nights when we're both in and I pretend I'm sleepy and I go up-stairs. See? But I don't go to bed. See? I have a little party all by myself. See? If I didn't, I'd die!"

"What do you mean, you'd die?"

"You're dumb, Barker! You may be sober, but you're dumb! Did you fall for all that apple sauce about the happy home and

the contented wife? Listen, Barker—I'd give anything in the world
to be out of this mess. I'd give anything to never see him again."

"Don't you love him any more? Doesn't he love you? Or
what?"

"Love! I never did love him! I didn't know what love was!
And all his love is for himself!"

"How did you happen to get married?"

"I was a kid; that's the answer. A kid and ambitious. See? He
was a director then and he got stuck on me and I thought he'd
make me a star. See, Barker? I married him to get myself a chance.
And now look at me!"

"I'd say you were fairly well off."

"Well off, am I? I'd change places with the scum of the earth
just to be free! See, Barker? And I could have been a star without any help if I'd only realized it. I had the looks and I had the
talent. I've got it yet. I could be a Swanson and get myself a
marquis; maybe a prince! And look what I did get! A self-satisfied,
self-centered —— ! I thought he'd *make* me! See, Barker? Well,
he's made me all right; he's made me a chronic mother and it's a
wonder I've got any looks left."

"I fought at first. I told him marriage didn't mean giving up
my art, my life work. But it was no use. He wanted a beautiful
wife and beautiful children for his beautiful home. Just to show
us off. See? I'm part of his chattels. See, Barker? I'm just like his
big diamond or his cars or his horses. And he wouldn't stand for
his wife 'lowering' herself to act in pictures. Just as if pictures
hadn't made him!

"You go back to your magazine tomorrow and write about our
love nest. See, Barker? And be sure and don't get mixed and call
it a baby ranch. Babies! You thought little Norma was pretty.
Well, she is. And what is it going to get her? A rich —— of a
husband that treats her like a —— ! That's what it'll get her if I
don't interfere. I hope I don't last long enough to see her grow up,
but if I do, I'm going to advise her to run away from home and
live her own life. And *be* somebody! Not a *thing* like I am! See,
Barker?"

"Did you ever think of a divorce?"

"Did I ever think of one! Listen—but there's no chance. I've got nothing on him, and no matter what he had on me, he'd never let the world know it. He'd keep me here and torture me like he does now, only worse. But I haven't done anything wrong, see? The men I might care for, they're all scared of him and his money and power. See, Barker? And the others are just as bad as him. Like fat old Morris, the hotel man, that everybody thinks he's a model husband. The reason he don't step out more is because he's too stingy. But I could have him if I wanted him. Every time he gets near enough to me, he squeezes my hand. I guess he thinks it's a nickel, the tight old —— ! But come on, Barker. Let's have a drink. I'm running down."

"I think it's about time you were running up—up-stairs," said Bartlett. "If I were you, I'd try to be in bed and asleep when Gregg gets home."

"You're all right, Barker. And after this drink I'm going to do just as you say. Only I thought of it before you did, see? I think of it lots of nights. And tonight you can help me out by telling him I had a bad headache."

Left alone, Bartlett thought a while, then read, and finally dozed off. He was dozing when Gregg returned.

"Well, well, Bartlett," said the great man, "did Celia desert you?"

"It was perfectly all right, Mr. Gregg. She had a headache and I told her to go to bed."

"She's had a lot of headaches lately; reads too much, I guess. Well, I'm sorry I had this date. It was about a new golf club and I had to be there. I mean I'm going to be president of it. I see you consoled yourself with some of the Bourbon. I mean the bottle doesn't look as full as it did."

"I hope you'll forgive me for helping myself so generously," said Bartlett. "I don't get stuff like that every day!"

"Well, what do you say if we turn in? We can talk on the way to town tomorrow. Though I guess you won't have much to ask me. I guess you know all about us. I mean you know all about us now."

"Yes, indeed, Mr. Gregg. I've got plenty of material if I can just handle it."

Celia had not put in an appearance when Gregg and his guest were ready to leave the house next day.

"She always sleeps late," said Gregg. I mean she never wakes up very early. But she's later than usual this morning. Sweetheart!" he called up the stairs.

"Yes, sweetheart," came the reply.

"Mr. Bartlett's leaving now. I mean he's going."

"Oh, good-by, Mr. Bartlett. Please forgive me for not being down to see you off."

"You're forgiven, Mrs. Gregg. And thanks for your hospitality."

"Good-by, sweetheart!"

"Good-by, sweetheart!"

OVER THE GREEN MOUNTAINS

By Erskine Caldwell

WAS READING A PIECE IN THE BOSTON PAPER LAST NIGHT ABOUT THE smartest people in the whole country coming from the State of Maine. Said at the time, and I'm still here to say it: you can take your pick of any ten men in the whole Union, and I'll back one Varmonter of my own choosing against them any day. Take ten men from any of the states you can find them in, and all of them put together won't have the smartness that my lone Varmonter has got. Have lived in the State of Maine all my life, ninety-odd years of it, but I've always said that if you want some smartness you shall have to go to Varmont to get it. Varmont is where it comes from.

Now, you take the farmers. Varmont farmers is that smart they can't keep from making money while the farmers in other places is all losing money. And here is why they are so smart: not long ago there was a Varmont farmer over here, riding around in his big auto having a good time and laughing at us farmers here because we hadn't made enough money to retire and maybe take a trip to Florida on, in even years. I asked this Varmont farmer how it was he had made so much money running a farm.

And this is what he told me: "Friend," he said, "the secret of making money out of a farm is this: Sell all you can; what you can't sell, feed to the hogs; what the hogs won't eat, eat yourself."

After he finished telling me that, he drove off laughing in his big auto to look at some more Maine farmers working and sweating in the fields because they ain't got sense enough to make money to retire on, and maybe take a winter trip to Florida, in even years.

That sporting farmer wasn't the first Varmonter I'd known, though. I used to know another one when I was a young man on the Penobscot.

This was a young fellow we called Jake Marks, one of them

old-time Varmonters who used to come over here to the State of Maine driving teams of oxen before the railroads was built across the mountains. This Jake Marks was a smart one, if there ever was a Varmonter who warn't. He used to drive his oxen over here hauling freight back and forth all the time. It was a long haul in them days, when you stop and think how slow them brutes travel, and Jake had a lot of mountain to cross coming and going. I don't recall how long it took him to make one of his trips, but it was quite a time in them days when there warn't no State roads, only trails wide enough for a yoke of oxen.

Jake was a real young man at that time, I should say about twenty-five, maybe twenty-seven. He warn't married then, neither. But pretty soon he took a liking to a young and handsome filly who cooked his meals for him at the house in Bangor where he put up while he was changing cargo between trips. She was just the kind of young filly that Jake wanted, too. She used to come into the room where he sat waiting for his meal and make herself real frisky in his presence. Jake, he was tormented something awful by the way she cut up in front of him, and he used to have to get up out of his chair sometimes and walk real fast around the house three-four times to get control over himself.

But this Jake Marks was a cautious man, and he never undertook a deal until he had thought it out a lot beforehand and saw that he had everything on his side. Then, when he had thought it all through, he turned loose and went after whatever it was he wanted like a real Varmonter. All them old-time Varmonters was like that, I guess; anyway, the ones who used to drive ox-freights over here to the State of Maine was, and Jake was just like all the rest of them.

This young filly of Jake's got so she pestered him about marrying of her all the time he was resting up between trips. Jake, he wanted her, all right. That was one thing he was wanting all the time he was over here. But Jake, he was taking his own good time about it, I'm telling you. He was figuring the thing out like all them Varmonters who drove ox-freights did. He had to be real certain that everything was on his side before he made any signs. He took the rest of the season for figuring the thing out, and he didn't make motions of a move toward the young filly that year at all.

The next spring when the frost had thawed out of the ground and when he could make his first trip of the year over the mountains, Jake he called at the house where this young filly stayed and told her to get ready to be married to him when he got back to Bangor on his next trip. That suited the young filly first-rate. She had been uneasy all winter about Jake, taking too much at heart all the gossip that was talked about them Varmont ox-freighters. But when Jake told her to get ready for marrying, she knew he would keep his promise right down to the last letter and come and marry her like he said he would.

So, Jake he went back to Varmont with his freight, promising to be ready to marry the young filly the same day he got back to Bangor on his next trip.

And just as he promised, Jake came back to get married to the young filly. He went straight to the house where she stayed, and there she was all waiting for him. Jake told her to get ready right away for the marriage, and then he went out to find a preacher somewhere. When he got back to the house with the preacher, he called her down to the room where all the guests had gathered to see the ceremony performed.

The minute she stepped into the room where Jake and the rest of the people was, Jake took one look at the young filly and told her to go back upstairs to her room and take off her dress. Well, that was all right and proper, because in those days there was a law in the State of Maine to the effect that a man could make what was called a shift-marriage. That was to say, the man could make the woman take off the dress she was wearing while the ceremony was being performed, and in that case he could not be held legally responsible for her past debts and would not have to pay them for her if he didn't have a mind to. Well, Jake he had heard all about this shift-law in Maine, and he was taking full advantage of its benefits. That was what he had been figuring out all the time he was driving them slow-footed oxen back and forth between Bangor and Varmont. Jake, he warn't no man's fool. Jake, he was a Varmonter.

After a while Jake's young filly came downstairs dressed according to this here shift-law. She had on what women wore under their dresses in those days, and that was all she had on. But Jake, he warn't satisfied, not completely. He told her to go back up-stairs and take off everything she had on. Jake, he was a hard-headed ox-freighter from Varmont, all right. He had figured all this out while he was driving them slow-footed oxen back and forth across the mountains.

In a little while his young filly came into the room again where Jake and the preacher and all the guests was, and she didn't have nothing on, except that she had a bedsheet wrapped around her, which was a good thing, I tell you. She was a handsome-looking filly if there ever was one.

They all got ready again for the ceremony, the preacher telling them where to stand and what to say to the questions he was get-ting ready to ask them. Then, just when they was beginning to get married, Jake he told his young filly to drop the bedsheet on the floor. Now, Jake he warn't taking no chances over here in the State of Maine. That shift-law said that if a woman was married without her dress on, her husband couldn't be held liable for her past debts, and Jake he figured that if the young filly didn't have nothing at all on her, there wouldn't be a chance in the world for to dun him for what she might owe, while if she had clothes on that he didn't know the true and legal names of, a storekeeper might try to say her underclothes was her overdress. Jake, he was thinking that he might by chance get cheated out of his rights to the full benefits of the shift-law if he didn't take-care, and Jake he warn't after taking no chances whatsoever over here in the State of Maine when he was so far away from Varmont. He was as cautious where he sat his foot as the next ox-freighter from Varmont.

"Drop the bedsheet on the floor," Jake he told the young filly again.

The young filly was getting ready to turn loose the bedsheet and let it drop on the floor like Jake told her to do, when the preacher he grabbed the bedsheet and held to it tight around her so she wouldn't show none of her naked self to him and Jake and the rest of the people in the house.

"No! No! No!" he yelled, getting red in the face and shaking his head at Jake. "That won't do, my man—that won't do at all! That would be indecent here before all of us! That can't be done! I'll never allow it!"

But the preacher he didn't know Jake Marks. Jake was one of them Varmont ox-freighters, and he was as hard-headed about what he wanted as the next one to come along. Jake, he told the young filly again to drop the bedsheet on the floor, and to drop it quick if she wanted to get married.

The handsome young filly was getting ready to let go of it like Jake said to, because she was that crazy about Jake she would have stood on her head right then and there if Jake had told her to do it, but just when she was getting ready to let go of it, the preacher he grabbed the bedsheet again and held it fast with both hands.

The preacher started in trying to argue with Jake about it being indecent for the handsome young filly to stand there naked while she was being married, but Jake he had his head set on getting the full benefits of the shift-law and he wouldn't give in an inch.

Then the preacher said he warn't going to perform the ceremony if that was what Jake was set on doing, and Jake he told the preacher he warn't going to get married at all without the bedsheet being dropped on the floor so that none of the cloth was touching the young filly.

Everybody got excited when Jake said that, and the people talked back and forth for an hour or more, arguing first on Jake's side, because they knew the law on the books, and then on the preacher's side, because they realized how it might upset the preacher if the handsome young filly stood there naked like Jake was set on having her do. The young filly didn't care which way the ceremony was done, just so long as Jake married her. She was willing to drop the bedsheet for Jake the minute the preacher let her. She was all excited about getting married, just like Jake had been all the time.

After a while the preacher gave in to Jake just a little. He saw what a fool he was, trying to argue with a Varmont ox-freighter.

"If she'll go inside the closet and shut the door so nobody can see her nakedness, I'll perform the ceremony," the preacher told Jake.

"That's all right by me," Jake said, "but I'll be compelled to have some witnesses on my side in case anybody tries to dispute me about us being married under the shift-law or not."

They finally settled that part when the preacher agreed to allow two of the older women to go in the closet with the young filly, just to make sure that everything was done in a legal manner. The preacher he didn't like to have Jake going in a closet with the naked filly, but he was pretty well worn out by that time after arguing for nearly two hours with a Varmont ox-freighter, and he said he would have to allow Jake to go in the closet, too.

Jake went in the closet where the filly and the two older women were.

"Now, you just look once, Jake," the preacher said, shaking his head back and forth, "and then you shut your eyes and keep them shut."

Jake was in the closet saying something to the young filly, but nobody in the room could hear what it was. The preacher he reached over and made a bit of a crack in the door while he was marrying them so he could hear their answers to the questions. And all that time Jake he was in there striking matches to make sure that the young filly was not putting the bedsheet on again, and to be certain that he was getting the full benefits of the shift-law.

When it was all done, the preacher he took the money Jake handed him and went off home without waiting to see what shape the young and handsome filly was in when the closet door was opened. When they came out into the room, the bedsheet was all awisted up into a knot; Jake handed it to her, and she didn't lose no time in getting upstairs where her clothes were. Jake he had told her to hurry and get dressed, because he wanted to get started with his ox-freight back to Varmont.

They started home to Varmont right away, the handsome young filly all dressed up in her wedding clothes and sitting on top of the freight-cargo while Jake he walked along beside the wagon bellowing at the oxen.

When Jake came back to Bangor on his next trip, a storekeeper tried to present him a bill for a hundred and forty dollars. The storekeeper told Jake that the young filly had bought a lot of dresses and things just before she got married, and he wanted to know if Jake had married her under the shift-law.

Jake just laughed a little, and started unloading his cargo.

"Well, was you married that way, or the other way?" the store-keeper asked him.

"You tell me this first," Jake said, "and then I'll answer your question. Does the State of Maine have a shift-law on the books?"

"Well, yes; but the shift-law says that the woman has to——"

"Never mind about explaining it to me," Jake said. "If the shift-law is on the statute books, then that's the law I married her with."

THE MURDER

By JOHN STEINBECK

THIS HAPPENED A NUMBER OF YEARS AGE IN MONTEREY COUNTY, in central California. The Cañon del Castillo is one of those valleys in the Santa Lucia range which lie between its many spurs and ridges. From the main Cañon del Castillo a number of little arroyos cut back into the mountains, oak-wooded canyons, heavily brushed with poison oak and sage. At the head of the canyon there stands a tremendous stone castle, buttressed and towered like those strongholds the Crusaders put up in the path of their conquests. Only a close visit to the castle shows it to be a strange accident of time and water and erosion working on soft, stratified sandstone. In the distance the ruined battlements, the gates, the towers, even the narrow slits, require little imagination to make out.

Below the castle, on the nearly level floor of the canyon, stand the old ranch house, a weathered and mossy barn and a warped feeding-shed for cattle. The house is deserted; the doors, swinging on rusted hinges, squeal and bang on nights when the wind courses down from the castle. Not many people visit the house. Sometimes a crowd of boys tramp through the rooms, peering into empty closets and loudly defying the ghosts they deny.

Jim Moore, who owns the land, does not like to have people about the house. He rides up from his new house, farther down the valley, and chases the boys away. He has put "No Trespassing" signs on his fences to keep curious and morbid people out. Sometimes he thinks of burning the old house down, but then a strange and powerful relation with the swinging doors, the blind and desolate windows, forbids the destruction. If he should burn the house he would destroy a great and important piece of his life. He knows that when he goes to town with his plump and still pretty wife, people turn and look at his retreating back with awe and some admiration.

Jim Moore was born in the old house and grew up in it. He knew every grained and weathered board of the barn, every smooth, worn manger-rack. His mother and father were both dead when he was thirty. He celebrated his majority by raising a beard. He sold the pigs and decided never to have any more. At last he bought a fine Guernsey bull to improve his stock, and he began to go to Monterey on Saturday nights, to get drunk and to talk with the noisy girls of the Three Star.

Within a year Jim Moore married Jelka Sepic, a Jugo-Slav girl, daughter of a heavy and patient farmer of Pine Canyon. Jim was not proud of her foreign family, of her many brothers and sisters and cousins, but he delighted in her beauty. Jelka had eyes as large and questioning as a doe's eyes. Her nose was thin and sharply faceted, and her lips were deep and soft. Jelka's skin always startled Jim, for between night and night he forgot how beautiful it was. She was so smooth and quiet and gentle, such a good housekeeper, that Jim often thought with disgust of her father's advice on the wedding day. The old man, bleary and bloated with festival beer, elbowed Jim in the ribs and grinned suggestively, so that his little dark eyes almost disappeared behind puffed and wrinkled lids.

"Don't be big fool, now," he said. "Jelka is Slav girl. He's not like American girl. If he is bad, beat him. If he's good too long, beat him too. I beat his mama. Papa beat my mama. Slav girl! He's not like a man that don't beat hell out of him."

"I wouldn't beat Jelka," Jim said.

The father giggled and nudged him again with his elbow, "Don't be big fool," he warned. "Sometime you see." He rolled back to the beer barrel.

Jim found soon enough that Jelka was not like American girls. She was very quiet. She never spoke first, but only answered his questions, and then with soft short replies. She learned her husband as she learned passages of Scripture. After they had been married a while, Jim never wanted for any habitual thing in the house but Jelka had it ready for him before he could ask. She was a fine wife, but there was no companionship in her. She never talked. Her great eyes followed him, and when he smiled, sometimes she smiled too, a distant and covered smile. Her knitting and mending and sewing were interminable. There she sat, watching her wise hands, and she seemed to regard with wonder and pride the little white hands that could do such nice and useful things. She was so much like an animal that sometimes Jim patted her head and neck under the same impulse that made him stroke a horse.

In the house Jelka was remarkable. No matter what time Jim came in from the hot dry range or from the bottom farm land, his dinner was exactly, steamingly ready for him. She watched while he ate, and pushed the dishes close when he needed them, and filled his cup when it was empty.

Early in the marriage he told her things that happened on the farm, but she smiled at him as a foreigner does who wishes to be agreeable even though he doesn't understand.

"The stallion cut himself on the barbed wire," he said.

And she replied, "Yes," with a downward inflection that held neither question nor interest.

He realized before long that he could not get in touch with her in any way. If she had a life apart, it was so remote as to be beyond his reach. The barrier in her eyes was not one that could be removed, for it was neither hostile nor intentional.

At night he stroked her straight black hair and her unbelievably smooth golden shoulders, and she whimpered a little with pleasure. Only in the climax of his embrace did she seem to have a life apart, fierce and passionate. And then immediately she lapsed into the alert and painfully dutiful wife.

"Why don't you ever talk to me," he demanded. "Don't you want to talk to me?"

"Yes," she said. "What do you want me to say?" She spoke the language of his race out of a mind that was foreign to his race.

When a year had passed, Jim began to crave the company of women, the chattery exchange of small talk, the shrill pleasant insults, the shame-sharpened vulgarity. He began to go again to town, to drink and to play with the noisy girls of the Three Star. They liked him there for his firm, controlled face and for his readiness to laugh.

"Where's your wife?" they demanded.

"Home in the barn," he responded. It was a never-failing joke.

Saturday afternoons he saddled a horse and put a rifle in the scabbard in case he should see a deer. Always he asked, "You don't mind staying alone?"

"No. I don't mind."

At once he asked, "Suppose someone should come?"

Her eyes sharpened for a moment, and then she smiled. "I would send them away," she said.

"I'll be back about noon tomorrow. It's too far to ride in the night." He felt that she knew where he was going, but she never protested nor gave any sign of disapproval. "You should have a baby," he said.

Her face lighted up. "Some time God will be good," she said eagerly.

He was sorry for her loneliness. If only she visited with the other women of the canyon she would be less lonely, but she had no gift for visiting. Once every month or so she put horses to the buckboard and went to spend an afternoon with her mother, and with the brood of brothers and sisters and cousins who lived in her father's house.

"A fine time you'll have," Jim said to her. "You'll gabble your crazy language like ducks for a whole afternoon. You'll giggle with that big grown cousin of yours with the embarrassed face. If I could find any fault with you, I'd call you a damn foreigner." He remembered how she blessed the bread with the sign of the cross before she put it in the oven, how she knelt at the bedside every night, how she had a holy picture tacked to the wall in the closet.

One Saturday of a hot dusty June, Jim cut oats in the farm flat. The day was long. It was after six o'clock when the mower tumbled the last band of oats. He drove the clanking machine up into the barnyard and backed it into the implement shed, and there he unhitched the horses and turned them out to graze on the hills over Sunday. When he entered the kitchen Jelka was just putting his dinner on the table. He washed his hands and face and sat down to eat.

"I'm tired," he said, "but I think I'll go to Monterey anyway. There's be a full moon."

Her soft eyes smiled.

"I'll tell you what I'll do," he said. "If you would like to go, I'll hitch up a rig and take you with me."

She smiled again and shook her head. "No, the stores would be closed. I would rather stay here."

"Well, all right, I'll saddle the horse then. I didn't think I was going. The stock's all turned out. Maybe I can catch a horse easy. Sure you don't want to go?"

"If it was early, and I could go to the stores—but it will be ten o'clock when you get there."

"Oh, no—well, anyway, on horseback I'll make it a little after nine."

Her mouth smiled to itself, but her eyes watched him for the development of a wish. Perhaps because he was tired from the long day's work, he demanded, "What are you thinking about?"

"Thinking about? I remember, you used to ask that nearly every day when we were first married."

"But what are you?" he insisted irritably.

"Oh—I'm thinking about the eggs under the black hen." She got up and went to the big calendar on the wall. "They will hatch tomorrow or maybe Monday."

It was almost dusk when he had finished shaving and putting on his blue serge suit and his new boots. Jelka had the dishes washed and put away. As Jim went through the kitchen he saw that she had taken the lamp to the table near the window, and that she sat beside it knitting a brown wool sock.

"Why do you sit there tonight?" he asked. "You always sit over here. You do funny things sometimes."

Her eyes arose slowly from her flying hands. "The moon," she said quietly. "You said it would be full tonight. I want to see the moon rise."

"But you're silly. You can't see it from that window. I thought you knew direction better than that."

She smiled remotely. "I will look out of the bedroom window, then."

Jim put on his black hat and went out. Walking through the dark empty barn, he took a halter from the rack. On the grassy sidehill he whistled high and shrill. The horses stopped feeding and moved slowly in towards him, and stopped twenty feet away.

Carefully he approached his bay gelding and moved his hand from its rump along its side and up and over its neck. The halter-strap clicked in its buckle. Jim turned and led the horse back to the barn. He threw his saddle on and cinched it tight, put his silver-bound bridle over the stiff ears, buckled the throat latch, knotted the tie-rope about the gelding's neck and fastened the neat coil-end to the saddle string. Then he slipped the halter and led the horse to the house. A radiant crown of soft red light lay over the eastern hills. The full moon would rise before the valley had completely lost the daylight.

In the kitchen Jelka still knitted by the window. Jim strode to the corner of the room and took up his 30-30 carbine. As he rammed cartridges into the magazine, he said, "The moon glow is on the hills. If you are going to see it rise, you better go outside now. It's going to be a good red one at rising."

"In a moment," she replied, "when I come to the end here." He went to her and patted her sleek head.

"Good night. I'll probably be back by noon tomorrow." Her dusky black eyes followed him out of the door.

Jim thrust the rifle into his saddle-scabbard, and mounted and swung his horse down the canyon. On his right, from behind the blackening hills, the great red moon slid rapidly up. The double light of the day's last afterglow and the rising moon thickened the outlines of the trees and gave a mysterious new perspective to the hills. The dusty oaks shimmered and glowed, and the shade under them was black as velvet. A huge, long-legged shadow of a horse and a half a man rode to the left and slightly ahead of Jim. From the ranches near and distant came the sound of dogs tuning up for a night of song. And the roosters crowed, thinking a new dawn had come too quickly. Jim lifted the gelding to a trot. The spattering hoof-steps echoed back from the castle behind him. He thought of blonde May at the Three Star in Monterey. "I'll be late. Maybe someone else'll have her," he thought. The moon was clear of the hills now.

Jim had gone a mile when he heard the hoofbeats of a horse coming towards him. A horseman cantered up and pulled to a stop. "That you, Jim?"

"Yes. Oh, hello, George."

"I was just riding up to your place. I want to tell you—you know the springhead at the upper end of my land?"

"Yes, I know."

"Well, I was up there this afternoon. I found a dead campfire and a calf's head and feet. The skin was in the fire, half burned, but I pulled it out and it had your brand."

"The hell," said Jim. "How old was the fire?"

"The ground was still warm in the ashes. Last night, I guess. Look, Jim, I can't go up with you. I've got to go to town, but I thought I'd tell you, so you could take a look around."

Jim asked quietly, "Any idea how many men?"

"No. I didn't look close."

"Well, I guess I better go up and look. I was going to town too. But if there are thieves working, I don't want to lose any more stock. I'll cut up through your land if you don't mind, George."

"I'd go with you, but I've got to go to town. You got a gun with you?"

"Oh yes, sure. Here under my leg. Thanks for telling me."

"That's all right. Cut through any place you want. Good night." The neighbour turned his horse and cantered back in the direction from which he had come.

For a few moments Jim sat in the moonlight, looking down at his stilted shadow. He pulled his rifle from its scabbard, levered a cartridge into the chamber, and held the gun across the pommel of his saddle. He turned left from the road, went up the little ridge, through the oak grove, over the grassy hogback and down the other side into the next canyon.

In half an hour he had found the deserted camp. He turned over the heavy, leathery calf's head and felt its dusty tongue to judge by the dryness how long it had been dead. He lighted a match and looked at his brand on the half-burned hide. At last he mounted his horse again, rode over the bald grassy hills and crossed into his own land.

A warm summer wind was blowing on the hilltops. The moon, as it quartered up the sky, lost its redness and turned the colour of strong tea. Among the hills the coyotes were singing, and the dogs at the ranch houses below joined them with broken-hearted howling. The dark green oaks below and the yellow summer grass showed their colours in the moonlight.

Jim followed the sound of the cowbells to his herd, and found them eating quietly, and a few deer feeding with them. He listened for the sound of hoofbeats or the voices of men on the wind.

It was after eleven when he turned his horse towards home. He rounded the west tower of the sandstone castle, rode through the shadow and out into the moonlight again. Below, the roofs of his barn and house shone dully. The bedroom window cast back a streak of reflection.

The feeding horses lifted their heads as Jim came down through the pasture. Their eyes glinted redly when they turned their heads.

Jim had almost reached the corral fence—he heard a horse stamping in the barn. His hand jerked the gelding down. He listened. It came again, the stamping from the barn. Jim lifted his rifle and dismounted silently. He turned his horse loose and crept towards the barn.

In the blackness he could hear the grinding of the horse's teeth as it chewed hay. He moved along the barn until he came to the occupied stall. After a moment of listening he scratched a match on the butt of his rifle. A saddle and bridled horse was tied in the stall. The bit was slipped under the chin and the cinch loosened. The horse stopped eating and turned its head towards the light.

Jim blew out the match and walked quickly out of the barn. He sat on the edge of the horse trough and looked into the water. His thoughts came so slowly that he put them into words and said them under his breath.

"Shall I look through the window? No. My head would throw a shadow in the room."

He regarded the rifle in his hand. Where it had been rubbed and handled, the black gun finish had worn off, leaving the metal silvery.

At last he stood up with decision and moved towards the house. At the steps, an extended foot tried each board tenderly before he put his weight on it. The three ranch dogs came out from under the house and shook themselves, stretched and sniffed, wagged their tails and went back to bed.

The kitchen was dark, but Jim knew where every piece of furniture was. He put out his hand and touched the corner of the table, a chair back, the towel hanger, as he went along. He crossed the room so silently that even he could hear only his breath and the whisper of his trousers legs together, and the beating of his watch in his pocket. The bedroom door stood open and spilled a patch of moonlight on the kitchen floor. Jim reached the door at last and peered through.

The moonlight lay on the white bed. Jim saw Jelka lying on her back, one soft bare arm flung across her forehead and eyes. He could not see who the man was, for his head was turned away. Jim watched, holding his breath. Then Jelka twitched in her sleep and the man rolled his head and sighed—Jelka's cousin, her grown, embarrassed cousin.

Jim turned and quickly stole back across the kitchen and down the back steps. He walked up the yard to the water-trough again, and sat down on the edge of it. The moon was white as chalk, and it swam in the water, and lighted the straws and barley dropped by the horses' mouths. Jim could see the mosquito wigglers, tumbling up and down, end over end, in the water, and he could see a newt lying in the sun moss in the bottom of the trough.

He cried a few dry, hard, smothered sobs, and wondered why, for his thought was of the grassed hilltops and of the lonely summer wind whisking along.

His thought turned to the way his mother used to hold a bucket to catch the throat blood when his father killed a pig. She stood as far away as possible and held the bucket at arms'-length to keep her clothes from getting spattered.

Jim dipped his hand into the trough and stirred the moon to broken, swirling streams of light. He wetted his forehead with his damp hands and stood up. This time he did not move so quietly, but he crossed the kitchen on tiptoe and stood in the bedroom door. Jelka moved her arm and opened her eyes a little. Then the eyes sprang wide, then they glistened with moisture. Jim looked into her eyes; his face was empty of expression. A little drop ran out of Jelka's nose and lodged in the hollow of her upper lip. She stared back at him.

Jim cocked the rifle. The steel click sounded through the house. The man on the bed stirred uneasily in his sleep. Jim's hands were quivering. He raised the gun to his shoulder and held it tightly to keep from shaking. Over the sights he saw the little white square between the man's brows and hair. The front sight wavered a moment and then came to rest.

The gun crash tore the air. Jim, still looking down the barrel, saw the whole bed jolt under the blow. A small, black, bloodless hole was in the man's forehead. But behind, the hollow-point took brain and bone and splashed them on the pillow.

Jelka's cousin gurgled in his throat. His hands came crawling out from under the covers like big white spiders, and they walked for a moment, then shuddered and fell quiet.

Jim looked slowly back at Jelka. Her nose was running. Her eyes had moved from him to the end of the rifle. She whined softly, like a cold puppy.

Jim turned in panic. His boot heels beat on the kitchen floor, but outside, he moved slowly towards the water-trough again. There was a taste of salt in his throat, and his heart heaved painfully. He pulled his hat off and dipped his head into the water. Then he leaned over and vomited on the ground. In the house he could hear Jelka moving about. She whimpered like a puppy. Jim straightened up, weak and dizzy.

He walked tiredly through the corral and into the pasture. His saddled horse came at his whistle. Automatically he tightened the cinch, mounted and rode away, down the road to the valley. The squat black shadow traveled under him. The moon sailed high and white. The uneasy dogs barked monotonously.

At daybreak a buckboard and pair trotted up to the ranch yard, scattering the chickens. A deputy sheriff and a coroner sat in the seat. Jim Moore half reclined against his saddle in the wagon-box. His tired gelding followed behind. The deputy sheriff set the brake and wrapped the lines around it. The men dismounted.

Jim asked, "Do I have to go in? I'm too tired and wrought up to see it now."

The coroner pulled his lip and studied. "Oh, I guess not. We'll tend to things and look around."

Jim sauntered away towards the water-trough. "Say," he called, "kind of clean up a little, will you? You know."

The men went on into the house.

In a few minutes they emerged, carrying the stiffened body between them. It was wrapped up in a comforter. They eased it up into the wagon-box. Jim walked back towards them. "Do I have to go in with you now?"

"Where's your wife, Mr. Moore?" the deputy sheriff demanded.

"I don't know," he said wearily. "She's somewhere around."

"You're sure you didn't kill her too?"

"No. I didn't touch her. I'll find her and bring her in this afternoon. That is, if you don't want me to go in with you now."

"We've got your statement," the coroner said. "And by God, we've got eyes, haven't we, Will? Of course there's a technical charge of murder against you, but it'll be dismissed. Always is in this part of the country. Go kind of light on your wife, Mr. Moore."

"I won't hurt her," said Jim.

He stood and watched the buckboard jolt away. He kicked his feet reluctantly in the dust. The hot June sun showed its face over the hills and flashed viciously on the bedroom window.

Jim went slowly into the house, and brought out a nine-foot, loaded bull whip. He crossed the yard and walked into the barn. And as he climbed the ladder to the hayloft, he heard the high, puppy whimpering start.

When Jim came out of the barn again, he carried Jelka over his shoulder. By the water-trough he set her tenderly on the ground. Her hair was littered with bits of hay. The back of her shirtwaist was streaked with blood.

Jim wetted his bandana at the pipe and washed her bitten lips, and washed her face and brushed back her hair. Her dusty black eyes followed every move he made.

"You hurt me," she said. "You hurt me bad."

He nodded gravely. "Bad as I could without killing you."

The sun shone hotly on the ground. A few blowflies buzzed about, looking for the blood.

Jelka's thickened lips tried to smile. "Did you have any breakfast at all?"

"No," he said. "None at all."

"Well, then, I'll fry you up some eggs." She struggled painfully to her feet.

"Let me help you," he said. "I'll help you get your shirtwaist off. It's drying stuck to your back. It'll hurt."

"No. I'll do it myself." Her voice had a peculiar resonance in it. Her dark eyes dwelt warmly on him for a moment, and then she turned and limped into the house.

Jim waited, sitting on the edge of the water-trough. He saw the smoke start out of the chimney and sail straight up into the air. In a very few moments Jelka called him from the kitchen door.

"Come, Jim. your breakfast."

Four fried eggs and four thick slices of bacon lay on a warmed plate for him. "The coffee will be ready in a minute," she said.

"Won't you eat?"

"No. Not now. My mouth's too sore."

He ate his eggs hungrily and then looked up at her. Her black hair was combed smooth. She had on a fresh white shirtwaist. "We're going to town this afternoon," he said. "I'm going to order lumber. We'll build a new house farther down the canyon."

Her eyes darted to the closed bedroom door and then back to him. "Yes," she said. "That will be good." And then, after a moment, "Will you whip me any more—for this?"

"No, not any more, for this."

Her eyes smiled. She sat down on a chair beside him, and Jim put out his hand and stroked her hair and the back of her neck.

I WANT TO KNOW WHY

By SHERWOOD ANDERSON

WE GOT UP AT FOUR IN THE MORNING, THAT FIRST DAY IN THE EAST. On the evening before we had climbed off a freight train at the edge of town, and with the true instinct of Kentucky boys had found our way across town and to the race track and the stables at once. Then we knew we were all right. Hanley Turner right away found a nigger we knew. It was Bildad Johnson who in the winter works at Ed Becker's livery barn in our home town, Beckersville. Bildad is a good cook as almost all our niggers are and of course he, like everyone in our part of Kentucky who is anyone at all, likes the horses. In the spring Bildad begins to scratch around. A nigger from our country can flatter and wheedle anyone into letting him do most anything he wants. Bildad wheedles the stable men and the trainers from the horse farms in our country around Lexington. The trainers come into town in the evening to stand around and talk and maybe get into a poker game. Bildad gets in with them. He is always doing little favors and telling about things to eat, chicken browned in a pan, and how is the best way to cook sweet potatoes and corn bread. It makes your mouth water to hear him.

When the racing season comes on and the horses go to the races and there is all the talk on the streets in the evenings about the new colts, and everyone says when they are going over to Lexington or to the spring meeting at Churchill Downs or to Latonia, and the horsemen that have been down to New Orleans or maybe at the winter meeting at Havana in Cuba come home to spend a week before they start out again, at such a time when everything talked about in Beckersville is just horses and nothing else and the outfits start out and horse racing is in every breath of air you breathe, Bildad shows up with a job as cook for some outfit. Often when I think about it, his always going all season to the races and working in the livery barn in the winter where horses are and where men like to come and talk about horses, I wish I was a nigger. It's a foolish thing to say, but that's the way I am about being around horses, just crazy. I can't help it.

Well, I must tell you about what we did and let you in on what I'm talking about. Four of us boys from Beckersville, all whites and sons of men who live in Beckersville regular, made up our minds we were going to the races, not just to Lexington or Louisville, I don't mean, but to the big eastern track we were always hearing our Beckersville men talk about, to Saratoga. We were all pretty young then. I was just turned fifteen and I was the oldest of the four. It was my scheme. I admit that and I talked the others into trying it. There was Hanley Turner and Henry Rieback and Tom Tumberton and myself. I had thirty-seven dollars I had earned during the winter working nights and Saturdays in Enoch Myer's grocery. Henry Rieback had eleven dollars and the others, Hanley and Tom had only a dollar or two each. We fixed it all up and laid low until the Kentucky spring meetings were over and some of our men, the sportiest ones, the ones we envied the most, had cut out—then we cut out too.

I won't tell you the trouble we had beating our way on freights and all. We went through Cleveland and Buffalo and other cities and saw Niagara Falls. We bought things there, souvenirs and spoons and cards and shells with pictures of the falls on them for our sisters and mothers, but thought we had better not send any of the things home. We didn't want to put the folks on our trail and maybe be nabbed.

We got into Saratoga as I said at night and went to the track. Bildad fed us up. He showed us a place to sleep in hay over a shed and promised to keep still. Niggers are all right about things like that. They won't squeal on you. Often a white man you might meet, when you had run away from home like that, might appear to be all right and give you a quarter or a half dollar or something, and then go right and give you away. White men will do that, but not a nigger. You ran trust them. They are squarer with kids. I don't know why.

At the Saratoga meeting that year there were a lot of men from home. Dave Williams and Arthur Mulford and Jerry Myers and others. Then there was a lot from Louisville and Lexington Henry Rieback knew but I didn't. They were professional gamblers and Henry Rieback's father is one too. He is what is called a sheet writer and goes away most of the year to tracks. In the winter when he is home in Beckersville he don't stay there much but goes away to cities and deals faro. He is a nice man and generous, is always sending Henry presents, a bicycle and a gold watch and a boy scout suit of clothes and things like that.

My own father is a lawyer. He's all right, but don't make much money and can't buy me things and anyway I'm getting so old now I don't expect it. He never said nothing to me against Henry, but Hanley Turner and Tom Tumberton's fathers did. They said to their boys that money so come by is no good and they didn't want their boys brought up to hear gamblers' talk and be thinking about such things and maybe embrace them.

That's all right and I guess the men know what they are talking about, but I don't see what it's got to do with Henry or with horses either. That's what I'm writing this story about. I'm puzzled. I'm getting to be a man and want to think straight and be O. K., and there's something I saw at the race meeting at the eastern track I can't figure out.

I can't help it, I'm crazy about thoroughbred horses. I've always been that way. When I was ten years old and saw I was growing to be big and couldn't be a rider I was so sorry I nearly died. Harry Hellinfinger in Beckersville, whose father is Postmaster, is grown up and too lazy to work, but likes to stand around in the street and get up jokes on boys like sending them to a hardware store for a gimlet to bore square holes and other jokes like that. He played one on me. He told me that if I would eat a half a cigar I would be stunted and not grow any more and maybe could be a rider. I did it. When father wasn't looking I took a cigar out of his pocket and gagged it down some way. It made me awful sick and the doctor had to be sent for, and then it did no good. I kept right on growing. It was a joke. When I told what I had done and why most fathers would have whipped me and mine didn't.

Well, I didn't get stunted and didn't die. It serves Harry Hellinfinger right. Then I made up my mind I would like to be a stable boy, but had to give that up too. Mostly niggers do that work and I knew father wouldn't let me go into it. No use to ask him.

If you've never been crazy about thoroughbreds it's because you've never been around where they are much and don't know any better. They're beautiful. There isn't anything so lovely and clean and full of spunk and honest and everything as some race horses. On the big horse farms that are all around our town Beckersville there are tracks and the horses run in the early morning. More than a thousand times I've got out of bed before daylight and walked two or three miles to the tracks. Mother wouldn't of let me go but father always says, "Let him alone." So I got some bread out of the bread box and some butter and jam, gobbled it and lit out.

At the tracks you sit on the fence with men, whites and niggers, and they chew tobacco and talk, and then the colts are brought out. It's early and the grass is covered with shiny dew and in another field a man is plowing and they are frying things in a shed where the track niggers sleep, and you know how a nigger can giggle and laugh and say things that make you laugh. A white man can't do it and some niggers can't but a track nigger can every time.

And so the colts are brought out and some are just galloped by stable boys, but almost every morning on a big track owned by a rich man who lives maybe in New York, there are always, nearly every morning, a few colts and some of the old horses and geldings and mares that are cut loose.

It brings a lump up into my throat when a horse runs. I don't mean all horses but some. I can pick them nearly every time. It's in my blood like in the blood of race track niggers and trainers. Even when they just go slop-jogging along with a little nigger on their backs I can tell a winner. If my throat hurts and it's hard for me to swallow, that's him. He'll run like Sam Hill when you let him out. If he don't win every time it'll be a wonder and because they've got him in a pocket behind another or he was pulled or got off bad at the post or something. If I wanted to be a gambler like Henry Rieback's father I could get rich. I know I could and Henry says so too. All I would have to do is to wait 'til that hurt comes when I see a horse and then bet every cent. That's what I would do if I wanted to be a gambler, but I don't.

When you're at the tracks in the morning—not the race tracks but the training tracks around Beckersville—you don't see a horse, the kind I've been talking about, very often, but it's nice anyway. Any thoroughbred, that is sired right and out of a good mare and trained by a man that knows how, can run. If he couldn't what would he be there for and not pulling a plow?

Well, out of the stables they come and the boys are on their backs and it's lovely to be there. You hunch down on top of the fence and itch inside you. Over in the sheds the niggers giggle and sing. Bacon is being fried and coffee made. Everything smells lovely. Nothing smells better than coffee and manure and horses and niggers and bacon frying and pipes being smoked out of doors on a morning like that. It just gets you, that's what it does.

But about Saratoga. We was there six days and not a soul from home seen us, and everything came off just as we wanted it to, fine weather and horses and races and all. We beat our way home and Bildad gave us a basket with fried chicken and bread and other eatables in, and I had eighteen dollars when we got back to Beckersville. Mother jawed and cried but Pop didn't say much. I told everything we done except one thing. I did and saw that alone. That's what I'm writing about. It got me upset. I think about it at night. Here it is.

At Saratoga we laid up nights in the hay in the shed Bildad had showed us and ate with the niggers early and at night when the race people had all gone away. The men from home stayed mostly in the grandstand and betting field, and didn't come out around the places where the horses are kept except to the paddocks just before a race when the horses are saddled. At Saratoga they don't have paddocks under an open shed as at Lexington and Churchill Downs and other tracks down in our country, but saddle the horses right out in an open place under trees on a lawn as smooth and nice as Banker Bohon's front yard here in Beckersville. It's lovely. The horses are sweaty and nervous and shine and the men come out and smoke cigars and look at them and the trainers are there and the owners, and your heart thumps so you can hardly breathe.

Then the bugle blows for post and the boys that ride come running out with their silk clothes on and you run to get a place by the fence with the niggers.

I always am wanting to be a trainer or owner, and at the risk of being seen and caught and sent home I went to the paddocks before every race. The other boys didn't but I did.

We got to Saratoga on a Friday and on Wednesday the next week the big Mullford Handicap was to be run. Middlestride was in it and Sunstreak. The weather was fine and the track fast. I couldn't sleep the night before.

What had happened was that both these horses are the kind it makes my throat hurt to see. Middlestride is long and looks awkward and is a gelding. He belongs to Joe Thompson, a little owner from home who only has a half dozen horses. The Mullford Handicap is for a mile and Middlestride can't untrack fast. He goes away slow and is always way back at the half, then he begins to run and if the race is a mile and a quarter he'll just eat up everything and get there.

Sunstreak is different. He is a stallion and nervous and belongs on the biggest farm we've got in our country, the Van Riddle place that belongs to Mr. Van Riddle of New York. Sunstreak is like a girl you think about sometimes but never see. He is hard all over and lovely too. When you look at his head you want to kiss him. He is trained by Jerry Tillford who knows me and has been good to me lots of times, lets me walk into a horse's stall to look at him close and other things. There isn't anything as sweet as that horse. He stands at the post quiet and not letting on, but he is just burning up inside. Then when the barrier goes up he is off like his name, Sunstreak. It makes you ache to see him. It hurts you. He just lays down and runs like a bird dog. There can't anything I ever see run like him except Middlestride when he gets untracked and stretches himself.

Gee! I ached to see that race and those two horses run, ached and dreaded it too. I didn't want to see either of our horses beaten. We had never sent a pair like that to the races before. Old men in Beckersville said so and the niggers said so. It was a fact.

Before the race I went over to the paddocks to see. I looked a last look at Middlestride, who isn't such a much standing in a paddock that way, then I went to see Sunstreak.

It was his day. I knew when I see him. I forgot all about being seen myself and walked right up. All the men from Beckersville were there and no one noticed me except Jerry Tillford. He saw me and something happened. I'll tell you about that.

I was standing looking at that horse and aching. In some way, I can't tell how, I knew just how Sunstreak felt inside. He was quiet and letting the niggers rub his legs and Mr. Van Riddle himself put the saddle on, but he was just a raging torrent inside. He was like the water in the river at Niagara Falls just before it goes plunk down. That horse wasn't thinking about running. He don't have to think about that. He was just thinking about holding himself back 'til the time for the running came. I knew that. I could just in a way see right inside him. He was going to do some awful running and I knew it. He wasn't bragging or letting on much or prancing or making a fuss, but just waiting. I knew it and Jerry Tillford his trainer knew. I looked up and then that man and I looked into each other's eyes. Something happened to me. I guess I loved the man as much as I did the horse because he knew what I knew. Seemed to me there wasn't anything in the world but that man and the horse and me. I cried and Jerry Tillford had a shine in his eyes. Then I came away to the fence to wait for the race. The horse was better than me, more steadier, and now I know better than Jerry. He was the quietest and he had to do the running.

Sunstreak ran first of course and he busted the world's record for a mile. I've seen that if I never see anything more. Everything came out just as I expected. Middlestride got left at the post and was way back and closed up to be second, just as I knew he would. He'll get a world's record too some day. They can't skin the Beckersville country on horses.

I watched the race calm because I knew what would happen. I was sure. Hanley Turner and Henry Rieback and Tom Tumberton were all more excited than me.

A funny thing had happened to me, I was thinking about Jerry Tillford the trainer and how happy he was all through the race. I liked him that afternoon even more than I ever liked my own father. I almost forgot the horses thinking that way about him. It was because of what I had seen in his eyes as he stood in the paddocks beside Sunstreak before the race started. I knew he had been watching and working with Sunstreak since the horse was a baby colt, had taught him to run and be patient and when to let himself out and not to quit, never. I knew that for him it was like a mother seeing her child do something brave or wonderful. It was the first time I ever felt for a man like that.

After the race that night I cut out from Tom and Hanley and Henry. I wanted to be by myself and I wanted to be near Jerry Tillford if I could work it. Here is what happened.

The track in Saratoga is near the edge of town. It is all polished up and trees around, the evergreen kind, and grass and everything painted nice. If you go past the track you get to a hard road made of asphalt for automobiles, and if you go along this for a few miles there is a road turns off to a little rummy-looking farm house set in a yard.

That night after the race I went along that road because I had seen Jerry and some other men go that way in an automobile. I didn't expect to find them. I walked for a ways and then sat down by a fence to think. It was the direction they went in. I wanted to be as near Jerry as I could. I felt close to him. Pretty soon I went up the side road—I don't know why—and came to the rummy farm house. I was just lonesome to see Jerry, like wanting to see your father at night when you are a young kid. Just then an automobile came along and turned in. Jerry was in it and Henry Rieback's father, and Arthur Bedford from home, and Dave Williams and two other men I didn't know. They got out of the car and went into the house, all but Henry Rieback's father who quarreled with them and said he wouldn't go. It was only about nine o'clock, but they were all drunk and the rummy looking farm house was a place for bad women to stay in. That's what it was. I crept up along the fence and looked through a window and saw.

It's what give me the fantods. I can't make it out. The women in the house were all ugly mean-looking women, not nice to look at or be near. They were homely too, except one who was tall and looked a little like the gelding Middlestride, but not clean like him, but with a hard ugly mouth. She had red hair. I saw everything plain. I got up by an old rose bush by an open window and looked. The women had on loose dresses and sat around in chairs. The men came in and some sat on the women's laps. The place smelled rotten and there was rotten talk, the kind a kid hears around a livery stable in a town like Beckersville in the winter but don't ever expect to hear talked when there are women around. It was rotten. A nigger wouldn't go into such a place.

I looked at Jerry Tillford. I've told you how I had been feeling about him on account of his knowing what was going on inside of Sunstreak in the minute before he went to the post for the race in which he made a world's record.

Jerry bragged in that bad woman house as I know Sunstreak wouldn't never have bragged. He said that he made that horse, that it was him that won the race and made the record. He lied and bragged like a fool. I never heard such silly talk.

And then, what do you suppose he did! He looked at the woman in there, the one that was lean and hardmouthed and looked a little like the gelding Middlestride, but not clean like him, and his eyes began to shine just as they did when he looked at me and at Sunstreak in the paddocks at the track in the afternoon. I stood there by the window—gee!—but I wished I hadn't gone away from the tracks, but had stayed with the boys and the niggers and the horses. The tall rotten looking woman was between us just as Sunstreak was in the paddocks in the afternoon.

Then, all of a sudden, I began to hate that man. I wanted to scream and rush in the room and kill him. I never had such a feeling before. I was so mad clean through that I cried and my fists were doubled up so my finger nails cut my hands.

And Jerry's eyes kept shining and he waved back and forth, and then he went and kissed that woman and I crept away and went back to the tracks and to bed and didn't sleep hardly any, and then the next day I got the other kids to start home with me and never told them anything I seen.

I been thinking about it ever since. I can't make it out. Spring has come again and I'm nearly sixteen and go to the tracks mornings same as always, and I see Sunstreak and Middlestride and a new colt named Strident I'll bet will lay them all out, but no one thinks so but me and two or three niggers.

But things are different. At the tracks the air don't taste as good or smell as good. It's because a man like Jerry Tillford, who knows what he does, could see a horse like Sunstreak run, and kiss a woman like that the same day. I can't make it out. Darn him, what did he want to do like that for? I keep thinking about it and it spoils looking at horses and smelling things and hearing niggers laugh and everything. Sometimes I'm so mad about it I want to fight someone. It gives me the fantods. What did he do it for? I want to know why.

PART IV

"Such tricks hath strong imagination,
That if it would but apprehend some joy,
It comprehends some bringer of that joy;
Or in the night, imagining some fear,
How easy is a bush supposed a bear!"
—SHAKESPEARE: *Midsummer Night's Dream*

THE VANISHING LADY

By ALEXANDER WOOLLCOTT

The adventure in Paris of a frightened girl whose travel-ing companion, together with the baseless fabric of her habitation, dissolves into thin air and leaves not a rock behind.

THEN THERE WAS THE STORY—TOLD ME SOME YEARS AGO AS A TRUE copy of a leaf from the dread secret archives of the Paris police—of the woman who disappeared during the World Exposition as suddenly, as completely, and as inexplicably as did Dorothy Arnold ten years later from the sidewalks of New York.

As I first heard the story, it began with the arrival from Marseilles of an Englishwoman and her young, inexperienced daughter, a girl of seventeen or thereabouts. The mother was the frail, pretty widow of an English officer who had been stationed in India, and the two had just come from Bombay, bound for home. In the knowledge that, after reaching there, she would soon have to cross to Paris to sign some papers affecting her husband's estate, she decided at the last minute to shift her passage to a Marseilles steamer, and, by going direct to Paris, look up the lawyers and there finish her business before crossing the Channel to settle for-ever and a day in the Warwickshire village where she was born.

Paris was so tumultuously crowded for the Exposition that they counted themselves fortunate when the *cocher* deposited them at the Crillon, and they learned that their precautionary telegram from Marseilles had miraculously caught a room on the wing—a double room with a fine, spacious sitting-room looking out on the Place de la Concorde. I could wish that they had wired one of those less magnificent caravansaries, if only that I might revel again in such a name as the Hotel of Jacob and of England, or, better still, the Hotel of the Universe and of Portugal. But, as the story reached me, it was to the Crillon that they went.

The long windows of their sitting-room gave on a narrow, stone-railed balcony and were half-shrouded in heavy curtains of plum-colored velvet. As again and again the girl later on had occasion to describe the look of that room when first she saw it, the walls were papered in old rose. A high-backed sofa, an oval satinwood table, a mantel with an ormolu clock that had run down—these also she recalled.

The girl was the more relieved that there would be no need of a house-to-house search for rooms, for the mother had seemed unendurably exhausted from the long train ride, and was now of such a color that the girl's first idea was to call the house physician, hoping fervently that he spoke English, for neither she nor her mother spoke any French at all.

The doctor, when he came—a dusty, smelly little man with a wrinkled face lost in a thicket of whiskers, and a reassuring Legion of Honor ribbon in the buttonhole of his lapel—did speak a little English. After a long, grave look and a few questions put to the tired woman on the bed in the shaded room, he called the girl into the sitting-room and told her frankly that her mother's condition was serious; that it was out of the question for them to think of going on to England next day; that on the morrow she might better be moved to a hospital, etc., etc.

All these things he would attend to. In the meantime he wanted the girl to go at once to his home and fetch him a medicine that his wife would give her. It could not be as quickly prepared in any chemist's. Unfortunately, he lived on the other side of Paris and had no telephone, and with all Paris *en fête* it would be perilous to rely on any messenger. Indeed, it would be a saving of time and worry if she could go, armed with a note to his wife he was even then scribbling in French at a desk in the sitting-room. In the lobby below, the manager of the hotel, after an excited colloquy with the doctor, took charge of her most sympathetically, himself putting her into a *sapin* and, as far as she could judge, volubly directing the driver how to reach a certain house in the Rue Val du Grâce, near the Observatoire.

It was then that the girl's agony began, for the ramshackle vic-

toria crawled through the festive streets and, as she afterwards
realized, more often than not crawled in the wrong direction. The
house in the Rue Val du Grâce seemed to stand at the other end
of the world, when the carriage came at last to a halt in front of it.
The girl grew old in the time which passed before any answer
came to her ring at the bell. The doctor's wife, when finally she
appeared, read his note again and again, then with much muttering
and rattling of keys stationed the girl in an airless waiting room
and left her there so long that she was weeping for very despera-
tion, before the medicine was found, wrapped, and turned over
to her.

A hundred times during that wait she rose and started for the
door, determined to stay no longer but to run back empty-handed
through the streets to her mother's bedside. A thousand times in
the wretched weeks that followed she loathed herself for not having obeyed that impulse. But always there was the feeling that
having come so far and having waited so long, she must not leave
without the medicine just for lack of the strength of will to stick
it out a little longer—perhaps only a few minutes longer.

Then the snail's pace trip back to the Right Bank was another
nightmare, and it ended only when, at the *cocher's* mulish determination to deliver her to some hotel in the Place Vendôme, she
leaped to the street and in sheer terror appealed for help to a
passing young man whose alien tweeds and boots told her he was
a compatriot of hers.

He was still standing guard beside her five minutes later when,
at long last, she arrived at the desk of the Crillon and called for
her key, only to have the very clerk who had handed her a pen
to register with that morning look at her without recognition and
blandly ask, "Whom does Mademoiselle wish to see?" At that a
cold fear clutched her heart, a sudden surrender to a panic that
she had fought back as preposterous when first it visited her as she
sat and twisted her handkerchief in the waiting room of the doctor's office on the Left Bank; a panic born when, after the doctor
had casually told her he had no telephone, she heard the fretful
ringing of its bell on the other side of his walnut door.

This then was the predicament of the young English girl as she
stood there at the desk of the hotel in Paris—a stranger in the city

and a stranger to its bewildering tongue. She had arrived that morning from India and had left her ailing mother in charge of the house physician while she went out in quest of medicine for her—a quest in which, through a malignant conspiracy between perverse circumstances and apparently motiveless passers-by, she had lost four hours.

But now with the bottle of medicine clutched in her hand, she reached the hotel at last, only to be stared down by the clerk at the desk, only to have the very man who had shown them their rooms with such a flourish that morning now gaze at her opaquely as though she were some slightly demented creature demanding admission to someone else's apartment.

But, no, Mam'zelle must be mistaken. Was it not at some other hotel she was descended? Two more clerks came fluttering into the conference. They all eyed her without a flicker of recognition. Did Mam'zelle say her room was No. 342? Ah, but 342 was occupied by M. Quelquechose. Yes, a French client of long standing. He had been occupying it these past two weeks and more. Ah, no, it would be impossible to disturb him. All this while the lobby, full of hurrying polyglot strangers, reeled around her.

She demanded the registration slips only to find in that day's docket no sign of the one she herself had filled out that morning on their arrival, the while her tired mother leaned against the desk and told her how. And even as the clerk now shuffled the papers before her eyes, the stupefying bloodstone, which she had noticed on his ring-finger when he handed her the pen five hours before, winked at her in confirmation.

From then on she came only upon closed doors. The same house physician who had hustled her off on her tragic wild-goose chase across Paris protested now with all the shrugs and gestures of his people that he had dispatched her on no such errand, that he had never been summoned to attend her mother, that he had never seen her before in all his life. The same hotel manager who had so sympathetically helped her into the carriage when she set forth on her fruitless mission denied her now as flatly and somehow managed to do it with the same sympathetic solicitude, suggesting that Mam'zelle must be tired, that she should let them provide another chamber where she might repose herself until such time

as she could recollect at what hotel she really belonged or until
some inquiries should bring in news of where her mother and her
luggage were, if——

For always there was in his ever polite voice the unspoken res-
ervation that the whole mystery might be a thing of her own disordered invention. Then, and in the destroying days that followed,
she was only too keenly aware that these evasive people—the personnel of the hotel, the attachés of the embassy, the reporters of
the Paris *Herald*, the officials at the Sûreté—were each and every
one behaving as if she had lost her wits. Indeed there were times
when she felt that all Paris was rolling its eyes behind her back and
significantly tapping its forehead.

Her only aid and comfort was the aforesaid Englishman who,
because a lovely lady in distress had come up to him in the street
and implored his help, elected thereafter to believe her against all
the evidence which so impressed the rest of Paris. He proved a
pillar of stubborn strength because he was some sort of well-born
junior secretary at the British Embassy with influence enough to
keep her agony from gathering dust in the official pigeon-holes.

His faith in her needed to be unreasoning because there slowly
formed in his mind a suspicion that for some unimaginable reason
all these people—the hotel attendants and even the police—were
part of a plot to conceal the means whereby the missing woman's
disappearance had been effected. This suspicion deepened when,
after a day's delay, he succeeded in forcing an inspection of Room
342 and found that there was no detail of its furnishing which
had not been altered from the one etched into the girl's memory.

It remained for him to prove the mechanism of that plot and to
guess at its invisible motive—a motive strong enough to enlist all
Paris in the silent obliteration of a woman of no importance, moreover a woman who, as far as her daughter knew, had not an enemy
in the world. It was the purchased confession of one of the paper-
hangers, who had worked all night in the hurried transformation
of Room 342, that started the unraveling of the mystery.

By the time the story reached me, it had lost all its content of
grief and become as unemotional as an anagram. Indeed, a few
years ago it was a kind of circulating parlor game and one was
challenged to guess what had happened to the vanished lady. Per-

haps you yourself have already surmised that the doctor had recognized the woman's ailment as a case of the black plague smug-
gled in from India; that his first instinctive step, designed only to
give time for spiriting her out of the threatened hotel, had, when
she died that afternoon, widened into a conspiracy on the part of
the police to suppress, at all costs to this one girl, an obituary
notice which, had it ever leaked out, would have emptied Paris
overnight and spread ruin across a city that had gambled heavily
on the great Exposition for which its gates were even then thrown
wide.

The story of this girl's ordeal long seemed to me one of the
great nightmares of real life and I was, therefore, the more taken
aback one day to have its historicity faintly impaired by my dis-
covering its essence in a novel called *The End of Her Honeymoon*
which the incomparable Mrs. Belloc-Lowndes wrote as long ago
as 1913. Then I find myself wondering if she unearthed it in the
archives of the Paris police or whether she spun its mystery out
of her own macabre fancy, making from whole cloth a tale of such
felicitous invention that, like Stockton's *The Lady or the Tiger*
or Anatole France's *The Procurator of Judea*, it had moved from
land to land with the seven-league-boots of folk-music and so been
told and retold at hearths the world around by people who had
never read it anywhere.

FOOTNOTE: The story of "The Vanishing Lady" is a fair specimen of folklore
in the making. For such a story to travel round the world by word of mouth,
it is necessary that each teller of it must believe it true, and it is a common
practice for the artless teller to seek to impart that belief to his listeners by
affecting kinship, or at least a lifelong intimacy, with the protagonist of the
adventure related. In my entertaining, desultory, and (with one exception) fruitless researches into the origin of twenty such world-girdling tales, I have often
challenged one of these straw-man authorities, only to have it vanish as utterly
as did the ailing lady from the Place de la Concorde. In the case of this story,
which was used not only by Mrs. Belloc-Lowndes but by Lawrence Rising in
a later novel called *She Who Was Helena Cass*, I can report that it is a favorite,
seemingly, with old ladies on shipboard, those rootless widows who wear but-
toned shoes with cloth tops and whose families, with ill-concealed delight, persuade them to do a good deal of traveling. The story will be whispered as
gospel truth from steamer-chair to steamer-chair, with such shakings of the head
and such Lord-have-mercy casting up of pious glances that it seems ever new,
and, with that air about it, gets submitted so regularly to the fiction magazines
that it has threaded many an editorial head with untimely silver. One day I
received word of its having been published as a news story in the *London Daily*

Mail as early as 1911, the bare facts substantiated by affidavits from attachés of the British Embassy in Paris. Here, I said with relief, is the end of my quest, only to have Richard Henry Little point out in the *Chicago Tribune* that the entire story had been dashed off by Karl Harriman one hot summer night in 1889 to fill a vacant column in the next morning's issue of the *Detroit Free Press*. Closing in on my quarry, I called upon the blushing Harriman to tell me whether he had invented the story or, like the rest of us, heard it somewhere in his travels. He said he could not remember. Thereupon I felt free to consider the question still open, for, without wishing to reflect on the fecundity of his imagination, I beg leave to doubt if any man could invent a tale like "The Vanishing Lady" and thereafter forget that he had done so.

SUSPICION

By Dorothy L. Sayers

AS THE ATMOSPHERE OF THE RAILWAY CARRIAGE THICKENED WITH tobacco smoke, Mr. Mummery became increasingly aware that his breakfast had not agreed with him.

There could have been nothing wrong with the breakfast itself. Brown bread, rich in vitamin content, as advised by the *Morning Star's* health expert; bacon fried to a delicious crispness; eggs just nicely set; coffee made only as Mrs. Sutton knew how to make it. Mrs. Sutton had been a real find, and that was something to be thankful for. For Ethel, since her nervous breakdown in the summer, had really not been fit to wrestle with the untrained girls who had come and gone in tempestuous succession. It took very little to upset Ethel nowadays, poor child. Mr. Mummery, trying hard to ignore his growing internal discomfort, hoped he was not in for an illness. Apart from the trouble it would cause at the office, it would worry Ethel terribly, and Mr. Mummery would cheerfully have laid down his rather uninteresting little life to spare Ethel a moment's uneasiness.

He slipped a digestive tablet into his mouth—he had taken lately to carrying a few tablets about with him—and opened his paper. There did not seem to be very much news. A question had been asked in the House about Government typewriters. The Prince of Wales had smilingly opened an all-British exhibition of footwear. A further split had occurred in the Liberal party. The police were still looking for the woman who was supposed to have poisoned a family in Lincoln. Two girls had been trapped in a burning factory. A film star had obtained her fourth decree nisi.

At Paragon Station, Mr. Mummery descended and took a tram. The internal discomfort was taking the form of a definite nausea. Happily he contrived to reach his office before the worst occurred. He was seated at his desk, pale but in control of himself, when his partner came breezing in.

"'Morning, Mummery," said Mr. Brookes in his loud tones, adding inevitably, "cold enough for you?"

"Quite," replied Mr. Mummery. "Unpleasantly raw, in fact."

"Beastly, beastly," said Mr. Brooks. "Your bulbs all in?"

"Not quite all," confessed Mr. Mummery. "As a matter of fact I haven't been feeling—"

"Pity," interrupted his partner. "Great pity. Ought to get 'em in early. Mine were in last week. My little place will be a picture in the spring. For a town garden, that is. You're lucky, living in the country. Find it better than Hull, I expect, eh? Though we get plenty of fresh air up in the Avenues. How's the missus?"

"Thank you, she's very much better."

"Glad to hear that, very glad. Hope we shall have her about again this winter as usual. Can't do without her in the Drama Society, you know. By Jove I shan't forget her acting last year in 'Romance.' She and young Welbeck positively brought the house down, didn't they? The Welbecks were asking after her only yesterday."

"Thank you, yes. I hope she will soon be able to take up her social activities again. But the doctor says she mustn't overdo it. No worry, he says—that's the important thing. She is to go easy and not rush about or undertake too much."

"Quite right, quite right. Worry's the devil and all. I cut out worrying years ago and look at me! Fit as a fiddle, for all I shan't see fifty again. *You're* not looking altogether the thing, by the way."

"A touch of dyspepsia," said Mr. Mummery. "Nothing much. Chill on the liver, that's what I put it down to."

"That's what it is," said Mr. Brookes, seizing his opportunity. "Is life worth living? It depends upon the liver. Ha, ha! Well now, well now—we must do a spot of work, I suppose. Where's that lease of Ferraby's?"

Mr. Mummery, who did not feel at his conversational best that morning, rather welcomed this suggestion, and for half an hour was allowed to proceed in peace with the duties of an estate agent. Presently, however, Mr. Brookes burst into speech again.

"By the way," he said abruptly, "I suppose your wife doesn't know of a good cook, does she?"

"Well, no," replied Mr. Mummery. "They aren't so easy to find nowadays. In fact, we've only just got suited ourselves. But why? Surely your old Cookie isn't leaving you?"

"Good lord, no!" Mr. Brookes laughed heartily. "It would take an earthquake to shake off old Cookie. No. It's for the Philipsons. Their girl's getting married. That's the worst of girls. I said to Philipson, 'You mind what you're doing,' I said. 'Get somebody you know something about, or you may find yourself landed with this poisoning woman—what's her name—Andrews. Don't want to be sending wreaths to your funeral yet awhile,' I said. He laughed, but it's no laughing matter and so I told him. What we pay the police for I simply don't know. Nearly a month now, and they can't seem to lay hands on the woman. All they say is, they think she's hanging about the neighbourhood and 'may seek a situation as cook.' As cook! Now I ask you!"

"You don't think she committed suicide, then?" suggested Mr. Mummery.

"Suicide my foot!" retorted Mr. Brookes coarsely. "Don't you believe it, my boy. That coat found in the river was all eyewash. *They* don't commit suicide, that sort don't."

"What sort?"

"Those arsenic maniacs. They're too damned careful of their own skins. Cunning as weasels, that's what they are. It's only to be hoped they'll manage to catch her before she tries her hand on anybody else. As I told Philipson—"

"You think Mrs. Andrews did it, then?"

"Did it? Of course she did it. It's plain as the nose on your face. Looked after her old father, and he died suddenly—left her a bit of money, too. Then she keeps house for an elderly gentleman, and *he* dies suddenly. Now there's this husband and wife—man dies and woman taken very ill, of arsenic poisoning. Cook runs away, and you ask, did she do it? I don't mind betting that when they dig up the father and the other old bird they'll find *them* bung full of arsenic, too. Once that sort gets started, they don't stop. Grows on 'em, as you might say."

"I suppose it does," said Mr. Mummery. He picked up his paper again and studied the photograph of the missing woman. "She looks harmless enough," he remarked. "Rather a nice, motherly-looking kind of woman."

"She's got a bad mouth," pronounced Mr. Brookes. He had a theory that character showed in the mouth. "I wouldn't trust that woman an inch."

As the day went on, Mr. Mummery felt better. He was rather nervous about his lunch, choosing carefully a little boiled fish and custard pudding and being particular not to rush about immediately after the meal. To his great relief, the fish and custard remained where they were put, and he was not visited by that tiresome pain which had become almost habitual in the last fortnight. By the end of the day he became quite light-hearted. The bogey of illness and doctor's bills ceased to haunt him. He bought a bunch of bronze chrysanthemums to carry home to Ethel, and it was with a feeling of pleasant anticipation that he left the train and walked up the garden path of *Mon Abri*.

He was a little dashed by not finding his wife in the sitting room. Still clutching the bunch of chrysanthemums he pattered down the passage and pushed open the kitchen door.

Nobody was there but the cook. She was sitting at the table with her back to him, and started up almost guiltily as he approached.

"Lor', sir," she said, "you give me quite a start. I didn't hear the front door go."

"Where is Mrs. Mummery? Not feeling bad again, is she?"

"Well, sir, she's got a bit of a headache, poor lamb. I made her lay down and took her up a nice cup o' tea at half past four. I think she's dozing nicely now."

"Dear, dear," said Mr. Mummery.

"It was turning out the dining room done it, if you ask me," said Mrs. Sutton. " 'Now, don't you overdo yourself, ma'am,' I says to her, but you know how she is, sir. She gets that restless, she can't abear to be doing nothing."

"I know," said Mr. Mummery. "It's not your fault, Mrs. Sutton. I've sure you look after us both admirably. I'll just run up and have a peep at her. I won't disturb her if she's asleep. By the way, what are we having for dinner?"

"Well, I *had* made a nice steak-and-kidney pie," said Mrs. Sutton, in accents suggesting that she would readily turn it into a pumpkin or a coach and four if it was not approved of.

"Oh!" said Mr. Mummery. "Pastry? Well, I—"

"You'll find it beautiful and light," protested the cook, whisking open the oven door for Mr. Mummery to see. "And it's made with butter, sir, you having said that you found lard indigestible."

"Thank you, thank you," said Mr. Mummery. "I'm sure it will be most excellent. I haven't been feeling altogether the thing just lately, and lard does not seem to suit me nowadays."

"Well, it don't suit some people, and that's a fact," agreed Mrs. Sutton. "I shouldn't wonder if you've got a bit of a chill on the liver. I'm sure this weather is enough to upset anybody."

She bustled to the table and cleared away the picture paper which she had been reading.

"Perhaps the mistress would like her dinner sent up to her?" she suggested.

Mr. Mummery said he would go and see, and tiptoed his way upstairs. Ethel was lying snuggled under the ciderdown and looked very small and fragile in the big double bed. She stirred as he came in and smiled up at him.

"Hullo, darling!" said Mr. Mummery.

"Hullo! You back? I must have been asleep. I got tired and headachy, and Mrs. Sutton packed me off upstairs."

"You've been doing too much, sweetheart," said her husband, taking her hand in his and sitting down on the edge of the bed.

"Yes—it was naughty of me. What lovely flowers, Harold. All for me?"

"All for you, Tiddleywinks," said Mr. Mummery tenderly. "Don't I deserve something for that?"

Mrs. Mummery smiled, and Mr. Mummery took his reward several times over.

"That's quite enough, you sentimental old things," said Mrs. Mummery. "Run away, now, I'm going to get up."

"Much better go to bed, my precious, and let Mrs. Sutton send your dinner up," said her husband.

Ethel protested, but he was firm with her. If she didn't take care of herself, she wouldn't be allowed to go to the Drama Society meetings. And everybody was so anxious to have her back. The Welbecks had been asking after her and saying that they really couldn't get on without her.

"Did they?" said Ethel with some animation. "It's very sweet of them to want me. Well, perhaps I'll go to bed after all. And how has my old Hubby been all day?"

"Not too bad, not too bad."

"No more tummyaches?"

"Well, just a *little* tummyache. But it's quite gone now. Nothing for Tiddleywinks to worry about."

Mr. Mummery experienced no more distressing symptoms the next day or the next. Following the advice of the newspaper expert, he took to drinking orange juice, and was delighted with the results of the treatment. On Thursday, however, he was taken so ill in the night that Ethel was alarmed and insisted on sending for the doctor. The doctor felt his pulse and looked at his tongue and appeared to take the matter lightly. An inquiry into what he had been eating elicited the fact that dinner had consisted of pig's trotters, followed by a milk pudding, and that, before retiring, Mr. Mummery had consumed a large glass of orange juice, according to his new régime.

"There's your trouble," said Dr. Griffith cheerfully. "Orange juice is an excellent thing, and so are trotters, but not in combination. Pig and oranges together are extraordinarily bad for the liver. I don't know why they should be, but there's no doubt that they are. Now I'll send you round a little prescription and you stick to slops for a day or two and keep off pork. And don't you worry about him, Mrs. Mummery, he's as sound as a trout. *You're* the one we've got to look after. I don't want to see those black rings under the eyes, you know. Disturbed night, of course —yes. Taking your tonic regularly? That's right. Well, don't be alarmed about your hubby. We'll soon have him out and about again.

The prophecy was fulfilled, but not immediately. Mr. Mummery, though confining his diet to Benger's food, bread and milk and beef tea skilfully prepared by Mrs. Sutton and brought to his bedside by Ethel, remained very seedy all through Friday, and was only able to stagger rather shakily downstairs on Saturday afternoon. He had evidently suffered a "thorough upset." However, he was able to attend to a few papers which Brookes had sent down from the office for his signature, and to deal with the household books. Ethel was not a business woman, and Mr. Mummery always ran over the accounts with her. Having settled up with the butcher, the baker, the dairy and the coal merchant, Mr. Mummery looked up inquiringly.

"Anything more, darling?"

"Well, there's Mrs. Sutton. This is the end of her month, you know."

"So it is. Well, you're quite satisfied with her, aren't you, darling?"

"Yes, rather—aren't you? She's a good cook, and a sweet, motherly old thing, too. Don't you think it was a real brain wave of mine, engaging her like that, on the spot?"

"I do, indeed," said Mr. Mummery.

"It was a perfect providence, her turning up like that, just after that wretched Jane had gone off without even giving notice. I was in absolute *despair*. It was a little bit of a gamble, of course, taking her without any references, but naturally, if she'd been looking after a widowed mother, you couldn't expect her to give references."

"N-no," said Mr. Mummery. At the time he had felt uneasy about the matter, though he had not liked to say much because, of course, they simply had to have somebody. And the experiment had justified itself so triumphantly in practice that one couldn't say much about it now. He had once rather tentatively suggested writing to the clergyman of Mrs. Sutton's parish, but, as Ethel had said, the clergyman wouldn't have been able to tell them anything about cooking, and cooking, after all, was the chief point.

Mr. Mummery counted out the month's money.

"And by the way, my dear," he said, "you might just mention to Mrs. Sutton that if she must *read* the morning paper before I come down, I should be obliged if she would fold it neatly afterwards."

"What an old fuss-box you are, darling," said his wife.

Mr. Mummery sighed. He could not explain that it was somehow important that the morning paper should come to him fresh and prim, like a virgin. Women did not feel these things.

On Sunday, Mr. Mummery felt very much better—quite his old self, in fact. He enjoyed the *News of the World* over breakfast in bed, reading the murders rather carefully. Mr. Mummery got quite a lot of pleasure out of murders—they gave him an agreeable thrill of vicarious adventure, for, naturally, they were matters quite remote from daily life in the outskirts of Hull.

He noticed that Brookes had been perfectly right. Mrs. Andrews' father and former employer had been "dug up" and had, indeed, proved to be "bung full" of arsenic.

He came downstairs for dinner—roast sirloin, with the potatoes done under the meat and Yorkshire pudding of delicious lightness, and an apple tart to follow. After three days of invalid diet, it was delightful to savour the crisp fat and underdone lean. He ate moderately, but with a sensuous enjoyment. Ethel, on the other hand, seemed a little lacking in appetite, but then, she had never been a great meat eater. She was fastidious and, besides, she was (quite unnecessarily) afraid of getting fat.

It was a fine afternoon, and at three o'clock, when he was quite certain that the roast beef was "settling" properly, it occurred to Mr. Mummery that it would be a good thing to put the rest of those bulbs in. He slipped on his old gardening coat and wandered out to the potting shed. Here he picked up a bag of tulips and a trowel, and then, remembering that he was wearing his good trousers, decided that it would be wise to take a mat to kneel on. When had he had the mat last? He could not recollect, but he rather fancied he had put it away in the corner under the potting shelf. Stooping down, he felt about in the dark among the flower pots. Yes, there it was, but there was a tin of something in the way. He lifted the tin carefully out. Of course, yes—the remains of the weed killer.

Mr. Mummery glanced at the pink label, printed in staring letters with the legend: "ARSENICAL WEED KILLER. *Poison*," and observed, with a mild feeling of excitement, that it was the same brand of stuff that had been associated with Mrs. Andrews' latest victim. He was rather pleased about it. It gave him a sensation of being remotely but definitely in touch with important events. Then he noticed, with surprise and a little annoyance, that the stopper had been put in quite loosely.

"However'd I come to leave it like that?" he grunted. "Shouldn't wonder if all the goodness has gone off." He removed the stopper and squinted into the can, which appeared to be half-full. Then he rammed the thing home again, giving it a sharp thump with the handle of the trowel for better security. After that he washed his hands carefully at the scullery tap, for he did not believe in taking risks.

He was a trifle disconcerted, when he came in after planting the tulips, to find visitors in the sitting room. He was always pleased to see Mrs. Welbeck and her son, but he would rather have had warning, so that he could have scrubbed the garden mould out of his nails more thoroughly. Not that Mrs. Welbeck appeared to notice. She was a talkative woman and paid little attention to anything but her own conversation. Much to Mr. Mummery's annoyance, she chose to prattle about the Lincoln Poisoning Case. A most unsuitable subject for the tea table, thought Mr. Mummery, at the best of times. His own "upset" was vivid enough in his memory to make him queasy over the discussion of medical symptoms, and besides, this kind of talk was not good for Ethel. After all, the poisoner was still supposed to be in the neighbourhood. It was enough to make even a strong-nerved woman uneasy. A glance at Ethel showed him that she was looking quite white and tremulous. He must stop Mrs. Welbeck somehow, or there would be a repetition of one of the old, dreadful, hysterical scenes.

He broke into the conversation with violent abruptness.

"Those Forsyth cuttings, Mrs. Welbeck," he said. "Now is just about the time to take them. If you care to come down to the garden I will get them for you."

He saw a relieved glance pass between Ethel and young Welbeck. Evidently the boy understood the situation and was chafing at his mother's tactlessness. Mrs. Welbeck, brought up all standing, gasped slightly and then veered off with obliging readiness on the new tack. She accompanied her host down the garden and chattered cheerfully about horticulture while he selected and trimmed the cuttings. She complimented Mr. Mummery on the immaculacy of his gravel paths. "I simply *cannot* keep the weeds down," she said.

Mr. Mummery mentioned the weed killer and praised its efficacy.

"That stuff!" Mrs. Welbeck stared at him. Then she shuddered. "I wouldn't have it in my place for a thousand pounds," she said, with emphasis.

Mr. Mummery smiled. "Oh, we keep it well away from the house," he said. "Even if I were a careless sort of person—"

He broke off. The recollection of the loosened stopper had come to him suddenly, and it was as though, deep down in his mind, some obscure assembling of ideas had taken place. He left it at that, and went into the kitchen to fetch a newspaper to wrap up the cuttings.

Their approach to the house had evidently been seen from the sitting-room window, for when they entered, young Welbeck was already on his feet and holding Ethel's hand in the act of saying good-bye. He manœuvred his mother out of the house with tactful promptness and Mr. Mummery returned to the kitchen to clear up the newspapers he had fished out of the drawer. To clear them up and to examine them more closely. Something had struck him about them, which he wanted to verify. He turned them over very carefully, sheet by sheet. Yes—he had been right. Every portrait of Mrs. Andrews, every paragraph and line about the Lincoln Poisoning Case, had been carefully cut out.

Mr. Mummery sat down by the kitchen fire. He felt as though he needed warmth. There seemed to be a curious cold lump of something at the pit of his stomach—something that he was chary of investigating.

He tried to recall the appearance of Mrs. Andrews as shown in the newspaper photographs, but he had not a good visual memory. He remembered having remarked to Brookes that it was a "motherly" face. Then he tried counting up the time since the disappearance. Nearly a month, Brookes had said—and that was a week ago. Must be over a month now. A month. He had just paid Mrs. Sutton her month's money.

"Ethel!" was the thought that hammered at the door of his brain. At all costs, he must cope with this monstrous suspicion on his own. He must spare her any shock or anxiety. And he must be sure of his ground. To dismiss the only decent cook they had ever had out of sheer, unfounded panic, would be wanton cruelty to both women. If he did it at all, it would have to be done arbitrarily, preposterously—he could not suggest horrors to Ethel. However, it was done, there would be trouble. Ethel would not understand and he dared not tell her.

But if by any chance there was anything in this ghastly doubt—how could he expose Ethel to the appalling danger of having the woman in the house a moment longer? He thought of the family at Lincoln—the husband dead, the wife escaped by a miracle with her life. Was not any shock, any risk, better than that?

Mr. Mummery felt suddenly very lonely and tired. His illness had taken it out of him.

Those illnesses—they had begun, when? Three weeks ago he had had the first attack. Yes, but then he had always been rather subject to gastric troubles. Bilious attacks. Not so violent, perhaps, as these last, but undoubted bilious attacks.

He pulled himself together and went, rather heavily, into the sitting room. Ethel was tucked up in a corner of the chesterfield.

"Tired, darling?"

"Yes, a little."

"That woman has worn you out with talking. She oughtn't to talk so much."

"No." Her head shifted wearily in the cushions. "All about that horrible case. I don't like hearing about such things."

"Of course not. Still, when a thing like that happens in the neighbourhood, people will gossip and talk. It would be a relief if they caught the woman. One doesn't like to think—"

"I don't want to think of anything so hateful. She must be a horrible creature."

"Horrible. Brookes was saying the other day—"

"I don't want to hear what he said. I don't want to hear about it at all. I want to be quiet. I want to be quiet!"

He recognised the note of rising hysteria.

"Tiddleywinks shall be quiet. Don't worry, darling. We won't talk about horrors."

No. It would not do to talk about them.

Ethel went to bed early. It was understood that on Sundays Mr. Mummery should sit up till Mrs. Sutton came in. Ethel was a little anxious about this, but he assured her that he felt quite strong enough. In body, indeed, he did; it was his mind that felt weak and confused. He had decided to make a casual remark about the mutilated newspapers—just to see what Mrs. Sutton would say.

He allowed himself the usual indulgence of a whisky and soda as he sat waiting. At a quarter to ten he heard the familiar click of the garden gate. Footsteps passed up the gravel—squeak, squeak, to the back-door. Then the sound of the latch, the shutting of the door, the rattle of bolts being shot home. Then a pause. Mrs. Sutton would be taking off her hat. The moment was coming.

The step sounded in the passage. The door opened. Mrs. Sutton in her neat black dress stood on the threshold. He was aware of a reluctance to face her. Then he looked up. A plump-faced woman, her eyes obscured by thick horn-rimmed spectacles. Was there, perhaps, something hard about the mouth? Or was it just that she had lost most of her front teeth?

"Would you be requiring anything tonight, sir, before I go up?"

"No, thank you, Mrs. Sutton."

"I hope you are feeling better, sir." Her eager interest in his health seemed to him almost sinister, but the eyes, behind the thick glasses, were inscrutable.

"Quite better, thank you, Mrs. Sutton."

"Mrs. Mummery is not indisposed, is she, sir? Should I take her up a glass of hot milk or anything?"

"No, thank you, no." He spoke hurriedly, and fancied that she looked disappointed.

"Very well, sir. Good night, sir."

"Good night. Oh! by the way, Mrs. Sutton—"

"Yes, sir?"

"Oh, nothing," said Mr. Mummery, "nothing."

Next morning Mr. Mummery opened his paper eagerly. He would have been glad to learn that an arrest had been made over the week-end. But there was no news for him. The chairman of a trust company had blown out his brains, and the headlines were all occupied with tales about lost millions and ruined shareholders. Both in his own paper and in those he purchased on the way to the office, the Lincoln Poisoning Tragedy had been relegated to an obscure paragraph on a back page, which informed him that the police were still baffled.

The next few days were the most uncomfortable that Mr. Mummery had ever spent. He developed a habit of coming down early in the morning and prowling about the kitchen. This made Ethel nervous, but Mrs. Sutton offered no remark. She watched him tolerantly, even, he thought, with something like amusement. After all, it was ridiculous. What was the use of supervising the breakfast, when he had to be out of the house every day between half past nine and six?

At the office, Brookes rallied him on the frequency with which he rang up Ethel. Mr. Mummery paid no attention. It was reassuring to hear her voice and to know that she was safe and well.

Nothing happened, and by the following Thursday he began to think that he had been a fool. He came home late that night. Brookes had persuaded him to go with him to a little bachelor dinner for a friend who was about to get married. He left the others at eleven o'clock, however, refusing to make a night of it. The household was in bed when he got back but a note from Mrs. Sutton lay on the table, informing him that there was cocoa for him in the kitchen, ready for hotting up. He hotted it up accordingly in the little saucepan where it stood. There was just one good cupful.

He sipped it thoughtfully, standing by the kitchen stove. After the first sip, he put the cup down. Was it his fancy, or was there something queer about the taste? He sipped it again, rolling it upon his tongue. It seemed to him to have a faint tang, metallic and unpleasant. In a sudden dread he ran out to the scullery and spat the mouthful into the sink.

After this, he stood quite still for a moment or two. Then, with a curious deliberation, as though his movements had been dictated to him, he fetched an empty medicine bottle from the pantry shelf, rinsed it under the tap and tipped the contents of the cup carefully into it. He slipped the bottle into his coat pocket and moved on tiptoe to the back door. The bolts were difficult to draw without noise, but he managed it at last. Still on tiptoe, he stole across the garden to the potting shed. Stooping down, he struck a match. He knew exactly where he had left the tin of weed killer, under the shelf behind the pots at the back. Cautiously he lifted it out. The match flared up and burnt his fingers, but before he could light another his sense of touch had told him what he wanted to know. The stopper was loose again.

Panic seized Mr. Mummery, standing there in the earthy-smelling shed, in his dress suit and overcoat, holding the tin in one hand the match box in the other. He wanted very badly to run and tell somebody what he had discovered.

Instead, he replaced the tin exactly where he had found it and went back to the house. As he crossed the garden again, he noticed a light in Mrs. Sutton's bedroom window. This terrified him more than anything which had gone before. Was she watching him? Ethel's window was dark. If she had drunk anything deadly there would be lights everywhere, movements, calls for the doctor, just as when he himself had been attacked. Attacked—that was the right word, he thought.

Still, with the same odd presence of mind and precision, he went in, washed out the utensils and made a second brew of cocoa, which he left standing in the saucepan. He crept quietly to his bedroom. Ethel's voice greeted him on the threshold.

"How late you are, Harold. Naughty old boy! Have a good time?"

"Not bad. You all right, darling?"

"Quite all right. Did Mrs. Sutton leave something hot for you? She said she would."

"Yes, but I wasn't thirsty."

Ethel laughed. "Oh! it was *that* sort of party, was it?"

Mr. Mummery did not attempt any denials. He undressed and got into bed and clutched his wife to him as though defying death and hell to take her from him. Next morning he would act. He thanked God that he was not too late.

Mr. Dimthorpe, the chemist, was a great friend of Mr. Mummery's. They had often sat together in the untidy little shop on Spring Bank and exchanged views on green-fly and club-root. Mr. Mummery told his story frankly to Mr. Dimthorpe and handed over the bottle of cocoa. Mr. Dimthorpe congratulated him on his prudence and intelligence.

"I will have it ready for you by this evening," he said, "and if it's what you think it is, then we shall have a clear case on which to take action."

Mr. Mummery thanked him, and was extremely vague and in-attentive at business all day. BBut that hardly mattered, for Mr. Brookes, who had seen the party through to a riotous end in the small hours, was in no very observant mood. At half past four, Mr. Mummery shut up his desk decisively and announced that he was off early, he had a call to make.

Mr. Dimthorpe was ready for him.

"No doubt about it," he said. "I used Marsh's test. It's a heavy dose—no wonder you tasted it. There must be four or five grains of pure arsenic in that bottle. Look, here's the mirror. You can see it for yourself."

Mr. Mummery gazed at the little glass tube with its ominous purple-black stain.

"Will you ring up the police from here?" asked the chemist.

"No," said Mr. Mummery. "No—I want to get home. God knows what's happening there. And I've only just time to catch my train."

"All right," said Mr. Dimthorpe. "Leave it to me. I'll ring them up for you."

The local train did not go fast enough for Mr. Mummery. Ethel—poisoned—dying—dead — Ethel—poisoned—dying—dead—the wheels drummed in his ears. He almost ran out of the station and along the road. A car was standing at his door. He saw it from the end of the street and broke into a gallop. It had happened already. The doctor was there. Fool, murderer that he was to have left things so late.

Then, while he was still a hundred and fifty yards off, he saw the front door open. A man came out followed by Ethel herself.

The visitor got into his car and was driven away. Ethel went in again. She was safe—safe!

He could hardly control himself to hang up his hat and coat and go in looking reasonably calm. His wife had returned to the armchair by the fire and greeted him in some surprise. There were tea things on the table.

"Back early, aren't you?"

"Yes—business was slack. Somebody been to tea?"

"Yes, young Welbeck. About the arrangement for the Drama Society. She spoke briefly but with an undertone of excitement.

A qualm came over Mr. Mummery. Would a guest be any protection? His face must have shown his feelings, for Ethel stared at him in amazement.

"What's the matter, Harold, you look so queer."

"Darling," said Mr. Mummery, "there's something I want to tell you about." He sat down and took her hand in his. "Something a little unpleasant, I'm afraid—"

"Oh, ma'am!"

The cook was in the doorway.

"I beg your pardon, sir—I didn't know you was in. Will you be taking tea or can I clear away? And, oh, ma'am, there was a young man at the fishmonger's and he's just come from Grimsby and they've caught that dreadful woman—that Mrs. Andrews. Isn't it a good thing? It's worritted me dreadful to think she was going about like that, but they've caught her. Taken a job as housekeeper she had to two elderly ladies and they found the wicked poison on her. Girl as spotted her will get a reward. I been keeping my eyes open for her, but it's at Grimsby she was all the time."

Mr. Mummery clutched at the arm of his chair. It had all been a mad mistake then. He wanted to shout or cry. He wanted to apologise to this foolish, pleasant, excited woman. All a mistake.

But there had been the cocoa. Mr. Dimthorpe. Marsh's test. Five grains of arsenic. Who, then—?

He glanced around at his wife, and in her eyes he saw something that he had never seen before. . . .

THE SHADOW

By BEN HECHT

THE MARVELOUS SARASTRO CAME FROM WARSAW ALTHOUGH HE sometimes hinted at Thibet and the Mountains of the Moon.

He was a Pole and a vaudeville magician, but given a sympathetic ear, he would fall to darkening his origins and clothing himself in such mysteries of parentage, race, and geography as gave one an uneasy feeling.

Never have I known a man to lie, boast, pose so tirelessly and childishly. But Sarastro was the true charlatan and one forgave him this. One even demanded it of him.

Often, while listening to his Mother Goose mysticism, his Munchausen adventures, his garbled and pompous chatter of genii, sylphs, and undines, I have grown annoyed at my own skepticism. How much more marvelous was the Marvelous Sarastro if one believed him! How much more entertaining this Arabian Night in which he lived, could one accept it with the heart of a child rather than the dull incredulity of a modern author.

And often, while smiling a bit condescendingly at my friend Sarastro as he unfolded his Brobdingnagian doings, I have been suddenly impressed by the thought of what a genius he would once have seemed; what a great man another age would have considered him—a savant, Magus, and dangerous kin of Lucifer. At such moments Sarastro's somewhat humorous appearance would take on an air of distinction and authority. His small eyes appeared sinister. His thin lips seemed cruel. His plump womanish face became a symbol of enigma. His long thin nose acquired a Papal dignity. His silken brown hair, falling in a Dutch bob almost to his neck, was transformed into a fascinating and medieval coiffure.

It was with the foregoing notions about Sarastro that I called on him in his dressing-room back stage at the Palace Theater. I had sat through his turn, thrilled as always by his dexterity and pompousness. For Sarastro was no glib magician apologizing for his pretenses with aged jokes and comical patter. He performed his levitations and disappearances, his transmutations and fears of legerdemain with the profound, unsmiling mein of one truly at work on Miracles. But I noticed, nevertheless, a change in his manner. He seemed nervous and preoccupied.

He greeted me coldly as I opened the door of his dressing-room and continued to remove his make-up in silence. I offered compliments. He nodded and said nothing. I remarked on his new feat—a disappearing cage full of birds. This was, said I, a miracle which would have astounded the great Herman.

"I am glad you saw it," said Sarastro. He was drying his face. "It is the last time."

"What is the last time?" I asked.

"The last time I perform," said Sarastro. "I leave tonight for Paris. You will never see me again. No one will ever see me again. It is the last of Sarastro."

"Why are you going to Paris?" I asked.

"To murder a man," said Sarastro. "I arrive on the 15th. On the morning of the 16th there will be one fiend less in the world."

I made no remark at this and disguised my delight with a sympathetic frown.

"What time do you sail?" I asked, as he put on his street clothes.

"At midnight."

"Would you care to honor me as my guest for supper?" I asked.

"Yes," said Sarastro. "Part of me being still human, I must continue to eat."

Twenty minutes later we entered a quiet, almost deserted café. Sarastro ordered food wearily but profusely.

"There is no hurry," he said. "My things are all on the boat. Here is my passport. Here is my ticket."

He showed me these documents.

"This is rather a new ambition," I said, "murder."

"Oh no," said Sarastro. "I have had this ambition for twenty years."

"The same man?"

"Yes."

"I have never suspected it."

"Hate," said Sarastro, "is not an emotion which one wears on one's sleeve. It is a soul. When it enters a man he may live on, he may laugh, work, and go about, and there will be no difference to those who are his friends; but his soul has only one color, his nights have only one dream. For twenty years I have dreamed only one thing—to kill a man."

I said nothing. We ate in silence for several minutes.

"His name is Rico Sansone," said Sarastro. "Have you ever heard of him?"

"No," I said.

"On the 16th," said Sarastro, "you will hear that he is dead."

"Why are you going to kill him?" I asked.

The medieval face smiled. A dreamy look filled the small eyes.

"Because," said Sarastro, "he is the most evil man in the world. I have been waiting for twenty years for his name to appear. For as long as he chose to hide there was no hope. He is too clever. Yes, even for me. Far too clever. But I knew that his vanity would betray him and that some day I would read again the name Rico Sansone. I knew he would return to the stage."

"Is he a magician?" I asked.

"Yes," said Sarastro. "The greatest that ever lived. The most profound and evil. He has no soul."

I nodded.

"He is greater than I," said Sarastro and closed his eyes as if overcome by this statement. "He begins his performance in Paris on the 15th."

"I would like to hear the story," I said frankly.

"You will," said Sarastro. "But I must have your oath not to interfere."

"You have it," I said.

"Very well," said Sarastro. "The story begins twenty years ago. I was a young man. I traveled with a small carnival through the villages of southeastern Europe. We were a company of clowns, gypsies, acrobats, and conjurors. We traveled in gilded wagons and performed for peasants and herdsmen on the outskirts of their villages.

"My powers developed early. I was young, but I was able to cast horoscopes, foretell the future, reveal the past, and converse with the gnomes and salamanders. I wore black tights and a small black jacket that came only to my waist. There was always a sword at my side, for in dealing with the spirits that infest the darkness beyond life one must always be armed. I was known as the Black Seer, and it was not only the peasants who held me in awe. My comrades themselves feared and respected me.

"One night we came to a village in Malo-Russia. Our cymbals sounded, our music played, our torches flickered in the spring wind, and the villagers crowded around our tents and wagons. I had taken my place in the black box on the platform outside my tent. There were holes in the box through which I could watch the crowd while the barker made his announcements. He ran up and down the platform, ringing his bell and shouting 'The Black Seer, the Marvel of Marvels, Sarastro the Magician, who speaks with the dead and reads the secrets of life. . . .'

"I saw her for the first time at this moment. Her young and gentle face surprised me among so many peasants. I said to myself, 'What a strange girl! What a beautiful child!' In a short while I began my performance in the tent. But I was restless. I kept watching the entrance. At length an old peasant led her in, holding her by the hand. I saw at once that she was blind.

"The old man led her to my side and asked that I tell her fortune. He said she was his daughter, but it needed no knowledge of the stars to see that he lied. I questioned him and learned her simple history. Se had been born blind and cast aside as an infant by a tyrant-noble of the vicinity and she had been found and raised by this old man and his wife.

"I studied her face as he talked. Pure as a seraph's, her large sightless eyes calm, resigned. She was eighteen and beautiful, pale, delicate, noble. But that does not describe her. It is in the eyes that the soul of a woman is usually to be seen. Anna's eyes were empty. She could neither see nor be seen by them. But the spirit which found these eyes closed lighted the rest of her face and body. A kindly, radiant child spoke from her lips. I held her white hands which she had offered me trustingly and I cast her horoscope. A dark mist passed over me and I listened to the voices which foretell the future. 'Sorrow, sorrow,' they breathed, 'pain and sorrow. Fly . . . run. . . .'

"But I smiled and my own voice was serene as I spoke.

" 'The spirits promise you happiness,' I told her, 'your hands will touch beautiful things. Love and delight await you.'

"I was rewarded for my lies by a smile such as one sees on a child's face when it is dreaming.

"That was the beginning. Her face haunted me that night and I could not sleep. I made inquiries the next morning and sought her out. We walked through the hills. She did not need my hand to guide her. She knew every stone, every turn of the paths we followed. She spoke of the trees around us. She had strange names for them. And she spoke of the flowers that were to come soon in these woods. I forgot that she was blind. I came again the next day—and the next. Her purity, her sweetness delighted me. But there was something else—a sense of disquiet. It had come to me first from the stars. I had heard a warning out of the dark mists in which the voices of the dead are hidden.

"But now more than before I felt it behind the child's smile of her lips. When her hands touched mine for the first time she shuddered and grew pale. I knew then that she was aware of her destiny. The stars had told me she would not live long and that agony and terror waited for her on the short journey.

"She was innocent, untouched as yet by life. But it is unnecessary to know the ways of the world to know how one's heart will break. Here, hidden away, she awaited her fate without too much knowledge or too much dread. Yet her soul knew it completely. Her hand, when it sought mine in the silent shadowed woods, sought the hands of a protector. In my supernatural talent, she fancied, lay a hope of escape. I understood this as I looked at her.

"We remained for two weeks in this village. When we left Anna came with me as my wife. More than her beauty and her gentleness, the sense of her ominous future had made the thought of leaving her impossible. Thus, in seeking to save her, I fulfilled the terrible message of the stars. For it was I—Sarastro—who was the instrument fate had selected for her ruin.

"She was happy. We rode together in the gilded wagon. Her pure, trusting face was always beside me. So that she might never be lonely I instructed her in a few of the elements of magic. In a little time she was able to take her place on the platform outside my tent. Dressed in the colorful robe I bought for her she sat blindfolded—for who would believe so perfect, so beautiful a creature was without sight?—and guessed numbers, told fortunes. Everything delighted her. Everything made her smile. She was happy.

"But I was not. From the moment that I embraced her as my wife I was haunted. How can I tell you of this dread, the continual dread of knowing something, of waiting for something that one knows, of waiting for life to despoil one?

"I tried to learn more, I sought for some clue that would enable me to anticipate the thing that menaced us and so, perhaps, overcome it. But my magic could tell me nothing more. It only repeated for me the words of dread, of horror.

"Then I knew, one night as I stood in the black box outside my tent, that I needed no further word from the mists of prophecy. It was there. It had come. He stood among the peasants before our tent—a graceful figure, smiling, leaning on his cane. A man of the world amusingly out of place in this far-away little village. I looked at him through the holes in my box. As I looked a glow of fear came to my heart.

"He had turned his face and I saw his remarkable eyes lighted by the flare of our torches. They were round, colorless eyes. They were proud and smiling and yet lifeless.

"I watched him and felt afraid. He was studying Anna. Never once did he stop looking at her. When we started to enter the tent for the performance he disappeared. I said nothing to Anna. What was there to say? That a man had looked at her. She would understand too much.

"I was waiting for him the next night. Yes, eagerly. You know the eagerness with which one waits for all certainties whether they are bright or dreadful. He came back. He stood once more leaning on his cane, graceful, smiling and sinister. His eyes were on her face.

"In the wagon that night she spoke to me.

" 'There is a man looking at me,' she said, as we lay side by side. Her hand crept into mine. There was nothing more to say. The same thing was in our minds.

"On the third night I decided to act. My temper was quick and fiery. I came up to him as he stood watching Anna. He followed me as if my enraged demand to speak to him were a gracious request. Ah, how subtle he was, how graceful! But that is the way of those whose souls are fashioned in Hell.

"On the outskirts of the crowd I seized his arm and demanded to know what he meant by coming every night and staring at my wife. He removed my hand as if it were a child's. I can tell you there was something terrifying in his strength as I felt it for the first time. For I knew . . . but that comes later. He looked at me with his cold lifeless eyes and he spoke softly and apologized for having given offense. He explained that he was a student of the occult traveling about the world in search of knowledge. He praised Anna as a woman of remarkable psychic powers. He said he had hoped to be able to induce her to join him as an assistant, for he was planning soon to go on the stage. But now that he knew she was my wife. . . . He shrugged his shoulders and apologized again for his seeming forwardness. Then he looked at me with a curious smile and said softly, 'She is blind, is she not?' In this moment as he smiled, I understood that he knew. Like myself, he had seen the ominous, the dreadful shadow around her.

"Yet I could do nothing. Despite my travels I was a rustic, young, hot-blooded, untutored in the ways of society. I had no words with which to resist his charm. Yes, even at that moment when I most understood him I found myself listening with interest to his talk—pleased, disarmed, moved somehow by the loneliness that underlay his eager, friendly manner. I recognized him as a genius. And he walked back to our tent with me, talking already as if I were his dearest friend.

"It was thus Rico entered our lives. Little by little, during the days that followed, he attached himself to us. He confessed simply that he had nothing to do, that he had no friends, no kin. He said he had been wandering alone over Europe since he was a boy. And he talked. Ah, his talk! We listened, Anna and I, to his tales. Yes, he had been everywhere, seen everything. He brought the world into our gilded wagon. He wooed us both as a lonely, brilliant man woos the friendship of those he likes.

"In his presence I always felt elated and flattered. But when he left and I was alone again with Anna a disquiet came. I waited darkly for her first words. You know the dangerous words a woman speaks when she finds herself interested in a man. But they did not come. Instead she would take my hands, press them to her cheeks and whisper, 'I do not like him, Sari. I do not like the way he looks at me. I feel something strange in him.'

"Then how eager I was to defend him, to remind her of his gay talk and of how he had made us laugh and feel happy. Thus does a man move in the grip of his destiny, thus do we dig with our own hands the appointed grave for our happiness. I was a fool, yes. But I was to be even a greater fool.

"For the time came when Anna took my hands one night and told me that our friend had made love to her. My heart grew black. I listened as she spoke for some telltale note in her voice. But, no. Anna's soul was as transparent, as pure as a child's. She clung to me as she had clung that first time in her native woods. And she repeated her fear of him. She told me he had come to her while she was alone, had taken her hand gently in his and asked her if she loved me and how deeply she loved me. Then he asked her if she loved me more than happiness or life. She had with-drawn her hand and answered only as a pure and noble soul can answer such questions. She had said, 'I cannot talk of love to you, even of my love for my husband. Please leave me.' And he had gone, pausing to ask her in the doorway to forgive him and to say that he understood now.

"It was late at night as she told me these things. And when she had finished and I was holding her in my arms there was a knock on the door. I opened it. It was Rico standing on the steps of our wagon. He held a heap of wild flowers in his arms.

"He entered without any word and laid the flowers on our table and I knew that he had picked them in woods beyond the village. Then he spoke. 'She has told you,' he said, and as I continued to stare at him blankly, he went on, 'it was not that I desired to hurt her, my friend. I asked only if she were happy. Because she has grown dear to me. She is the first woman to whom my heart has turned. And I asked, because for a moment I grew weak. I knocked at a forbidden door as a lonely beggar might knock timidly and foolishly at the door of a great house within which he had caught a glimpse of feasting. Forget my weakness. Let me remain your friend. I am heartbroken to think I have brought a moment of unhappiness or alarm to either of you. . . .'

"I remember more of his words. But what are words compared to the emotion that kindles them? And I will perhaps seem like a greater fool than I was when I tell you that tears filled my eyes and that I seized his hand. For I had never before heard so deep, so melancholy a voice as his. A voice so resigned, so caressing. I poured wine for the three of us. We drank—Rico and I. But Anna did not touch her glass. She did not speak once during his visit. When he left she sat motionless for a long time. I came to her and she raised her gentle, brooding face, and her words, uttered softly, brought the dread back into my heart.

" 'I'm afraid of him,' she murmured. 'I'm afraid, Sari.'

"This was in the third month of our friendship. We were in Bavaria. Rico had come with us to Baumburg. Our carnival had planned to remain here for several weeks and Anna and I had moved into a pension. And gradually we saw less and less of Rico. He came occasionally to talk and sometimes the three of us took walks. But I began to feel it was my companionship he desired, not Anna's. He had undertaken to initiate me into the mysteries of magic and we spent long hours together—without Anna. He was learned. He knew things that are not known by many men. I was again flattered, lured, disarmed. Under his care my mind was expanding, my powers developing.

"Then one day I was sitting in my tent preparing for the afternoon performance when a curious sense overcame me. I felt a pressure on my heart as if a hand were closing around it. It was a warning. When one is close to the secrets of life and death one understands their voice, their inner voice.

"I left the tent quickly and hurried to the pension. Anna had remained behind as she frequently did in the afternoon. I tried to rid myself of the oppression as I approached our home. It would not do to frighten Anna. Yet I found myself running toward the door. I paused, waited till I had recovered my breath and then, smiling, opened the door quietly. I saw Rico standing with his arms around her, her face raised to his lips.

"Speechless, powerless, I looked at them. I heard her voice murmuring words of love. Her arms moved around his neck and she kissed him. My head grew black. In another instant I would have fallen as one falls under a heavy blow. Yes, death seemed to enter me. Then I heard his voice. He spoke her name. He caressed her with words. At their sound a horror seized me. It was my voice. It was Sarastro talking. It was a voice that seemed to come from my own throat. A horrible, familiar voice. And I understood what had happened.

"I sprang forward shouting his name . . . Rico! He turned and faced me. He pointed his finger at me as if he were an image in a mirror. 'Rico,' he echoed.

"I heard Anna scream. But murder was in my heart. I fought with this monster. I flew at him with a knife. We struggled across the room and he answered my cries with cries that eachoed each note, each inflection of my voice. I saw him through my rage. His face was contorted like my own. His every feature had changed. He was Sarastro. There were two Sarastros screaming together, tumbling over each other.

"Then he held me in hands that were like steel fetters. Powerless I lay, mad with rage and terror, under him. I could not move or cry out. His hand was on my throat. I lay gasping and crazed, and it was Sarastro who was holding me. Then this horrible and familiar figure changed. It became Rico. It was Rico Sansone who spoke. The breath was leaving my body. I was strangling, dying, yet I could hear him—'Sarastro. God! You are killing me. Sari—Sari. Have mercy. I am dying!' His voice was faint. I felt in this moment the agonies of a hundred deaths, for as my eyes grew dark I saw with horror the thing he had in his mind. He was pretending it was I who was killing him. And thus he would kill me and go to her as Sarastro. It would be Rico Sansone who was buried. It would be Sarastro who remained.

"For a moment I caught a glimpse of his cold, lifeless eyes burning now over my face as he enacted his false death-groaning, pleading for mercy. And a strength drawn from the soul filled my lungs. I cried out the name Anna—once, twice, knowing that by this she would understand it was I—I who was dying. And darkness seized me.

"An hour had passed when I opened my eyes. My head was splitting. My throat was stiffened. I raised myself and looked. He was gone. I saw her. She was standing in a corner of the room, crouched against the wall, her hand against her teeth and staring into the terrible dark around her.

" 'It is I,' I whispered, 'Anna!'

"She shrank from my voice. I dragged myself to her feet, calling her name, sobbing, pleading. But when I touched her she sank to the floor.

"It had come—the agonies and terror foretold by the stars. I lifted her to the bed. She recovered her senses, but the touch of my hand was enough to make her scream. I sat beside her through the night. I talked quietly of the little things that had been between us, of secrets only a husband may share with a woman. I recalled myself to her as one who has been away for years might struggle vainly to prove who he was. She lay silent, her face drawn with terror and listened. Finally at dawn she whispered my name.

"This was the beginning. Rico had disappeared. I had frustrated his diabolical plan with my last cry. With his evil happiness a moment away he had released me and fled. But I kept this part of the horror a secret from her.

"We laid our plans. As soon as she was able to walk we abandoned the carnival and left Baumburg. We went to Munich. We were inseparable. She could not bear to have me away even for a moment. The darkness in which she had found peace and love had become filled with terror for her. I understood everything in her soul. Yes, even the trembling that would seize her sometimes when I took her hand.

"It would be folly to engage an attendant, a third one to watch, to guard. It was I alone he could not deceive. To everyone else he could become Sarastro. Even to her whose senses had learned every breath, every inflection of the man she loved, he had been Sarastro.

"Yes, we made our plans. We invented codes of greeting and secret handclasps and intimate caresses by which she might know me. Ah, how curious and terrible were these first months; With what foolish ruses, desperate childish ruses, we struggled to evade the terror that had closed around us! She was brave. She grew to smile again. The months passed. She whispered to me now as we lay together that her spirit was recovered. She was not afraid any more, she said. The thing she had feared had come and had passed. It was ended now. We were free.

"I agreed with her. I feigned exuberance, carelessness. You understand how it was. It was her soul I must cure of its dread, for in this dread alone she would go mad. When she insisted I return to work I went. I begged her to accompany me so that we might be together while we performed. But she answered strangely that she no longer felt the power in her to perform. Something had passed from her. And I understood this, too. But I would not let her see. It would not do to alarm her. I went alone. I pretended I was without fear. But it was a lie. I was still waiting. . . .

"I thought first of flying to another part of the world. But one does not escape terror by running. He would be there—wherever I was. I knew this, because it was given to me to know my fate. I remembered his genius. He had been made in Hell. He was a shadow from which I could not hope to hide. So we remained in Munich. I secured employment in a cabaret. Eight months passed. The dread, although it never left me, grew vaguer. And our life had become again almost like a honeymoon. Almost, I say, for there were moments in which I caught a glimpse of Anna's inner soul. I would wake at night to find her fingers tracing the contours of my face and body. I would lie motionless listening to her moan out of the nightmare whose nature I knew only too well. In the morning she would waken, tired and nervous. On such days I pretended to be ill and remained at her side. We said nothing, but we knew the shadow in each other's mind.

"These occasions, however, grew rarer. Ah, this fool's peace in which we struggled to live, this empty and ominous security we built around our love. Yes, for he was waiting. This monster, this fiend was hovering near us and I had only to close my eyes to feel his shadow.

"I entered the cabaret where I performed one evening, feeling unusually disturbed. It was winter. The cold had numbed me during my walk to the place. I was removing my overcoat in the dressing room and it came again as I had known it would. The warning . . . the hand closing over my heart. Without a word to anyone I left the place. In the street I felt choked, dizzy. I hailed a carriage with difficulty and drove to within a block of our home. And during this ride I kept muttering to myself that my terror was only a folly of the nerves.

"I entered our cottage by a back door quietly like a thief. And I stood listening. The room was in darkness but in the room beyond a light burned. 'She had gone to bed early,' I thought, and then, through the half-opened door of her bedroom I heard her voice. She was talking softly, happily. She was saying, 'My darling, you are ill again. We will go to sleep and in the morning you will feel better.' And a voice answered her caressingly, adoringly. My own voice it was, as before, but tender and gentle. . . .

"One does not reason in the midst of nightmare. Yet terror can wake the mind to a clairvoyance, an understanding beyond thought. I stood motionless, silent, listening. The light was turned out. I heard her laugh like a child in the dark, and this sound killed me. Yes, one is dead forever when happiness is torn from the heart. I slipped from the house like a thief. I walked in the cold streets. My thought returned. I had acted out of one clear impulse. Through the terror and agony of those moments when I heard him take her in his arms there had remained the certainty that above everything else I must save Her.

"Now I knew I had acted wisely. Had I rushed into the room, had I made a noise—she would have died. She would have known in that moment, as I knew listening to him, that he had been there before. That he had crept through our defenses as a shadow creeps. That despite our plans, despite everything, he had stolen into her soul.

"He lay beside her now embracing her, wooing her, and she with her arms holding him. I thought of this thing as I walked. And I thought again that I had only to rush back, to speak her name. Yes, and destroy her. No, I kept on moving in the cold night. I had slunk away in order to save her. And as I walked I began to understand him. Yes, we were dealing with a monster. He would manage to leave her before I was due to return from the cabaret. And if I sensed something wrong he would rely on my love for her to keep this sense a secret. He knew me well, well enough to take my place in her arms, well enough to take my place in her soul and to reason with my own thoughts. He understood I would allow my heart to be eaten away with grief and I would not make a sign lest I destroy her whom I loved more than myself. It was I who must be careful, not he. Yes, he knew me. He gambled on me.

"I returned. I undressed as he had directed I should undress quietly. She lay with her lips parted and the faint odor of a drug was on her breath. This I understood, too, and was grateful—grateful to him. I stretched myself beside her, closed my eyes and waited. She awoke in the morning and I felt her hands caress me solicitously. She asked if I felt better and when I turned to her she started back in alarm. But I saw, thank God, it was only my cold fingers on her hand that had frightened her. I held my breath, however, waiting as one waits for death. I was ill, she cried. She must send for a doctor. Her lips covered my face with kisses and I choked back the tears. I strangled the agony in my heart. I said nothing. I pretended to be weary and I distracted her attention by continuous and querulous demands. She nursed me through the day.

"And thus it began again. My illness lasted for two weeks. I thought during these days that i would die. But I realized I must recover. She would begin to fear that there was something wrong. I left the bed finally. I postponed returning to the cabaret. But this, too, had to be done. I decided, however, to leave Munich. I explained to her that the climate was better in Berlin. We went to Berlin.

"What followed is hard to tell you. Terror leaves no memory. Yes, I no longer lived. There was only one thing in my mind. Perhaps it drove me mad. It has seemed to me always that all this time in Berlin I was able to eat, work, even sleep, only because of my desire to save her. This desire was greater than myself.

"I had determined to kill him the first moment I saw him—alone. I knew he was near us. He had tasted of the fruit of heaven and he would not go away now. I must be careful. Then I began to think he would kill me as he had at first intended and that he would go on living with her as Sarastro. She would never know I was dead. She would continue to love me in his arms, to press her kisses upon my murderer, until . . . This was the thought that contained in it the fullest measure of horror. The thought of that moment when she saw him and not me. . . .

"With this in view I wrote a long letter, sealed it and deposited it with a lawyer with instructions that he open it if I failed to communicate with him a single day and act immediately on the information it contained. For the rest I managed, God knows how, to spare her. The months passed and she felt no moment of dread. This was my reward. I asked questions, vague, subtle, disarming questions, and waited for her answers as one waits for a reprieve or a doom. Gradually I noticed that she spoke of things that were strange to me. She would continue his conversations—with me. She would speak of endearments I had never bestowed, of foolish, tender things I had never uttered.

"Do you understand the grief of these months? Yes, it is fortunate I cannot remember it. I can remember only prowling the streets like a madman, crawling into corners to weep, waking at night with my agony echoing through dreams of horror. I was like a thing in a trap, while he came and went, stealing her love, stealing my soul from under my eyes. But it was I, not he, who was afraid. It was I who held her life in my hands.

"I will pass over these months. What use is there now to remember them? They came to an end. I returned home one night after my performance. I was no longer so careful about my own comings and goings. I trusted him, do you understand—that out of his evil he would spare her as I spared her out of love. But when I entered the bedroom this time, when I opened the door of her bedroom this night, I knew he had blundered. She was alone.

"At the sound of my voice she turned. She stood facing me for a moment. Then she screamed. It is this scream I remember, it is with this voice she comes back to me. This cry of horror is my memory of Anna. She seized her face with her hands as if she wear tearing something—yes, the darkness. As I rushed to her she fell. She did not speak again. In the morning she died."

I have written the story as nearly in Sarastro's words as I can remember.

I went with him to the boat. We said good-by. Three weeks

later my friend Sarastro was dead. I stared at the dispatch in a theatrical weekly with sadness and confusion. Under a Paris date line it recounted the end of the Marvelous Sarastro. He had been killed in an automobile accident. While motoring through the country his automobile had stalled on a railroad track and been demolished by an oncoming train. Sarastro, read the dispatch, had been cut to pieces. A friend who had been driving with him had escaped with slight injuries. The friend's name was given. It was Enrico Sansone.

THE MOST DANGEROUS GAME

By Richard Connell

"OFF THERE TO THE RIGHT—SOMEWHERE—IS A LARGE ISLAND," SAID Whitney. "It's rather a mystery—"

"What island is it?" Rainsford asked.

"The old charts called it Ship-Trap Island," Whitney replied. "A suggestive name, isn't it? Sailors have a curious dread of the place. I don't know why. Some superstition—"

"Can't see it," remarked Rainsford, trying to peer through the dank tropical night that pressed its thick warm blackness in upon the yacht.

"You've got good eyes," said Whitney with a laugh, "and I've seen you pick off a moose moving in the brown fall bush at four hundred yards, but even you can't see four miles or so through a moonless Caribbean night."

"Not four yards," admitted Rainsford. "Ugh! It's like moist black velvet."

"It will be light enough in Rio," promised Whitney. "We should make it in a few days. I hope the jaguar guns have come from Purdey's. We should have some good hunting up the Amazon. Great sporting, hunting."

"The best sport in the world," agreed Rainsford.

"For the hunter," amended Whitney. "Not for the jaguar."

"Don't talk rot, Whitney. You're a big-game hunter, not a philosopher. Who cares how a jaguar feels?"

"Perhaps the jaguar does."

"Bah! They've no understanding."

"Even so, I rather think they understand one thing—fear. The fear of pain and the fear of death."

"Nonsense," laughed Rainsford. "This hot weather is making you soft, Whitney. Be a realist. The world is made up of two classes—the hunters and the huntees. Luckily you and I are hunters. Do you think we have passed that island yet?"

"I can't tell in the dark. I hope so."

"Why?"

"The place has a reputation—a bad one."

"Cannibals?"

"Hardly. Even cannibals wouldn't live in such a God-forsaken place. But it's gotten into sailor lore, somehow. Didn't you notice that the crew's nerves seemed a bit jumpy today?"

"They were a big strange, now you mention it. Even Captain Neilson."

"Yes, even that tough-minded old Swede, who'd go up to the devil himself and ask him for a light. Those fishy blue eyes held a look I never saw there before. All I could get out of him was: 'This place has an evil name among seafaring men, sir.' Then he said, gravely: 'Don't you feel anything? Now you mustn't laugh but I did feel a sort of chill, and there wasn't a breeze. What I felt was a—a mental chill, a sort of dread."

"Pure imagination," said Rainsford. "One superstitious sailor can taint a whole ship's company with his fear."

"Maybe. Sometimes I think sailors have an extra sense which tells them when they are in danger . . . anyhow I'm glad we are getting out of this zone. Well, I'll turn in now, Rainsford."

"I'm not sleepy. I'm going to smoke another pipe on the after deck."

There was no sound in the night as Rainsford sat there but the muffled throb of the yacht's engine and the swish and ripple of the propeller.

Rainsford, reclining in a steamer chair, puffed at his favourite briar. The sensuous drowsiness of the night was on him. "It's so dark," he thought, "that I could sleep without closing my eyes; the night would be my eyelids—"

An abrupt sound startled him. Off to the right he heard it, and his ears, expert in such matters, could not be mistaken. Again he heard the sound, and again. Somewhere, off in the blackness, someone had fired a gun three times.

Rainsford sprang up and moved quickly to the rail, mystified. He strained his eyes in the direction from which the reports had come, but it was like trying to see through a blanket. He leaped upon the rail and balanced himself there, to get greater elevation; his pipe, striking a rope, was knocked from his mouth. He lunged for it; a short, hoarse cry came from his lips as he realized he had reached too far and had lost his balance. The cry was pinched off short as the blood-warm waters of the Caribbean Sea closed over his head.

He struggled to the surface and cried out, but the wash from the speeding yacht slapped him in the face and the salt water in his open mouth made him gag and strangle. Desperately he struck out after the receding lights of the yacht, but he stopped before he had swum fifty feet. A certain cool-headedness had come to him for this was not the first time he had been in a tight place. There was a chance that his cries could be heard by someone aboard the yacht, but that chance was slender and grew more slender as the yacht raced on. He wrestled himself out of his clothes and shouted with all his power. The lights of the boat became faint and vanishing fireflies; then they were blotted out by the night.

Rainsford remembered the shots. They had come from the right, and doggedly he swam in that direction, swimming slowly, conserving his strength. For a seemingly endless time he fought the sea. He began to count his strokes; he could do possibly a hundred more and then—

He heard a sound. It came out of the darkness, a high, screaming sound, the cry of an animal in an extremity of anguish and terror. He did not know what animal made the sound. With fresh vitality he swam towards it. He heard it again; then it was cut short by another noise, crisp, staccato.

"Pistol shot," muttered Rainsford, swimming on.

Ten minutes of determined effort brought to his ears the most welcome sound he had ever heard, the breaking of the sea on a rocky shore. He was almost on the rocks before he saw them; on a night less calm he would have been shattered against them. With his remaining strength he dragged himself from the swirling waters. Jagged crags appeared to jut into the opaqueness; he forced himself up hand over hand. Grasping, his hands raw, he reached a flat place at the top. Dense jungle came down to the edge of the cliffs, and careless of everything but his weariness

Rainsford flung himself down and tumbled into the deepest sleep of his life.

When he opened his eyes he knew from the position of the sun that it was late in the afternoon. Sleep had given him vigour; a sharp hunger was picking at him.

"Where there are pistol shots there are men. Where there are men there is food," he thought; but he saw no sign of a trail through the closely knit web of weeds and trees; it was easier to go along the shore. Not far from where he landed, he stopped.

Some wounded thing, by the evidence a large animal, had crashed about in the underwood. A small glittering object caught Rainsford's eyes and he picked it up. It was an empty cartridge.

"A twenty-two," he remarked. "That's odd. It must have been a fairly large animal, too. The hunter had his nerve with him to tackle it with a light gun. It is clear the brute put up a fight. I suppose the first three shots I heard were when the hunter flushed his quarry and wounded it. The last shot was when he trailed it here and finished it."

He examined the ground closely and found what he had hoped to find—the print of hunting boots. They pointed along the cliff in the direction he had been going. Eagerly he hurried along, for night was beginning to settle down on the island.

Darkness was blacking out sea and jungle before Rainsford sighted the lights. He came upon them as he turned a crook in the coast line, and his first thought was that he had come upon a village as there were so many lights. But as he forged along he saw all the lights were in one building—a château on a high bluff.

"Mirage," thought Rainsford. But the stone steps were real enough. He lifted the knocker and it creaked up stiffly as if it had never before been used.

The door, opening, let out a river of glaring light. A tall man, solidly built and black-bearded to the waist, stood facing Rainsford with a revolver in his hand.

"Don't be alarmed," said Rainsford, with a smile that he hoped was disarming. "I'm no robber. I fell off a yacht. My name is Sanger Rainsford of New York City."

The man gave no sign that he understood the words or had even heard them. The menacing revolver pointed as rigidly as if the giant were a statue.

Another man was coming down the broad, marble steps, an erect slender man in evening clothes. He advanced and held out his hand.

In a cultivated voice marked by a slight accent which gave it added precision and deliberateness, he said: "It is a great pleasure and honour to welcome Mr. Sanger Rainsford, the celebrated hunter, to my home."

Automatically Rainsford shook the man's hand.

"I've read your book about hunting snow leopards in Tibet," explained the man. "I am General Zaroff."

Rainsford's first impression was that the man was singularly handsome; his second, that there was a bizarre quality about the face. The general was a tall man past middle age, for his hair was white; but his eyebrows and moustache were black. His eyes, too, were black and very bright. He had the face of a man used to giving orders. Turning to the man in uniform he made a sign. The fellow put away his pistol, saluted, withdrew.

"Ivan is an incredibly strong fellow," remarked the general, "but he has the misfortune to be deaf and dumb. A simple fellow, but a bit of a savage."

"Is he Russian?"

"A Cossack," said the general, and his smile showed red lips and pointed teeth. "So am I."

"Come," he said, "we shouldn't be chatting here. You want clothes, food, rest. You shall have them. This is a most restful spot."

Ivan had reappeared and the general spoke to him with lips that moved but gave forth no sound.

"Follow Ivan if you please, Mr. Rainsford. I was about to have my dinner, but will wait. I think my clothes will fit you."

It was to a huge beam-ceilinged bedroom with a canopied bed large enough for six men that Rainsford followed the man. Ivan laid out an evening suit and Rainsford as he put it on noticed that it came from a London tailor.

"Perhaps you were surprised," said the general as they sat down to dinner in a room which suggested a baronial hall of feudal times, "that I recognized your name; but I read all books on hunting published in English, French and Russian. I have but one passion in life, and that is the hunt."

"You have some wonderful heads here," said Rainsford, glancing at the walls. "That Cape buffalo is the largest I ever saw."

"Oh, that fellow? He charged me, hurled me against a tree and fractured my skull. But I got the brute."

"I've always thought," said Rainsford, "that the Cape buffalo is the most dangerous of all big game."

For a moment the general did not reply, then he said slowly: "No, the Cape buffalo is not the most dangerous." He sipped his wine. "Here in my preserve on this island I hunt more dangerous game.

"Is there big game on this island?"

The general nodded. "The biggest."

"Really?"

"Oh, it isn't here naturally. I have to stock the island."

"What have you imported, General? Tigers?"

The general grinned. "No, hunting tigers ceased to interest me when I exhausted their possibilities. No thrill left in tigers, no real danger. I live for danger, Mr. Rainsford."

The general took from his pocket a gold cigarette case and offered his guest a long black cigarette with a silver tip; it was perfumed and gave off a smell like incense.

"We will have some capital hunting, you and I," said the general.

"But what game—" began Rainsford.

"I'll tell you. You will be amused, I know. I think I may say in all modesty, that I have done a rare thing. I have invented a new sensation. May I pour you another glass of port?"

"Thank you, General."

The general filled both glasses and said: "God makes some men poets. Some he makes kings, some beggars. Me he made a hunter. But after years of enjoyment I found that the hunt no longer fascinated me. You can perhaps guess why?"

"No—why?"

"Simply this, hunting had ceased to be what you call a 'sporting proposition.' I always got my quarry . . . always . . . and there is no greater bore than perfection."

The general lit a fresh cigarette.

"The animal has nothing but his legs and his instinct. Instinct is no match for reason. When I realized this, it was a tragic moment for me."

Rainsford leaned across the table, absorbed in what his host was saying.

"It came to me as an inspiration what I must do."

"And that was?"

"I had to invent a new animal to hunt."

"A new animal? You are joking."

"I never joke about hunting. I needed a new animal. I found one. So I bought this island, built this house, and here I do my hunting. The island is perfect for my purpose—there are jungles with a maze of trails in them, hills, swamps—"

"But the animal, General Zaroff?"

"Oh," said the general, "it supplies me with the most exciting hunting in the world. Every day I hunt, and I never grow bored now, for I have a quarry with which I can match my wits."

Rainsford's bewilderment showed in his face.

"I wanted the ideal animal to hunt, so I said, 'What are the attributes of an ideal quarry?' and the answer was, of course: 'It must have courage, cunning, and, above all, it must be able to reason.'"

"But no animal can reason," objected Rainsford.

"My dear fellow," said the general, "there is one that can."

"But you can't mean—"

"And why not?"

"I can't believe you are serious, General Zaroff. This is a grisly joke."

"Why should I not be serious? I am speaking of hunting."

"Hunting? Good God. General Zaroff, what you speak of is murder."

The general regarded Rainsford quizzically. "Surely your experiences in the war—"

"Did not make me condone cold-blooded murder," finished Rainsford stiffly.

Laughter shook the general. "I'll wager you'll forget your notions when you go hunting with me. You've a genuine new thrill in store for you, Mr. Rainsford."

"Thank you, I am a hunter, not a murderer."

"Dear me," said the general, quite unruffled, "again that unpleasant word; but I hunt the scum of the earth—sailors from tramp ships—lascars, blacks, Chinese, whites, mongrels."

"Where do you get them?"

The general's left eyelid fluttered down in a wink. "This island is called Ship-Trap. Come to the window with me."

Rainsford went to the window and looked out towards the sea.

"Watch; Out there!" exclaimed the general, as he pressed a button. Far out Rainsford saw a flash of lights. "They indicate a channel where there's none. Rocks with razor edges crouch there like a sea-monster. They can crush a ship like a nut. Oh, yes, that is electricity. We try to be civilized."

"Civilized? And you shoot down men?"

"But I treat my visitors with every consideration," said the general in his most pleasant manner. "They get plenty of good food and exercise. They get into splendid physical condition. You shall see for yourself tomorrow."

"What do you mean?"

"We'll visit my training school," smiled the general. "It is in the cellar. I have about a dozen there now. They're from the Spanish bark, *Sanlucar*, which had the bad luck to go on the rocks out there. An inferior lot, I regret to say, and more accustomed to the deck than the jungle."

He raised his hand and Ivan brought thick Turkish coffee. "It is a game, you see," pursued the general blandly. "I suggest to one of them that we go hunting. I give him three hours' start. I am to follow, armed only with a pistol of smallest caliber and range. If my quarry eludes me for three whole days, he wins the game. If I find him"—the general smiled—"he loses."

"Suppose he refuses to be hunted?"

"I give him the option. If he does not wish to hunt I turn him over to Ivan. Ivan once served as official knouter to the Great White Tsar and he has his own ideas of sport. Invariably they choose the hunt."

"And if they win?"

The smile on the general's face widened. "To date I have not lost."

Then he added, hastily: "I don't wish you to think me a braggart, Mr. Rainsford, and one did almost win. I eventually had to use the dogs."

"The dogs?"

"This way, please. I'll show you."

The general led the way to another window. The lights sent a flickering illumination that made grotesque patterns on the courtyard below, and Rainsford could see a dozen or so huge black shapes moving about. As they turned towards him he caught the green glitter of eyes.

"They are let out at seven every night. If anyone should try to get into my house—or out of it—something regrettable would happen to him. And now I want to show you my new collection of heads. Will you come to the library?"

"I hope," said Rainsford, "that you will excuse me tonight. I'm really not feeling at all well."

"Ah, indeed? You need a good restful night's sleep. Tomorrow you'll feel like a new man. Then we'll hunt, eh? I've one rather promising prospect—"

Rainsford was hurrying from the room.

"Sorry you can't go with me tonight," called the general. "I expect rather fair sport. A big, strong black. He looks resourceful—"

The bed was good and Rainsford was tired, but nevertheless he could not sleep, and had only achieved a doze when, as morning broke, he heard, far off in the jungle, the faint report of a pistol.

General Zaroff did not appear till luncheon. He was solicitous about Rainsford's health. "As for me," he said, "I do not feel so well. The hunting was not good last night. He made a straight trail that offered no problems at all."

"General," said Rainsford firmly, "I want to leave the island at once."

He saw the dead black eyes of the general on him studying

him. The eyes suddenly brightened. "Tonight," said he, "we will hunt—you and I."

Rainsford shook his head. "No, General," he said, "I will not hunt."

The general shrugged his shoulders. "As you wish. The choice rests with you, but I would suggest that my idea of sport is more diverting than Ivan's."

"You don't mean—" cried Rainsford.

"My dear fellow," said the general, "have I not told you I always mean what I say about hunting? This is really an inspiration. I drink to a foeman worthy of my steel at last."

The general raised his glass, but Rainsford sat staring at him. "You'll find this game worth playing," the general said, enthusiastically. "Your brain against mine. Your woodcraft against mine. Your strength and stamina against mine. Outdoor chess! And the stake is not without value, eh?"

"And if I win—" began Rainsford huskily.

"If I do not find you by midnight of the third day, I'll cheerfully acknowledge myself defeated," said General Zaroff. "My sloop will place you on the mainland near a town."

The general read what Rainsford was thinking.

"Oh, you can trust me," said the Cossack. "I will give you my word as a gentleman and a sportsman. Of course, you, in turn, must agree to say nothing of your visit here."

"I'll agree to nothing of the kind."

"Oh, in that case—but why discuss that now? Three days hence we can discuss it over a bottle of Veuve Cliquot, unless—"

The general sipped his wine.

Then a business-like air animated him. "Ivan," he said, "will supply you with hunting clothes, food, a knife. I suggest you wear moccasins; they leave a poorer trail. I suggest, too, that you avoid the big swamp in the southeast corner of the island. We call it Death Swamp. There's quicksand there. One foolish fellow tried it. The deplorable part of it was that Lazarus followed him. You can't imagine my feelings, Mr. Rainsford, I loved Lazarus; he was the finest hound in my pack. Well, I must beg you to excuse me now. I always take a siesta after lunch. You'll hardly have time for a nap, I fear. You'll want to start, no doubt. I shall not follow until dusk. Hunting at night is so much more exciting than by day, don't you think? Au revoir, Mr. Rainsford, au revoir."

As General Zaroff, with a courtly bow strolled from the room, Ivan entered by another door. Under one arm he carried hunting clothes, a haversack of food, a leathern sheath containing a long-bladed hunting knife; his right hand rested on a cocked revolver thrust in the crimson sash about his waist. . . .

Rainsford had fought his way through the bush for two hours, but at length he paused saying to himself through tight teeth, "I must keep my nerve."

He had not been entirely clear-headed when the château gates closed behind him. His first idea was to put distance between himself and General Zaroff and, to this end, he had plunged along, spurred by the sharp rowels of something approaching panic. Now, having got a grip on himself he had stopped to take stock of himself and the situation.

Straight flight was futile for it must inevitably bring him to the sea. Being in a picture with a frame of water, his operations, clearly, must take place within that frame.

"I'll give him a trail to follow," thought Rainsford, striking off from the path into trackless wilderness. Recalling the lore of the fox-hunt and the dodges of the fox, he executed a series of intricate loops, doubling again and again on his trail. Night found him leg-weary, with hands and face lashed by the branches. He was on a thickly wooded ridge. As his need for rest was imperative, he thought: "I have played the fox, now I must play the cat of the fable."

A big tree with a thick trunk and outspread branches was near by, and, taking care to leave no marks, he climbed into the crotch and stretched out on one of the broad limbs. Rest brought him new confidence and almost a feeling of security.

An apprehensive night crawled slowly by like a wounded snake. Towards morning, when a dingy grey was varnishing the sky, the cry of a startled bird focussed Rainsford's attention in its direction. Something was coming through the bush, coming slowly, carefully, coming by the same winding way that Rainsford had come. He flattened himself against the bough and, through a screen of leaves almost as thick as tapestry, watched.

It was General Zaroff. He made his way along, with his eyes fixed in concentration on the ground. He paused, almost beneath the tree, dropped to his knees and studied the ground. Rainsford's impulse was to leap on him like a panther, but he saw that the general's right hand held a small automatic.

The hunter shook his head several times as if he were puzzled. Then, straightening himself he took from his case one of his black cigarettes; its pungent incense-like smoke rose to Rainsford's nostrils.

Rainsford held his breath. The general's eyes had left the ground and were traveling inch by inch up the tree. Rainsford froze, every muscle tensed for a spring. But the sharp eyes of the hunter stopped before they reached the limb where Rainsford lay. A smile spread over his brown face. Very deliberately he blew a smoke ring into the air; then he turned his back on the tree and walked carelessly away along the trail he had come. The swish of the underbrush against his hunting boots grew fainter and fainter.

The pent-up air burst hotly from Rainsford's lungs. His first thought made him feel sick and numb. The general could follow a trail through the woods at night; he could follow an extremely difficult trail; he must have uncanny powers; only by the merest chance had he failed to see his quarry.

Rainsford's second thought was more terrible. It sent a shudder through him. Why had the general smiled? Why had he turned back?

Rainsford did not want to believe what his reason told him was true—the general was playing with him, saving him for another day's sport. The Cossack was the cat; he was the mouse. Then it was that Rainsford knew the meaning of terror.

"I will not lose my nerve," he told himself, "I will not."

Sliding down from the tree, he set off into the woods. Three hundred yards from his hiding-place he stopped where a huge dead tree leaned precariously on a smaller, living one. Throwing off his sack of food, he took his knife from its sheath and set to work.

When the job was finished, he threw himself down behind a

fallen log a hundred feet away. He did not have to wait long. The cat was coming back to play with the mouse.

Following the trail with the sureness of a bloodhound came General Zaroff. Nothing escaped those searching black eyes, no crushed blade of grass, no bent twig, no mark, no matter how faint, in the moss. So intent was the Cossack on his stalking that he was upon the thing Rainsford had made before he saw it. His foot touched the protruding bough that was the trigger. Even as he touched it, the general sensed his danger, and leaped back with the agility of an ape. But he was not quite quick enough; the dead tree, delicately adjusted to rest on the cut living one, crashed down and struck the general a glancing blow on the shoulders as it fell; but for his alertness he must have been crushed beneath it. He staggered but he did not fall; nor did he drop his revolver. He stood there, rubbing his injured shoulder, and Rainsford, with fear again gripping his heart, heard the general's mocking laugh ring through the jungle.

"Rainsford," called the general, "if you are within sound of my voice let me congratulate you. Not many men know how to make a Malay man catcher. Luckily for me I, too, have hunted in Malacca. You are proving interesting, Mr. Rainsford. I am now going to have my wound dressed; it is only a slight one. But I shall be back. I shall be back."

When the general, nursing his wounded shoulder, had gone, Rainsford again took up his flight. It was flight now, and it carried him on for some hours. Dusk came, then darkness, and still he pressed on. The ground grew softer under his moccasins; the vegetation grew ranker, denser; insects bit him savagely. He stepped forward and his foot sank into ooze. He tried to wrench it back, but the mud sucked viciously at his foot as if it had been a giant leech. With a violent effort he tore his foot lose. He knew where he was now. Death Swamp and its quicksand.

The softness of the earth had given him an idea. Stepping back from the quicksand a dozen feet, he began, like some huge prehistoric beaver, to dig.

Rainsford had dug himself in, in France, when a second's delay would have meant death. Compared to his digging now, that had been a placid pastime. The pit grew deeper; when it was above his shoulders he climbed out and from some hard saplings cut stakes, sharpening them to a fine point. These stakes he planted at the bottom of the pit with the points up. With flying fingers he wove a rough carpet of weeds and branches and with it covered the mouth of the pit. Then, wet with sweat and aching with tiredness, he crouched behind the stump of a lightning-blasted tree.

By the padding sound of feet on the soft earth he knew his pursuer was coming. The night breeze brought him the perfume of the general's cigarette. It seemed to the hunted man that the general was coming with unusual swiftness; that he was not feeling his way along, foot by foot. Rainsford, from where he was crouching, could not see the general, neither could he see the pit. He lived a year in a minute. Then he heard the sharp crackle of breaking branches as the cover of the pit gave way; heard the sharp scream of pain as the pointed stakes found their mark. Then he cowered back. Three feet from the pit a man was standing with an electric torch in his hand.

"You've done well, Rainsford," cried the general. "Your Burmese tiger pit has claimed one of my best dogs. Again you score. I must now see what you can do against my whole pack. I'm going home for a rest now. Thank you for a most amusing evening."

At daybreak, Rainsford, lying near the swamp, was awakened by a distant sound, fain and wavering, but he knew it for the baying of a pack of hounds.

Rainsford knew he could do one of two things. He could stay where he was. That was suicide. He could flee. That was postponing the inevitable. For a moment, he stood there thinking. An idea that held a wild chance came to him, and, tightening his belt, he headed away from the swamp.

The baying of the hounds drew nearer, nearer. Rainsford climbed a tree. Down a watercourse, not a quarter of a mile away, he could see the bush moving. Straining his eyes, he saw the lean figure of General Zaroff. Just ahead of him Rainsford made out another figure, with wide shoulders, which surged through the jungle reeds. It was the gigantic Ivan and he seemed to be pulled along. Rainsford realized that he must be holding the pack in leash.

They would be on him at any moment now. His mind worked frantically, and he thought of a native trick he had learned in Uganda. Sliding down the tree, he caught hold of a springy young sapling and to it fastened his hunting knife, with the blade pointing down the trail. With a bit of wild grape-vine he tied back the sapling . . . and ran for his life. As the hounds hit the fresh scent, they raised their voices and Rainsford knew how an animal at bay feels.

He had to stop to get his breath. The baying of the hounds stopped abruptly, and Rainsford's heart stopped, too. They must have reached the knife.

Shinning excitedly up a tree he looked back. His pursuers had stopped. But the hope in Rainsford's brain died for he saw that General Zaroff was still on his feet. Ivan, however, was not. The knife, driven by the recoil of the springing tree, had not wholly failed.

Hardly had Rainsford got back to the ground when, once more, the pack took up the cry.

"Nerve, nerve, nerve!" he panted to himself as he dashed along. A blue gap showed through the trees dead ahead. The hounds drew nearer. Rainsford forced himself on towards that gap. He reached the sea, and across a cove could see the gray stone of the château. Twenty feet below him the sea rumbled and hissed. Rainsford hesitated. He heard the hounds. Then he leaped far out into the water.

When the general and his pack reached the opening, the Cossack stopped. For some moments he stood regarding the blue-green expanse of water. Then he sat down, took a drink of brandy from a silver flask, lit a perfumed cigarette, and hummed a bit from *Madame Butterfly*.

General Zaroff ate an exceedingly good dinner in his great panelled hall that evening. With it he had a bottle of Pol Roger and half a bottle of Chambertin. Two slight annoyances kept him from perfect enjoyment. One was that it would be difficult to replace Ivan; the other, that his quarry had escaped him. Of course—so thought the general, as he tasted his after-dinner liqueur—the American had not played the game.

To soothe himself, he read in his library from the works of Marcus Aurelius. At ten he went to his bedroom. He was comfortably tired, he said to himself, as he turned the key of his door. There was a little moonlight, so before turning on the light he went to the window and looked down on the courtyard. He could see the great hounds, and he called: "Better luck another time." Then he switched on the light.

A man who had been hiding in the curtains of the bed, was standing before him.

"Rainsford!" screamed the general. "How in God's name did you get here?"

"Swam. I found it quicker than walking through the jungle."

The other sucked in his breath and smiled. "I congratulate you. You have won the game."

Rainsford did not smile. "I am still a beast at bay," he said, in a low, hoarse voice. "Get ready, General Zaroff."

The general made one of his deepest bows. "I see," he said. "Splendid. One of us is to furnish a repast for the hounds. The other will sleep in this very excellent bed. On guard, Rainsford. . . ."

He had never slept in a better bed, Rainsford decided.

THUS I REFUTE BEELZY

By JOHN COLLIER

"THERE GOES THE TEA BELL," SAID MRS. CARTER. "I HOPE SIMON hears it."

They looked out from the window of the drawing-room. The long garden, agreeably neglected, ended in a waste plot. Here a little summer-house was passing close by beauty on its way to complete decay. This was Simon's retreat: it was almost completely screened by the tangled branches of the apple tree and the pear tree, planted too close together, as they always are in suburban gardens. They caught a glimpse of him now and then, as he strutted up and down, mouthing and gesticulating, performing all the solemn mumbo-jumbo of small boys who spend long afternoons at the forgotten ends of long gardens.

"There he is, bless him," said Betty.

"Playing his game," said Mrs. Carter. "He won't play with the other children any more. And if I go down there—the temper! And comes in tired out."

"He doesn't have his sleep in the afternoons?" asked Betty.

"You know what Big Simon's ideas are," said Mrs. Carter. "'Let him choose for himself,' he says. That's what he chooses, and he comes in as white as a sheet."

"Look. He's heard the bell," said Betty. The expression was justified, though the bell had ceased ringing a full minute ago. Small Simon stopped in his parade exactly as if its tinny dingle had at that moment reached his ear. They watched him perform certain ritual sweeps and scratchings with his little stick, and come lagging over the hot and flaggy grass towards the house.

Mrs. Carter led the way down to the play-room, or garden-room, which was also the tea-room for hot days. It had been the huge scullery of this tall Georgian house. Now the walls were cream-washed, there was coarse blue net in the windows, canvas-covered armchairs on the stone floor, and a reproduction of Van Gogh's *Sunflowers* over the mantelpiece.

Small Simon came drifting in, and accorded Betty a perfunctory greeting. His face was an almost perfect triangle, pointed at the chin, and he was paler than he should have been. "The little elf-child!" cried Betty.

Simon looked at her. "No," said he.

At that moment the door opened, and Mr. Carter came in, rubbing his hands. He was a dentist, and washed them before and after everything he did. "You!" said his wife. "Home already!"

"Not unwelcome, I hope," said Mr. Carter, nodding to Betty. "Two people cancelled their appointments: I decided to come home. I said, I hope I am not unwelcome."

"Silly!" said his wife. "Of course not."

"Small Simon seems doubtful," continued Mr. Carter. "Small Simon, are you sorry to see me at tea with you?"

"No, Daddy."

"No, what?"

"No, Big Simon."

"That's right. Big Simon and Small Simon. That sounds more like friends, doesn't it? At one time little boys had to call their father 'sir.' If they forgot—a good spanking. On the bottom, Small Simon! On the bottom!" said Mr. Carter, washing his hands once more with his invisible soap and water.

The little boy turned crimson with shame or rage.

"But now, you see," said Betty, to help, "you can call your father whatever you like."

"And what," asked Mr. Carter, "has Small Simon been doing this afternoon? While Big Simon has been at work."

"Nothing," muttered his son.

"Then you have been bored," said Mr. Carter. "Learn from experience, Small Simon. Tomorrow, do something amusing, and you will not be bored. I want him to learn from experience, Betty. That is my way, the new way."

"I have learned," said the boy, speaking like an old, tired man, as little boys so often do.

"It would hardly seem so," said Mr. Carter, "if you sit on your behind all the afternoon, doing nothing. Had *my* father caught me doing nothing, I should not have sat very comfortably."

"He played," said Mrs. Carter.

"A bit," said the boy, shifting on his chair.

"Too much," said Mrs. Carter. "He comes in all nervy and dazed. He ought to have his rest."

"He is six," said her husband. "He is a reasonable being. He must choose for himself. But what game is this, Small Simon, that is worth getting nervy and dazed over? There are very few games as good as all that."

"It's nothing," said the boy.

"Oh, come," said his father. "We are friends, are we not? You can tell me. I was a Small Simon once, just like you, and played the same games you play. Of course there were no aeroplanes in those days. With whom do you play this fine game? Come on, we must all answer civil questions, or the world would never go round. With whom do you play?"

"Mr. Beelzy," said the boy, unable to resist.

"Mr. Beelzy?" said his father, raising his eyebrows inquiringly at his wife.

"It's a game he makes up," said she.

"Not makes up!" cried the boy. "Fool!"

"That is telling stories," said his mother. "And rude as well. We had better talk of something different."

"No wonder he is rude," said Mr. Carter, "if you say he tells lies, and then insist on changing the subject. He tells you his fantasy: you implant a guilt feeling. What can you expect? A defence mechanism. Then you get a real lie."

"Like in *These Three*," said Betty. "Only different, of course. *She* was an unblushing little liar."

"I would have made her blush," said Mr. Carter, "in the proper part of her anatomy. But Small Simon is in the fantasy stage. Are you not, Small Simon? You just make things up."

"No, I don't," said the boy.

"You do," said his father. "And because you do, it is not too late to reason with you. There is no harm in a fantasy, old chap. There is no harm in a bit of make-believe. Only you have to know the difference between day dreams and real things, or your brain

will never grow. It will never be the brain of a Big Simon. So
come on. Let us hear about this Mr. Beelzy of yours. Come on.
What is he like?"

"He isn't like anything," said the boy.

"Like nothing on earth?" said his father. "That's a terrible
fellow."

"I'm not frightened of him," said the child, smiling. "Not a bit."

"I should hope not," said his father. "If you were, you would
be frightening yourself. I am always telling people, older people
than you are, that they are just frightening themselves. Is he a
funny man? Is he a giant?"

"Sometimes he is," said the little boy.

"Sometimes one thing, sometimes another," said his father.
"Sounds pretty vague. Why can't you tell us just what he's like?"

"I love him," said the small boy. "He loves me."

"That's a big word," said Mr. Carter. "That might be better
kept for real things, like Big Simon and Small Simon."

"He is real," said the boy, passionately. "He's not a fool. He's
real."

"Listen," said his father. "When you go down the garden there's
nobody there. Is there?"

"No," said the boy.

"Then you think of him, inside your head, and he comes."

"No," said Small Simon. "I have to do something with my
stick."

"That doesn't matter."

"Yes, it does."

"Small Simon, you are being obstinate," said Mr. Carter. "I am
trying to explain something to you. I have been longer in the
world than you have, so naturally I am older and wiser. I am
explaining that Mr. Beelzy is a fantasy of yours. Do you hear?
Do you understand?"

"Yes, Daddy."

"He is a game. He is a let's pretend."

The little boy looked down at his plate, smiling resignedly.

"I hope you are listening to me," said his father. "All you have
to do is to say, 'I have been playing a game of let's-pretend. With
someone I make up, called Mr. Beelzy.' Then no one will say you

tell lies, and you will know the difference between dreams and reality. Mr. Beelzy is a day dream."

The little boy still stared at his plate.

"He is sometimes there and sometimes not there," pursued Mr. Carter. "Sometimes he's like one thing, sometimes another. You can't really see him. Not as you see me. I am real. You can't touch him. You can touch me. I can touch you." Mr. Carter stretched out his big, white, dentist's hand, and took his little son by the shoulder. He stopped speaking for a moment and tightened his hand. The little boy sank his head still lower.

"Now you know the difference," said Mr. Carter, "between a pretend and a real thing. You and I are one thing; he is another. Which is the pretend? Come on. Answer me. Which is the pretend?"

"Big Simon and Small Simon," said the little boy.

"Don't!" cried Betty, and at once put her hand over her mouth, for why should a visitor cry "Don't!" when a father is explaining things in a scientific and modern way?

"Well, my boy," said Mr. Carter, "I have said you must be allowed to learn from experience. Go upstairs. Right up to your room. You shall learn whether it is better to reason, or to be perverse and obstinate. Go up. I shall follow you."

"You are not going to beat the child?" cried Mrs. Carter.

"No," said the little boy. "Mr. Beelzy won't let him."

"Go on up with you!" shouted his father.

Small Simon stopped at the door. "He said he wouldn't let anyone hurt me," he whimpered. "He said he'd come like a lion, with wings on, and eat them up."

"You'll learn how real he is!" shouted his father after him. "If you can't learn it at one end, you shall learn it at the other. I'll have your breeches down. I shall finish my cup of tea first, however," said he to the two women.

Neither of them spoke. Mr. Carter finished his tea, and unhurriedly left the room, washing his hands with his invisible soap and water.

Mrs. Carter said nothing. Betty could think of nothing to say. She wanted to be talking: she was afraid of what they might hear.

Suddenly it came. It seemed to tear the air apart. "Good God!"

she cried. "What was that? He's hurt him." She sprang out of her chair, her silly eyes flashing behind her glasses. "I'm going up there!" she cried, trembling.

"Yes, let us go up," said Mrs. Carter. "Let us go up. That was not Small Simon."

It was on the second-floor landing that they found the shoe, with the man's foot still in it, like that last morsel of a mouse which sometimes falls from the jaws of a hasty cat.

THE MOST MADDENING STORY
IN THE WORLD

By RALPH STRAUS

I

THE FIRST MAN I MET IN MY CLUB WAS JOHN CHESTER, M.P. IT
must have been some time in the March of 1920, and I was just
home from four years' service in India. And to be candid I was not
at all certain that I altogether appreciated this changed England
into which I had come. Some things I did not at first understand;
others I soon discovered would never be in the least to my liking.
But it was good to see John Chester again, he, I knew well, would
not have changed for all the wars in the world. And to see him
there, cool and dignified, in the well-remembered grey morning
coat, was like finding a piece of the old England which for all
those four years had for ever been in my mind.

He stared at me in that curiously magisterial manner of his, and
held my hand in his own for a rather longer time than Englishmen
generally give to the business. Then he took me away to his own
particular corner.

"Since you went away," he said, "the powers that be have made
many astonishing discoveries. The one that chiefly concerns us at
the moment has reference to drink. I am sorry to say, my dear
friend, that for years we have all been drinking far too much
alcohol. Far too much," he repeated solemnly, and then smiled.
"We are now forbidden to drink during the hours when a drink
is most welcome." He looked at his watch. "H'm, just an hour and
a half to wait. Well, that will be enough for a short history of
India during the Great War, and with details of the Hunnish
plots you unearthed, and what the Amir of Afghanistan——"

I was lighting my pipe. "For four years," I told him, "I have
been soldiering after a fashion, and occasionally playing detective.
I don't want to hear another word about the Army or the Police.
Both are excellent bodies, but you can have too much of them.

Here I am back in my club and you're the first person I see.
Doesn't that suggest something to you? Don't you think that after
four years away I deserve something in the nature of a—story?"

"A story?" John Chester repeated the word with the air of a
man who has never told a story in his life. "A story from a man
who has spent four years of his life making crutches very slowly
and very badly for soldiers who had never done him any harm?
What sort of a story d'you suppose I have to tell you?" But I
could see that he was pleased. There was that queer little twinkle
in his eye—the preparatory twinkle.

"I'm waiting," said I, "and in India I learnt patience."

"There is one story," he went on after a moment's pause, "but
I doubt whether it would amuse you. The war does not venture
to intrude, and that is in its favour, but on the other hand I am
afraid it is rather unsatisfactory. Very unsatisfactory. In fact, I'm
not at all sure that it isn't the most maddening story in the world."

"Exactly what I require."

"But when I've told it to you, you'll never speak to me again."

"We can see about that."

"Very well then."

I settled myself back in the huge easy-chair, and prepared to
be maddened.

"It is not really my story," he began, putting the tips of his fingers together. "I dare say you may even have heard it before. For
myself I know of at least three different accounts of the strange
experience of Lord Brassington, and rather fancy to have seen a
fourth, badly garbled, in one of the popular magazines. Brassington, as I dare say you know, was killed on the Somme."

"I remember something——"

"Yes, a very brave man. . . . But his strange experience had
nothing to do with the war. It happened, I think, in 1910 or the
following year, at the time of the first Commission on Housing.
He worked like a Trojan. You met him once or twice on the Terrace with me—a tall dark man, you remember, who stooped, and
dressed very shabbily indeed. An earnest person like his father
before him. It was the old man who wrote those two volumes on
the *Psychology of Crowds*—a remarkable production which I
commend to your attention. Very well. Brassington overworked

himself and very wisely determined to take a long holiday. For some time he had wanted to travel about, and he finally decided upon a sort of irregular pilgrimage throughout Europe. It was typical of him that he should travel alone and with no settled plans."

"He could certainly have afforded a valet," said I, recalling the square solidity of Brassington House in Mayfair.

"He could," agreed John Chester. "It is perhaps a pity that he did not. As it happened, not all the cheques in the world could have made that pilgrimage a success."

He paused for a moment or two in the old Chester way.

"Yes, it was at Brussels that he met the Comte d'Anoury. He was staying at one of the smaller hotels at the time. He had dined alone and was enjoying his coffee in the lounge and wondering whether he would go on the next morning to Paris or stay and see something of Belgium. Ypres, I remember was one of the places he wanted to see. He could not make up his mind. And that, you know, was essentially Brassington's weak point. He was one of those unfortunate people who so often look to somebody else to make up their minds for them. On this particular evening it was the Comte d'Anoury who decided for him.

"A gentleman with one of those square beards which Leopold made so fashionable, came into the lounge and went straight up to Brassington.

"'Pardon me,' he said with a bow, 'but have I the pleasure of addressing the Earl of Brassington?'

"'You have,' replied Brassington.

"It then appeared that the Belgian had known the old lord very well, and had been in repeated communication with him over the publication of the *Psychology of Crowds*. In fact it was D'Anoury who had been largely responsible for the French translation.

"You can imagine that the two men soon found much to talk about. The Comte ultimately invited the son of his old friend to visit his château, an invitation that was at once accepted. And it was in the Château d'Anoury that the fatal card was presented to our friend. . . .

"It seems that Brassington mentioned his proposed European pilgrimage to his host, who speedily showed himself to be a much travelled man. There was hardly a good hotel in Europe, Brassington told me, which he did not know. Information of a kind which falls to the lot of no Cook's tourist was placed unreservedly at Brassington's disposal. Their relation became even more cordial, and on the last evening of our friend's stay at the château the card was proffered and accepted.

"Now I must tell you that one of Brassington's weak points was his ignorance of foreign languages. His French was of the *table d'hôte* order, and his German negligible. Of Russian, Italian, or Spanish he knew nothing at all. I doubt whether he'd realized that in the south-eastern corner of Europe over a hundred distinct languages were in daily use. He was sufficiently insular to imagine that English, particularly when spoken in a loud voice, and a smattering of French would carry him through—as they so often do. Well, the Comte d'Anoury discovered this fact, and in his hospitable way suggested that he might be of some little assistance. He took out of his card-case a blank card—exactly similar, I mean, to an ordinary visiting card, but quite plain. Then he scribbled a few words on it, and handed it over.

" 'If you should go to any of the hotels I've mentioned,' said he, 'this may be of use. Often a stranger is not given the most comfortable room.'

"Brassington thanked him and looked at the writing. He did not recognize the language, although he was convinced that it was neither French nor German. It did not seem to be Italian or Spanish, but, as Brassington told me afterwards, he thought, without knowing why, that it might be Russian."

"Didn't he inquire?" I asked.

John Chester looked at me. "I was expecting that question. In point of fact, he was about to inquire when the Comtesse came into the room. He just put the card in his pocket and forgot all about it. The next morning he journeyed to Paris and was driven to the hotel of which the Belgian had spoken. I've forgotten the name, but it was a small, comfortable sort of place, rather old-fashioned. The guide-books would have called it select and possibly have omitted to tell you its rate of charges. Brassington found it entirely to his liking. It was not too dull, and the proprietor spoke English extremely well. He had been an hotel manager in London, and was enough of a snob to find pleasure in having a British peer under his roof. And there was a particular old brandy in his possession which Brassington greatly appreciated. In fact, I gather they drank quite a number of glasses together in the privacy of the proprietor's own sanctum. Don't think for one moment that Brassington ever took too much in his life. He didn't. He was the last sort of man to do anything of the kind. But he liked the old man and he liked the old brandy, and he was enjoying a holiday.

"He stayed a fortnight at that hotel and had a right joyous time. In fact, he was in no hurry to continue his pilgrimage. Paris, as you probably know, has its own fascinations, and Brassington would have been well content to stay there for months. He went to the play, he heard fine music, and he went for long walks. And so pleased was he with the few Frenchmen whose acquaintance he made that he had almost decided to treat himself to a *pied-à-terre* in their capital. He did, indeed, seek the proprietor's advice on this very point. But the hotel proprietor did not seem too keen on the proposition. Doubtless he saw no reason why milord should not continue to put money into his own pocket. And it was then that Brassington, without knowing why, remembered the Belgian's card.

" 'By the way,' he said suddenly, 'I think you know the Comte d'Anoury.'

" 'Monsieur?'

" 'A frequent visitor here, surely?'

"The proprietor shrugged his shoulders. 'Possibly,' said he, with no sign of his usual enthusiasm.

"Brassington, I think, was piqued. He took out the card, and immediately experienced the curious idea that he was embarking on an adventure altogether outside his ken. That is how he expressed himself to me when he told me his story. Well, he took out his card, and handed it over.

"And then something odd immediately happened."

II

"I lay stress," continued John Chester, "on Brassington's feelings at this moment. He never quite understood why he handed over the card. It would have been easy for him to have visited an ordinary house-agent without the proprietor's help. In fact, had he thought about the matter at all, he would surely have seen that the proprietor would naturally not be too keen to see the departure of his guest. But he didn't think. He just took the card out of his pocket and handed it over.

"And then a queer little pang raced through his body, a pang of shame or horror or—fright. He told me afterwards that before the proprietor spoke, he was convinced that he'd made the biggest mistake of his life. And he was angry with himself. But he was also unmistakably afraid, for it suddenly seemed to him that, to use one of our modern turns of slang, he was up against *something* which would render him powerless and absurd if nothing worse. He tried to pull himself together. What significance could the mere handing over of a card with some half-dozen words scribbled on it, possibly have? His commonsense told him none, but his instinct sent a warning in that tiny pang. And so he just sat there and waited."

There came another of those little pauses of which John Chester made such frequent use. I think he likes to see the mouth of his audience open a little, awaiting some expression of tense interest.

"You pique my curiosity," I told him.

"Yes, it was certainly rather curious," he continued with irritating deliberation. "The hotel proprietor behaved so very oddly. As I have told you, Brassington knew immediately that something was wrong, but he'd no means of knowing just *what* would account for the extraordinary change in the proprietor's manner. For over the man's face there had come an expression which was interpreted without much difficulty. As Brassington told me, he looked angry, insulted, and—disgusted. And it was the man's ill-hidden disgust which he could never forget. 'I felt a cad,' he said, 'a dirty cad, guilty of all the most horrible crimes you can think of. And the odd thing was that although I knew I was absolutely innocent I felt that the man's attitude was—justified. In some curious way, it did seem to me that I had been guilty of foul horrors. He handed me back the card, and I faced him shivering like a criminal in the dock for the first time.'

"That was what our good Brassington felt—a criminal, and the feeling was intensified when the proprietor with another look of disgust spat on the floor and walked over to the telephone. And Brassington listened as in a dream to the conversation that followed. He could not fully understand, but he knew enough to learn that the police were being summoned. And still he sat there, unable to move, unable to think.

"Well, they fetched him. They took him away, him and his luggage, in the middle of the night. He tried to protest. He mentioned our Ambassador, who happened to be a distant cousin of his mother's. He tried to be angry. He tried to behave in that rather silly way most Englishmen do behave when they become unexpectedly involved in a police row abroad. But he could do nothing. . . . He was put in a train with three detectives and escorted to the German frontier, and the three detectives lost no opportunity of showing what they thought of him. Obviously they hated their job; obviously they found the mere presence of the Englishman unspeakably offensive. And he felt more than ever like a criminal. It didn't occur to him that he could have demanded to know the reason for his expulsion: he just sat in the train half-dazed."

"But I can't understand——"

"Wait a little," begged John Chester, smiling; "there was worse to come. Our friend Brassington arrived in Cologne, where, you may remember, there is an Englishehof, and there under that solemn roof he was able in some measure to recover. He found the stolid, orderly methods of the Germans extraordinarily soothing and peaceful after his untoward experience in France, and although some days passed before he felt able to walk out in the streets like an ordinary tourist, he succeeded in persuading himself that the old brandy must have been stronger than he had supposed, and was in some way responsible for the affair. It was a poor enough explanation, but it was all he could summon to his aid. The brandy, he found himself thinking, might have been drugged. . . . Something of that sort. . . .

"And then for a fortnight nothing happened. He spent his time exploring Cologne, where, by the way, there is much that is usually interesting. He made an effort to learn German. He met in casual fashion two or three English friends. And once or twice behind locked doors he took out the Belgian's card and attempted to decipher the words. And here I would have you notice a curious point. When Brassington looked at the card, locked up alone in his own room, it seemed harmless and even vaguely helpful. It was only when it was shown. . . . But I am anticipating.

"Brassington went on to Berlin, where an uncle of his was in the Embassy. They spent an enjoyable week together, and no mention was made of the card. Then our friend crossed the Austrian frontier and ultimately arrived in Prague. Yes, Prague," repeated John Chester thoughtfully. "At Prague something else happened."

"Not exactly. The card was asked for. It seemed that Brassington chose his hotel by the merest chance. At the station there were several hotel porters waiting. He picked out one of them at random, and had his luggage placed on a shabby old omnibus which rumbled slowly along the picturesque streets. Prague, you know, is one of the most romantically picturesque cities in Europe. I remember in '89. . . ." For a moment he became vague. "Yes, well, as I was telling you, Brassington chose his hotel haphazard. He found it on the outskirts of the town, a rather lonely old pile, once, no doubt, some Czech nobleman's house, but now disfigured in the usual way by gigantic gold letters. I forget the name those letters formed, but it was vaguely familiar to Brassington. And then, when they were showing him to his room, he remembered: the Comte d'Anoury had mentioned this particular hotel as a favourite resort of his own. . . .

"Five minutes later a thin fair man in some uniform which Brassington did not recognize had come into his room. He spoke broken English, and seemed to be in a very bad temper.

" 'You 'ave come from Berlin?' he snapped.

" 'Yes.'

" 'An' you 'ave ze card?'

"Our friend was horribly startled, not only by the unexpected question, but also by the look on the man's face. It was a look of devilish hate and cruelty. But he pulled himself together. After all, it was surely nobody's business if he chose to carry the damned card. He was an Englishman travelling for pleasure—with a banking account that would have roused the envy of every Austrian official, had its full extent been known. He was not going to be bullied. He attempted to bluster.

" 'I don't know what you mean,' he said in a loud voice. 'You've evidently made some mistake. I am Lord Brassington, a British subject.'

"The man in uniform seemed to be almost trembling with fury. 'Dere are some men,' he said with incredible bitterness, 'too bad to 'ave ze nationality. Show me ze card.'

" 'I absolutely decline,' Brassington spoke warmly.

"The thin man blew a whistle. Four soldiers appeared, and in another moment our poor friend was being searched none too kindly. The card of course was easily found—Brassington still kept it in his card-case—and handed over to the leader of the party.

"Half an hour later the fifth Earl of Brassington was confined in the filthiest cell of the prison-fortress of Prague."

III

"Now, if you or I were to find ourselves in such a position we should know what to do. We would talk very loudly of the mighty arm of Britannia, and threaten all sorts of personal reprisals. And the Governor would be gravely polite and full of regrets that he was unable to help us. And then in some way or other we should succeed in getting a message through to the Consulate. I don't know myself how one does such things, but I feel convinced that we should." John Chester smiled. "Possibly nothing more than a few judicious bribes and nice crisp English bank-notes. And then, there'd be a coming and going of all sorts of higher officials, and delays and telegrams, and finally a grovel from some semi-royal personage. Whereupon we should walk out with our heads very high, secretly rather pleased with ourselves that the affair had really occurred. Something to talk about, you understand, on our return home."

"Quite so," I agreed laughing, "but I can hardly see myself languishing in a Bohemian jail—at least, before the war—without a pretty good effort to find out the reason. . . ."

"And yet our friend took no steps at all. He found himself all unconceivably a prisoner in an Austrian dungeon, which I gather is even nastier than most other dungeons, unable to eat the appalling food he was given, quite helpless and stunned. He became, of course, physically ill. He admitted to me that he more than once began to cry like a child. And I fancy he must have become lightheaded, because he told me that at the time he could hardly be certain that he was Brassington at all. The card had been returned to him, and he spent hours with it in his hands, trying to fathom its mystery. A little piece of pasteboard! Some half-dozen words! But it might be symbolic? Yet even so how. . . . There seemed to him to be no solution whatsoever. Moreover, he was by no means unconscious of the change in himself. He knew that he ought to be rousing himself to fight against the enigma, whatever it might be; but he couldn't. As you know, Brassington was ordinarily a strong healthy man. I remember seeing him box for Oxford. But in the prison at Prague he could do nothing—nothing at all."

"I should have thought he might have found it advisable to destroy the card."

"My dear man, that was my first question when he told me what happened in Prague. Why on earth didn't he destroy it? There were two reasons, I think. In the first place he could never persuade himself when alone that the card held any undue significance at all. In the second place he never gave up hope that the day would come when a complete explanation would appear."

"Of course it did?" I interrupted with some eagerness.

"Lord Brassington," continued my friend imperturbably, "remained in that prison-fortress for nearly three weeks. Then one evening when he was so weak that he could hardly stand up, he was taken away in the Austrian equivalent of our Black Maria. He told me that this was the most painful journey he had ever experienced. The roads must have been awful, but just as he was deciding that he could not stand another yard of jolting, the Black Maria stopped. He was helped out. A huge grey motor-car stood there in the moonlight. To his surprise he found that his own luggage had been placed in the tonneau. The next day he was over the Italian frontier. . . .

"It is true that Italy had been included in his pilgrimage, and for a week or so Brassington basked in the sun. He stayed in some small inn, and for some reason or other gave a false name. He wanted, he told me, to lose himself entirely—to forget what he had gone through. Incidentally he came to the conclusion that nothing should make him show the card to anybody else. True, at Prague they had asked for it, but he had stayed at half a dozen other places and they had not asked for it. For some reason he did not think that they would ask him for it in Italy.

"And then he met the Greek.

"A Greek gentleman came to the little inn: a diminutive, dark, pasty-faced man, very dapper and polite. Brassington hardly noticed him at first, but they happened to meet one evening on a bridge outside the village. The Greek gentleman bowed and spoke of the scenery. Brassington made some reply, and then found himself listening to an enthusiastic account of the beauties of Greece. So immeasurably superior, it seemed, to this flamboyant Italy. Brassington spoke of our English landscapes, and the Greek appeared extraordinarily interested. For England, he said, the home of true liberty, he had always entertained the warmest admiration and respect, and it was while he was giving tongue to these pleasant opinions that the strange idea about the card came into Brassington's mind. It suddenly seemed to him absolutely certain that the words which Comte d'Anoury had so hurriedly scribbled must be modern Greek. And in his excitement he forgot his resolution.

" 'I wonder,' he said abruptly, 'if you would do me a favour?'

"The Greek, it seemed, would be enchanted.

" 'I have reason to believe that some words on a card I possess are written in your language. You could possibly translate them for me.'

"The Greek gentleman would be delighted.

"Now, so far as I can gather, this is what happened. With a strong feeling that the mystery was about to be solved, Brassington handed over the card. He experienced no sense of shame or disgust as he did so. The Greek gentleman, it seemed to him, would just translate, and then they would continue to speak of the scenery. . . . The next moment he was lying on his back in the road with a sharp pain in his side.

"The Greek gentleman had stabbed him and was gone . . ."

John Chester looked at me. "To be frank with you," he continued, "I know very little about knife-wounds, but this one of Brassington's seems to have been no more than superficial. He saw his own blood, but seems to have easily stanched the flow. In any case he was able to stagger back to the inn, there to learn that the Greek gentleman had suddenly departed. The people were kind to him. They asked no questions, but sent for a doctor and helped him to bed. And it was while he was being undressed that he found the card sticking out of his waistcoat pocket. . . .

"It was a bad shock. Anywhere else I suppose there would have been no little rumpus, but here nothing was said. The English gentleman had met with an accident and would be leaving in a few days' time. And leave he did as soon as he felt well enough. He did not know what he wanted to do, but he felt he must travel. He debated the idea of an immediate return to England, but something was preventing it. Ultimately he came to Naples, nervously apprehensive and yet at the same time convinced that before going home he must in some way solve the enigma.

"He stayed at the Hotel de Vesuve and almost immediately ran into Archie Summers and his wife."

IV

"You know Sir Archibald Summers? The cricketer, I mean—one of the splendidest fellows I ever knew. He got his Brigade early on in the war and was killed at Loos. Brassington and he were old friends. They used to meet at White's. Lady Summers was one of those pretty Hemingway girls, the eldest I fancy. At any rate the two men were delighted to meet, and Brassington joined their table. He told me that the relief of finding an old friend here in Naples was extraordinary. At dinner that night he could hardly believe that anything untoward had happened to him. And yet barely an hour later. . . .

"I'll tell you, but I want you to understand that Archie Summers was absolutely loyal, a level-headed man of the world, the sort of man you naturally went to when in trouble. As I happen to know, he got more than one youngster out of a scrape. A splendid friend to have. And it is important you should realize this, because it makes what followed on their meeting so strange. You have to think of Summers, not as a narrow-minded saint, but as an honourable man, certainly not unaware of the seamier side of life, though of course absolutely untouched by it himself, and unselfishly devoted to his friends. Brassington, I suppose, was one of his oldest friends, if not his best. Lady Summers herself once told me how well they had always got on together. And so on this particular evening it was quite natural that after dinner the two of them should forgather over their liqueurs for an intimate chat.

"Archie, it seemed, was bound ultimately for a long stay in Egypt, where his brother was stationed. They were going slowly eastwards. And then when he asked for details of his friend's travels, it seemed to Brassington that here was an admirable opportunity for unburdening himself.

" 'I've a mighty queer story to tell you, Archie,' he said.

" 'Fire away.'

" 'But you may——' Brassington hesitated. A moment before, it had seemed simple to tell his friend of the strange affair of the card, but now there crossed his mind the possibility that even Archie Summers might find something sinister in the business. 'It's very silly of me,' he continued, 'but I've had rather a shock, rather a bad shock, to tell you the truth.'

"Archie showed his solicitude. 'Why, man, you look upset now.'

" 'I am,' admitted Brassington. 'It's quite absurd——'

" 'Have another brandy and tell me the yarn,' suggested Archie Summers, and they filled up their glasses.

"And then Brassington gave a plain account of what had occurred. He looked sharply at his friend as he finished and was enormously relieved to see him laughing outright.

" 'It strikes me you must have been doing yourself very well, old man.'

" 'You don't believe me?'

" 'Oh, certainly I do. I believe you've been locked up and all the rest of it, but I can't believe that half-a-dozen words on a card caused all the trouble.'

" 'I might,' continued Brassington, nervous again, 'show you the card.'

" 'Do, by all means,' laughed the other, 'but if you expect me to be disgusted and horrified and angry, you're quite mistaken.'

" 'You swear that?"

" 'Swear? Good God, man, what's come over you? Some damned nonsense on a card—what on earth is there to swear about? You don't think a few words could turn me into a raging lunatic ready to stab an old pal or send him to jail?'

" 'No, old man, but somehow——'

" 'Show me the card,' said Archie Summers, laughing again, 'and if I can, I'll translate it for you. I'm not bad at languages. And if it's very awful,' he added with mock seriousness, 'mum's the word.'

"In silence Brassington handed over the card. Archie Summers glanced almost carelessly at it, and for a moment it looked as if the spell had been broken. Then he saw that Summers had gone very white. He had got up from his chair and was pacing excitedly up and down the room. He did not look at Brassington. For a while he was angrily muttering to himself, and Brassington watched him as some wretched bird might watch a snake. Then came words which he could not easily forget.

" 'You'll have to resign,' said Archie Summers in a queer strained voice. 'Your clubs, I mean. At once. We have been friends, I know, and I shall say nothing myself. Nothing. That goes without saying, but if you ever dare to show your face again in decent society, I'll— And my wife here too!' He had turned now towards the wretched man. 'How *dare* you, Brassington,' he shouted. 'My God, if I'd ever thought. . . .' He couldn't say any more, but threw down the card and rushed from the room.

"Half an hour later the very polite hotel-keeper was regretting the fact that the signor's room would be wanted the next day. An old customer. . . ."

V

"He seems to have got almost as far south as Messina, but could tell me little enough about that time. There was no mistaking the menace of Archie Summers's words, and as he worried and groped, his fears increased. He began to imagine things. His thoughts became stranger and stranger. He found himself afraid to go to bed. Fearsome dreams would cause him to wake up in an agony of fear. And then he noticed that he was making excuses to himself for not going out into the streets. Once he tried to write a letter to D'Anoury, but could find no words.

"There came, you will understand, a general nervous breakdown.

"And still the card reposed in his case . . . though Brassington could no longer bring himself to look at it. Once or twice he felt minded to fling it away, but always something came to prevent him. But no longer did he particularly wish to have its meaning explained to him. A heavy languor was setting upon him. And little gaps appeared in his memory. It seemed to him that he would remain, for all time unnoticed and alone, in this corner of Italy.

"Then one night he had a bad fright. I'm not quite clear as to what happened. Possibly he had some sort of fit—what the doctors call the night-terrors in children—and in the morning he felt so ill that he was unable to leave his bed. He was staying in a little farmhouse now, and for some weeks he lay there, tended very lovingly by the farm-people. The local doctor visited him and could find nothing organically wrong. He gave one piece of good advice. The Englishman ought certainly to return to England to consult his own physician.

"For some time Brassington debated that admirable suggestion. The whole thing, he tried to think, might be nerves. Why not rush home to see Aylmer? He need not even mention the card. No one need know he had returned to England, and if necessary he could recross the Channel almost at once. And so, one day, he took his courage in his hands and came home.

"I don't know Dr. Aylmer myself, but I've always heard that he's a first-class man. Neurologist at Guy's for some years, and now in Harley Street. Brassington hired him from Dover, asking for an immediate appointment. Luckily Aylmer was at home and saw him at once. He was shocked at the change in Brassington's appearance. Told him he looked like a haunted man and wanted to know what frightful concoctions he had been trying to eat. I gather that Brassington himself was so exhausted that for some time he could hardly speak. The doctor was seriously worried, and soon diagnosed one of those distressing phobias which seem to be so common to-day.

" 'Just tell me everything quite slowly and coolly,' he said, 'and when you come to the unpleasant parts, remember I'm a doctor who hasn't been shocked since Derby Day of 1896.'

"And Brassington somehow managed to tell his story. To his surprise there was no detail which seemed to cause Dr. Aylmer any astonishment at all: he just listened and occasionally nodded his head.

"His attitude was undoubtedly the right one, for Brassington seemed no little relieved.

" 'You've been through a considerable strain, you see, Lord Brassington,' he told him. 'We shall have to go thoroughly into the whole matter. Probably I have heard only half at the moment. So far as I can see, your unfortunate adventures have somehow grouped themselves round some words on a card. Very well, the first thing to do is to solve the mystery of those words. I am particularly interested in such things. Let me see it.'

" 'But that's the one thing, Doctor, that I don't feel I have courage enough to do.'

"Aylmer smiled. 'The doctor's consulting-room . . .' he began.

" 'Oh, I know, I know, but what can I think when Archie Summers, one of my oldest friends. . . .'

" 'Shall I tell you what I think, Lord Brassington? I think that on the evening when you met Sir Archibald you were not at all well.'

"Brassington put up a hand to his forehead. 'I sometimes do forget things,' he muttered, 'but I swear I remember every incident of that evening.'

" 'No doubt,' agreed Aylmer, 'Just give me the card, then, and we'll see what can be done.'

"Brassington was painfully hesitating.

" 'I believe you can't even trust your own doctor,' said Aylmer, laughing. 'You ought to know by this time that a doctor is accustomed to hear many things which the average layman doesn't usually speak about.'

" 'I know, I know, but you see, if you fail me. . . .'

" 'My dear sir, there is not a chance I shall fail you, for the simple reason that I'm almost positive I have already solved the mystery.'

" 'You believe. . . .'

" 'Show me the card, and I promise that not a human soul shall be told anything about it.'

" 'Your word of honour?'

" 'My word of honour.'

"Brassington took out his card-case.

" 'Here it is,' he said, and held out the card.

"The doctor took it up and examined it carefully. He turned it over and held it up to the light.

"Then he smiled. 'Exactly what I expected to find,' he said.

" 'You mean. . . . I. . . .' Brassington sat down and stared at him. 'I don't understand. . . .'

" '*There is nothing on the card*,' said Dr. Aylmer. 'Both sides are quite blank.' "

"But," I exclaimed, "I don't understand either. There must have been something. . . ."

"I told you," said John Chester, "that this was the most maddening story in the world, and you mustn't ask me any more questions. I can only tell you that when the doctor saw the card it was blank, but whether it had always been blank— Hullo, the old General has obtained his drink! Waiter, you may bring us two whiskies-and-sodas."

CATERPILLARS

By E. F. BENSON

I SAW A MONTH AGO IN AN ITALIAN PAPER THAT THE VILLA Cascana, in which I once stayed, had been pulled down, and that a manufactory of some sort was in process of erection on its site. There is therefore no longer any reason for refraining from writing of those things which I myself saw (or imagined I saw) in a certain room and on a certain landing of the villa in question, nor from mentioning the circumstances which followed, which may or may not (according to the opinion of the reader) throw some light on, or be somehow connected with this experience.

The Villa Cascana was in all ways but one a perfectly delightful house, yet, if it were standing now, nothing in the world—I use the phrase in its literal sense—would induce me to see foot in it again, for I believe it to have been haunted in a very terrible and practical manner. Most ghosts, when all is said and done, do not do much harm; they may perhaps terrify, but the person whom they visit usually gets over their visitation. They may on the other hand be entirely friendly and beneficent. But the appearances in the Villa Cascana were not beneficent, and had they made their "visit" in a very slightly different manner, I do not suppose I should have got over it any more than Arthur Inglis did.

The house stood on an ilex-clad hill not far from Sestri di Levante on the Italian Riviera, looking out over the iridescent blues of that enchanted sea, while behind it rose the pale green chestnut woods that climb up the hillsides till they give place to the pines that, black in contrast with them, crown the slopes. All round it the garden in the luxuriance of mid-spring bloomed and was fragrant, and the scent of magnolia and rose, borne on the salt freshness of the winds from the sea, flowed like a stream through the cool, vaulted rooms.

On the ground floor a broad pillared *loggia* ran round three sides of the house, the top of which formed a balcony for certain rooms on the first floor. The main staircase, broad and of grey marble steps, led up from the hall to the landing outside these rooms, which were three in number, namely, two big sitting-rooms and a bedroom arranged *en suite*. The latter was unoccupied, the sitting-rooms were in use. From here the main staircase continued up to the second floor, where were situated certain bedrooms, one of which I occupied, while on the other side of the first-floor landing some half-dozen steps led to another suite of rooms, where, at the time I am speaking of, Arthur Inglis, the artist, had his bedroom and studio. Thus the landing outside my bedroom, at the top of the house, commanded both the landing of the first floor, and also the steps that led to Inglis' rooms. Jim Stanley and his wife, finally (whose guest I was), occupied rooms in another wing of the house, where also were the servants' quarters.

I arrived just in time for lunch on a brilliant noon of mid-May. The garden was shouting with colour and fragrance, and not less delightful after my broiling walk up from the *marina*, should have been the coming from the reverberating heat and blaze of the day into the marble coolness of the villa. Only (the reader has my bare word for this, and nothing more), the moment I set foot in the house I felt that something was wrong. This feeling, I may say, was quite vague, though very strong, and I remember that when I saw letters waiting for me on the table in the hall I felt certain that the explanation was here: I was convinced that there was bad news of some sort for me. Yet when I opened them I found no such explanation of my premonition: my correspondents all reeked of prosperity. Yet this clear miscarriage of a presentiment did not dissipate my uneasiness. In that cool fragrant house there was something wrong.

I am at pains to mention this because it may explain why it was that, though I am as a rule so excellent a sleeper that the extinction of a light on getting into bed is apparently contemporaneous with being called on the following morning, I slept very badly on my first night in the Villa Cascana. It may also explain the fact that when I did sleep (if it was indeed in sleep that I saw what I thought I saw) I dreamed in a very vivid and original manner, original, that is to say, in the sense that something which, as far as I knew, had never previously entered into my consciousness, usurped it then. But since, in addition to this evil premonition, certain words and events occurring during the rest of the day, might have suggested something of what I thought happened that night, it will be well to relate them.

After lunch, then, I went round the house with Mrs. Stanley, and during our tour she referred, it is true, to the unoccupied bedroom on the first floor, which opened out of the room where we had lunched.

"We left that unoccupied," she said, "because Jim and I have a charming bedroom and dressing room, as you saw, in the wing, and if we used it ourselves we should have to turn the dining room into a dressing room and have our meals downstairs. As it is, however, we have our little flat there, Arthur Inglis has his little flat in the other passage; and I remembered (aren't I extraordinary?) that you once said that the higher up you were in a house the better you were pleased. So I put you at the top of the house, instead of giving you that room."

It is true that a doubt, vague as my uneasy premonition, crossed my mind at this. I did not see why Mrs. Stanley should have explained all this, if there had not been more to explain. I allow, therefore, that the thought that there was something to explain about the unoccupied bedroom was momentarily present to my mind.

The second thing that may have borne on my dream was this.

At dinner the conversation turned for a moment on ghosts. Inglis, with the certainty of conviction, expressed his belief that anybody who could possibly believe in the existence of supernatural phenomena was unworthy of the name of an ass. The subject instantly dropped. As far as I can recollect, nothing else occurred or was said that could bear on what follows.

We all went to bed rather early, and personally I yawned my way upstairs, feeling hideously sleepy. My room was rather hot, and I threw all the windows wide, and from without poured in the white light of the moon, and the love song of many nightingales. I undressed quickly, and got into bed, but though I had felt so sleepy before, I now felt extremely wide-awake. But I was quite content to be awake: I did not toss or turn, I felt perfectly happy listening to the song and seeing the light. Then, it is possible, I may have gone to sleep, and what follows may have been a dream. I thought anyhow that after a time the nightingales ceased singing and the moon sank. I thought also that if, for some unexplained reason, I was going to lie awake all night, I might as well read, and I remembered that I had left a book in which I was interested in the dining room on the first floor. So I got out of bed, lit a candle, and went downstairs. I entered the room, saw on a side table the book I had come to look for, and then, simultaneously, saw that the door into the unoccupied bedroom was open. A curious grey light, not of dawn nor of moonshine, came out of it, and I looked in. The bed stood just opposite the door, a big four-poster, hung with tapestry at the head. Then I saw that the greyish light of the bedroom came from the bed, or rather from what was on the bed. For it was covered wtih great caterpillars, a foot or more in length, which crawled over it. They were faintly luminous, and it was the light from them that showed me the room. Instead of the sucker-feet of ordinary caterpillars they had rows of pincers like crabs, and they moved by grasping what they lay on with their pincers, and then sliding their bodies forward. In colour these dreadful insects were yellowish grey, and they were covered with irregular lumps and swellings. There must have been hundreds of them, for they formed a sort of writhing, crawling pyramid on the bed. Occasionally one fell off onto the floor, with a soft fleshy thud, and though the floor was of hard concrete, it yielded to the pincer-feet as if it had been putty, and crawling back, the caterpillar would mount on to the bed again, to rejoin its fearful companions. They appeared to have no faces, so to speak, but at one end of them there was a mouth that opened sideways in respiration.

Then, as I looked, it seemed to me as if they all suddenly became conscious of my presence. All the mouths at any rate were turned in my direction, and the next moment they began dropping off the bed with those soft fleshy thuds onto the floor, and wriggling towards me. For one second the paralysis of nightmare was on me, but the next I was running upstairs again to my room, and I remember feeling the cold of the marble steps on my bare feet. I rushed into my bedroom, and slammed the door behind me, and then—I was certainly wide awake now—I found myself standing by my bed with the sweat of terror pouring from me. The noise of the banged door still rang in my ears. But, as would have been more usual, if this had been mere nightmare, the terror that had been mine when I saw those foul beasts crawling about the bed or dropping softly onto the floor did not cease then. Awake now, if dreaming before, I did not at all recover from the horror of dream: it did not seem to me that I had dreamed. And until dawn, I sat or stood, not daring to lie down, thinking that every rustle or movement that I heard was the approach of the caterpillars. To them and the claws that bit into the cement the wood of the door was child's play: steel would not keep them out.

But with the sweet and noble return of day the horror vanished: the whisper of wind became benignant again: the nameless fear, whatever it was, was smoothed out and terrified me no longer. Dawn broke, hueless at first; then it grew dove-coloured, then the flaming pageant of light spread over the sky.

The admirable rule of the house was that everybody had breakfast where and when he pleased, and in consequence it was not till lunch-time that I met any of the other members of our party, since I had breakfast on my balcony, and wrote letters and other things till lunch. In fact, I got down to that meal rather late, after the other three had begun. Between my knife and fork there was a small pillbox of cardboard, and as I sat down Inglis spoke.

"Do look at that," he said, "since you are interested in natural history. I found it crawling on my counterpane last night, and I don't know what it is."

I think that before I opened the pillbox I expected something of the sort which I found in it. Inside it, anyhow, was a small caterpillar, greyish-yellow in colour, with curious bumps and excrescences on its rings. It was extremely active, and hurried round the box, this way and that. Its feet were unlike the feet of any caterpillar I ever saw: they were like the pincers of a crab. I looked, and shut the lid down again.

"No, I don't know it," I said, "but it looks rather unwholesome. What are you going to do with it?"

"Oh, I shall keep it," said Inglis. "It has begun to spin: I want to see what sort of a moth it turns into."

I opened the box again, and saw that these hurrying movements were indeed the beginning of the spinning of the web of its cocoon. Then Inglis spoke again.

"It has got funny feet, too," he said. "They are like crabs' pincers. What's the Latin for crab? Oh, yes, Cancer. So in case it is unique, let's christen it: 'Cancer Inglisensis'."

Then something happened in my brain, some momentary piecing together of all that I had seen or dreamed. Something in his words seemed to me to throw light on it all, and my own intense horror at the experience of the night before linked itself onto what he had just said. In effect, I took the box and threw it, caterpillar and all, out of the window. There was a gravel path just outside, and beyond it a fountain playing into a basin. The box fell onto the middle of this.

Inglis laughed.

"So the students of the occult don't like solid facts," he said. "My poor caterpillar!"

The talk went off again at once on to other subjects, and I have only given in detail, as they happened, these trivialities in order to be sure myself that I have recorded everything that could have borne on occult subjects or on the subject of caterpillars. But at the moment when I threw the pillbox into the fountain, I lost my head: my only excuse is that, as is probably plain, the tenant of it was, in miniature, exactly what I had seen crowded onto the bed in the unoccupied room. And though this translation of those phantoms into flesh and blood—or whatever it is that caterpillars are made of—ought perhaps to have relieved the horror of the night, as a matter of fact it did nothing of the kind. It only made the crawling pyramid that covered the bed in the unoccupied room more hideously real.

After lunch we spent a lazy hour or two strolling about the garden or sitting in the *loggia*, and it must have been about four o'clock when Stanley and I started off to bathe, down the path that led by the fountain into which I had thrown the pillbox. The water was shallow and clear, and at the bottom of it I saw its white remains. The soaking had disintegrated the cardboard, and it had become no more than a few strips and shreds of sodden paper. The centre of the fountain was a marble Italian Cupid which squirted the water out of a wineskin held under its arm. And crawling up its leg was the caterpillar. Strange and scarcely credible as it seemed, it must have survived the falling-to-bits of its prison, and made its way to shore, and there it was, out of arm's reach, weaving and waving this way and that as it evolved its cocoon.

Then, as I looked at it, it seemed to me again that, like the caterpillars I had seen last night, it saw me, and breaking out of the threads that surrounded it, it crawled down the marble leg of the Cupid and began swimming like a snake across the water of the fountain towards me. It came with extraordinary speed (the fact of a caterpillar being able to swim was new to me), and in another moment was crawling up the marble lip of the basin. Just then Inglis joined us.

"Why, if it isn't old 'Cancer Inglisensis' again," he said, catching sight of the beast. "What a tearing hurry it is in."

We were standing side by side on the path, and when the caterpillar had advanced to within about a yard of us, it stopped, and began waving again, as if in doubt as to the direction in which it should go. Then it appeared to make up its mind, and crawled onto Inglis' shoe.

"It likes me best," he said, "but I don't really know that I like it. And as it won't drown I think perhaps—"

He shook it off his shoe onto the gravel path and trod on it.

All the afternoon the air got heavier and heavier with the Sirocco that was without doubt coming up from the south, and that night again I went up to bed feeling very sleepy, but below my drowsiness, so to speak, there was the consciousness, stronger than before, that there was something wrong in the house, that something dangerous was close at hand. But I fell asleep at once, and— how long after I do not know—either woke or dreamed I awoke, feeling that I must get up at once, *or I should be too late*. Then (dreaming or awake) I lay and fought this fear, telling myself that I was but the prey of my own nerves disordered by Sirocco or what not, and at the same time quite clearly knowing in another part of my mind, so to speak, that every moment's delay added to the danger. At last this second feeling became irresistible, and I put on coat and trousers and went out of my room onto the landing. And then I saw that I had already delayed too long, and that I was now too late.

The whole of the landing of the first floor below was invisible under the swarm of caterpillars that crawled there. The folding doors into the sitting-room from which opened the bedroom where I had seen them last night, were shut, but they were squeezing through the cracks of it, and dropping one by one through the keyhole, elongating themselves into mere string as they passed, and growing fat and lumpy again on emerging. Some, as if exploring, were nosing about the steps into the passage at the end of which were Inglis' rooms, others were crawling on the lowest steps of the staircase that led up to where I stood. The landing, however, was completely covered with them: I was cut off. And of the frozen horror that seized me when I saw that, I can give no idea in words.

Then at last a general movement began to take place, and they grew thicker on the steps that led to Inglis' room. Gradually, like some hideous tide of flesh, they advanced along the passage, and I saw the foremost, visible by the pale grey luminousness that came from them, reach his door. Again and again I tried to shout and warn him, in terror all the time that they should turn at the sound of my voice and mount my stair instead, but for all my efforts I felt that no sound came from my throat. They crawled along the hinge-crack of his door, passing through as they had done before, and still I stood there making impotent efforts to shout to him, to bid him escape while there was time.

At last the passage was completely empty: they had all gone, and at that moment I was conscious for the first time of the cold of the marble landing on which I stood barefooted. The dawn was just beginning to break in the Eastern sky.

Six months later I met Mrs. Stanley in a country house in England. We talked on many subjects, and at last she said:

"I don't think I have seen you since I got that dreadful news about Arthur Inglis a month ago."

"I haven't heard," said I.

"No? He has got cancer. They don't even advise an operation, for there is no hope of a cure: he is riddled with it, the doctors say."

Now during all these six months I do not think a day had passed on which I had not had in my mind the dreams (or whatever you like to call them) which I had seen in the Villa Casana.

"It is awful, is it not?" she continued, "and I feel, I can't help feeling, that he may have—"

"Caught it at the villa?" I asked.

She looked at me in blank surprise.

"Why did you say that?" she asked. "How did you know?"

Then she told me. In the unoccupied bedroom a year before there had been a fatal case of cancer. She had, of course, taken the best advice and had been told that the utmost dictates of prudence would be obeyed so long as she did not put anybody to sleep in the room, which had also been thoroughly disinfected and newly whitewashed and painted. But—

THE OPEN WINDOW

By "Saki" (H. H. Munro)

"MY AUNT WILL BE DOWN PRESENTLY, MR. NUTTEL," SAID A VERY self-possessed young lady of fifteen; "in the meantime you must try and put up with me."

Framton Nuttel endeavoured to say the correct something which should duly flatter the niece of the moment without unduly discounting the aunt that was to come. Privately he doubted more than ever whether these formal visits on a succession of total strangers would do much towards helping the nerve cure which he was supposed to be undergoing.

"I know how it will be," his sister had said when he was preparing to migrate to this rural retreat; "you will bury yourself down there and not speak to a living soul, and your nerves will be worse than ever from moping. I shall just give you letters of introduction to all the people I know there. Some of them, as far as I can remember, were quite nice."

Framton wondered whether Mrs. Sappleton, the lady to whom he was presenting one of the letters of introduction, came into the nice division.

"Do you know many of the people round here?" asked the niece, when she judged that they had had sufficient silent communion.

"Hardly a soul," said Framton. "My sister was staying here, at the rectory, you know, some four years ago, and she gave me letters of introduction to some of the people here."

He made the last statement in a tone of distinct regret.

"Then you know practically nothing about my aunt?" pursued the self-possessed young lady.

"Only her name and address," admitted the caller. He was wondering whether Mrs. Sappleton was in the married or widowed state. An undefinable something about the room seemed to suggest masculine habitation.

"Her great tragedy happened just three years ago," said the child; "that would be since your sister's time."

"Her tragedy?" asked Framton; somehow in this restful country spot tragedies seemed out of place.

"You may wonder why we keep that window wide open on an October afternoon," said the niece, indicating a large French window that opened on to a lawn.

"It is quite warm for the time of the year," said Framton; "but has that window got anything to do with the tragedy?"

"Out through that window, three years ago to a day, her husband and her two young brothers went off for their day's shooting. They never came back. In crossing the moor to their favorite snipe-shooting ground they were all three engulfed in a treacherous piece of bog. It had been that dreadful wet summer, you know, and places that were safe in other years gave way suddenly without warning. Their bodies were never recovered. That was the dreadful part of it." Here the child's voice lost its self-possessed note and became falteringly human. "Poor aunt always thinks that they will come back some day, they and the little brown spaniel that was lost with them, and walk in at that window just as they used to do. That is why the window is kept open every evening till it is quite dusk. Poor dear aunt, she has often told me how they went out, her husband with his white waterproof coat over his arm, and Ronnie, her youngest brother, singing 'Bertie, why do you bound?' as he always did to tease her, because she said it got on her nerves. Do you know, sometimes on still, quiet evenings like this, I almost get a creepy feeling that they will all walk in through that window—"

She broke off with a little shudder. It was a relief to Framton when the aunt bustled into the room with a whirl of apologies for being late in making her appearance.

"I hope Vera has been amusing you?" she said.

"She has been very interesting," said Framton.

"I hope you don't mind the open window," said Mrs. Sappleton briskly; "my husband and brothers will be home directly from shooting, and they always come in this way. They've been out

for snipe in the marshes today, so they'll make a fine mess over
my poor carpets. So like you men-folks, isn't it?"

She rattled on cheerfully about the shooting and the scarcity
of birds, and the prospects for duck in the winter. To Framton
it was all purely horrible. He made a desperate but only partially
successful effort to turn the talk on to a less ghastly topic; he was
conscious that his hostess was giving him only a fragment of her
attention, and her eyes were constantly straying past him to the
open window and the lawn beyond. It was certainly an unfortunate coincidence that he should have paid his visit on this
tragic anniversary.

"The doctors agree in ordering me complete rest, an absence of
mental excitement, and avoidance of anything in the nature of
violent physical exercise," announced Framton, who laboured under the tolerably wide-spread delusion that total strangers and
chance acquaintances are hungry for the least detail of one's ail-
ments and infirmities, their cause and cure. "On the matter of diet
they are not so much in agreement," he continued.

"No?" said Mrs. Sappleton, in a voice which only replaced a
yawn at the last moment. Then she suddenly brightened into alert
attention—but not to what Framton was saying.

"Here they are at last!" she cried. "Just in time for tea, and
don't they look as if they were muddy up to the eyes!"

Framton shivered slightly and turned towards the niece with a
look intended to convey sympathetic comprehension. The child
was staring out through the open window with dazed horror in
her eyes. In a chill shock of nameless fear Framton swung round
in his seat and looked in the same direction.

In the deepening twilight three figures were walking across the
lawn towards the window; they all carried guns under their arms,
and one of them was additionally burdened with a white coat hung
over his shoulders. A tired brown spaniel kept close at their heels.
Noiselessly they neared the house, and then a hoarse young voice
chanted out of the dusk: "I said, Bertie, why do you bound?"

Framton grabbed wildly at his stick and hat; the hall-door, the
gravel-drive, and the front gate were dimly noted stages in his
headlong retreat. A cyclist coming along the road had to run into
the hedge to avoid imminent collision.

"Here we are, my dear," said the bearer of the white mackintosh, coming in through the window; "fairly muddy, but most of it's dry. Who was that who bolted out as we came up?"

"A most extraordinary man, a Mr. Nuttel," said Mrs. Sappleton; "could only talk about his illness, and dashed off without a word of good-bye or apology when you arrived. One would think he had seen a ghost."

"I expect it was the spaniel," said the niece calmly; "he told me he had a horror of dogs. He was once hunted into a cemetery somewhere on the banks of the Ganges by a pack of parish dogs, and had to spend the night in a newly dug grave with the creatures snarling and grinning and foaming just above him. Enough to make any one lose their nerve."

Romance at short notice was her specialty.

TWO SHARP KNIVES

By DASHIELL HAMMETT

ON MY WAY HOME FROM THE REGULAR WEDNESDAY NIGHT POKER game at Ben Kamsley's I stopped at the railroad station to see the 2:11 come in—what we called putting the town to bed—and as soon as this fellow stepped down from the smoking-car I recognized him. There was no mistaking his face, the pale eyes with lower lids that were as straight as if they had been drawn with a ruler, the noticeably flat-tipped bony nose, the deep cleft in his chin, the slightly hollow grayish cheeks. He was tall and thin and very neatly dressed in a dark suit, long dark overcoat, derby hat, and carried a black Gladstone bag. He looked a few years older than the forty he was supposed to be. He went past me towards the street steps.

When I turned around to follow him I saw Wally Shane coming out of the waiting-room. I caught Wally's eye and nodded at the man carrying the black bag. Wally examined him carefully as he went by. I could not see whether the man noticed the examination. By the time I came up to Wally the man was going down the steps to the street.

Wally rubbed his lips together and his blue eyes were bright and hard. "Look," he said out of the side of his mouth, "that's a ringer for the guy we got—"

"That's the guy," I said, and we went down the steps behind him.

Our man started towards one of the taxicabs at the curb, then saw the lights of the Deerwood Hotel two blocks away, shook his head at the taxi driver, and went up the street afoot.

"What do we do?" Wally asked. "See what he's—?"

"It's nothing to us. We take him. Get my car. It's at the corner of the alley."

I gave Wally the few minutes he needed to get the car and then

544

closed in. "Hello, Furman," I said when I was just behind the tall man.

His face jerked around to me. "How do you—" He halted. "I don't believe I—" He looked up and down the street. We had the block to ourselves.

"You're Lester Furman, aren't you?" I asked.

He said "Yes" quickly.

"Philadelphia?"

He peered at me in the light that was none too strong where we stood. "Yes."

"I'm Scott Anderson," I said, "Chief of Police here. I—"

His bag thudded down on the pavement. "What's happened to her?" he asked hoarsely.

"Happened to who?"

Wally arrived in my car then, abruptly, skidding into the curb. Furman, his face stretched by fright, leaped back away from me. I went after him, grabbing him with my good hand, jamming him back against the front wall of Henderson's warehouse. He fought with me there until Wally got out of the car. Then he saw Wally's uniform and immediately stopped fighting.

"I'm sorry," he said weakly. "I thought—for a second I thought maybe you weren't the police. You're not in uniform and—It was silly of me. I'm sorry."

"It's all right," I told him. "Let's get going before we have a mob around us." Two cars had stopped just a little beyond mine and I could see a bellboy and a hatless man coming towards us from the direction of the hotel.

Furman picked up his bag and went willingly into my car ahead of me. We sat in the rear. Wally drove.

We rode a block in silence, then Furman asked, "You're taking me to police headquarters?"

"Yes."

"What for?"

"Philadelphia."

"I—" he cleared his throat, "—I don't think I understand you."

"You understand that you're wanted in Philadelphia, don't you, for murder?"

He said indignantly, "That's ridiculous. Murder! That's—" He put a hand on my arm, his face close to mine, and instead of indignation in his voice there now was a desperate sort of earnestness. "Who told you that?"

"I didn't make it up. Well, here we are. Come on, I'll show you."

We took him into my office. George Propper, who had been dozing in a chair in the front office, followed us in. I found the Trans-American Detective Agency circular and handed it to Furman. In the usual form it offered fifteen hundred dollars for the arrest and conviction of Lester Furman, alias Lloyd Fields, alias J. D. Carpenter, for the murder of Paul Frank Dunlap in Philadelphia on the 26th of the previous month.

Furman's hands holding the circular were steady and he read it carefully. His face was pale, but no muscles moved in it until he opened his mouth to speak. He tried to speak calmly. "It's a lie." He did not look up from the circular.

"You're Lester Furman, aren't you?" I asked.

He nodded, still not looking up.

"That's your description, isn't it?"

He nodded.

"That's your photograph, isn't it?"

He nodded, and then, staring at his photograph on the circular, he began to tremble—his lips, his hands, his legs.

I pushed a chair up behind him and said, "Sit down," and he dropped down on it and shut his eyes, pressing the lids together. I took the circular from his limp hands.

George Propper, leaning against a side of the doorway, turned his loose grin from me to Wally and said, "So that's that and so you lucky stiffs split a grand and a half reward money. Lucky Wally! If it ain't vacations in New York at the city's expense it's reward money."

Furman jumped up from the chair and screamed, "It's a lie. It's a frame-up. You can't prove anything. There's nothing to prove. I never killed anybody. I won't be framed. I won't be—"

I pushed him down on the chair again. "Take it easy," I told him. "You're wasting your breath on us. Save it for the Philadelphia police. We're just holding you for them. If anything's wrong it's there, not here."

"But it's not the police. It's the Trans-American De—"

"We turn you over to the police."

He started to say something, broke off, sighed, made a little hopeless gesture with his hands, and tried to smile. "Then there's nothing I can do now?"

"There's nothing any of us can do till morning," I said. "We'll have to search you, then we won't bother you any more till they come for you."

In the black Gladstone bag we found a couple of changes of clothes, some toilet articles, and a loaded .38 automatic. In his pockets we found a hundred and sixty-some dollars, a book of checks on a Philadelphia bank, business cards and a few letters that seemed to show he was in the real estate business, and the sort of odds and ends that you usually find in men's pockets.

While Wally was putting these things in the vault I told George Propper to lock Furman up.

George rattled keys in his pocket and said, "Come along, darling. We ain't had anybody in our little hoosegow for three days. You'll have it all to yourself, just like a suite in the Ritz."

Furman said "Good night and thank you" to me and followed George out.

When George came back he leaned against the door frame again and asked, "How about you big-hearted boys cutting me in on a little of that blood money?"

Wally said, "Sure. I'll forget that two and a half you been owing me three months."

I said, "Make him as comfortable as you can, George. If he wants anything sent in, O.K."

"He's valuable, huh? If it was some bum that didn't mean a nickel to you. . . . Maybe I ought to take a pillow off my bed for him." He spit at the cuspidor and missed. "He's just like the rest of 'em to me."

I thought, "Any day now I'm going to forget that your uncle is county chairman and throw you back in the gutter." I said, "Do all the talking you want, but do what I tell you."

It was about four o'clock when I got home—my farm was a little outside the town—and maybe half an hour after that before I went to sleep. The telephone woke me up at five minutes past six.

Wally's voice: "You better come down, Scott. The fellow Furman's hung himself."

"What?"

"By his belt—from a window bar—deader'n hell."

"All right. I'm on my way. Phone Ben Kamsley I'll pick him up on my way in."

"No doctor's going to do this man any good, Scott."

"It won't hurt to have him looked at," I insisted. "You'd better phone Douglassville too." Douglassville was the county seat.

"O.K."

Wally phoned me back while I was dressing to tell me that Ben Kamsley had been called out on an emergency case and was somewhere on the other side of town, but that his wife would get in touch with him and tell him to stop at headquarters on his way home.

When, riding into town, I was within fifty or sixty feet of the Red Top Diner, Heck Jones ran out with a revolver in his hand and began to shoot at two men in a black roadster that had just passed me.

I leaned out and yelled, "What's it?" at him while I was turning my car.

"Holdup," he bawled angrily. "Wait for me." He let loose another shot that couldn't have missed my front tire by more than an inch and galloped up to me, his apron flapping around his fat legs. I opened the door for him, he squeezed his bulk in beside me, and we set off after the roadster.

"What gets me," he said when he had stopped panting, "is they done it like a joke. They come in, they don't want nothing but ham and eggs and coffee and then they get kind of kidding together under their breath and then they put the guns on me like a joke."

"How much did they take?"

"Sixty or thereabouts, but that ain't what gripes me so much. It's them doing it like a joke."

"Never mind," I said. "We'll get 'em."

We very nearly didn't, though. They led us a merry chase. We lost them a couple of times and finally picked them up more by luck than anything else, a couple of miles over the state line.

We didn't have any trouble taking them, once we had caught

up to them, but they knew they had crossed the state line and they insisted on regular extradition or nothing, so we had to carry them on to Badington and stick them in the jail there until the necessary papers could be sent through. It was ten o'clock before I got a chance to phone my office.

Hammill answered the phone and told me Ted Carroll, our district attorney, was there, so I talked to Ted—though not as much as he talked to me.

"Listen, Scott," he asked excitedly, "what is all this?"

"All what?"

"This fiddle-de-dee, this hanky-panky."

"I don't know what you mean," I said. "Wasn't it suicide?"

"Sure it was suicide, but I wired the Trans-American and they phoned me just a few minutes ago and said they'd never sent out any circulars on Furman, didn't know about any murder he was wanted for. All they knew about him was he used to be a client of theirs."

I couldn't think of anything to say except that I would be back in Deerwood by noon. And I was.

Ted was at my desk with the telephone receiver clamped to his ear, saying, "Yes. . . . Yes. . . . Yes," when I went into the office. He put down the receiver and asked, "What happened to you?"

"A couple of boys knocked over the Red Top Diner and I had to chase 'em almost to Badington."

He smiled with one side of his mouth. "The town getting out of your hands?" He and I were on opposite sides of the fence politically and we took our politics seriously in Candle County.

I smiled back at him. "Looks like it—with one felony in six months."

"And this." He jerked a thumb towards the rear of the building, where the cells were.

"What about this? Let's talk about this."

"It's plenty wrong," he said. "I just finished talking to the Philly police. There wasn't any Paul Frank Dunlap murdered there that they know about; they've got no unexplained murder on the 26th of last month." He looked at me as if it were my fault. "What'd you get out of Furman before you let him hang himself?"

"That he was innocent."

"Didn't you grill him? Didn't you find out what he was doing in town? Didn't you—"

"What for?" I asked. "He admitted his name was Furman, the description fitted him, the photograph was him, the Trans-American's supposed to be on the level. Philadelphia wanted him: I didn't. Sure, if I'd known he was going to hang himself— You said he'd been a client of the Trans-American. They tell you what the job was?"

"His wife left him a couple of years ago and he had them hunting for her for five or six months, but they never found her. They're sending a man up tonight to look it over." He stood up. "I'm going to get some lunch." At the door he turned his head over his shoulder to say, "There'll probably be trouble over this."

I knew that; there usually is when somebody dies in a cell.

George Propper came in grinning happily. "So what's become of that fifteen hundred fish?"

"What happened last night?" I asked.

"Nothing. He hung hisself."

"Did you find him?"

He shook his head. "Wally took a look in there to see how things was before he went off duty and found him."

"You were asleep, I suppose."

"Well, I was catching a nap, I guess," he mumbled; "but everybody does that sometimes—even Wally sometimes when he comes in off his beat between rounds—and I always wake up when the phone rings or anything. And suppose I had been awake. You can't hear a guy hanging hisself."

"Did Kamsley say how long he'd been dead?"

"He done it about five o'clock, he said he guessed. You want to look at the remains? They're over at Fritz's undertaking parlor."

I said, "Not now. You'd better go home and get some more sleep, so your insomnia won't keep you awake tonight."

He said, "I feel almost as bad about you and Wally losing all that dough as you do," and went out; went out chuckling.

Ted Carroll came back from lunch with the notion that perhaps there was some connection between Furman and the two men who had robbed Heck Jones. That didn't seem to make much sense, but

I promised to look into it. Naturally, we never did find any such connection.

That evening a fellow named Rising, assistant manager of the Trans-American Detective Agency's Philadelphia branch, arrived. He brought the dead man's lawyer, a scrawny, asthmatic man named Wheelock, with him. After they had identified the body we went back to my office for a conference.

It didn't take me long to tell them all I knew, with the one additional fact I had picked up during the afternoon, which was that the police in most towns in our corner of the state had received copies of the reward circular.

Rising examined the circular and called it an excellent forgery: paper, style, type were all almost exactly those ordinarily used by his agency.

They told me the dead man was a well-known, respectable, and prosperous citizen of Philadelphia. In 1928 he had married a twenty-two-year-old girl named Ethel Brian, the daughter of a respectable, if not prosperous, Philadelphia family. They had a child born in 1930, but it lived only a few months. In 1931 Furman's wife had disappeared and neither he nor her family had heard of her since, though he had spent a good deal of money trying to find her. Rising showed me a photograph of her, a small-featured, pretty blonde with a weak mouth and large, somewhat staring eyes.

"I'd like to have a copy made," I said.

"You can keep that. It's one of them that we had made. Her description's on the back."

"Thanks. And he didn't divorce her?"

Rising shook his head with emphasis. "No, sir. He was a lot in love with her and he seemed to think the kid's dying had made her a little screwy and she didn't know what she was doing." He looked at the lawyer. "That right?"

Wheelock made a couple of asthmatic sounds and said, "That is my belief."

"You said he had money. About how much, and who gets it?"

The scrawny lawyer wheezed some more, said, "I should say his estate will amount to perhaps a half a million dollars, left in its entirety to his wife."

That gave me something to think about, but the thinking didn't help me out then.

They couldn't tell me why he had come to Deerwood. He seemed to have told nobody where he was going, had simply told his servants and his employees that he was leaving town for a day or two. Neither Rising nor Wheelock knew of any enemies he had. That was the crop.

And that was still the crop at the inquest the next day. Everything showed that somebody had framed Furman into our jail and that the frame-up had driven him to suicide. Nothing showed anything else. And there had to be something else, a lot else.

Some of the else began to show up immediately after the inquest. Ben Kamsley was waiting for me when I left the undertaking parlor, where the inquest had been held. "Let's get out of the crowd," he said. "I want to tell you something."

"Come on over to the office."

We went over there. He shut the door, which usually stayed open, and sat on a corner of my desk. His voice was low: "Two of those bruises showed."

"What bruises?"

He looked curiously at me for a second, then put a hand on the top of his head. "Furman—up under the hair—there were two bruises."

I tried to keep from shouting. "Why didn't you tell me?"

"I am telling you. You weren't here that morning. This is the first time I've seen you since."

I cursed the two hoodlums who had kept me away by sticking up the Red Top Diner and demanded, "Then why didn't you spill it when you were testifying at the inquest?"

He frowned. "I'm a friend of yours. Do I want to put you in a spot where people can say you drove this chap to suicide by third-degreeing him too rough?"

"You're nuts," I said. "How bad was his head?"

"That didn't kill him, if that's what you mean. There's nothing the matter with his skull. Just a couple of bruises nobody would notice unless they parted the hair."

"It killed him just the same," I growled. "You and your *friendship* that—"

The telephone rang. It was Fritz. "Listen, Scott," he said, "there's a couple of ladies here that want to look at that fellow. Is it all right?"

"Who are they?"

"I don't know 'em—strangers."

"What do they want to see him for?"

"I don't know. Wait a minute."

A woman's voice came over the wire: "Can't I please see him?" It was a very pleasant, earnest voice.

"Why do you want to see him?" I asked.

"Well, I,"—there was a long pause—"I am"—a shorter pause, and when she finished the sentence her voice was not much more than a whisper—" his wife."

"Oh, certainly," I said. "I'll be right over."

I hurried out.

Leaving the building, I ran into Wally Shane. He was in civilian clothes, since he was off duty. "Hey, Scott!" He took my arm and dragged me back into the vestibule, out of sight of the street. "A couple of dames came into Fritz's just as I was leaving. One of 'em's Hotcha Randall, a baby with a record as long as your arm. You know she's one of that mob you had me in New York working on last summer."

"She know you?"

He grinned. "Sure. But not by my right name, and she thinks I'm a Detroit rum-runner."

"I mean did she know you just now?"

"I don't think she saw me. Anyways, she didn't give me a tumble."

"You don't know the other one?"

"No. She's a blonde, kind of pretty."

"O.K.," I said. "Stick around a while, but out of sight. Maybe I'll be bringing them back with me." I crossed the street to the undertaking parlor.

Ethel Furman was prettier than her photograph had indicated. The woman with her was five or six years older, quite a bit larger, handsome in a big, somewhat coarse way. Both of them were attractively dressed in styles that hadn't reached Deerwood yet.

The big woman was introduced to me as Mrs. Crowder. I said, "I thought your name was Randall."

She laughed. "What do you care, Chief? I'm not hurting your town."

I said, "Don't call me Chief. To you big-city slickers I'm the Town Whittler. We go back through here."

Ethel Furman didn't make any fuss over her husband when she saw him. She simply looked gravely at his face for about three minutes, then turned away and said, "Thank you," to me.

"I'll have to ask you some questions," I said, "so if you'll come across the street—"

She nodded. "And I'd like to ask you some." She looked at her companion. "If Mrs. Crowder will—"

"Call her Hotcha," I said. "We're all among friends. Sure, she'll come along, too."

The Randall woman said, "Aren't you the cut-up?" and took my arm.

In my office I gave them chairs and said, "Before I ask you anything I want to tell you something. Furman didn't commit suicide. He was murdered."

Ethel Furman opened her eyes wide. "Murdered?"

Hotcha Randall said as if she had had the words on the tip of her tongue right along. "We've got alibis. We were in New York. We can prove it."

"You're likely to get a chance to, too," I told her. "How'd you people happen to come down here?"

Ethel Furman repeated, "Murdered?" in a dazed tone.

The Randall woman said, "Who's got a better right to come down here? She was still his wife, wasn't she? She's entitled to some of his estate, isn't she? She's got a right to look out for her own interests, hasn't she?"

That reminded me of something. I picked up the telephone and told Hammill to have somebody get hold of the lawyer Wheelock —he had stayed over for the inquest, of course—before he left town and tell him I wanted to see him. "And is Wally around?"

"He's not here. He said you told him to keep out of sight. I'll find him, though."

"Right. Tell him I want him to go to New York tonight. Send

Mason home to get some sleep; he'll have to take over Wally's night trick."

Hammill said, "Oke," and I turned back to my guests.

Ethel Furman had come out of her daze. She leaned forward and asked, "Mr. Anderson, do you think I had—had anything to do with Lester's—with his death?"

"I don't know. I know he was killed. I know he left you something like half a million."

The Randall woman whistled softly. She came over and put a diamond-ringed hand on my shoulder. "Dollars?"

When I nodded, the delight went out of her face, leaving it serious. "All right, Chief," she said, "now don't be a clown. The kid didn't have a thing to do with whatever you think happened. We read about him committing suicide in yesterday morning's paper, and about there being something funny about it, and I persuaded her she ought to come down and—"

Ethel Furman interrupted her friend: "Mr. Anderson, I wouldn't have done anything to hurt Lester. I left him because I wanted to leave him, but I wouldn't have done anything to him for money or anything else. Why, if I'd wanted money from him all I'd've had to do would've been to ask him. Why, he used to put ads in papers telling me if I wanted anything to let him know, but I never did. You can—his lawyer—anybody who knew anything about it can tell you that."

The Randall woman took up the story: "That's the truth, Chief. For years I've been telling her she was a chump not to tap him, but she never would. I had a hard enough time getting her to come for her share now he's dead and got nobody else to leave it to."

Ethel Furman said, "I wouldn't've hurt him."

"Why'd you leave him?"

She moved her shoulders. "I don't know how to say it. The way we lived wasn't the way I wanted to live. I wanted—I don't know what. Anyway after the baby died I couldn't stand it any more and cleared out, but I didn't want anything from him and I wouldn't've hurt him. He was always good to me. I was—I was the one that was wrong."

The telephone rang. Hammill's voice: "I found both of 'em.

Wally's home. I told him. The old guy Wheelock is on his way over."

I dug out the phony reward circular and showed it to Ethel Furman. "This is what got him into the can. Did you ever see that picture before?"

She started to say "No"; then a frightened look came into her face. "Why, that's—it can't be. It's—it's a snapshot I had—have. It's an enlargement of it."

"Who else has one?"

Her face became more frightened, but she said, "Nobody that I know of. I don't think anybody else could have one."

"You've still got yours?"

"Yes. I don't remember whether I've seen it recently—it's with some old papers and things—but I must have it."

I said, "Well, Mrs. Furman, it's stuff like that that's got to be checked up, and neither of us can dodge it. Now there are two ways we can play it. I can hold you here on suspicion till I've had time to check things up, or I can send one of my men back to New York with you for the check-up. I'm willing to do that if you'll speed things up by helping him all you can and if you'll promise me you won't try any tricks."

"I promise," she said. "I'm as anxious as you are to—"

"All right. How'd you come down?"

"I drove," the Randall woman said. "That's my car, the big green one across the street."

"Fine. Then he can ride back with you, but remember, no funny business."

The telephone rang again while they were assuring me there would be no funny business. Hammill: "Wheelock's here."

"Send him in."

The lawyer's asthma nearly strangled him when he saw Ethel Furman. Before he could get himself straightened out I asked, "This is really Mrs. Furman?"

He wagged his head up and down, still wheezing.

"Fine," I said. "Wait for me. I'll be back in a little while." I herded the two women out and across the street to the green car. "Straight up to the end of the street and then two blocks left," I told the Randall woman, who was at the wheel.

"Where are we going?" she asked.

"To see Shane, the man who's going to New York with you."

Mrs. Dober, Wally's landlady, opened the door for us.

"Wally in?" I asked.

"Yes, indeedy, Mr. Anderson. Go right on up." She was staring with wide-eyed curiosity at my companions while talking to me.

We went up a flight of stairs and I knocked on his door.

"Who is it?" he called.

"Scott."

"Come on in."

I pushed the door open and stepped aside to let the women in.

Ethel Furman gasped, "Harry!" and stepped back, treading on my foot.

Wally had a hand behind him, but my gun was already out in my hand. "I guess you win," he said.

I said I guessed I did and we all went back to headquarters.

"I'm a sap," he complained when he and I were alone in my office. "I knew it was all up as soon as I saw those two dames going into Fritz's. Then, when I was ducking out of sight and ran into you, I was afraid you'd take me over with you, so I had to tell you one of 'em knew me, figuring you'd want to keep me under cover for a little while anyhow—long enough for me to get out of town. And then I didn't have sense enough to do it.

"I drop in home to pick up a couple of things before I scram and that call of Hammill's catches me and I fall for it plenty. I figure I'm getting a break. I figure you're not on yet and are going to send me back to New York as the Detroit rum-runner again to see what dope I can get out of these folks and I'll be sitting pretty. Well, you fooled me, brother, or didn't— Listen, Scott, you didn't just stumble into that accidentally, did you?"

"No. Furman had to be murdered by a copper. A copper was most likely to know reward circulars well enough to make a good job of forging one. Who printed that for you?"

"Go on with your story," he said. "I'm not dragging anybody in with me. It was only a poor mug of a printer that needed dough."

"O.K. Only a copper would be sure enough of the routine to know how things would be handled. Only a copper—one of my coppers—would be able to walk into his cell, bang him across the head and string him up on the— Those bruises showed, you know."

"They did? I wrapped the blackjack in a towel, figuring it would knock him out without leaving a mark anybody'd find under the hair. I seem to've slipped up a lot."

"So that narrows it down to my coppers," I went on, "and—well —you told me you knew the Randall woman, and there it was, only I figured you were working with them. What got you into this?"

He made a sour mouth. "What gets most saps in jams? A yen for easy dough. I'm in New York, see, working on that Dutton job for you, palling around with bootleggers and racketeers, passing for one of them; and I get to figuring that here my work takes as much brains as theirs, and is as tough and dangerous as theirs, but they're taking in big money and I'm working for coffee and doughnuts. That kind of stuff gets you; anyway, it got me.

"Then I run into this Ethel and she goes for me like a house afire. I like her, too, so that's dandy; but one night she tells me about this husband of hers and how much dough he's got and how nuts he is about her and how he's still trying to find her, and I get to thinking. I think she's nuts enough about me to marry me. I still think she'd marry me if she didn't know I killed him. Divorcing him's no good, because the chances are she wouldn't take any money from him and, anyway, it would only be part. So I got to thinking about suppose he died and left her the roll.

"That was more like it. I ran down to Philly a couple of afternoons and looked him up and everything looked fine. He didn't even have anybody else close enough to leave more than a little of his dough to. So I did it. Not right away; I took my time working out the details, meanwhile writing to her through a fellow in Detroit.

"And then I did it. I sent those circulars out—to a lot of places— not wanting to point too much at this one. And when I was ready I phoned him, telling him if he'd come to the Deerwood Hotel that night, sometime between then and the next night, he'd hear from Ethel. And, like I thought, he'd've fallen for any trap that was baited with her. You picking him up at the station was a break. If you hadn't I'd've had to discover he was registered at the hotel that night. Anyway, I'd've killed him and pretty soon I'd've started drinking or something and you'd've fired me and I'd've gone off and married Ethel and her half-million under my Detroit name." He made the sour mouth again. "Only I guess I'm not as sharp as I thought I was."

"Maybe you are," I said, "but that doesn't always help. Old man Kamsley, Ben's father, used to have a saying, 'To a sharp knife comes a tough steak.' I'm sorry you did it, Wally. I always liked you."

He smiled wearily. "I know you did," he said. "I was counting on that."

A ROSE FOR EMILY

By William Faulkner

WHEN MISS EMILY GRIERSON DIED, OUR WHOLE TOWN WENT TO HER funeral: the men through a sort of respectful affection for a fallen monument, the women mostly out of curiosity to see the inside of her house, which no one save an old man-servant—a combined gardener and cook—had seen in at least ten years.

It was a big, squarish frame house that had once been white, decorated with cupolas and spires and scrolled balconies in the heavily lightsome style of the Seventies, set on what had once been our most select street. But garages and cotton gins had encroached and obliterated even the august names of that neighborhood; only Miss Emily's house was left, lifting its stubborn and coquettish decay bove the cotton wagons and the gasoline pumps—an eyesore among eyesores. And now Miss Emily had gone to join the representatives of those august names where they lay in the cedar-bemused cemetery among the ranked and anonymous graves of Union and Confederate soldiers who fell at the battle of Jefferson.

Alive, Miss Emily had been a tradition, a duty, and a care; a sort of hereditary obligation upon the town, dating from that day in 1894 when Colonel Sartoris, the mayor—he who fathered the edict that no Negro woman should appear on the streets without an apron—remitted her taxes, the dispensation dating from the death of her father on into perpetuity. Not that Miss Emily would have accepted charity. Colonel Sartoris invented an involved tale to the effect that Miss Emily's father had loaned money to the town, which the town, as a matter of business, preferred this way of repaying. Only a man of Colonel Sartoris' generation and thought could have invented it, and only a woman could have believed it.

When the next generation, with its more modern ideas, became mayors and aldermen, this arrangement created some little dissatisfaction. On the first of the year they mailed her a tax notice. February came, and there was no reply. They wrote her a formal letter, asking her to call at the sheriff's office at her convenience. A week later the mayor wrote her himself, offering to call or to send his car for her, and received in reply a note on paper of an archaic shape, in a thin, flowing calligraphy in faded ink, to the effect that she no longer went out at all. The tax notice was also enclosed, without comment.

They called a special meeting of the Board of Aldermen. A deputation waited upon her, knocked at the door through which no visitor had passed since she ceased giving china-painting lessons eight or ten years earlier. They were admitted by the old Negro into a dim hall from which a stairway mounted into still more shadow. It smelled of dust and disuse—a close, dank smell. The Negro led them into the parlor. It was furnished in heavy, leather-covered furniture. When the Negro opened the blinds of one window, they could see that the leather was cracked; and when they sat down, a faint dust rose sluggishly about their thighs, spinning with slow motes in the single sun-ray. On a tarnished gilt easel before the fireplace stood a crayon portrait of Miss Emily's father.

They rose when she entered—a small, fat woman in black, with a thin gold chain descending to her waist and vanishing into her belt, leaning on an ebony cane with a tarnished gold head. Her skeleton was small and spare; perhaps that was why what would have been merely plumpness in another was obesity in her. She looked bloated, like a body long submerged in motionless water, and of that pallid hue. Her eyes, lost in the fatty ridges of her face, looked like two small pieces of coal pressed into a lump of dough as they moved from one face to another while the visitors stated their errand.

She did not ask them to sit. She just stood in the door and listened quietly until the spokesman came to a stumbling halt. Then they could hear the invisible watch ticking at the end of the gold chain.

Her voice was dry and cold. "I have no taxes in Jefferson.

Colonel Sartoris explained it to me. Perhaps one of you can gain access to the city records and satisfy yourselves."

"But we have. We are the city authorities, Miss Emily. Didn't you get a notice from the sheriff, signed by him?"

"I received a paper, yes," Miss Emily said. "Perhaps he considers himself the sheriff . . . I have no taxes in Jefferson."

"But there is nothing on the books to show that, you see. We must go by the—"

"See Colonel Sartoris. I have no taxes in Jefferson."

"But, Miss Emily—"

"See Colonel Sartoris." (Colonel Sartoris had been dead almost ten years.) "I have no taxes in Jefferson. Tobe!" The Negro appeared. "Show these gentlemen out."

II

So she vanquished them, horse and foot, just as she had vanquished their fathers thirty years before about the smell. That was two years after her father's death and a short time after her sweetheart—the one we believed would marry her—had deserted her. After her father's death she went out very little; after her sweetheart went away, people hardly saw her at all. A few of the ladies had the temerity to call, but were not received, and the only sign of life about the place was the Negro man—a young man then—going in and out with a market basket.

"Just as if a man—any man—could keep a kitchen properly," the ladies said; so they were surprised when the smell developed. It was another link between the gross, teeming world and the high and mighty Griersons.

A neighbor, a woman, complained to the mayor, Judge Stevens, eighty years old.

"But what will you have me do about it, madam?" he said.

"Why, send her word to stop it," the woman said. "Isn't there a law?"

"I'm sure that won't be necessary," Judge Stevens said. "It's probably just a snake or a rat that nigger of hers killed in the yard. I'll speak to him about it."

The next day he received two more complaints, one from a man who came in diffident deprecation. "We really must do something about it, Judge. I'd be the last one in the world to bother Miss Emily, but we've got to do something." That night the Board of Aldermen met—three graybeards and one younger man, a member of the rising generation.

"It's simple enough," he said. "Send her word to have her place cleaned up. Give her a certain time to do it in, and if she don't . . ."

"Dammit, sir," Judge Stevens said, "will you accuse a lady to her face of smelling bad?"

So the next night, after midnight, four men crossed Miss Emily's lawn and slunk about the house like burglars, sniffing along the base of the brickwork and at the cellar openings while one of them performed a regular sowing motion with his hand out of a sack slung from his shoulder. They broke open the cellar door and sprinkled lime there, and in all the outbuildings. As they recrossed the lawn, a window that had been dark was lighted and Miss Emily sat in it, the light behind her, and her upright torso motionless as that of an idol. They crept quietly across the lawn and into the shadow of the locusts that lined the street. After a week or two the smell went away.

That was when people had begun to feel really sorry for her. People in our town, remembering how Old Lady Wyatt, her great-aunt, had gone completely crazy at last, believed that the Griersons held themselves a little too high for what they really were. None of the young men was quite good enough for Miss Emily and such. We had long thought of them as a tableau: Miss Emily a slender figure in white in the background, her father a spraddled silhouette in the foreground, his back to her and clutching a horsewhip, the two of them framed by the back-flung front door. So when she got to be thirty and was still single, we were not pleased exactly, but vindicated; even with insanity in the family she wouldn't have turned down all of her chances if they had really materialized.

When her father died, it got about that the house was all that was left to her; and in a way, people were glad. At last they could pity Miss Emily. Being left alone, and a pauper, she had become humanized. Now she too would know the old thrill and the old despair of a penny more or less.

The day after his death all the ladies prepared to call at the house and offer condolence and aid, as is our custom. Miss Emily met them at the door, dressed as usual and with no trace of grief on her face. She told them that her father was not dead. She did that for three days, with the ministers calling on her, and the doctors, trying to persuade her to let them dispose of the body. Just as they were about to resort to law and force, she broke down, and they buried her father quickly.

We did not say she was crazy then. We believed she had to do that. We remembered all the young men her father had driven away, and we knew that with nothing left, she would have to cling to that which had robbed her, as people will.

III

She was sick for a long time. When we saw her again, her hair was cut short, making her look like a girl, with a vague resemblance to those angels in colored church windows—sort of tragic and serene.

The town had just let the contracts for paving the sidewalks, and in the summer after her father's death they began the work. The construction company came with niggers and mules and machinery, and a foreman named Homer Barron, a Yankee—a big, dark, ready man, with a big voice and eyes lighter than his face. The little boys would follow in groups to hear him cuss the niggers, and the niggers singing in time to the rise and fall of picks. Pretty soon he knew everybody in town. Whenever you heard a lot of laughing about the square, Homer Barron would be in the center of the group. Presently we began to see him and Miss Emily on Sunday afternoons driving in the yellow-wheeled buggy and the matched team of bays from the livery stable.

At first we were glad that Miss Emily would have an interest, because the ladies all said, "Of course a Grierson would not think seriously of a Northerner, a day laborer." But there were still others, older people, who said that even grief could not cause a real lady to forget noblesse oblige—without calling it noblesse oblige. They just said, "Poor Emily. Her kinsfolk should come to her." She had some kin in Alabama; but years ago her father had fallen out with them over the estate of Old Lady Wyatt, the crazy woman, and there was no communication between the two families. They had not even been represented at the funeral.

And as soon as the old people said, "Poor Emily," the whispering began. "Do you suppose it's really so?" they said to one another. "Of course it is. What else could . . ." This behind their hands; rustling of craned silk and satin behind jalousies closed upon the sun of Sunday afternoon as the thin, swift clop-clop-clop of the matched team passed: "Poor Emily."

She carried her head high enough—even when we believed that she was fallen. It was as if she demanded more than ever the recognition of her dignity as the last Grierson; as if it had wanted that touch of earthiness to reaffirm her imperviousness. Like when she bought the rat poison, the arsenic. That was over a year after they had begun to say "Poor Emily," and while the two female cousins were visiting her.

"I want some poison," she said to the druggist. She was over thirty then, still a slight woman, though thinner than usual, with cold, haughty black eyes in a face the flesh of which was strained across the temples and about the eye-sockets as you imagine a lighthouse-keeper's face ought to look. "I want some poison," she said.

"Yes, Miss Emily. What kind? For rats and such? I'd recom—"

"I want the best you have. I don't care what kind."

The druggist named several. "They'll kill anything up to an elephant. But what you want is—"

"Arsenic," Miss Emily said. "Is that a good one?"

"Is . . . arsenic? Yes, ma'am. But what you want—"

"I want arsenic."

The druggist looked down at her. She looked back at him, erect, her face like a strained flag. "Why, of course," the druggist said. "If that's what you want. But the law requires you to tell what you are going to use it for."

Miss Emily just stared at him, her head tilted back in order to look him eye for eye, until he looked away and went and got the arsenic and wrapped it up. The Negro delivery boy brought her the package; the druggist didn't come back. When she opened the package at home there was written on the box, under the skull and bones: "For rats."

IV

So the next day we all said, "She will kill herself"; and we said it would be the best thing. When she had first begun to be seen with Homer Barron, we had said, "She will marry him." Then we said, "She will persuade him yet," because Homer himself had remarked—he liked men, and it was known that he drank with the younger men in the Elks' Club—that he was not a marrying man. Later we said, "Poor Emily" behind the jalousies as they passed on Sunday afternoon in the glittering buggy. Miss Emily with her head high and Homer Barron with his hat cocked and a cigar in his teeth, reins and whip in a yellow glove.

Then some of the ladies began to say that it was a disgrace to the town and a bad example to the young people. The men did not want to interfere, but at last the ladies forced the Baptist minister—Miss Emily's people were Episcopal—to call upon her. He would never divulge what happened during that interview, but he refused to go back again. The next Sunday they again drove about the streets, and the following day the minister's wife wrote to Miss Emily's relations in Alabama.

So she had blood-kin under her roof again and we sat back to watch developments. At first nothing happened. Then we were sure that they were to be married. We learned that Miss Emily had been to the jeweler's and ordered a man's toilet set in silver, with the letters H.B. on each piece. Two days later we learned that she had bought a complete outfit of men's clothing, including a nightshirt, and we said, "They are married." We were really glad. We were glad because the two female cousins were even more Grierson than Miss Emily had ever been.

So we were not surprised when Homen Barron—the streets had been finished some time since—was gone. We were a little disappointed that there was not a public blowing-off, but we believed that he had gone on to prepare for Miss Emily's coming, or to give her a chance to get rid of the cousins. (By that time it was a cabal, and we were all Miss Emily's allies to help circumvent the cousins.) Sure enough, after another week they departed. And, as we had expected all along, within three days Homer Barron was back in town. A neighbor saw the Negro man admit him at the kitchen door at dusk one evening.

And that was the last we saw of Homer Barron. And of Miss Emily for some time. The Negro man went in and out with the market basket, but the front door remained closed. Now and then we would see her at a window for a moment, as the men did that night when they sprinkled the lime, but for almost six months she did not appear on the streets. Then we knew that this was to be expected too; as if that quality of her father which had thwarted her woman's life so many times had been too virulent and too furious to die.

When we next saw Miss Emily, she had grown fat and her hair was turning gray. During the next few years it grew grayer and grayer until it attained an even pepper-and-salt iron-gray, when it ceased turning. Up to the day of her death at seventy-four it was still that vigorous iron-gray, like the hair of an active man.

From that time on her front door remained closed, save for a period of six or seven years, when she was about forty, during which she gave lessons in china-painting. She fitted up a studio in one of the downstairs rooms, where the daughters and granddaughters of Colonel Sartoris' contemporaries were sent to her with the same regularity and in the same spirit that they were sent to church on Sundays with a twenty-five-cent piece for the collection plate. Meanwhile her taxes had been remitted.

Then the newer generation became the backbone and the spirit of the town, and the painting pupils grew up and fell away and did not send their children to her with boxes of color and tedious brushes and pictures cut from the ladies' magazines. The front door closed upon the last one and remained closed for good. When the town got free postal delivery, Miss Emily alone refused to let them fasten the metal numbers above her door and attach a mailbox to it. She would not listen to them.

Daily, monthly, yearly we watched the Negro grow grayer and more stooped, going in and out with the market basket. Each December we sent her a tax notice, which would be returned by the post office a week later, unclaimed. Now and then we would see her in one of the downstairs windows—she had evidently shut up the top floor of the house—like the carven torso of an idol in a niche, looking or not looking at us, we could never tell which. Thus she passed from generation to generation—dear, inescapable, impervious, tranquil, and perverse.

And so she died. Fell ill in the house filled with dust and shadows, with only a doddering Negro man to wait on her. We did not even know she was sick; we had long since given up trying to get any information from the Negro. He talked to no one, probably not even to her, for his voice had grown harsh and rusty, as if from disuse.

She died in one of the downstairs rooms, in a heavy walnut bed with a curtain, her gray head propped on a pillow yellow and moldy with age and lack of sunlight.

V

The Negro met the first of the ladies at the front door and let them in, with their hushed, sibilant voices and their quick, curious glances, and then he disappeared. He walked right through the house and out the back and was not seen again.

The two female cousins came at once. They held the funeral on the second day, with the town coming to look at Miss Emily beneath a mass of bought flowers, with the crayon face of her father musing profoundly above the bier and the ladies sibilant and macabre; and the very old men—some in their brushed Confederate uniforms—on the porch and the lawn, talking of Miss Emily as if she had been a contemporary of theirs, believing that they had danced with her and courted her perhaps, confusing time with its mathematical progression, as the old do, to whom all the past is not a diminishing road but, instead, a huge meadow which no winter ever quite touches, divided from them now by the narrow bottle-neck of the most recent decade of years.

Already we knew that there was one room in that region above stairs which no one had seen in forty years, and which would have to be forced. They waited until Miss Emily was decently in the ground before they opened it.

The violence of breaking down the door seemed to fill this room with pervading dust. A thin, acrid pall as of the tomb seemed to lie everywhere upon this room decked and furnished as for a bridal: upon the valance curtains of faded rose color, upon the rose-shaded lights, upon the dressing table, upon the delicate array of crystal and the man's toilet things backed with tarnished silver, silver so tarnished that the monogram was obscured. Among them lay a collar and tie, as if they had just been removed, which, lifted, left upon the surface a pale crescent in the dust. Upon a chair hung the suit, carefully folded; beneath it the two mute shoes and the discarded socks.

The man himself lay in the bed.

For a long while we just stood there, looking down at the profound and fleshless grin. The body had apparently once lain in the attitude of an embrace, but now the long sleep that outlasts love, that conquers even the grimace of love, had cuckoled him. What was left of him, rotted beneath what was left of the nightshirt, had become inextricable from the bed in which he lay; and upon him and upon the pillow beside him lay that even coating of the patient and biding dust.

Then we noticed that in the second pillow was the indentation of a head. One of us lifted something from it, and leaning forward, that faint and invisible dust dry and acrid in the nostrils, we saw a long strand of iron-gray hair.